C0-AXC-134

Ego Development and the Personality Disorders

Ego Development and the Personality Disorders

A Developmental Approach to Psychopathology

DAVID P. AUSUBEL, M.D., Ph.D.

Bureau of Research and Service
College of Education
University of Illinois, Urbana

GRUNE & STRATTON • New York 1952

381 Fourth Avenue
New York City 16

Printed and bound in U.S.A. for Grune & Stratton
PRINTED BY MARSTIN PRESS, NEW YORK
I. LONDON, *President* 438

Contents

Preface

THE AIM OF THIS BOOK is to present a systematic and comprehensive developmental theory of psychopathology that is consonant with modern concepts of genetic psychology and with the empirical data on which they are based. It seeks to synthesize the fields of child development and abnormal psychology around the central theme of ego development.

This approach is by no means original. Freudians, neo-Freudians and the critics of both schools have been explaining psychopathological phenomena for a long time on the basis of developmental factors. Of the three schools, however, only orthodox psychoanalysis has evolved a complete system of psychopathology. But for reasons which will be discussed later, many psychologists and psychiatrists have reservations about the adequacy of psychoanalytic theory. Nevertheless they feel reluctant about discarding it for want of an acceptable alternative of comparable comprehensiveness, and, therefore, usually take refuge in eclecticism. It is largely to this group of individuals that the present theory of psychopathology is addressed.

In accordance with the writer's conception of the learning process, the organization of this book is concentric rather than additive. That is, the major concepts are first presented in rough outline with very little elaboration so that the total design is apparent from the start. Then, once the main conceptual relationships are unfolded, detailed analytical attention is given to the component parts in later separate chapters. This practice of repeating the same concepts in different and ever more differentiated contexts does not conform to traditional criteria of logical exposition or of textbook organization. It does, however, conform to modern concepts of the learning process and tends to make rereading of chapters relatively unnecessary.

Part I provides an historical orientation to the concepts employed in this book. It is not intended as a definitive or original critique of psychoanalysis, but as a brief summary of the major criticisms levelled at psychoanalytic theories of ego development during the past twenty years. The citation of specific evidence is meant to be illustrative only.

A more extensive treatment of psychoanalytic theory was felt to be not only out of place in this volume, but also completely unnecessary in view of the many definitive expositions and critiques currently available. In certain instances, however, where particular psychoanalytic theories are especially relevant to the discussion of various concepts of ego development, they are reintroduced in later sections of the book and subjected to more detailed scrutiny.

Part II, *The Natural History of Ego Development,* is concerned with a descriptive survey of ego development from birth through adolescence. In Part III, *The Dynamics of Ego Development,* the theoretical framework of the volume is elaborated. Considerable attention is given to the variables influencing the course of ego development, to periods of crisis and transition, to modes of resistance, and to causes and consequences of developmental progress and failure.

Part IV, *Ego Development and the Personality Disorders,* offers a classification and analysis of the behavior disorders in terms of the theoretical structure of ego development, followed by a brief discussion of implications for therapy.

In the effort to present a complete theoretical system which at the same time would not be made unwieldy by constant reference to the rules of evidence, the following scheme was adopted: Where supporting evidence for a theoretical position is available, it is explicitly cited. Pure speculation is clearly identified as such. In all other cases, the only foundation for an expressed opinion lies in the writer's observations and deductions as a psychiatrist, teacher, father, and research worker in child development. It is not intended that these latter statements should be dignified by any status other than as hypotheses.

It is indeed regrettable that the present state of knowledge in psychopathology makes this procedure necessary if theoretical completeness is desired. But if the reader will constantly bear in mind the rules of evidence set forth above, it may be possible to avoid many misunderstandings that frequently arise regarding the scientific basis of psychopathology. All too frequently, hypotheses and speculation are presented in the same breath with empirical data; and by implication the uncritical reader is invited to believe that psychopathology enjoys equal status with such empirical sciences as physiology and pathology. In the writer's opinion, this is an optimistic but not impossible expression of hope rather than a realistic appraisal of the current situation in the field.

In general, the use of case and anecdotal material has been avoided, since the main concern has been with presenting a concise outline of theory. Furthermore, in view of the fact that any theorist can explain any case to suit his theory, the citation of such material adds neither empirical nor logical support to the argument. It does have a certain illustrative value and offers relief to the reader, but is frequently misleading since illustrations are often implicitly accepted as evidence.

The writer's conceptual debt to the writings of Sherif and Cantril, Krech and Crutchfield, Norman Cameron, Nathaniel Cantor, Gardner Murphy, Erich Fromm, Kurt Lewin, and Jean Piaget will be readily apparent to anyone familiar with the works of these authors. In addition, I am indebted to many colleagues for critical review of various portions of the manuscript, notably, Ruth Cunningham, A. T. Jersild, Nathaniel Cantor, William E. Martin, Celia B. Stendler, Herbert M. Schiff, Edward B. Gasser, Foster McMurray, Kenneth Benne, and to my wife, Pearl Ausubel. I am also indebted to Mrs. Shirley S. Deusch for assistance in the preparation of the manuscript.

DAVID P. AUSUBEL

Champaign, Illinois
December, 1951

Acknowledgments

THE AUTHOR wishes to acknowledge the courtesy of the following authors and publishers in permitting quotations from their publications:

American Psychological Association, Inc., for excerpts from Bruno Bettelheim, *Individual and Mass Behavior in Extreme Situations,* Journal of Abnormal and Social Psychology, Volume 38, 1943, pages 428, 431, 437, 439, 440, and 447; also for an excerpt from Harold Orlansky, *Infant Care and Personality,* Psychological Bulletin, Volume 46, 1949, page 15.

National Association of Secondary-School Principals, for excerpts from David P. Ausubel, *Problems of Adolescent Adjustment,* The Bulletin, Volume 34, January 1950, pages 7, 8, 15, 17, 27, 38, 42, 63, 69, 70, 72, and 77.

Dr. Norman Cameron for excerpts from his book, *The Psychology of Behavior Disorders,* published by Houghton, Mifflin, 1947, pages 23, 25, 29, 30, 33-35, 41, and 42.

Child Development Publications, for excerpts from Sybil Escalona, *A Commentary Upon Some Recent Changes in Child Rearing Practices,* Child Development, Volume 20, 1949, pages 161 and 162.

Columbia University Press, for an excerpt from Abram Kardiner, *The Individual and His Society,* copyright 1939, page 336.

Dr. Erich Fromm for excerpts from his book, *Man For Himself,* published by Rinehart & Co., Inc., 1947, pages 21-23, 26, 129-131, 135, 144-148, 155, 156, 158, 173, 181, 182, 190, 196, 220, 231-234, 236, and 237.

Harcourt, Brace, and Co., Inc., for an excerpt from Jean Piaget, *The Moral Judgment of the Child,* copyright 1932, page 409.

Harper and Brothers, for excerpts from Gardner Murphy, *Personality,* copyright 1947, pages 553 and 570.

The Institute of Living, for an excerpt from Leo Kanner, *A Discussion of Early Infantile Autism,* Digest of Neurology and Psychiatry, Volume 19, 1951, page 158.

The National Society for the Study of Education, for the following excerpts from the 43rd Yearbook, Part I, *Adolescence,* University of Chicago Press, 1944; Caroline Zachry, *Preparing Youth to be Adults,* pages 334 and 340; and Allison Davis, *Socialization and Adolescent Personality,* pages 200 and 203.

The Psychiatric Quarterly for excerpts from David P. Ausubel, *The Psychopathology and Treatment of Drug Addiction in Relation to the Mental Hygiene Movement,* Psychiatric Quarterly Supplement, Volume 22, Part II, 1948, pages 231, 232, 248, and 249; also for excerpts from David P. Ausubel, *A Psychopathological Classification of Schizophrenia,* Psychiatric Quarterly, Volume 23, 1949, pages 127, 128, 136, 138, and 140-142.

The Ronald Press Company, for excerpts from Rollo May, *The Meaning of Anxiety,* copyright 1950, pages 336, 341, 342 and 356; also for the following excerpts from J. McVickers Hunt (editor), *Personality and the Behavior Disorders,* copyright 1944: O. H. Mowrer and Clyde Kluckhohn, *Dynamic Theory of Personality,* pages 96 and 110-111; Lois B. Murphy, *Childhood Experience in Relation to Personality Development,* page 669; M. A. Ribble, *Infantile Experience in Relation to Personality Development,* pages 621 and 622.

The Scientific Monthly, for excerpts from N. R. F. Maier, *Experimentally Induced Abnormal Behavior,* Scientific Monthly, Volume 67, 1948, pages 214 and 215.

Dr. Percival M. Symonds for excerpts from his book, *The Dynamics of Parent-Child Relationships,* published by Bureau of Publications, Teachers College, Columbia University, 1949, pages v, vi, vii, ix, xii, xiii, 5, 8, 9, 23, 52, and 57.

The William Alanson White Psychiatric Foundation, for excerpts from Harry Stack Sullivan, *Conceptions of Modern Psychiatry,* copyright 1947, pages 21 and 22.

John Wiley and Sons, for excerpts from Robert J. Havighurst and Hilda Taba, *Adolescent Character and Personality,* copyright 1949, pages 5, 6, 11, 34, 66, 68, 86-90, 95, 116, 183, and 311; also for excerpts from Muzafer Sherif and Hadley Cantril, *The Psychology of Ego-Involvements,* copyright 1947, pages 492, 493, 496, and 505.

To my son Freddy, artful teacher of the intricacies of ego development

Introduction

THE RELEVANCE of infantile and childhood experience for adult personality structure and the behavior disorders is no longer a subject of serious controversy among students of personality development and psychopathology. This is by no means an indication that abundant empirical evidence is available or that unanimity prevails regarding its interpretation [*303*].* On the contrary, after an exhaustive review of "the empirical data bearing on the theory that various features of *infantile care* determine adult personality," Orlansky [*303*] declares: "Our conclusion has been largely negative, and we have been led to substitute a theory which emphasizes instead the importance of constitutional factors and of the total cultural situation in personality formation; the importance of post-infantile experience is also indicated." Thus, when it comes to interpretation of the meager data that exist, the area of agreement is reduced even further to the general statement that *some* relationship prevails.

It is the precise nature of this relationship which occasions such heated controversy. Through what channels are parental influences on the offspring's character structure transmitted? Which are more important—specific practices of infant and child care or broader patterns of parental attitudes? How modifiable are personality "traits" and reaction patterns developed in early infancy or childhood? How are we to view the general process of personality growth —as the inevitable unfolding of phylogenetically-determined drives and "stages," or as the product of continuous biosocial interaction between a "unique organism undergoing maturation and a unique physical and social environment" [*303*]?

In this welter of theoretical controversy and paucity of data what rationale is there for the appearance of the present volume? Simply the writer's firm conviction that no task in psychopathology is more

* Italic numerals within brackets refer to the Bibliography, page 519.

deserving of attention than the systematic relation of behavior disorders to personality development in terms of the growing self. It is felt that since the concept of the self is the most significant mirror of a human being's biosocial status and its fluctuations through successive stages in maturation (as well as his interpretation of same), the most comprehensive and integrated interpretation of personality can be gained through the study of ego development. The systematic consideration of these relationships can not await the collection of sufficient data, because before we can have fruitful observation and experimentation, we need a more careful formulation and sharper definition of relevant problems [*178*]. This in turn depends upon a systematic integration of existing evidence into a coherent framework of reference in relation to which "gaps in knowledge can be discovered which evidence can fill" [*178*].

It should be noted that in this volume we will be concerned with psychopathology only from the point of view of ego development. There is no presumption of presenting a complete textbook of psychopathology but rather the contribution of distorted ego development to the predisposing matrix of factors resulting in the production of the personality disorders. In so delimiting our task, no attempt is being made to minimize the importance of constitutional or situational factors, psychosexual maturation, mechanisms of adjustment, the evolution of symptoms, and other considerations customarily covered in textbooks of psychopathology.

In effect, then, this volume is an attempt at the formulation of a systematic theory of psychopathology based upon a nonpsychoanalytic interpretation of personality development. As a preliminary exploratory venture it can not hope to go beyond the bare outlines of such a theory. More precise formulations must await the accumulation of considerably more data than are presently available.

PART I

Historical and Conceptual Orientation

CHAPTER 1

Psychoanalytic Approaches to Personality Development

THE ORTHODOX FREUDIAN APPROACH[1]*

OUR INSISTENCE on a systematic formulation of personality development does not overlook the fact that Freudian theorists have devised a most elaborate scheme for adult characterology based upon the psychological development of infant and child [*109, 128 129, 133, 205, 257*]. The contention is, however, that such a theory founded upon immutable instincts, predetermined and rigid sequences of personality development, and well-defined "layers" of reified personality structure is in conflict with modern conceptions of psychology and anthropology, and hence inevitably doomed to unfruitful speculation. This statement is not intended in any way to disparage the tremendous contributions made by Freud and his followers to general psychopathological theory. However, acceptance of such Freudian principles as "mechanisms" of adjustment, "unconscious" motivation, conflict between individual impulses and social conventions, etc. does not necessarily imply indorsement of the "metapsychological theories" [*382*] which Freud himself regarded as belonging to the "mythology" of psychoanalysis [*133*].

Critique of Freudian Conceptions of Ego Development

The Freudian conception of the ego as a precipitate of outlawed sex impulses made socially acceptable through various compromise formations (e.g., sublimation) is open to many fundamental objections: (1) *The specific content and course of development of the basic drives are not innately given but determined by unique*

* Notes for this chapter appear on page 10.

factors of culture, constitution and personal history [*141, 187, 218, 265, 303, 354*]. Although modern psychology recognizes the importance of biological impulses, it accords to them no innate structuration or predetermined development[2] in the sense of the complex and specific content which instinct theory demands. One need not adopt any naive *tabula rasa* conception to insist on the fact that these biological drives father only very general impulses to action. Social anthropology has abundantly proven that the specific form of expression which any drive assumes can be understood only as an outcome of the "interaction between biology and culture" [*178*]. In the light of evidence which indicates that there is tremendous social variability in the mode of gratifying even relatively basic human drives, any division of personality development into preformed, inevitable and universal sequences, such as oral, anal, genital and oedipal, is hardly tenable [*265, 339, 382*].

(2) *Drives related to the ego are not merely modified social derivatives of instinctual impulses but are also continuous products of social experience* [*141, 354*]. Human motives are constantly emerging under the impact of new experiences, new social pressures and expectations, new ways of perceiving the same experience [*233, 354*]. These motives are also outcomes of *positive* impulses to manipulate and explore the environment as well as adjustive reactions to frustration and anxiety [*201*]. Hence psychoanalytic formulations which maintain that all of man's constructive motives are only indirect by-products (via sublimation and reaction-formation) of a single socially-inacceptable fountainhead of drive [*334*] cannot be very realistic.

The psychoanalytic position follows logically from the Freudian conception of the ego as a resultant of the interplay between dichotomous forces—the id as the source of drive, and reality as the source of frustration and of the social censure necessitating repression. It would be gratuitous to point out that society creates as many needs as it suppresses. And even though we conceive of many adult motives as *historically* related to primitive organic needs [*90*], Allport's insistence on their functional autonomy is quite plausible [*223*].

In further criticism of the Freudian doctrine of sublimation, it may also be noted that to speak of one motive as substituting for another which is blocked (and hence relieving some of the associated tension) is not the same as contending that the energy of the first is directly channeled into the second. With respect to the erogenous zones, for example, Sears [*346*] could find no evidence to support the view that one could serve as a substitute for another. And Kinsey [*225*], confirming the earlier work of Taylor [*391*] and Kirkendall [*226*], demonstrated that instances of extremely low sexual outlet were very rare among men in our culture, and in all cases understandable in simpler terms than sublimation.

(3) *Psychosexual development is not coextensive with ego development.* The Freudian conception of the ego as "that part of the id which has been modified by the direct influence of the external world" [*134*] leads to the view that the process of ego development in a given individual can be envisaged only as a personal variation of a universal theme of psychosexual maturation. It is important to bear this fact in mind in evaluating psychoanalytic "ego psychology" and other systems of personality description which make use of the attractive "layer" scheme of personality organization. These constructs (ego, superego and id) appear on the face of it to be so much more inclusive of general personality development than the course of infantile sexuality that we tend to forget that the former are merely derived creatures of the latter. "Layers" of personality structure such as the psychoanalytic ego or superego are allegedly fashioned out of an inherited id [*134*] as it comes into contact with a repressive reality. Hence, proponents of "ego psychology" [*9, 124, 319*] while "less preoccupied with the instinctual life of the individual" [*382*] than earlier psychoanalytic writers must either implicitly or explicitly subscribe to the latter's theoretical formulations.

These instinctual implications become clear when we examine some of the ambiguity surrounding terms like "ego," "ego ideal" and "superego." The ego, besides constituting a precipitate of the id, is supposed to evolve into an active conciliating agent which seeks to both subjugate the latter and serve as legal procurer to its impulses. But is all this activity of the ego—both active and passive—only in the service of an innately given set of psychosexual urges? Are there no other sources of drive for which the ego will "exert itself"?

What is the genetic distinction between ego and superego? If the ego tests reality and represses socially-unacceptable elements of the id, why then do we need a superego which is the "heir" of an instinctual oedipus conflict[3] [*134*]? Why must instincts be invoked when the acquisition of moral values can be understood developmentally as in the case of any interiorized ego value [*308, 354*]? Why must a special unconscious office be erected for the superego apart from the ego [*188*]? And what is the rationale for distinguishing between an unconscious superego and a conscious "ego ideal" on the one hand [*958, 167, 268*], and between the "ego ideal" and the ego on the other hand, when goals and standards of behavior are both assimilated into the ego by essentially the same processes and when either may or may not operate apart from awareness?

In clinical psychopathology also, it is clear that when psychoanalysts refer to ego development they mean mostly the history of psychosexual maturation and its characterological precipitates in a given individual. Federn, for example, in discussing the development of ego feelings places major emphasis upon the differentiation of erogenous zones [*104*]. According to him, each step in this process of differentiation constitutes a fixation point in relation to which regression may later occur [*104*]. This results in varying degrees of neurotic and psychotic ego damage, the severity of which corresponds to the depths of regression.

(4) *The tendency to reify the ego* [*354*]. Psychoanalytic literature [*9, 58, 134, 321*] is full of references to the ego as an agent which does things—strives, struggles, liberates, etc.—just as if it were a teleologically functioning individual. The ego as an abstraction can be correctly conceived of as an entity as long as we do not endow it with any independent existence apart from the concrete manifestations out of which it is abstracted. To do so is to fall into the logical and anthropomorphic error reminiscent of the "group mind" fallacy [*396*]: An abstraction becomes a corporeal being with a separate life and purpose of its own.

(5) *Reliance on basic assumptions unrelated to developmental observations of children* [*303, 354*]. Freudian theory has for the most part arisen from clinical investigation of adult neurotics. Hence its assumptions regarding personality development in infant

and child must necessarily be subject to all of the errors and distortions produced by forgetting, bias, and the manifest impossibility of an adult retaining childhood experiences intact and untainted by interpretations derived fron an adult frame of reference.[4]

No one could quarrel with the commendable aim to suggest organizing hypotheses which unify and illuminate the processes of personality development. Canons of adequate scientific theory require, however, that hypotheses either bear some relationships to existing or potential naturalistic data in the real world [*354*] or else have self-evident validity [*346*]; and that lacking same, only the fewest and simplest necessary assumptions can be made. In the light of these criteria, Freudian concepts such as the id, superego, oedipus complex, sequences of psychosexual development, life and death instincts, etc., constitute highly unsatisfactory systematic formulations for a scientific theory of personality development.

NEO-FREUDIAN APPROACHES[5]

It is somewhat difficult to comprehend the theoretical position of a group of writers (i.e., Fromm, Horney, Kardiner) who have repudiated Freud's phylogenetic determinism and have recognized the role of cultural influences in producing the type of structures and mechanisms which were hitherto declared to be innately given [*100, 123, 141, 187, 189, 218, 294*]. To the present writer, it seems like indulging in verbal magic to deny the prepotency of instincts on the one hand, and on the other hand to describe personality in terms of the very same "layers" and "stages" which imply acceptance of instinctual origins and predetermined sequences of development.[6] If it is genuinely believed that concepts of conscience and self are genetic products of interaction between a unique organism and a unique social environment, what justification is there for retaining phylogenetic terms like "superego" and "id" or in using "ego" as if it were a mere social variation of an instinctual precipitate? Also to retain the same basic concepts of Freud but merely to give them a social derivation is a poor compromise indeed when these concepts are themselves inextricably bound up with a set of "simple, sovereign" assumptions such as "libido" and "sublimation" [*354*]. And as Sherif and Cantril point out [*354*], there is little improvement in replacing one set of "simple sovereign principles" with another (e.g., Fromm's inherent "strivings for justice and truth" and "need to avoid aloneness"). Just like conscience they can be derived genetically under certain biosocial conditions and require no assumptions such as a phylogenetic oedipus complex [*354*].

NOTES

[1] It is not the purpose of this volume to present a condensed version or an historically-complete, systematic critique of Freudian doctrines. However, it would be quite artificial to discuss ego development in relation to the personality disorders without some reference to the historical framework in which this problem is embedded. For treatment of more specific problems in this general area the reader is referred to Fenichel's [*109*] exhaustive treatise on psychoanalytic theory and to Sherif and Cantril's [*354*] excellent critical survey of psychoanalysis from the point of view of personality, ego development and social psychology.

[2] Erikson [*98*], for example, goes so far as to compare this predetermination of developmental sequences in personality development to the inevitable sequences in structural development preordained by embryological constitution. If for any reason variations were to occur in the order or rate of development of the former, he predicts the same dire consequences to personality structure as would occur to physical structure, granted a comparable disturbance in embryological process. The same point of view also seems implicit in Gesell's [*149*] descriptions of sequences of motor development, but in this area it is more plausible if accepted in very general terms (see pp. 43-44).

[3] The solution of this conflict is further aided (according to Freud) by identifications rooted in the "collective unconscious" [*134*].

[4] Such obvious considerations are completely ignored by writers like Ribble [*327*] who declares: "A rich clinical experience in the study and treatment of neurotic individuals revealed consistently that their sufferings derived from a struggle to repress or to disguise infantile pleasure strivings connected with the basic bodily functions."

Available today, of course, is a considerable body of evidence emanating from the psychoanalysis of children. But "child analysts like Melanie Klein and Anna Freud . . . have generally been more interested in applying psychoanalytic theory than in testing it" [*354*]. To be sure, evidence of hostility toward the father has been uncovered in male children, but this in no sense proves that the basis of the rivalry is sexual in nature or that the rivalry is rooted in the phylogenetic unconscious. It may prove that in our culture the primary emotional attachment of the male (or female) child is to the mother; that most of the child's experience with father is in the latter's role as moral arbitrator and dispenser of punishment; and that in some cases of marital discord, the male child is cast by the mother in the role of the preferred emotional (but sexless) rival of the father.

[5] For a fuller critical survey, see Sherif and Cantril [*354*], F. Bartlett [*36*] and J. Stone [*382*]. Reference to Alfred Adler's contributions is made in a later section.

[6] Murray and Kluckhohn [*294*] thus speak of an individual as "id-dominated," if "the primary biological impulses remain unchecked." Erikson [*100*] while denying that "the individual is . . . merely the sum of his childhood identifications" refers to " 'id resistances' as derivates of the infantile fear of being restrained and deprived of the satisfactions of needs inherent in the organism and its early satisfactions." Frenkel-Brunswick, Levinson and Sanford insist that "the determinants of personality . . . are mainly social" [*123*], but at the same time interpret anti-Semitism in puritanical college girls as a projection of "id impulses into the Jew" [*122*]. L. B. Murphy [*291*] believes that the emotional relationships between parent and child should be viewed in a wider context than the psychoanalytic one, but still refers to the ego as "caught between the urgings of the id or impulse-life and the pressure of super-ego or conscience."

CHAPTER 2

Genetic Concepts of Self and Ego[1*]

THE CONCEPTS of self and ego have come into their own in modern psychology because of the manifest impossibility of explaining the major portion of man's behavior without assuming some reference to self. In the experimental psychology of motivation, concepts such as *level of aspiration* [*250*] have assumed a central place, and no approach to the social psychology of attitude-formation can afford to overlook the question of ego-involvement[2] [*354*]. Yet in the effort to find an acceptable functional concept of self, considerable difficulty has arisen because of the historical association of various religious, philosophical and psychoanalytic meanings with this concept [*354*].

It is important at the outset to differentiate between body, self, ego and personality, which in the order given constitute an ascending hierarchy of inclusiveness (see Fig. 1). "The ego is only one portion, one region . . . of the personality. Many skills, habits, memories are components of personality but seldom if ever become ego-involved" [*12*]. Also as Chein [*66*] points out, "the self is not identical with the ego. If it were, then the knowledge of the ego would be as immediate as the knowledge of the self . . . For while each individual recognizes himself, he has no immediate knowledge of ego-processes such as repression or self-actualization."

The self-concept[3] arises genetically in the course of infantile experience as "a content of awareness . . . It has no reality apart from awareness" [*66*]. The body,[4] on the other hand, is only "the object of awareness . . . that is, what is in between the space in front and the space behind" [*66*]. Thus, the self, although inclusive of an image of the body, does not correspond perfectly to it, and includes much more besides. "The thing known as the self is a

* Notes for this chapter appear on page 18.

BODY — visual image of one's appearance in space	+	Auditory images of one's name, kinaesthetic sensations, visceral tensions, personal memories	=	SELF

SELF	+	self-attitudes self-ideals self-motives self-values	=	EGO	+	other non- ego-involved skills, habits, memories, etc.	=	PERSON- ALITY

FIG. 1.—*Diagram of Relationships Between Body, Self, Ego and Personality*

selection and organization of its experiences involving the visceral tensions, muscular strains, the sound of one's name" [*289*]. It includes the "continuity of memories" which is responsible for the maintenance of self-identity [*178*].

The ego,[5] in contradistinction to the self, is an abstratcion referring to the inter-related set of experiences, perceptions, attitudes, motives and values which revolve about the awareness of self. Naturally, the self by virtue of its central position within ego structure becomes itself a "supreme value and the core of an evaluative system" [*66*]. The ego is "coextensive with neither consciousness nor with unconsciousness, for much that we are conscious of is indifferent to our egos and many unconscious stimuli silently but effectively engage them" [*12*]. But whether motives are conscious or unconscious, their organization maintains a certain developmental consistency as long as we survey them from a "genotypical" standpoint [*178*].

Also arising in genetic fashion and in no more mysterious way than the ego itself, are a group of moral values and standards which may be referred to collectively as "conscience" and a set of self-evaluative attitudes which may be abstracted as a "self-critical faculty."

THE EGO AS AN ENTITY

We have already referred to the unfortunate habit of reifying the ego, a tendency which is a heritage of the psychoanalytic tradition. Even Chein [*66*] in his careful and lucid analysis of the ego refers to its capacity to be "selfish, strive for dominance or look to the future." We cannot agree too strongly with Sherif and Cantril that the ego can do none of these things but is itself only an abstraction referring to attitudes, motives, etc. that have reference to the self-concept [*354*]. However, as these same writers point out, this does not negate the fact that the ego is an entity.[6] It seems perfectly legitimate to refer to an identifiable abstraction as an entity as long as one does not reify it. To say that the ego is not an entity because it is constantly in a state of flux is to set up a philosophical criterion for identity that has no psychological reality. All of nature is in a state of constant flux as well as all concepts in the mind; hence in a phenomenal sense there can be no absolute entity. To have psychological reality as an entity, a concept must be endowed only with personal indentifiability and some measure of continuity. Thus, although "the subjective sense of the ego varies from time to time . . . and its content keeps shifting . . . this shifting scene does not mean that there is no stable and recurring structure" [*12*]. Through the web of memory thus formed, the ego retains its phenomenological identity [*178*].

But once attaining this highly differentiated and abstracted form endowed with continuity and personal identifiability, the ego becomes an entity in a more complete sense of the term than is implied by Sherif and Cantril's use of the phrase, "constellation of ego-attitudes" [*354*]. The process of conceptualization has already proceeded one step beyond the stage of "constellations of attitudes" to a stage which exists at a higher level of abstraction and enjoys a certain measure of psychological substantiveness but none of the corporeal, personified, or teleological properties of the reified ego. The end result may be conceived of as a personalized common denominator (rather than as a constellation) of ego attitudes. This genetic, non-reified ego (unlike the psychoanalytic ego) can be systematically related to naturalistic data. It makes no untenable assumptions, instinctual or otherwise, and does not require any "unfolding of an inevitable pattern" [*178*]. Hence, it can qualify as a respectable scientific construct. And "like any other scientific construct . . . it will be useful to the extent that it simplifies the understanding of events" [*178*].

THE ORGANIZING ROLE OF EGO VALUES

The ego, however, is more than a derivative product of experiences related to the self. It also plays a crucial role in the hierarchical ordering of experience. By serving as a "dead center of gravity," objects, persons and events can be arranged along a gradient of affective proximity in relation to it. Thus, as Murphy points out [*288*], it is difficult to speak of a self-not self dichotomy. More comprehensible is the notion of an ever-expanding gradient of objects in the external world organized heirarchically by an individual on the basis of intensity of ego-involvement. It is this "central polarity of the self" which is responsible for such varied phenomena as narcissism, egocentrism, invariable "self-rightness" and ethnocentrism (the self-evident superiority of in-group practices). For the very same reason, experience has a crucial effect on personality structure when it creates needs relative to ego status. As will be seen later, so much emphasis is placed upon the experiences of rejection or over-valuation in childhood because they give rise to more or less permanent constellations of ego needs. It is these needs and the characteristic modes of self-evaluation and ego defense in a given person which give continuity to his personality structure.

Nevertheless, because we are required to invest the processes of perception and motivation with a directive self-reference, we are not simultaneously committed to the hypothesis that "the more and better selfhood a person has, the less is available for others—that no one can enhance or defend himself without encroaching upon the self-enhancement and self-defense of others" [*288*]. This point of view is by no means universal or inevitable [*287, 288*]. It flourishes especially in a highly competitive society, and, as will be pointed out later, as a consequence of a certain type of ego development (see page 150).

INTROVERSION AND EXTRAVERSION

These concepts have historically been associated with problems of self and ego since they imply characteristic differences in the tendency to be concerned with self as against the outside world

[*288*]. Actually it would seem more fruitful to use these terms in describing the varying degrees of emotional *directness* with which different persons participate in the problems of living. The extravert prefers to participate directly in his emotional relationships with objects and persons in the environment. The introvert recoils from direct emotional participation and interposes a buffer of symbols and abstractions. Since introversion implies a great deal of solitary cerebration, the illusion is created that the introvert is primarily preoccupied with self as such; and since extraversion customarily involves more manipulation of objects and social situations, it is assumed that the extravert's focus of interest is in the outside world and not in the self.[7] Although this difference is almost inevitable, it is more of a distinction in terms of *product* than of *process*. The introvert, for example, may be intensely interested in mechanical or social relationships without *participating* in them directly at all; they may merely furnish raw material for his abstractions. The extravert, on the other hand, may be intensely interested in inner psychological processes, but less from the point of view of finding abstractions than as a rich source of vivid personal experience.

The factors accounting for these differences in directness of emotional involvement are not too clear. Constitutional predispositions undoubtedly play a part. A highly endomorphic individual, for example, would hardly be content with symbolic satisfaction of his pressing visceral needs. A dominant, ascendant and "tough-skinned" individual is not apt to be too concerned about the opinions of others or overly sensitive to rebuffs. As Gardner Murphy puts it, "extraversion may prove to consist primarily of the capacity to retain self-confidence despite social onslaughts upon it" [*288*]. Equally crucial perhaps, are environmental factors relating to ego defense or enhancement. In the personal history of the introvert there can usually be found "early distasteful experience with reality 'in the raw,' setting up a need for 'cushioning' " [*21*]. The parent may have differentially rewarded introverted activity. Early social rebuffs or rejection by the parent may have been traumatic enough to create powerful inhibitions in the child about directly exposing himself emotionally to environmental vicissitudes.

As a characteristic mode of reacting emotionally to life problems, introversion-extraversion is obviously an important dimension of personality structure. In addition—when acting with other psychopathological determinants—it furnishes predispositions towards adopting certain types of undesirable adjustive techniques. Withdrawing reactions are obviously more in line with the introverted tendency to be always one step removed from direct contact with reality; whereas the frustrated extravert is much more likely to attempt solutions involving more direct manipulation of reality (i.e., hedonistic regressions, rationalization, projection, etc.).

SELF-REFERENCE AND THE MECHANISMS OF DEFENSE

Because the self is such a central value, "however poor, confused, and incoherent it is, . . . it must be defended not only against outer attacks but against a clear perception of its unloveliness . . . This cherished possession must forever be made more adequate, more worthy; and it must forever be defended against stain and injury whether from the acts of others or of the valuing organism" [*288*]. Hence, as Hilgard states, "the mechanisms are comprehensible only if we accept a conception of the self" [*178*].

Interpreted in this light, mechanisms such as compensation, and identification primarily serve the function of ego enhancement. "The really critical compensations are ego problems. Whatever in the environment threatens the self or robs it of its defences or its means of enhancement, leads to a compensatory effort of the system as a whole . . . There is a perpetual struggle to make the actual self as much as possible like the ideal self, a self which has been enhanced and freed of its limitations to the highest degree imaginable" [*288*]. On the other hand, the main function of mechanisms such as rationalization, projection, repression, and "reaction-formation" is to put the self in a more favorable light. "The need for self-deception arises because of a more fundamental need to maintain or to restore self-esteem" [*178*]. The guilty self presents a highly unacceptable, anxiety-laden picture which must be reconstructed as soon as possible. The "inadequate self" is a similarly unpalatable dish to swallow, inviting the intervention of rationalizing mechanisms which help adjust "the ego to the aspiration level" [*288*].

Withdrawing techniques (negativism, fantasy, insulation, etc.) utilize still another approach: They remove the self beyond the reach of threatening influences in the distasteful environment, and make it invulnerable to attack while autistic satisfactions are enjoyed.

Gardner Murphy [*288*] also interprets love and aggression as means of ego enhancement rather than as direct sources of the mechanisms of defense. Love, he believes, is primarily self-oriented since the lover expects to be loved in return. And "what passes for aggression may be self-expression arising from the fact than in most societies, satisfaction with the self comes from power" [*288*].

The following quotation from the same author may be adopted as expressing the point of view of the present volume on the relationship between ego development and the personality disorders:

> "The tensions which at the level of the rat or sheep or dog relate to food and pain are likely in man to relate to alternative self-pictures . . . The physiological wear and tear which these two types of conflict entail seems to be largely a problem of ego-organization . . . The psychosomatic problem is partly one of conflict in maintaining an acceptable picture of self . . . The whole organism is sick when problems of the self are basically insoluble . . . Most serious personality trouble is ego problem" [*288*].

NOTES

[1] The best critical discussions of this topic are to be found in Allport [*12*], Chein [*66*], Hilgard [*178*], Sherif and Cantril [*354*], Snygg and Combs [*363*], Murphy [*288*], Murphy, Murphy and Newcomb [*289*], and Symonds [*390*].

[2] Ego-involvement as used in this volume refers to the degree of self-implication in a given task or performance, i.e., whether the outcome is a matter of concern or importance to self. The underlying motivation, however, is another matter. In an ego-involved task, the primary object of the activity might be self-enhancement (prestige motivation) in which case we speak of level of ego aspiration. On the other hand, there may be intense ego-involvement in a task in which the outcome *per se* rather than its relation to self-enhancement is the major focus of concern (intrinsic motivation). One might also refer to this latter situation as "task-involvement," which is a more defensible use of the term than its use to denote absence of ego-involvement.

[3] Snygg and Combs [*363*] differentiate between the *phenomenal self* and the

self-concept which is an abstraction of the self: "The self concept includes those parts of the phenomenal field which the individual has differentiated as definite and fairly stable characteristics of himself." Symonds [*390*] defines *ego* and *self* in much the same way as we do in this chapter, but stresses more than we think necessary the distinction between *self* as subject and *ego* as object.

[4] *Body* as used here is equivalent to Schilder's term *body image* [*342*]. The *body image* is the core of the self-concept and undergoes gradual and imperceptible change with age except during adolescence when the change is more abrupt and noticeable (see page 88).

[5] Hilgard [*178*] lucidly points out that the concept of self (ego) "does not necessarily imply unity. Conflict as well as harmony may be perpetuated through genotypical organization." He then goes on to differentiate between an "integrative" personality who can adapt realistically to pluralistic demands, and an "integrated" personality who if not integrative at the same time may achieve complete consistency in relation to an autistic or delusional framework of reference. Bateson [*38*] observes that the individual can enact various incompatible roles, each in its own appropriate situation without precipitating inner conflict.

[6] In a recent letter to the writer, Sherif reinforces this position by stating that he does not object to calling the ego an entity as long as it refers in a "naturalistic sense" to a "functional structure."

[7] The terms *egocentrism* and *sociocentrism* can be used to indicate the relative distribution of interest and attention in matters pertaining to self and others respectively. A highly egocentric individual, for example, cannot absorb himself in or pay attention to the problems of others. On the level of affective concern, the terms *intro- and extra-relatedness* can be employed. The degree of *intro-relatedness* is largely a reflection of the individual's level of ego aspiration. *Ego-* and *sociocentrism,* on the other hand, depend more on his level of socialization and sense of security. A highly *intro-related* individual, for example, who is secure and well socialized can show considerable interest in the problems of others (sociocentrism) on an objective and superficial level without relating himself emotionally to them. Introversion-extraversion constitutes still another dimension which has reference to the directness of emotional participation in experience (i.e., with or without a buffering layer of symbolism and abstraction).

CHAPTER 3

Childhood Experience and Adult Personality[1*]

PSYCHOANALYTIC DOCTRINE, as we have already noted, postulated an instinctual pattern of psychosexual development which unfolded in accordance with a predetermined design. This does not mean, however, that no allowance was made for individual differences in childhood experience. Such differences were conceived of as constituting individual variations on a universal theme. At each stage of development, several possibilities presented themselves: an adequate degree of gratification could be achieved, following which the child would pass on normally to the next stage; or else, either excessive gratification or frustration might result in a certain amount of fixation.[2] These vicissitudes in psychosexual development were held to be dependent on differences in parental care and discipline in relation to such factors as suckling, weaning, toilet training and genital manipulation. And far from being trifling matters, such vicissitudes were related in point to point fashion to specific attributes of adult personality.[3]

Originally the only "data" bearing on this subject were obtained from the recollections of adult neurotic subjects who had undergone psychoanalytic treatment. As noted above, however, "the reconstructions of infant experience obtained from the analytic couch do not constitute empirical findings on the infantile situation" [*303*]. But in the last ten years, some empirical evidence bearing on these hypotheses has become available. Reference has already been made to the conclusions reached by Orlansky [*303*] after surveying this evidence (see page 1). These conclusions are consistent with those reached by a number of recent writers [*92, 141,*

*Notes for this chapter appear on page 29.

187, 188, 219, 275, 287, 291] who stress the fact that personality structure is a product of multiple causality, and that hence no *single item* of parental discipline is likely to be of crucial significance[4]; that the emotional and cultural context in which a particular item of training is imbedded is more important that the specific practice itself [*292*]; that neither constitutional factors nor later childhood, adolescent or adult experience can be ignored [*100, 123, 303*]; that due account must be taken of the social factors of class, caste, sex, and peer group affiliations [*292, 303, 354*] and of the possibility of "emergent qualities" developing in the course of "personal and group interactions" and social change [*354*].

THE QUESTION OF "INFANTILE SEXUALITY"

Basic, of course, to the entire structure of psychoanalytic characterology is the assumption that the oral, and genital activity of the infant must be conceived of as qualitatively continuous with adult sexuality. This assumption has received amazingly widespread acceptance (even outside psychoanalytic circles) despite the complete absence of any convincing empirical evidence.[5] L. B. Murphy [*291*], for example, makes the following statement: "The child's interest in sex differences and other experiences connected with the genitals (observation of which is believed to be the basis for the castration complex or fear of loss of the penis or even loss of love), and the child's intense love relation to the parents in the preschool life (which becomes involved in the Oedipus complex) together with the prevalence of self-comfort patterns (thumbsucking and masturbation) *have not been successfully challenged.*"

The confusion springs from the definition of the term "sexuality." No one would deny that children are intensely emotional in relation to their parents, that they are interested in sex differences or that they derive *visceral pleasure* from sucking and genital manipulation. However, it is an assumption of quite another order to equate these activities with adult sexuality or to see in them proof of complex predetermined patterns such as the Oedipus complex. To the argument that one can define terms in any way that one chooses as long as one uses them consistently, there is the simple answer that scientific progress is seldom made by subsuming different discriminable variables under the same conceptual category. One could define the term "horse" broadly enough to include cats, dogs, and apes, but it is difficult to see what benefits could possibly ensue from this liberalization. It is reasonable to conceive of adult sexuality as a form of self-expression (functionally or historically related to hormonal stimulation) which is related to the individual's experience of himself in a biological sex role.[6] This type of self-expression, occurring after puberty, is *qualitatively* different from the exploratory and manipulative activity giving rise to pleasurable sensations from "erogenous zones," or from curiosity about sexual anatomy, even if it is true that similar organs are involved in both instances. A child and a biologist may both peer through a microscope, but one would hesitate to refer to the former as a scientist on this basis.[7]

The origin of this fallacy is not difficult to locate. In adult life, sensuous and sexual pleasure *are* interwoven in sexual experience. Hence it is easy for an adult in retrospecting about childhood experience to impute sexual significance to his infantile sensuality. The child also associates the anal and genital regions together because of their proximity and the pleasure and shame attached to both. Thus, if there had been much preoccupation with infantile anal sensuality, he may as an adult transfer *sexual* pleasure from the genitals to the anus because of the original sensuous association of the two areas. This, of course, does not prove that the infantile anal sensuality was originally sexual but that the adult is superimposing adult genital sexuality on the anus because of the previous close relationship.

Acceptance of "infantile sexuality" forms the core of Mowrer and Kluckhohn's "dynamic theory of personality." They state: "The fact that aggressive and sexual prerogatives are denied to the small child throws him into conflict and prevents complete identification with the otherwise loving and protective parents. This dilemma is resolved by means of repression which introduces the latency period. At puberty, this solution is undone and accomplished anew by repudiation of the parent's earlier tabus, and attainment at last of more or less complete identification with them" [*287*]. Again we witness psychosexual development made coextensive with ego development and the brushing aside of other crucial elements in the parent-child relationship.[8]

More germane to the problem of ego development than the issue of whether children's sex interests are comparable in content to those of adults is the process whereby the former learn to identify with their own sex group. Very early in their social careers, children learn to think of themselves as either male or female. Very little, for example, is known about the process of how a boy comes to regard himself as a member of the male clan or to learn the acceptable attributes of male behavior. In contrast to the psychoanalytic view, however, we would stress the point that sex role differentiation is not a product of endogenous impulses of a physiological or emotional nature. The datum of sex type would not go unnoticed if a child were left to his own devices; but it is not of such intrinsic importance as to constitute *per se* an important aspect of his ego development.[9] Its actual importance for ego development is derived from the fact that maleness and femaleness are important characteristics of adult personality structure, and adults project this importance into the life of the child through their expectations that sex differences receive early and sharp recognition from the moment of birth. Hence, sex differences are important to the child's concept of self simply because of social pressures and expectations. Were his culture correspondingly to emphasize the difference between brown and blue eyes he would be similarly preoccupied with learning the appropriate behavior of his like-eyed group.[10]

During the pre-school and elementary school period, therefore, sex role differentiation is an important aspect of ego development, but in a social sense rather than in terms of its psychophysiological or psycho-affectional implications. The pressures exerted in children for assimilating appropriate sex behavior originate in the adult culture, but this function is taken over by the peer group. The opportunities and models for learning are also provided chiefly by the latter. And since sex differences can be made so obvious and unambiguous, learning is facilitated by continual reinforcement. During adolescence, the child is faced with the additional problem of learning a biological sex role (see page 88).

CAUSE AND EFFECT IN DEVELOPMENTAL SEQUENCES

Both Mead [*275*] and Murphy, Murphy and Newcomb [*289*] have criticized the uncritical psychoanalytic imputation of cause and effect relationships to developmental sequences. The former has pointed out that while the child is being subjected to a given aspect of infant care, he is *simultaneously* being exposed to many of the unique cultural values and aspects of adult personality that prevail in his society; and that it is therefore ridiculous to conclude that the latter products are *caused* by the child training practices. "Because . . . symptoms are part of a syndrome, they are always found to be correlated and present at the same time or in a certain sequence; they are then erroneously thought to be cause and effect" [*289*]. For example, both homosexual trends and a marked tendency to distort experience unfavorable to the self are tendencies frequently found in the personality type which is characterized by "ego hypertrophy" and predisposed towards the development of paranoid trends. The first tendency is a modified expression of the exaggerated self-love characteristic of persons with "hypertrophied egos," and the second is a device which is often employed for ego enhancement. But according to psychoanalytic teachings, repressed homosexual trends are the *cause* of paranoid delusions.

CULTURE AND CONSTITUTION

In the eagerness to recognize the role of cultural factors in personality development, there has been a certain amount of understandable overenthusiasm as an inevitable reaction to the phylogenetic views of the orthodox Freudians. As a result, individual differences in constitution and growth pattern, and variability in subcultural and familial patterns within a given culture have tended to be overlooked.

Hereditary Factors in Personality Development

Considerable evidence from many sources is available to support the belief that hereditary factors cannot be dismissed in accounting for the course of personality development. Sontag and Jost [*212*] demonstrated that the locus and degree of autonomic reactivity is at least partially determined by genetic constitution. They found twins to be more alike in the patterning of their autonomic responses than siblings, who in turn showed closer correspondence than unrelated children. Kallman showed that morbidity rate in schizophrenia increases in proportion to an individual's degree of blood relationship to the patient [*214*]. 86 per cent of the monozygotic co-twins of schizophrenic patients were discovered to have schizophrenia. This exceeded by six times the morbidity rate for dizygotic co-twins and ordinary siblings. The strength of the genetic factor in etiology was further indicated by the fact that separation of the monozygotic twins in different familial environments made little difference in eventual rate of incidence, and that in no case was one monozygotic twin diagnosed as suffering from manic-depressive psychosis while his co-twin partner was diagnosed as a schizophrenic.

We cannot deduce from this evidence that hereditary factors are *always* crucial in determining the eventual outcome of any personality trait. They do set the limits and determine the initial direction of growth, but the final outcome is always a resultant of continuous interaction between a genetic predisposition and the environment in which it operates. Even an instant after conception takes place, the morphogenic matrix which shapes the nature of the growth process is not simply the sum total of genetic elements, but rather the resultant of these plus the influence of the existing cellular structure and the maternal environment. It is not that the genes change, but that genes alone do not constitute a growth matrix except at the moment of conception. For the determination of present behavior, only the present effective predisposition (which is a precipitate of all the influences that have ever impinged on an individual's growth), is the immediate relevant variable contributed by the organism. And in many areas of behavior the effective predisposition operating at any given time may be a far cry from the original genetic predisposition.

On the basis of the very same reasoning, to prove that a hereditary factor is operative in personality development, it is not required that one demonstrate its overt consequences in present personality structure. The criterion of universality of occurrence is equally unreasonable since a given biological determinant may be overwhelmed and negated by contrary cultural forces and find only spasmodic and attenuated expression. A variable functions regardless of whether it is crucial for eventual outcome. Although the losing team obviously does not prevail, who would be so rash as to deny that it put in an appearance on the field?

Because the influence of environment is exerted so early in the growth process, it becomes exceedingly difficult to isolate and measure the relative contribution of genetic factors to the development of any personality or behavioral trait. Even the method of monozygotic co-twin control permits only a relative degree of isolation. However, it is reasonable to infer that if individual differences between children appear at birth or shortly afterwards, they are largely determined by hereditary factors since environmental differences have not had sufficient time in which to exert much differential effect. Neonates, for example, display marked individual differences with respect to such gross factors as kinetic level, distribution of energy and irritability [*138, 201*]. Fries and Lewi have detected early differences even in responsiveness to frustration [*140*].

Constitutional Correlates of Personality

Sheldon [*352*] has recently presented convincing evidence that various dimensions of bodily form are highly correlated with certain clusters of personality traits. By defining these bodily dimensions in terms of relative degree of development of organ systems derived from the three primitive embryonic layers, e.g., endomorphy, mesomorphy, and ectomorphy, they acquire additional genetic significance.[11] For example, the general finding that the degree of structural development of an organ system is related to the magnitude of motivations and interests associated with it (e.g., gastrointestinal prominence and greed for affection and approval) points to a genetic common denominator responsible for both the somatic and personality manifestations. Comparable data are presented by Levy who found a significant relationship between duration of menstrual flow and degree of motherliness [*246*].

Lest the conclusions indicated by the above findings be overdrawn, it should be emphasized that the correlations obtained are far from perfect and cannot be used effectively for purposes of individual prediction. Furthermore, it is possible that much of the relationship is acquired through experience rather than through genetic factors; that is, overdevelopment of a given organ predisposes towards frequent exercise, development of aptitude, successful performance, gratification, increased interest, and canalization of motivation in relation to the function subserved by it. These results in turn tend to accentuate the original hypertrophy.

Nevertheless, the implications of this approach cannot be overlooked. If constitutional factors are instrumental in determining tendencies toward introversion or extraversion, hedonism, need for affection, kinetic level, etc., it is reasonable to expect that "a given experience will mean different things to different children . . . Often we discuss the child's behavior in terms of what the parents have done and fail to ask what the child was like to start with, and how his sensitivities and resources have affected the parent" [*291*]. If a six-year-old still sucks his thumb, one need not necessarily choose between excessive deprivation of affectional needs, fixation, or regression to explain the phenomenon. Merely on a constitutional basis he may require a great deal of oral gratification.

Variability in growth pattern—acceleration and retardation in different areas—acts in the same direction as constitutional differences. It helps add to the growth matrix a tough inner core of individuality which makes the child more than a puppet of environmental forces playing upon him. By sensitizing a given child's reaction to a particular pattern of cultural or familial attitudes it insures the fact that even if all children could be ground through the same environmental mill, assembly-line uniformity of product would still not ensue.

Heterogeneity of Cultural Patterning

The description of unique personality types for various primitive cultures [*41, 274*] must not blind us to the fact that such descriptions can be valid only for substantially homogeneous cultures [*275*]. Only in recent years have we awakened to the importance of the fact that in our complex civilization, "cultural environment" is a meaningless abstraction unless further differentiated with respect to such subcultural factors as caste, class, sex, and ethnic origin [*73, 74, 275, 291, 292*].

Neither can we assume any uniformity of parental attitudes or training procedures within a given cultural or sub-cultural area. Influences arising from such sources primarily affect the child indirectly in the early years through the medium of the parents, and only later operate more directly on the child himself. Mowrer and Kluckhohn aptly comment in this connection: "The conditions under which tuition occurs are partly but only partly prescribed by the culture. Mothers vary greatly in the flexibility or rigidity with which they follow the cultural pattern. Even if prescriptions are rigorously adhered to, one mother will handle the child impersonally, another with active distaste, another with emotional warmth" [*287*]. As a result, despite an infinite variety of cultural patterns in child rearing, there is a certain universality in the distribution of certain broad categories of parental practices and attitudes. The writer would hazard the guess that these latter factors (e.g., emotional acceptance or rejection) which (as individual family differences in executing the cultural pattern) overlap cultural boundaries, are more crucial for personality development than the formal uniformities characterizing the culture as a whole.[12]

SITUATIONAL DETERMINISM

A good deal of controversy has waxed in recent years over the issue of "situational determinism." Bartlett [*36*] and Sherif and Cantril [*354*] have both berated the psychoanalytic school for neglecting situational and over-emphasizing genetic factors in the causation of neurosis. No one can deny that the present individual represents a precipitate of his past history, or that traumatic situations tend to precipitate acute or unusual behavioral adjustments. Symptoms of anxiety can be developed by an exhausted and overwrought infantryman exposed to continuous gunfire for a week, even if he had the most optimal childhood environment imaginable. On the other hand the very same symptoms may be developed by an officer (emotionally rejected as a child) who is 3000 miles from the front following a disappointing session with his superior in which the latter appears unaware or unappreciative of his special efforts. Both men breathe rapidly, complain of precordial pain, flatulence, and "choking" sensations. But are they *qualitatively* suffering from the same syndrome? The infantryman can usually be cured by a week's rest; the officer, if at all, only by an intensive reorganization of personality structure.

This dilemma is a product of the statistical concept of behavioral disorder which places abnormal behavior at either extreme of a continuum of behavioral normality. This concept might be valid if we were concerned only with symptomatology, i.e., the physiological signs of anxiety. But it is completely invalid to include similar symptoms reflective of *different* psychopathological mechanisms and significance on the *same* behavioral continuum. The reaction of the infantryman can be placed along a gradient of psychophysiological responses to situational stress; the officer's reaction must be considered along a gradient of developmental predispositions to anxiety growing out of aberrant parent-child relationships.

Thus, while we must agree with Allison Davis that "many concepts of personality economy developed by psychopathology do not hold for individuals in our culture who are mentally ill" [*30*], we must insist that the converse is equally true. There is a range of normal anxieties and aggressions which at the extremes of the continuum are still only exaggerations of the normal; but except for superficial aspects of symptomatology, these have little in common with psychopathological mechanisms whose roots are found in childhood.

NOTES

[1] Fenichel [*109*] presents the psychoanalytic viewpoint adequately. Critical surveys may be found in Ribble [*327*], L. B. Murphy [*291*], and especially Orlansky [*303*].

[2] In relation to this conception, Gardner Murphy [*288*] reaches the following conclusion: "According to Freud and Abraham, a part of the infant's body may become the seat of such intensely satisfying experience that experience in relation to it may serve to mold both subsequent body processes and subsequent conceptions of the self. The observations are meager and the theory overpretentious; but for all that it is a highly stimulating conception, some aspects of which have been experimentally confirmed."

[3] A new system of infant care, the Cornelian Corner, stressing the importance of breast feeding, self-demand feeding schedules, and delayed toilet training, is historically related to this point of view. However (although empirical evidence in support of these practices is sparse) it is possible to advocate them on the basis of sound developmental principles of child care without in the least subscribing to their psychoanalytic implications for adult personality structure.

[4] Margaret Mead [*275*] points out that in cases where a specific practice is an

expression of a more general pattern of parental attitudes, other concrete manifestations of these attitudes are usually available. Du Bois [*92*] comments that "a single discipline of childhood or a single traumatic experience is rarely sufficient in itself to set cultural personality types. Repeated experiences in different behavioral, value and institutional contexts alone will create personality constellations of force and consistency."

[5] Mowrer and Kluckhohn [*287*] refer to the "disputed" [*346*] fact of the so-called "equivalence" of the erogenous zones (as a result of which "inhibition of gratification in one sphere is likely to be followed by increased activity in the other") as evidence in support of infantile sexuality. But even if this fact *were* true it would indicate only that one form of *pleasurable* activity can to a certain extent compensate for the loss of another.

[6] The differentiation between the historical and functional roles of the sex hormones in producing adult sex drive can be seen in the fact that castration prior to puberty rules out the possibility of sex desire; whereas after puberty it reduces sexual potency but does not eliminate sex desire.

[7] This break in continuity of psychosexual development is not incompatible with principles of genetic psychology. The addition of a potent new variable, i.e., sex hormones, may quite conceivably result in behavioral changes that are discontinuous with previous development. This discontinuity is reported by half of Kinsey's male subjects [*225*]. In the other half, continuity may have been retrospective illusion rather than historical fact.

[8] That such psychoanalytic interpretations are neither inevitable nor self-evident can be seen from Gardner Murphy's [*288*] penetrating analysis of the Oedipus situation: "Aggression which develops toward the restricting or frustrating parent . . . may result from injury to the self and not from the sexuality of the child . . . What hurts anyone . . . is to be pushed aside in favor of another." Perhaps it is later, if and as fondling by the parents begins to show consistent sex preferences on *their* part, that a preference for the parent of the opposite sex appears; and even here it seems likely that it is enhancement or frustration of selfhood, differentially induced by the behavior of father or mother, that causes much of the strain, rather than primarily sexual aims in the children themselves.

[9] This position does not necessarily refute the possibility that sex differences in the behavior of boys and girls might in part be biologically conditioned. It merely holds that such behavioral differences as are conditioned by anatomical and physiological factors, (just as the primary sex differences themselves) would not without cultural emphasis constitute crucial aspects of ego development. Prior to adolescence we cannot conceive of psychosexual impulses as important determinants of personality structure. Afterwards, also, they are more of an expression of existing personality structure functioning in a particular cultural climate with respect to sanctioned sexual activity than a primary influence shaping the development of personality.

[10] A parallel situation to sex role differentiation which demonstrates that the eye analogy is not at all far-fetched is the importance of skin-color differentiation for ego development in American culture. This discussion would obviously be in the nature of a truism were the issue not so thoroughly beclouded by psychoanalysis.

[11] Sheldon's typology is generally considered to be superior to Kretschmer's well-known classification of constitutional types (asthenic, pyknic, athletic and dysplastic [*234*]) because each individual can be rated on a one to seven scale along each of three separate dimensions. This eliminates much of the ambiguity, arbitrariness and subjectivity of judgment inevitably inhering in qualitative, "all-or-none" categories such as Kretschmer's.

[12] This explanation of basic differences found between individuals in the same culture differs from the following explanation offered by Margaret Mead: "If we think of culture in terms of regularities instead of similarities, it is possible to refer differences between individuals to a cultural base . . . Such differences are explicable in cultural terms to the extent that the common culture provides the background for different choices" [*275*]. While this explanation suffices in understanding why "one of a pair of brothers turns out to be a devout Baptist and the other a fervid agnostic" [*275*], it will not explain why two adults one in New York and one in Samoa both have secure emotionally responsive personalities, while two other adults similarly located have hostile, insecure and anxiety-ridden personalities.

CHAPTER 4

Personality and the Parent-Child Relationship

FROM AN HISTORICAL STANDPOINT, this volume can be viewed as part of a growing movement to establish a general theory of psychopathology which is derived from a broader base than the psychoanalytic approach via psychosexual maturation. It starts with the thesis that the most important determinants of future personality structure are *not* to be found in the individual vicissitudes impinging upon a predetermined gradient of psychosexual development, but rather in the changing aspects of the child-parent, and child-society relationship through the successive stages of maturation. Implicit in this thesis is the belief that "parent-child relationships are determined primarily by the attitudes of the parents . . . that it is in the small and subtle aspects of these relationships that the security of the child develops . . . that the essence of parent-child relations lies more in how a parent *feels* than in what a parent *does*" [*389*].

In developing this thesis, attention will first be directed to the normal course of ego development and then to deviations resulting from aberrant parent-child relationships. Finally, these distortions in ego organization will be related to the categories of personality disorder toward which they predispose the affected individual.

INFANTILE VERSUS LATER EXPERIENCE

Accordingly, as the significance of specific items of infant care for adult personality structure was discounted, greater attention was devoted to the broader aspects of parental attitudes[1]* embodied

* Notes for this chapter appear on page 37.

in such concepts as "rejection," "overprotection," etc. Some evidence has been presented in support of the hypothesis that such emotional attitudes can be communicated to the infant through subtle cues of handling in the early months of life [*303*]. This channel of "early personality conmmunication" [*303*] has been given an important place in concepts of personality development advanced by such writers as Plant [*309*], Sullivan [*387*], Cantor [*63*] and Lois B. Murphy [*291, 292*].

While such hypotheses[2] have intriguing possibilities, it would seem reasonable to impose at least two qualifications at the outset: (1) A review of the emotional development of the child indicates that his susceptibility to phobic stimuli increases as he matures and becomes more capable of appreciating their implications [*201*]. Threats to the ego can not be very significant while the concept of self is still vague and amorphous. It is therefore quite difficult to appreciate Rank's conception of the "birth trauma" [*314*] or Freud's "nuclear prototype" of anxiety referable to the same experience [*135*]. (2) The permanence or irreversibility of the effects of early parental attitudes on personality structure can be described only in relative terms. At least in the first two years of life, there seems to be much room for reversibility, with somewhat less possibility for fundamental revisions remaining in later years.[3] At any rate, we must bear in mind that "like biological heredity, infant experiences while placing certain constraints upon personality give mainly potentialities. Whether these potentialities become actualized or not or the extent to which they become actualized depends upon later social and other conditions which structure the individual's experiences. Only an external condition of adult life brings out fully a predisposition, the basis for which has been laid in the experiences of infancy and early childhood . . . Substantially the same personality trait may be caused by different patterns of childhood experience" [*287*]. As will be seen in the later discussion of ego development, some of the most significant changes take place between the third and fifth years. And while it is true that defects referable to this period may have lasting effects, normal development at this stage does not necessarily guarantee a favorable outcome for the crucial period of adolescence.

DESCRIPTIONS OF PERSONALITY DEVELOPMENT ORIENTED AROUND THE PARENT-CHILD RELATIONSHIP

Conceptions of personality development which emphasize the crucial role of the parent-child relationship in its broader aspects are of course commonplace today [*5, 61, 63, 123, 141, 188, 219, 247, 267, 287, 288, 291, 294, 309, 315, 354, 389*], and not a few attempts have been made to relate these concepts to psychopathology.[4] Adler made the child's feeling of helplessness in relation to his parents the basis of his longing for superiority, and emphasized the importance of sequential position (in the order of children in a family) for the patterning of the "style of life" [*5*]. While reserving more detailed appraisal of Adler's theories for a later section, it may be noted here that he deserves a large share of the credit for bringing ego problems into a central position in present-day psychopathology. Kardiner's concept of "basic personality structure" as "the precipitate of the reactions of the individual to specific institutions in the order in which they affect him [*218*] naturally stressed the prepotency of the parent-child relationship. In delineating the contrasting trends towards self-assertion and self-subservience[5] [*315*], Rank emphasized the child's earlier tendency to identify with his parents and his later efforts to differentiate himself from them. Plant[5] distinguished between feelings of security ("who"-status) and feelings of adequacy ("what"-status) by associating the former with the intrinsic acceptance of the child for himself in the family circle [*309*].

Following upon these more theoretical conceptions of the parent-child relationship were the pioneering studies of Levy [*243, 245, 247*] and Symonds [*389*] which helped to delineate the origins and consequences of "maternal overprotection," and parental domination. It is not at all surprising that "observational and experimental studies have contributed less than have case studies to our knowledge of parent-child relationships . . . Study by techniques of observation, ratings, questionnaire is difficult on account of the subtlety with which parent attitudes are expressed . . . A parent like everyone else may have an official self, which he presents to the world and a true self which may often think and feel in ways that are not socially approved" [*389*].

It is apparent, therefore, that the writer is making no claim to originality in employing this approach to personality development. However, the hopeful intention is (by rigorous systematization of existing data and reformulation of existing concepts) to fill some of the gaps in a theory of personality development to which L. B. Murphy was referring in making the following statement: "There is as yet no adequate longitudinal study of the processes of character formation, either starting from the hypotheses intrinsic in the oral, anal, genital type of theory of Freud and Abraham or any other framework oriented to the question of the integrated personality as a whole" [*291*]. While it is obvious that a complete theory of personality development must await the completion of studies now in progress or yet to be done, it is the writer's contention that systematization and clarification of the existing theoretical structure is a logical prerequisite to clear formulation of fruitful research problems.

To illustrate the type of systematization that is being attempted, a brief listing will be made of some of the deficiencies found in discussions and systems of personality development referred to in this section:

1. There is a general tendency to discuss concepts such as "security" and "anxiety" without relating them to various stages of completeness and sophistication in the self-concept and in maturational capacity for responsiveness to emotional stimuli (e.g, Plant [*309*], Adler [*5*], Rank [*314, 315*], Freud [*135*].

2. While it is appreciated that most normal children go through a period of dependent identification with their parents, (a situation referred to as "satellization" by the writer), little notice is taken of the sizeable number of children who fail to pass through this stage. As a result there is no systematic treatment of (a) the types of parental attitudes which give rise to this maturational failure; (b) the consequences of this developmental defect for later maturational sequences; (c) the differential effects of practices such as "indulgence" or "domination" on "satellizers" and "non-satellizers"; (d) different methods of value formation and learning found in

the two types; (e) differences in predisposition to various personality disorders related to the above distinction.

3. The various attributes of infantile ego structure are not followed through developmentally in a systematic fashion from childhood to adult life or related systematically to the personality disorders on the basis of maturational defects.

4. In discussing the child's needs for dependence or independence, no distinction is drawn between the *volitional*[6] and the *executive*[6] aspects of the problem. It is tacitly assumed that both aspects vary concomitantly, an assumption, which, as will be seen later, is far from the truth.

5. There has been a lamentable lack of precision in defining and using various terms descriptive of parental attitudes and practices. "Indulgence," "overvaluation," "underdomination" and "extrinsic valuation" are often lumped together or used interchangeably. Similarly, the aspects of parental solicitousness and domination are frequently confused.

In using such constructs as "infantile omnipotence," "satellization," "volitional independence," etc., does not the writer leave himself open to the same charge of employing "simple sovereign" assumptions which Sherif and Cantril [*354*] levelled at the psychoanalysts? In defense, it can be stated only that these constructs are either related to an accumulated mass of developmental observations in accordance with the law of parsimony, or else have a certain self-evident validity. They are primarily intended to apply to developmental sequences in our culture. Further cross-cultural research would be needed to establish their applicability on a wider basis.

To avoid possible misunderstanding later, it may be restated now that any statements regarding psychopathology for which evidence is not cited must not be interpreted as having any empirical validity. They have the status merely of hypotheses derived from clinical observations or from logical inferences of relationships between existing data. In most instances they are systematically related to naturalistic observations, or are capable of so being related. However, in certain cases, e.g., the neonate's conception of self and universe, speculation is unavoidable, and one can only hope to maintain a certain logical consistency between the situation at this stage and the developments which follow. It is felt that this procedure is more satisfactory from a theoretical standpoint than leaving gaps the closure of which is presently not even a remote possibility.

NOTES

[1] Outstanding studies illustrating this point of view include those of P. M. Symonds [*388*] and D. M. Levy [*247*].

[2] Ribble [*327*], for example, maintains: "It is becoming evident that psychological care of the infant is fully as important for his emotional, intellectual and social development as is careful feeding for adequate nutrition and good digestive functioning... It is reasonable enough to suppose that the sensitive organism of the human infant would register the experiences related to body security and well-being or to insecurity and lack of personal care. Once registered, these experiences of security or insecurity would be expected to foster responses of positive groping on the one hand or of negative resistance on the other. These early mechanisms of reaction might then readily gain momentum so as to alter or even to distort the succeeding phases of personality development."

[3] Although longitudinal studies of personality development [*207*] have shown that adjustive techniques may shift in the face of crises produced by critical situations or by developmental lags or spurts in growth, it is still questionable whether more than *mode* of reaction is involved in the change. Further research of this kind is needed to determine how much of the core of personality can be changed after the first six years of life. And more basic to the question of core than the types of adjustive techniques employed by the individual at various stages in his career, are the aspirations and evaluations standing in relation to his concept of self. For a discussion of the possibility of later fundamental changes in personality, see pp. 72-73.

[4] The relatively belated recognition given to the importance of parent-child relationships for personality development can, of course, be attributed to the influence of Freud. He and his followers were among the first to stress the importance of childhood experience for character formation. However, they selected out of this experience only those factors which impinge on the course of the child's predetermined psychosexual development, and more or less neglected broader emotional aspects growing out of parental attitudes of rejection, overprotection, domination, etc.

[5] See pp. 74-75 and 339-340 for a critical discussion of Rank's and Plant's views.

[6] *Executive* refers to the manipulative activity involved in completing a need-satisfaction sequence, whereas *volitional* refers solely to the act of willing the satisfaction of a given need apart from any consideration as to how this is to be consummated. An infant, for example, displays marked notions of volitional independence and omnipotence, but at the same time may conceive of himself as executively impotent and dependent. In adult life there is greater correspondence between these two aspects of dependence-independence.

PART II

The Natural History of Ego Development

CHAPTER 5

Theoretical Assumptions Underlying a Psychology of Ego Development

---

SCIENTIFIC HAZARDS

THE INVESTIGATION of anything as formidable as the concept of self prior to the development of language is admittedly an unsatisfactory and highly conjectural matter [*24*]. The neonate or the infant cannot *tell* us how it regards self and the universe. After freeing oneself as far as possible from anthropomorphic bias, one can at best evaluate infantile biosocial status and perceptual capacity, and then attempt to draw intelligent inferences as to what a perception of self might possibly be like under such circumstances.

Speculation, however, does not lie outside the realm of science. Global hypotheses lacking immediate verifiability through direct empirical data, e.g., the nebular hypothesis, the atomic theory, the theory of evolution, have played significant roles in the ordering and interpretation of immediate data in their respective sciences. Such hypotheses are scientifically allowable as long as they remain consistent with available empirical fact, and provided that they are uttered with the humility befitting their status as hypotheses. In the area of ego development, there is the additional requirement that speculation be psychologically plausible in terms of the child's actual perceptual capacities rather than in terms of an adult framework of reference grafted on an infantile organism.

THE SELF: HOMUNCULAR OR DEVELOPMENTAL PRODUCT

Until comparatively recently—because of the dominant influence of theological doctrines—the prevailing conception of ego development was homuncular. That is, the ego at birth was thought to be a fully-formed, ready-made instrument, a kind of veritable ego in miniature or tabloid representation of an adult ego. Appreciation of self and individuality with all of its implications was confidently held to be an axiomatic correlate of consciousness.

This homuncular conception of the ego had an obvious and more concrete pictorial counterpart in a formerly popular notion of reproduction and ante-natal existence. According to this view the sperm was not the fertilizing half of a zygote out of which layers, tissues and organs were gradually differentiated as the outcome of an ontogenetic process. It was instead a little man in miniature. No new parts developed in the process of gestation; the fully formed organs merely gained in bulk until they attained full-term fetal size.

In the realm of idea-acquisition, apart from the self-concept, homunculism had been successfully combated by the empiricism of Locke, which insisted that ideas evolve as the product of experience. In biology, the homuncular concept is remembered only as a quaint relic of pre-scientific embryology. And instincts—the ultimate in homunculism as applied to behavior theory—had already fallen into disrepute even before behaviorism had apparently dealt it the death blow.

The roots of homuncular thinking, however, were too deeply ingrained in our culture to disappear so gracefully from the psychological scene. Banished from the sphere of intellectual and behavior development, homunculism was resurrected by psychoanalysis in the more tolerant area of personality development. Populating a phylogenetic id were a whole host of psychosexual motivations, each accompanied by appropriate emotional overtones. It is true that in accordance with psychoanalytic theory all of these motivations do not appear at once but inevitably undergo unfolding in predetermined sequence. However, the crucial distinction between developmentalism and homunculism does not lie with the issue of latency of appearance. The former demands a concept of gradual evolution in qualitative aspects of form; the latter implies that final form is complete from the start and subject only to quantitative modification.

In the more limited and special meaning given to the ego by

psychoanalysis, a good deal of ontogenesis is accepted. That is, the ego becomes a layer of personality which evolves through interaction of id and reality. However, how reasonable is this limited concept of the ego? Can we exempt psychosexual motivations (which psychoanalysis derives exclusively from the id) from all developmental connection with ego? Are they not related to the concept of self? If so, they must also have an ontogenesis rather than a preformed existence in the id. But it is obvious that no developmental process is envisaged since infantile sexuality is qualitatively equated with adult sexuality. As a matter of fact, psychoanalysis places the entire genesis of motivation beyond the ego by allowing for ego motivations only as by-products of id sublimation.

Yet even within this limited definition of ego, psychoanalysis lacks self-consistency. The infant is supposed to experience a primal anxiety as a result of the trauma of birth [*135*]. But anxiety is a response of fear evoked when the ego is threatened. Hence, this notion of Freud's must necessarily assume the existence of ego before any experience with reality could possibly occur. The same assumption of an ante-natal ego is also made in postulating a phylogenetic identification of the male child with his father which aids in overcoming the Oedipal conflict, since identification is inconceivable prior to ego formation.

A variety of homunculism has also found its way back into developmental psychology through another devious route, i.e., through unwarranted extension of the concept of *maturation*. Operationally speaking, maturation can refer only to the achievement of a degree of development of a given function in the absence of specific training opportunities. It does not imply *per se* that the course of development is essentially molded by directional factors inherent in the organism, rather than by factors impinging on the organism from without. Yet Gesell makes the former assumption when he states: "Growth is a unifying concept which resolves the dualism of heredity and environment. Environmental factors support, inflect and modify; but they do not generate the progressions of development" [*148*].

Thus, instead of acknowledging that the relative influence of internal and external factors can be expected to vary depending on the particular function considered, Gesell assumes that *all* functions are primarily patterned from within with respect to sequence of developmental changes. Such a hypothesis fulfills the criteria of developmentalism since is presupposes a qualitative evolution of form. But if inner directional factors are so potent in development—even in emotional, conceptual and motivational areas—that uniformities in sequential progress are predictable in terms of detailed content, the net effect is almost the same as if everything were preformed from the start.

The theoretical implications of this point of view for ego development are obvious. It implies that the patterning and the uniformities which prevail even from one culture to the next are exclusively the outcome of common internal morphogenic factors. In the next section, therefore, a refutation of this orientation will be presented together with the thesis that uniformities in ego development issue from those "universal biological and psychological conditions and limitations relevant to the process of maturation" [*24*] which confront growing human beings in every culture.

EGO DEVELOPMENT: A PRODUCT OF BIOSOCIAL INTERACTION

Ego development is the outcome of continuous biosocial interaction. There is no predetermined course or sequence of events which reflects the unfolding of a detailed blueprint designed by inner impulses. Genetic predispositions, to be sure, are not lacking. They provide initial direction for growth and predetermine its absolute limits. But their influence is absolute and unopposed only at the moment of conception. Thereafter, this influence operates with only relative and varying degrees of effectiveness in shaping ultimate form. In no case, however, can we conceive of absolute inevitability; and in no case is the genetic factor the immediately antecedent variable. Environmental forces always intervene to insure that the effective matrix of developmental forces impinging on any ongoing growth process is not a simple genetic determinant but a complex resultant of interaction between heredity and environment.

The relative importance of hereditary factors in determining the degree of variability possible in the form and sequential appearance of new behavior patterns is a function of their "phylogenetic origin and importance" [*271*]. Every child must learn to walk if he is to fulfill the expectations of his species membership. Hence, we can predict that an unusual degree of regularity will prevail in the patterning of developmental steps incident to the acquisition of human locomotion, a uniformity which reflects the prepotency of similar phylogenetic factors operating in all members of the species. This uniformity is so striking in its specific aspects —despite diversity in culturally provided opportunities for exercise—that we can assume environmental influences to be of negligible significance in the emergence of the new function. To speak of such a phenomenon as the outcome of an "unfolding process" is, therefore, not too inaccurate or far afield for practical purposes.

It is quite another matter, however, when we deal with adjustive behavior, which is relevant only to the unique organism-environment relationships embodied in the personal history of a single member of the species. In this case, the possibilities for variability in behavior patterning are almost limitless. The genetic component is still present and cannot be dismissed; but its expression is so modified by unique factors of individual experience that the resulting behavior pattern can be predicted only in very general terms from known properties of the organism. Such predictions are made possible by virtue of the fact that processes of interaction can never exceed the organism's psychological capacity for responding to his environment at any given point in his developmental career. This consideration perforce imposes certain arbitrary sequences in the development of functions. Concept formation, for example, cannot take place prior to the occurrence of sufficient concrete experience (with enough commonality in diversity) to make abstraction possible. It is important to remember, however, that these predictions are always in terms of process and never in terms of specific content.

Because the very meaning of ego implies abstraction of the individuality derived from unique personal experience, ego development must primarily be a reflection of ontogenetic rather than of phytogenetic factors. Hence the suggestion that the specific content of ego structure unfolds in accordance with certain ancestrally predetermined engrams is grossly lacking in plausibility.

Uniformities in ego development do prevail, but they are uniformities in process which issue from a common core of problems associated with shifts in biosocial status, and from a common set of psychological capacities for perceiving self and environment. Hence, one can easily conceive of many different male children possessing a comparable capacity for possibly identifying with their fathers as a consequence of relevant antecedent experience under a wide variety of circumstances. Less credible, however, is the notion that this identification inevitably exists preformed at birth in all male infants prior to any opportunity for interpersonal experience, and is then elicited *only* as a means of solving an Oedipal conflict. And to say that the identification is not preformed but must arise anyway because of inner morphogenic trends is hardly more satisfactory.

The ego can be nothing more or less than an organization of values, attitudes and aspirations related to an abstraction of self. It is a joint product of the unique interpersonal relations which define an individual's biosocial status and of his perceptual and adjustive responses to awareness of this status. As he develops new behavior capacities, as social expectations change in relation to him, as dependency relationships become altered, and as his ability realistically to appraise his status improves, ego attitudes and their organization adopt new forms. In common with biological evolution there is both continuity and modification in the course of ego development. The existing properties of a given structural organization always selectively direct and limit the type of change that can be expected from the introduction of new experience.

The thesis of this book is that behavior disorders are largely the outcome of unfavorable modifications in ego development which predispose toward undesirable adjustments to life situations. As the biosocial status of the individual shifts, changes in ego structure are made necessary. These alterations may or may not be in accordance with the socially-approved direction of adult maturation. They may or may not help produce a stable, secure and well-integrated personality resistant to behavioral distortion. It will be our task in this and succeeding chapters to trace the changes in ego structure that are correlated with modifications in role and status, to identify differences in ego organization that follow from significant differences in interpersonal experience, and finally to inquire into the relationship between specific defects and distortions in ego development and the particular types of behavior disorder to which they predispose the affected individual.

CHAPTER 6

The Omnipotent Phase of Ego Development

DEVELOPMENT OF A PRE-VERBAL EMPIRICAL SELF

PERCEPTION is largely a matter of defining boundaries between figure and ground [*231*]. As boundary lines become sufficiently sharpened, the organism becomes capable of differentially responding to different perceptual cues. Later if it is able to generalize, common elements are abstracted from related perceptions and a concept is formed which permits a higher order of response integration.

So it is with ego development. Self and the world: which is figure and which is ground [*231*], where does one end and the other begin? The newborn infant does not know. To him the boundaries are blurred; stimulus and sensation constitute an undifferentiated field. Then as boundaries emerge they are multi-dimensional in nature. At countless points of junction between organism and environment, distinctions in quality are made: inside and outside, feeling-surface and object-surface, moving hand and feeling of motion, violent contact and feeling of pain. Finally, "all of these separately differentiated perceptions of self . . . become organized into a unified [concept] as they occur [sequentially or] concurrently and hence interact" [*24*].

The first step in ego development, therefore, requires the delimitation of the boundary of self from the wider environment of objects and persons with which it is fused [*149, 268, 288, 354*]. This distinction is gradually brought about as the child explores his environment: The sense of touch acquaints him with the presence of objects outside himself [*149*]; kinaesthetic sensations make him aware of his own movements in space; and the sense of pain vividly informs him that transgressions of the self-not self boundary are unpleasant [*354*].

The most acute consciousness of self, however, develops as an outgrowth of inevitable delays in the gratification of his organic needs [*109, 116*]. For here is awareness of intense unpleasant stimulation referable to the body and of the existence of environmental objects and persons associated with the termination of deprivation. A biosocial relationship has already arisen defined in terms of absolute dependency in this need-satisfaction sequence. But this is an objective description of the actual situation by an adult rather than an account of what the infant perceives. Because he stops crying when he hears his mother's footsteps, we cannot assume that he appreciates the causal relationship between her presence and the anticipated reduction of his hunger, and hence that he understands his dependence on her for need-satisfaction. Mother is only a conditioned stimulus which he has learned to associate with food. Yet this whole sequence of hunger, displeasure, mother, food and placidity provides a most vivid opportunity for self-perception by interposing two environmental variables (mother and food) between the only two poles of emotional expression (displeasure and quiescence) that define inner experience at birth.

Self-perception is further facilitated by the infant's reaction to mother as a person—as a psychosocial rather than as a conditioned physical stimulus. This seems to occur "for the first time in the third month when the infant smiles in response to a human partner's face" [*369*]. Thus, "mother's outline serves an an anchorage point for the slowly accumulating self-pattern" [*288*]. It provides a scaffolding for the elaboration of his own self-portrait as a person from which he must later differentiate that which is he and that which is his mother.

When a sense of volition emerges in relation to the need-satisfaction sequence, the empirical distinction between self and environment is already well-established on a functional basis and becomes further reinforced. The voluntary aspects of this situation are differentiated from the generalized emotional response of displeasure (thrashing, crying, etc.) which even at birth appears in reaction to an intense internal or external simulus. This response has unlearned adaptive value; but it is not until its efficacy in relieving the tensions of need are perceived by the infant that it can be utilized as a volitional device for this purpose. Volitional crying then becomes a conscious instrument for relieving unpleasant sensations referable to self. The act of willing becomes a directed expression of self as an entity, and the aid it invokes from the outside serves to highlight the distinction between self and environment.

Thus, long before a verbal concept of self makes its appearance, a functional appreciation of the ego boundary is apparent in the child's behavior [*109, 288, 308, 354*]. He can distinguish between phenomena occurring within himself and those transpiring in the outer world. Yet there is no reason to believe that the capacity to make this practical distinction in many different areas implies a unified concept of self. This concept, which is the fruit of difficult abstraction, must await the facilitating influence of language.

THE ORIGIN OF EGO OMNIPOTENCE[1]*

Even if the empirical self does not constitute a unified concept which can be abstracted, the several parts of it are endowed with value by the infant. He occupies a biosocial position characterized by complete dependency on others for the satisfaction of his needs. Nevertheless, his value in the eyes of his parents is not discounted by this fact. They organize his environment in a way which is peculiarly benevolent in catering to his needs while making relatively few demands upon him [*268*]. It is true that he soon becomes aware of the causal relationship between the presence of parental figures and the reduction of organic need. Hence he comes to appreciate his executive dependency. But at the same time crying becomes a volitional response which can be employed at will to satisfy inner needs. Since he obviously cannot appreciate the role of parental love and duty in ministering to his helplessness, this solicitude can appear only as an act of obedience to his irresistibly omnipotent will.[2]

This latter misinterpretation of parental altruism which contributes to the infant's self-concept of omnipotence springs from his perceptual immaturity in evaluating his own status in relation to others. The difficulty does not lie in an inability realistically to perceive the actual attitudes and behavior of individuals in his

* Notes for this chapter appear on page 53.

tiny, interpersonal world. He does not, for example, expect to receive the same degree of deference from older siblings as he does from parents. In small, intimate groups his proximate perception of interpersonal attitudes is quite accurate. His perceptual immaturity first becomes evident at the level of perceiving the underlying bases for these attitudes. At this stage of developmental maturity he can conclude only that parents are deferential and permissive because of an obligatory need to submit to his powerful will. The attribution of altruism to their behavior becomes possible later as both perceptual maturity increases and as his notion of omnipotence is no longer supported by a proximate perception of relatively invariable parental deference to his desires.

Consider this sequence and its effects on self-perception in the six-month-old infant: The child is hungry. He cries because he has learned that crying is an effective adaptive response. His mother hears but cannot come immediately. The hunger becomes more uncomfortable and evokes a generalized reaction of displeasure. More intense crying and thrashing about. Mother hurries to fetch a bottle. Footsteps are heard and satisfaction is anticipated. The crying ceases.

What has the child perceived in relation to himself? He was hungry but he was helpless to satisfy his hunger. He was dependent on his mother to bring him a bottle. But does he interpret this as a sign of impotence on his part? Quite the contrary. He willed that she bring the bottle and she brought it. Surely his will must be quite powerful. The fact that he is executively dependent only strengthens this belief. What further proof of omnipotence does he need when, as a manifestly helpless individual, he is still so successful in the matter of self-gratification?

It also seems probable that the early notion of volitional omnipotence is related to the differentiation of anger from the single primitive emotion of displeasure. Spitz does not report the appearance of rage until the tenth month of life [*369*]. By this time the feeling of omnipotence is well-grounded. When the child is exposed to need-frustration, to the original reaction of displeasure in the face of unpleasant stimulation is added a new component which is a response to the thwarting of the supposed omnipotent attributes of will. This is the emotion of anger. In time, as the range of volitional expression is extended beyond the desire for gratification of organic needs, anger will appear whenever goal-directed activity is opposed. But "whether or not restraint of movement will cause negative reactions in the older infant depends upon whether or not the restraint interferes with customary sequences which have been built up" [*80*]. It is immaterial whether objective evidence of deprivation is apparent to the observer. The crucial factor determining the adequacy of a stimulus for eliciting rage is its capacity for producing subjective feelings of frustration in the child.

But even if this hypothesis regarding the development of anger fails to hold up, the emotion of anger itself helps to reinforce and enhance "the solipsistic qualities of the infantile ego by investing it with emotional tone. The process of self-assertion, thus, becomes charged with emotional overtones; and its frustration gives rise to the temper tantrum which is the nuclear prototype for all aggressive reactions to ego-denial, including the negativism of the three-year-old child" [*24*].

THE VERBAL STAGE OF EGO DEVELOPMENT

The ego attains status as a concept with the advent of language. Symbols free the child from direct dependence on objects for the expression of meaning. The resulting enhancement of the possibilities for interaction of related perceptions greatly facilitates abstraction and generalization.

Two earlier developments antedate the appearance of the final conceptualization of self in personal pronoun form. By the eighth month "possessive emotions towards toys are manifested . . . Between the tenth and twelfth months . . . a positive sense of property becomes observable" [*369*]. By twenty-one months, this is conceptualized as "mine" [*149*]. It represents a sharpening of the distinction between self and others to the point where objects come to belong to the persons habitually using them. Although natural egocentricity first makes him conscious of his own property, awareness of the belongings of others accentuates the concepts of possession. "My toothbrush" acquires more definite meaning as an assertion of personal priority of use after he gets the idea of "Mommy's toothbrush" and "Daddy's toothbrush."

The next development in the growth of a verbal concept of self arises when he becomes objectively aware of his own doings as a person and makes third-person reference to them. His own activities acquire the same distinctiveness that he associates with other integral selves. First he conceives of another child as a "baby." It is a step forward when at 24 months he subsumes his own perceived form under the same concept [*149*]. Likewise it shows that he appreciates his functional role as a person when in referring to himself, he says, "Jimmy threw the ball."

The next higher degree of abstraction in relation to self appears at 27 months [*149*] when the child uses the personal pronoun "I." This "I" includes all of the separate perceptions of self. It implies a genuine self-consciousness. He no longer equates his own activities to the doings of others by referring to both in the third-person. His own functions are characterized by the distinctiveness of his own individuality. "After this point is reached, a new abstract level of self-reactions becomes possible: identification with persons, goals, and values; incorporation of standards; and finally self-judgments, self-criticism, guilt feelings and conscience" [*24, 149, 157, 354*].

The growth of language consolidates the ego as a concept. It allows its attributes to "stand out in sharper relief." By coinciding with the height of the omnipotent phase at two-and-one-half, the verbalization of ego induces an accelerated expansion and clearer expression of its essential characteristics.

NOTES

[1] As early as 1915, Ferenczi [*110*] wrote about four stages of omnipotence in the differentiation of the ego: (a) a period of "unconditional acceptance" prior to birth when all "wishes" are automatically satisfied; (b) a period of "magic hallucinatory omnipotence" shortly after birth when mere wishing is translated into actuality; (c) a third stage of "magic cries and gestures"; and lastly (d) a period of omnipotence through "magic thoughts and words".

The first two stages prior to the development of *voluntary* articulation of needs are obviously a product of homuncular reasoning, since feelings of omnipotence cannot antedate a functional concept of self. A self concept exists neither before birth nor shortly after birth. Ferenczi's last two stages are compatible with the concept of omnipotence presented in this section, although he fails to make clear their origin in distorted self-perception and fails to distinguish between feelings of volitional and executive power (see page 38). This latter confusion persists to this very day in psychoanalytic literature: It is simultaneously alleged (without any further explanation) that the infant both regards himself as omnipotent as well as feels overwhelmed by his dependence on parents.

[2] The feeling of omnipotence, of course, cannot be definitely observed until the advent of language. Many beliefs of magical power persist into adult life, but are seldom communicated except in the psychoses. "There are many ways in which individuals believe themselves to have magical powers, to be among the specially gifted, to be so precious as to be specially vulnerable, to be able to shape events through willing them to be" [*178*].

CHAPTER 7

Devaluation of the Omnipotent Ego

PRESSURES TOWARD DEVALUATION

AT ABOUT THE TIME that the ego becomes established on a conceptual basis, the omnipotent attributes of ego organization approach the height of their development. They have flourished in an idyllic child-centered world which has demanded but little in the way of conformity from the child. But violent changes are soon in the offing, changes in his biosocial status and changes in his capacity to perceive this status realistically. As a result, these "delusions" of omnipotence must give way and be replaced by ego attributes which reflect the influence of these new developments.

The culture tends to be tolerant of infantile dependency. Generally speaking, it provides through the parents an atmosphere of benevolent protection asking nothing in return save that the infant grow and realize the phylogenetic capacities of the species. But there is a limit to cultural and parental indulgence. Parents are not willing to continue indefinitely as "slaves" to their offspring. In addition, they begin to feel the responsibility for superimposing on the infant's biological acquisitions the distinguishing characteristics which will make him a creature of his culture.

The culture, therefore, demands that the infant graduate to the status of child. Before taking steps to effect this transformation, parents wait, depending on the culture, for a longer or shorter period of time, more or less patiently, for some indications of maturity. As some of the infant's more primitive helplessness recedes, as motor, intellectual and social growth gives rise to greater manifest capacity for responsiveness to parental desires, parents "make increasingly greater demands on the child" [*24*]. They demand more and more that he conform to certain standards which possess self-evident validity to them but only stubborn arbitrariness to the child.

Simultaneously, as the child is subjected to the greater pressures for conforming to the general expectations of his culture and to the more specific requirements of his parents, intellectual maturation greatly increases his capacity for appreciating the true nature of his biosocial status. He acquires insight into his own relative insignificance in the ordering of events that impinge on his welfare. He begins to perceive that he is dependent on his parents' good will as well as on their executive agency for the gratification of his needs.

Thus, for the first time he realizes that his dependence is volitional as well as executive in nature and that his parents are not *obliged* to serve him just because he is helpless. Helplessness is no longer a regal badge of volitional omnipotence, but a perceived condition for impotent dependence on the will of others. Now he is obliged to help himself to the limits of his motor competence instead of ignoring this competence in favor of being waited upon. Hence, this limited degree of compulsory self-help set within a larger framework of insufficient capacity for complete executive independence becomes symbolic of the end of the infantile era of volitional omnipotence.

SATELLIZATION AS A DEVALUING PROCEDURE

A crisis in ego organization is now inevitable, making necessary a reorganization on a vastly devalued basis. This devaluation is a protective device which avoids severe traumatic injury to self-esteem. For obviously if a child continued to retain grandiose conceptions of himself in the face of a reality which continually belied his pretensions of omnipotence, he would have little chance of emerging with any sense of adequacy. Self-esteem or the feeling of adequacy is largely the outcome of achieving a status commensurate with one's conception of self-importance. If realistic expectations of attaining high status are groundless, self-esteem can only be maintained by a downward revision of aspirational level. With the illusion of volitional omnipotence shattered by modifications in biosocial status, the child is left with all of the deflating implications of his executive dependence.

But there are limits to the degree of devaluation which is possible. If ego importance were to be devalued to the point required to bring it into line with actual ability to manipulate the environment, the resulting trauma to self-esteem would probably be greater than if the untenable notions of omnipotence were retained. The formula for self-esteem given above holds true on a relativistic basis provided that a minimum absolute degree of self-importance is maintained, i.e., provided that devaluation is not carried too far.

Fortunately, however, most children are not required to choose between either of these two unfavorable alternatives, i.e., maintaining notions of omnipotence which inevitably face frustration, or grossly devaluing self in line with realistic levels of volitional independence and performance ability. A less damaging compromise solution available is a reorganization of ego structure by a process of satellization or identification of the child in a dependent position with the dominant parental figures. Since he cannot manipulate reality successfully enough to gratify omnipotent fancies, the next best thing, therefore, is to become a satellite of persons who obviously *are* omnipotent. Mother and father hold the key to his universe. All manners of rewards, privileges and good things are at their disposal. They know everything and can do everything. They determine pain and pleasure, right and wrong, good and bad. In short, they inherit the mantle of omnipotence which formerly adorned his shoulders. Master and servants change positions in accordance with the newly instituted realities of life, just as Lord and butler exchange roles on shipwreck island in James Barrie's play "The Admirable Crichton" [*34*]. The former humble and efficient ministers of his majesty ascend the throne to rule, and the ex-king becomes a courtier who basks vicariously in reflected regal glory.

The great advantage inherent in satellization as a solution to the crisis in ego organization is its capacity for providing the child with intrinsic feelings of security and adequacy. He is relieved of the burden of justifying his adequacy on the basis of actual performance ability, which in fact could be meager at best. Instead, he acquires an indirect status which has nothing to do with his own ability to manipulate reality, but is vicariously derived from the fact of his dependent identification with his parents who are omnipotent in this respect. As a result of this identification, he does not vicariously become possessed of their powers, but shares (in a highly diluted form) in their magnificence—in the same way as the retainers of a powerful potentate would revel in the glory of their liege.

PREREQUISITES FOR SATELLIZATION

Satellization is not necessarily an inevitable outcome of the dilemma confronting the child when the omnipotent phase of his ego development becomes less tenable. Whether or not it becomes a relavant possibility depends more on the attitudes and behavior of the parents than on the willingness of the child. To the latter it is the most satisfactory and stable solution available despite his understandable initial reluctance to part with the prerogatives of omnipotence.

The process of satellization is made possible in the first place by virtue of the child's affectionate regard for his parents, which is built up as a consequence of the latters' predominantly altruistic role in the satisfaction of his needs. Acceptance of volitional dependency on powerful figures is a hazardous venture unless one feels assured of their benevolent protective interest in advance.

Equally important is the consideration that if the child is to derive intrinsic feelings of security and adequacy (apart from his actual competence) from the satellizing relationship, he must be loved and valued by the parent on the same basis as that on which his satellizing attutude is predicated, i.e., the parent must value him not for what he can do or become, but merely because he is his parents' child. In other words, the benefits of satellization can be realized only if the dominant partner in the relationship is willing to grant unconditional acceptance to the subordinate partner, and to confer an intrinsic value or status which is derived solely from the fact of the relationship apart from any consideration of merit or competence. In the child's eyes, this feat is easily within the parent's power. The latter, who is all-powerful and omniscient, is the sole determiner of what objects have value and on what basis. If he behaves as if the child has intrinsic value and is worthwhile for himself, that settles the matter once and for all. It is a definitive and absolute judgment which is not open to question. The child accepts it unreservedly as his own judgment of himself. Thus, it becomes the core of his self-respect and self-acceptance, and the basis of an inner feeling of security and adequacy which only the severest type of subsequent ego-trauma could successfully undermine.

It, therefore, follows that neither the rejected nor the extrinsically-valued child can satellize. The former cannot identify with a parent who regards him as an unwanted burden instead of extending benevolent support and protection. No derived status can be gained unless the parent confers acceptance and an intrinsic sense of worth. Rejection is the most extreme method of indicating to the child that the omnipotent and omniscient one considers him unworthy.

The extrinsically-valued child can also derive no intrinsic status from satellization. Sooner or later he realizes that he is not valued for himself but in terms of his potential capacity for gratifying projected parental ambitions. In his case, however, the infantile ego structure is more tenable and less subject to the usual pressures forcing devaluation. The over-valuing parent has no interest in deflating infantile notions of omnipotence and grandiosity. He interprets these characteristics either as portentous of future greatness or as invaluable assets in the struggle for power. Hence through indulgence and adulation he provides an environment which helps to maintain for some time the fiction of infantile omnipotence and to postpone the ego crisis which normally makes devaluation a relevant possibility.

A parental attitude of extreme permissiveness—overindulging a child's volitional whims by playing an overly submissive role—will not in itself prevent satellization from taking place. It is true that the parents' failure to "take active steps to alter the child's status in the household" [*24*] will delay the crisis in ego development which forces contemplation of devaluation. But if the child is truly accepted and valued for his own sake, if the parent does not overvalue him for ulterior motives of his own, he will eventually perceive his new biosocial status and choose satellization. Arapesh children quite typically show strong satellizing trends despite an extremely permissive upbringing. Unrestrained temper tantrums, however, seem to be prolonged beyond the age range commonly attributed to children in our culture [*274*].

The remarkable thing, however, is that the only two parental attitudes which definitely preclude satellization—rejection and extrinsic valuation— should on the face of it appear to have so little in common. The rejecting parent usually undervalues, overdominates, overcriticizes and underprotects his child, whereas the overvaluing parent does precisely the opposite. But basically, the two attitudes have much in common. Both parents are narcissistic and intrinsically disinterested in the child as a person. The former, however, is completely preoccupied with himself and regards the child as a burden. The latter regards his offspring as mere extensions of his own ego, and hence as convenient instruments for fulfilling projected ambitions which seem to lie beyond his own immediate grasp.

ALTERNATIVES TO SATELLIZATION

If satellization cannot occur, what then? In the absence of any intrinsic status, the source of security and adequacy feelings must forever remain extrinsic. And since grandiosity can no longer be taken for granted (as in the early days of infancy when reality was perceived through solipsistic glasses), the achievement of status must be related to actual capacity to manipulate the environment. Given this orientation, there is now a choice between devaluation of ego omnipotence to the extent required to make it compatible with the new biosocial status, or retention of the old ego structure despite its long-range untenability, predisposing toward chronic frustration and lowered self-esteem. Although the former alternative is conceivable under certain circumstances, it is not very probable.

In the first place, it involves more abrupt and immediate ego deflation. Secondly, acceptance of a very low aspirational level (which can be achieved without any gap between aspiration and achievement) involves a greater loss of self-esteem than maintenance of an unrealistically high level which favors the occurrence of such a discrepancy. To aim high is in itself an enhancement of self-esteem, whereas immediate capitulation (without resistance or striving) to the most unpalatable ego status available implies defeat and degradation. Considerable resistance (negativism) arises even in relation to accepting the more favorable status of satellite on the part of those children who eventually satellize. There is always time to accept "the last resort": As long as striving is maintained, there is a possibility of success; the very worst that could happen would be attainment of the lowly status that acceptance of the other alternative guarantees from the start.

There are also other specific factors which favor retention of the grandiose ego structure in the event that satellization does not occur. One who fancies himself omnipotent does not accept parental rejection passively. All indications point to the fact that children react to rejection with aggressive counter-hostility and self-assertion. Denied intrinsic status, they compensate for its lack by asserting the omnipotent attributes of ego structure all the more vigorously and belligerently. The intention is to achieve an extrinsic status commensurate with infantile notions of self-importance—to acquire self-esteem in relation to the higher (rather than to the lower) ranges of aspirational level. By setting their sights on power and prestige they hope someday to negate parental judgments as to their worthlessness. Only the powerful can obtain revenge.

To be sure, these omnipotent fancies are driven underground by an austere and hostile environment. An hypertrophied (un-devalued) ego can expect precious little satisfaction from a home in which normal recognition and appreciation are replaced by neglect, deprivation and humiliation. Self-esteem must necessarily remain at a low ebb as expediency compels conformity to a hateful authority. But conceptions of volitional omnipotence are carefully nurtured within; the need for survival demands outward subservience to overwhelming force, but there is no inner yielding of independence, and no true subordination of self to others. There is hope in the coming of a better day when the omnipotent self will break its bonds and carve out of reality an ego status consistent with its fondest dreams of power and glory.

There is little doubt as to which course the extrinsically and over-valued child will elect when faced with the issue of devaluation in relation to achieving extrinsic status. His environment "values him on his own terms and grants free reign to his expansive will" [*23*]. Hence if the enjoyment of self-esteem seems assured at this high level, there is surely little incentive for devaluation to take place.

CONSEQUENCES OF SATELLIZATION

So far we have referred only to certain quantitative aspects in ego organization, the magnitude of which fluctuates as the child passes from the omnipotent to the satellizing phases of ego development. In addition, there are other qualitative properties of personality structure which are closely bound up with the self-concept because of their central importance for all goal-directed activity. These characteristics are readily recognized in all descriptive accounts of child behavior and undergo progressive maturation with age. Hence, as the grandiose conceptions of ego importance and volitional omnipotence become devalued in the process of satellization, we can expect correlative changes in these other aspects of ego organization. The chief areas involved are the extent of hedonistic motivation, the need for immediacy in gratification, the degree of executive dependency, and the concept of moral responsibility.

With respect to all of these components, the infant is characteristically at one pole and the mature adult at the other. The former manifests an exaggerated hedonism and need for immediate gratification, regards himself as executively dependent, and exhibits complete moral irresponsibility. Satellization modifies all of this because the attitude of self-subordination (which leads to the relinquishment of omnipotent notions and the acceptance of parental direction) creates a need for parental approval; and parental training efforts are all directed toward maturation of these factors of personality. Hence, the child's uninhibited need for pleasure and immediate gratification becomes reduced and partly redirected into more acceptable channels. His recalcitrance in matters of self-help is gradually overcome. And lastly, the infantile belief of exemption from all responsibility undergoes displacement as the child gradually begins to accept the authority of his parents, and to assume some responsibility for behaving in greater conformity to their moral expectations.[1]*

* Notes for this chapter appear on page 64.

In the event that satellization does not occur, these additional components of ego structure fail to undergo the modifications described above. Their fate is considered in a later section when the consequences of non-satellization are described in detail.

Satellization, however, is the end result rather than the immediate reaction to the need for ego devaluation. The child first resists the threatened loss of his infantile ego status by more vigorous and aggressive assertion of its dominant characteristics. This leads to the resistive and negativistic behavior of two-and-one-half, characterized by petulance and frequent temper tantrums. The latter are less an indication of conscious perverseness than a stubborn perseveration of a biosocially outmoded concept of self. The emphasis is on self-assertion rather than on opposition to others. The apparent contrariness evidenced by dogged pursuit of a self-determined goal is merely the product of "reinforcement of self-sustained activity when obstacles are encountered"[*288*].

The birth of a sibling is often such a traumatic process because it comes at a time when the ego is already bearing the brunt of a violent devaluing process. If this is made even more abrupt by a complete dethroning and transfer of love to the new child, the normal stage of negativism is intensified. In many cases, the redistribution of affection may be radical enough to constitute emotional rejection and prevent satellization. A more gradual redistribution of affection, on the other hand, as is found in a secure, balanced home or upon introduction to nursery school, may have a wholesome realistic effect, promoting satellization.

Evidence for this point of view may be found in the fact that sibling rivalry tends to be less severe if the younger child is born either before or after the crucial stage of devaluation in the older sibling (18 to 42 months) [*20*]. But nevertheless even in a much older child, emotional rejection occasioned by the arrival of a sibling may (see page 347) cause profound changes in personality structure. These changes are most marked in the case of a previously overvalued child, but are not inconsiderable even if normal satellization had taken place.

As for the almost universal prevalence of intense sibling rivalry in our culture, Mowrer and Kluckhohn propose the convincing explanation that it is a product of the "dominant . . . cultural motif from childhood on . . . that 'a gain to your ego means a loss to mine' " [*287*].

NOTES

[1] As Gardner Murphy puts it: "The self becomes less and less a pure perceptual object and more and more a conceptual trait system" [*288*]. The more responsive the child becomes to parental and social pressures (the more he internalizes their standards) the more he tries to live up to the traits he accepts.

CHAPTER 8

Progress Toward Satellization

AT THREE,[1]* the growth of satellization makes itself felt by a marked decline in resistive behavior. The child is less self-assertive and more anxious to please and conform. He is more responsive to direction, and can be bargained with or put off until "later" [*149*]. He becomes somewhat sensitive to both praise and blame.

However, the gradient of satellization does not proceed in a straight line. Developmental disequilibrium tends to revive residual vestiges of the infantile ego structure. At three and a half, he is still "very affectionate toward and possessive of (his) parent" [*149*], but there is a return of some imperiousness in his attempt to restrain the talking and laughter of others [*149*]. The common interchange of parent-child role [*149*] at this age is more indicative of an incorporation of parental prerogatives than it is a sign of satellization.

FOUR-YEAR-OLD AGGRESSION: LEARNING TO ACCEPT PARENTAL AUTHORITY

The four-year-old is more conscious of his own power and capacity. Marked strides have taken place in intellectual, motor and social growth; the child is much less dependent on his parents. With this increased self-consciousness of capacity comes a resurgance of infantile ego characteristics. He becomes expansive, boisterous, obstreperous and less anxious to please, obey, conform [*149*]. It is almost as if he regretted the haste with which he abandoned his infantile ego structure. If only he could have held out one year longer! His behavior shows resistiveness to direction, and is typically "out of bounds." He is "bigger" than everyone,[2] "can do everything, brags about his power, and flourishes threats

* Notes for this chapter appear on page 76.

such as 'I'll chop your head off,' or 'I'll knock your house down' " [*149*]. He frequently plays at being "wolf."

Four ushers in a period of intense rivalry with other persons. Everything that he has or can do is compared with the possessions and abilities of others; and the decision regarding relative superiority is invariably made in his favor. Dad is a convenient rival in the absence of an older sibling, and mother must be careful to see that he does not get a bigger portion of dessert than Junior. He is acutely resentful of the privileges accorded older brother since he feels that he is just as grown-up and just as capable. Many sibling conflicts at this age arise from his insistence on "tagging along" against the will of his older contemporaries.

It is most important to differentiate between the self-assertion and negativism current at four and the variety previously encountered at two and a half. That the former is more verbal, less physical, and less frequently expressed in the form of temper tantrums is easily observed. More crucial, however, is the basis in ego development from which each proceeds. At four, self-assertion is a reflection of the increased self-confidence and exuberance which result from the child's first intoxication with his executive competence and independence rather than a reflection of infantile notions of omnipotence. The earlier self-assertion was largely autistic and unrelated to reality. Now there is a more realistic attempt at self-appraisal in relation to the social setting. But the child's skill in self-evaluation is still primitive; he is over-awed by his new powers to cope with the environment, and fails to note their relative insufficiency. His expansiveness, thus, is an outcome of an unrealistic self-appraisal, derived from social immaturity rather than a reflection of dereistic autism. When he asserts himself he is venturing an experiment in social behavior based on a distorted perception of superiority. It is at this stage and not at the age of two and a half [*24*] that explanations of negativism in terms of a "gap between biological and social maturity" [*61*] or of conflict regarding the issue of self-help [*201, 288, 291*] first become relevant. And not only is he asserting himself as an end in itself, but also with some conscious awareness of deliberate opposition to others.

Four-year-old aggression is also distinguished by its relation to the newly developing moral sense. At two and a half, parental opposition was regarded for the most part as a physical impediment. Now it involves issues of conscience and guilt. The expectation of punishment becomes more of a moral than a physical deterrent. There is a pronounced tendency to rationalize self-assertive negativism and to disclaim responsibility for it. One four-year-old, for example, when upbraided for banging on the table said "I had to scratch my head, and my hands just came down fast and hit the table." As he begins to appreciate the social consequences of his behavior and their moral implications, his threats tend to wane in ferocity. Before threatening to knock down the dish cabinet, he may first offer to remove the dishes; or he talks about breaking down a neighbor's house instead of his own.

In this stage of early satellization, there is still considerable concern with power and prestige. "Experiments on competition in three- and four-year-olds have indicated the important and constantly increasing role of the effort toward applause. A large part of the quest for possession as contrasted with the search for immediate satisfaction is rooted in the need to display the broadening selfhood which property brings; and a large part of the 'naughtiness' pattern—interference with other children's play, the snatching of their toys . . . is a pattern of power seeking" [*288*]. In this same category of behavior must be placed the teasing and calculatingly cruel treatment of animals and younger children which is such a vexatious feature of this age period. And how else are we to understand the increasing preference for white dolls which Negro children manifest from the third to the fifth year [*68*]? To identify with the prestige of the socially dominant caste seems to be more important than identification with parents.

We can best understand the resurgence of self-assertion in the four-year-old by viewing it as a second stage in the process of satellization.[3] At two, the child could not view reality clearly enough to realize that the parental deference shown him in spite of his helplessness was not proof of volitional omnipotence. At three, however, it became apparent to him that his executive incompetence was the main factor responsible for the volitional dependency he was now forced to acknowledge. He had already begun to exchange an omnipotent ego structure for a highly devalued conception of self in which his sense of security and adequacy depended upon his acceptance of a satellizing position in relation to his parents (provided, of course, that he was emotionally accepted and intrinsically valued by them). Hence, at the end of the first negativistic period, with acceptance of the deflated status, the three-year-old appears pliable and almost humble in the face of his executive incompetence.

By the fourth year, however, as the result of rapid strides in the acquisition of motor, verbal and social skills, his confidence in his ability to manipulate the environment grows apace. There are times when he apparently believes that he is capable enough to regain volitional independence and cast aside satellization in favor of seeking an extrinsic status on the basis of his own competence. Deference to parental direction and authority can become a burdensome thing, especially when it is so obvious to him that he "knows better." Parents are also the chief frustrating agents in his environment. They are always interfering with his desire for experiencing immediate pleasure.

At other times, however, he becomes painfully aware that he is only a child. His threats to impose reprisals on his parents for punitive measures have an empty ring. He proposes to run away from home but notes that no one is awed. Then as soon as he can do so without losing face, he seeks to crawl back into the good graces of his parents and regain the intrinsic security he feels in their approval and affection. Thus, he is torn by a conflict between two opposing trends—a longing for independence based on an exaggerated self-estimate of his executive competence, and a frightened desire to recapture the comfort and protection of his dependent status as he stretches his wings too far and falls. And, hence, he teeters back and forth from "good boy" to "bad boy" until the issue is finally decided.

This conflict which appears in the second stage of the satellizing process is generally resolved in favor of the need to retain parental approval (that is, in the case of all children who are not emotionally rejected or extrinsically valued). The eventual triumph of satellization is not only aided by the development of a more realistic self-critical faculty, but is almost an inevitable product of the child's dependent biosocial satus in all cultures. As will be seen later (see pp. 122-123), the resolution of this conflict results in the formation of conscience. The child internalizes the frustrating moral standards imposed by his parents, and begins to demand from himself what he formerly resisted bitterly.

In addition to the two factors already mentioned as facilitating the acceptance of parental authority, four other factors play a subsidiary role: (a) the unquestioned prestige status of the parents; (b) the importance of prestige suggestion where no frame of reference exists for attitude formation [*233*]; (c) a type of "sweet lemon" mechanism in the early stages, in the course of which "face can be saved" if mandatory frustrating standards can somehow be perceived as desirable or preferable; and (d) the reinforcing value of reward and "anxiety-reduction" (anticipation of punishment) [*280, 284*].

Despite the fact that the cards seem stacked in favor of satellization, situations other than parental rejection or extrinsic valuation may provide considerable difficulty: Where marital discord prevails, the child can not identify with either (parent) without coming into conflict with one or the other of them [*287*]. Where father is a "dreaded nightly visitor" or a brutal "animated whip," identification does not come easily, and then more as a technique of mastering fear (as in overcoming fear of wolves by "making believe" he is a wolf). This situation is aggravated for the boy in our culture; because of the predominantly feminine influence in home and school, identification with father's authority is difficult.

Cultural factors may add to these difficulties. We have already referred to the reluctance of Negro children to identify with their own skin color which does not enjoy high social status. The same situation prevails with other minority groups, especially in the case of first generation immigrants. Finally it should be mentioned that "even though identification is psychologically normal, difficulty may also arise if the person identified with does not happen to provide a socially appropriate model" [*287*] (i.e., delinquent parents).

EARLY SATELLIZATION AND THE SOCIALIZING PROCESS

The type of social relationship of which the child is capable is largely a reflection of his stage of ego development. The predominance of non-cooperative play until the age of four can not be attributed only to ignorance of social techniques. It is also a reflection of an egocentric attitude which makes him say, " 'I want someone to play with me.' " At five and six, "we more often hear, 'I want to go and play with the other children' " [*157*]. Four's expansiveness makes him a quarrelsome playmate. But as a result of more realistic self-appraisal, he passes from "a stage of self-assertiveness and interference with the liberties of others to a stage in which he shows consideration, sympathy, and kindness for others" [*51*]. After finding his proper role in the group, "cumulative experience in these positions enables each child to hold his place as leader or follower thereafter with a minimum of effort and resistance from others" [*304*].

The type of socialization pattern exhibited by an individual child, however, will do more than serve as a reflection of his level of ego development. To a large extent it will also mirror the type of interpersonal relationship prevailing between him and his earliest socializers, the parents. "For it is these attitudes toward the latter individuals which they largely generalize or 'transfer' to other persons. It is . . . on the basis of their experiences with their parents and early teachers that childrens' expectations develop of what to expect from people in general" [*287*]. This fact assumes greater significance in those cases where the parent-child relationship is atypical in any way (see pp. 275-278), especially since there is a tendency for these early social techniques to persist, even if manifestly unsuccessful [*61*].

LATER STAGES OF SATELLIZATION

Five[4] is a relatively quiet, well-conforming age. The child is more dependent on adult emotional support, tends to be "friendly, sympathetic, affectionate, and helpful" [*150*], and is likely to invite supervision. All of this betokens progress on the road to satellization. A truly affectional conscience in relation to parental dicta is now an established, going concern. The marked degree of acceptance of parental value-judgments is indicated by his almost tearful sensitivity to disapproval [*150*]. And appropriately enough, the Clarks [*68*] note a sharp drop between five and seven in Negro children's preference for white dolls.

Most striking at five is the marked decline in self-exuberance [*150*]. There is a sudden sharpening of the self-critical faculty with a resulting loss of confidence in and enthusiasm for his own powers. He may even go to the opposite extreme and underestimate his own abilities, becoming executively dependent in areas where he was formerly self-sufficient. But this resurgence of executive dependency recedes easily enough in response to parental pressure, since it is no longer believed to be a sign of volitional omnipotence.

The whole quality of the child's emotional attachment to his parents changes. Not only does it become more intense but it also acquires a more dependent, clinging and affectionate tone. The parents are idealized and appear more omnipotent than ever. The father may for the first time become emotionally important to the child and receive his due share of affection [*150*].

The intensity of the five-year-old's emotional dependence on his parents may reach the point where he feels apprehensive when out of their sight. He may suddenly pose objections to their leaving him in another's care when they go out at night, or become recalcitrant about playing outdoors alone [*150*]. On the other hand, the problem of discipline almost vanishes. A minor threat or mild show of disapproval is remarkably effective in effecting compliance. Resistance is seldom prolonged or intense. The grateful parent sorely tried by the boisterousness and defiance of the fourth year can think of his child only as a "little angel" [*150*].

But the fluctuating balance between satellization and the revival of infantile self-assertiveness has still to pass through several more cycles. The general tendency seems to be towards greater satellization up to the age of eight, at which time, identification with the parent is at a maximum [*150*]. However, developmental disequilibrium ascribable to tensions between the child and the environment [*150*] tend to reinstate negativistic behavior at six and eight. The six-year-old, experiencing for the first time another pattern of adult values and authoritarian techniques (the school), tends to be aggressive, expansive, boastful, resistive to direction, excitable and defiant[4] [*150*]. At eight, the "out-of-bounds" behavior is again mostly on a verbal plane [*150*]. Yet he "begins to recognize that the adult may know more than he does, . . . tries to live up to the standards of others, and may feel guilty if he thinks he doesn't [*150*]."

REVERSIBILITY OF SATELLIZING PATTERNS

Just how basic is this satellizing pattern with its corollary conditions of intrinsic security and adequacy? How well will it bear up under the strain and trauma of later childhood, adolescence, and adult life? Definite answers can not be given now, but certain trends are indicated.

To be sure, the very next step in ego development is a process of desatellization with a resurgence of volitional independence and self-assertion. But this does not mean a complete abrogation of satellizing patterns. There is a shift in the dependence-independence ratio, the parents are displaced by other models, biosocial fluctuations in introversion-extraversion and conformity to group standards take place. However, if satellization once occurred—barring unusual ego trauma[5]—it leaves a permanent residue in basic personality structure. Regardless of external vicissitudes, a certain inner feeling of security and adequacy always remains, and changes in self-valuation which occur with later success and failure always remain peripheral to and superimposed upon this basic self-acceptance. And as will be pointed out in a later section, future methods of value-acquisition still tend to follow the same pattern of emotional identification with parental surrogates prior to the assimilation of their values.

But it is also true that the occurrence of satellization does not in and of itself guarantee the emergence of a normal adult personality. For unless maturation results through desatellization in the ensuing years, the basis is laid for an inadequate personality, or possibly for evolutionary schizophrenia (see pp. 490-494). But a history of satellization (or not) is a crucial element in preserving that genotypical continuity in personality organization [*178*] which Kardiner referred to as "basic personality structure" [*218*] and Adler as the "style of life" [*5*]. "Although this underlying personality structure may find expression in many different ways," [*291*] and although adjustive techniques may shift in different environmental crises, the fundamental meaning still remains consistent.[6]

A NOTE ON THE VIEWS OF ADLER AND RANK

Alfred Adler has made the awareness of childhood dependency with consequent feelings of helplessness and inferiority the basis of his "drive for superiority" or "will to power" [*5*]. In normally satellizing children, however, the emotional identification with the parent is so complete that economic or intellectual dependency is in no way suggestive of inferiority. Connotations of inferiority in this context do become relevant, as will be seen later, in the case of the non-satellizing child. However, it must be admitted that the child's complete dependence on his parents, and his manifest helplessness in the face of their arbitrariness and unpredictability must give rise to some undertone of insecurity and uneasiness which may find displaced expression in the form of imaginary fears or forebodings of improbable calamities[7] which are so common in this age period [*201*]. Since these fears cannot be discounted by experience, they are more stable than the more concrete variety which everyday experience eventually shows to be baseless.

Adler's emphasis on awareness of organic defects as providing a widespread need for compensatory ego aggrandizement [*5*] also seems largely exaggerated. Although admittedly physical deformity or weakness may sometimes be great enough to result in a repudiation of basic self-acceptance and the creation of compensatory power needs, this situation is far from being universal, or even common. Somatic defects and deviations occur frequently enough, and especially during adolescence tend to be exaggerated. The resulting ego trauma, however, can hardly be conceived of as severe enough to produce an irreversible change in a satellizing pattern of ego development.

In short, Adler's postulation of a primary feeling of inferiority resulting from the dependency situation of childhood ignores the main functions of satellization in relation to ego structure—to provide *intrinsic* feelings of security and adequacy. It is for this reason—and not, as Adler believed, vicariously to further a will to power—that children identify with their parents. Adlerian psychology holds true only for that group of children who do not satellize; and as a keen and penetrating analysis of the ego development of the non-satellizing individual, it is one of the most significant contributions ever made to psychopathology and the theory of personality development.

Rank's failure to account for the maturational capacity of the organism in reacting to ego threats has already been mentioned in connection with the "birth trauma." Psychologically it also seems rather fanciful (if philosophically plausible) to conceive of the infant as *feeling* a sense of loss or separateness upon separation from either embryonic, physical or psychological unity with his mother. Here it surely seems that Rank, the mature adult philosopher, is endowing the child with his own retrospective capacity for interpreting prenatal, neonatal and infantile experience. To be sure, formulations concerning the child's concept of self must be speculative at this point. Such speculations, however, must be consistent with the infant's perceptual capacity, and not with criteria of plausibility which assume that the latter is functioning at the abstract level of a college professor.

The core of Rank's system lies in his postulation of two contrasting trends in personality development—a need for totality, distinctiveness or independence in the experience of self, versus a need to surrender some of this individuality in relating oneself to others. Thus, the main function of the child's identification with his parents is considered to be a means of obtaining enough of the raw material of personality structure with which later to establish an independent, differentiated individuality of his own [*315*]. And the difficulties of adolescence are largely attributed to a reluctance for the surrender of part of this painfully acquired independence and individuality that goes with the establishment of an adult love relationship [*163*].

It is undeniable that some type of balance between dependence and independence must be struck before any individual can hope to maintain effective interpersonal relationships. This is a universal feature of the socializing process at any stage of development. The Rankian formulation, however, describes personality development in relation to achieving such a balance without taking into consideration such qualitative differences in process as are referable to satellizers and non-satellizers respectively. Manifestations of independence in the former can not be equated to similar phenomena in the latter—in terms of either the ego needs they satisfy or of the mode of learning involved. The intrinsically secure satellizing, adolescent, for example, becomes volitionally independent in order to fulfill biosocial expectations of mature personality status; his mode of learning recapitulates the earlier method of identifying primarily with the preceptor and incidentally with his values. His non-satellizing counterpart on the other hand, who lacks intrinsic feelings of adequacy, has *always* been independent; because to him dependence is equivalent to an admission of defeat in his compensatory striving to attain the symbols of prestige and power on which extrinsic feelings of adequacy are founded. And far from learning by a process of dependent identification with another, he incorporates goals and values which may enhance his ego status, aiming as far as possible to avoid acknowledgment of dependence on anyone.

It should also be pointed out that the differentiation of the self-concept as distinct from the rest of the environment (as developed by Rank) is in no sense coextensive with the entire problem of dependence and independence in ego development. In fact, it is meaningless to speak of these latter concepts apart from an individual's formulation of ego magnitude (in the omnipotent, satellizing, and desatellizing phases), which to a large extent determines his relative needs for and notions of same. A person with hypertrophic ego demands can not tolerate the slightest suggestion of dependence. Another who values himself more modestly can tolerate a great deal of it with equanimity.

NOTES

[1] It must be realized that by citing a specific age for a given phase of ego development, we are referring to the mean of an age *range* for the particular group under observation. This age range varies for different socio-economic groups and from one generation of children to the next, depending on cultural shifts in child-rearing practices.

For example, Gesell's population was atypical since it was drawn from an upper middle-class group attending private school or the Yale Clinic of Child Development. Furthermore, parents in this subcultural group are presently leaning more towards permissiveness in child-rearing than in the era when Gesell was collecting his data (see note 4 below).

An interesting shift in the developmental cycle is the acceleration of segregation of the sexes which was formerly described as occurring at about the age of eight. As a result of the cowboy culture which has currently captured American children, this segregation tends to occur at a much earlier age.

[2] "This sense of bigness in the nursery group at four, which is sometimes accompanied by an aggressive and dominating expression of the ego enhancement to which it gives rise, may be followed by deflation as the child goes to the still larger group of kindergarten in a school where he is once again among the littlest. In our culture where the educational system is divided into a sequence of schools—elementary school, junior high school, high school and college or technical school—the child has a sequence of inflating experiences in being among the oldest in each group, which are followed by deflation as he becomes one of the youngest in the next school" [*291*].

[3] Reference has already been made to the psychoanalytic explanation of this stage of ego development presented by Mowrer and Kluckhohn [*287*] (see page 22). This explanation emphasizes the appearance of sexual and aggressive urges at this time, conflict with the frustrating parents (preventing complete identification with them) and resolution of the conflict by repression of these urges during the "latent period." Feelings of guilt, inferiority and anxiety during this period are referred to these completely or partially repressed erotic impulses which parents and teachers regard as shameful. Although it is undoubtedly true that children are made to feel guilty on account of "sexual" curiosity or genital explorations, it has already been pointed out that this theory rests upon the unproven assumption that childhood and adult "sexuality" are qualitatively continuous. It also ignores the more self-evident considerations of ego status making for and resolving parent-child conflict during this age period.

[4] As a result of the current fetish of permissiveness among middle-class parents, the five-year-old stage of conformity and pliancy described by Gesell tends to come more often at six. School exerts a sobering influence on these children, since it is generally more authoritarian and makes greater demands than the home with respect to discipline and obedience. Thus, Stendler and Young [*378*] found the same ego-bolstering effects of initial school experience

on six-year-olds reported by Gesell (due to the sudden increase of extrinsic status), but at the same time, parents reported an improvement in general behavior.

[5] An example of such unusual trauma, later rejection of the child upon the birth of a sibling, has already been cited. Another example is furnished by the occurrence of chronic crippling diseases in later childhood and adolescence (see page 298).

[6] For a discussion of factors which make for consistency and continuity in personality development, see pp. 256-258, 263-265, 275-281, 337-339.

[7] This statement in no way implies acceptance of the hypothesis of "free-floating anxiety." Apart from neonates, any type of emotional or perceptual *reaction* can hardly be expressed in a generalized non-specific form completely undifferentiated as to meaningful objects in the individual's psychological world. What passes for "free-floating" anxiety or aggression is merely a generalized *lowering of the threshold of responsiveness* to fear- or rage-producing stimuli. The tension accompanying such a state of increased readiness tends to be more disagreeable than a specific fear reaction for two reasons: (a) Specific fears can be relieved by avoidance of the phobic situation; and (b) they usually represent considerable displacement from the actual stimuli responsible for the state of tension. Unless displacement occurs, the lowered threshold for anxiety-reaction produced by a general atmosphere of insecurity tends to result in anxieties referable to the insecure situation itself.

CHAPTER 9

The Beginning of Desatellization: Pre-Adolescence

THE GROWING ESTRANGEMENT OF PARENT AND CHILD

BEFORE EGO DEVELOPMENT is complete, one more important maturational step is necessary: emancipation from the home, and preparation to assume the role of an independent adult in society. Traditionally the process of emancipation is placed in the adolescent era. Actually this is hardly the case; the groundwork for emancipation is laid in the middle and late years of childhood, and is an important factor in influencing the outcome of adolescent emancipation.

At eight the child is already more outgoing and in greater contact with his environment [*150*]. "His chief interest is in relationships with others—children and adults. He resents being treated as a child and wants to be like an adult . . . He can't wait to grow up." The nine-year-old is more independent, responsible, cooperative and dependable [*150*]. His "own individuality and personality is making itself clearly apparent" [*150*]. The decrease in overt resistance to adult authority, however, is more deceptive than appears on the surface. It is not accepted without some inner reservations and rebellion. And perhaps were it not for the compensatory outlets in movies, comics, and opportunities for fighting with peers and bullying younger children, it would come more into the open [*292*]. Also, as Lois Murphy has pointed out, a certain "social security and even prestige" lies in the acceptance of parental authority as manifested in the boast, " 'My Mom brings us up right' " [*292*].

At nine we already see well-established barriers existing between children and adults. This growing alienation is a consequence of our family and cultural traditions which provide children with little opportunity for exercising independence, responsibility and identification with the world of adult concerns. At eight the child makes a futile attempt to draw the adult into his world [*150*]. By nine, he seems to accept the fact that fusion is impossible. Desatellization and the assumption of adult goals are achieved by a course other than gradual participation in communal responsibilities. Denied a place in adult reality, he finds other outlets for the independence and more mature interests which personality growth has stimulated. "He becomes very busy with his own concerns and doesn't have time for routines or parents' demands" [*150*]. There is "much planning, in great and practical detail" [*150*]. He "may prefer work to play" [*150*]. But these concerns are "now oriented more toward his contemporaries than toward his parents . . . and he verbally expresses indifference to adult commands or adult standards" [*150*].

THE ROLE OF THE PEER GROUP: DESATELLIZING INFLUENCE AND COMPENSATORY SOURCE OF STATUS

It is through the mechanism of ego identification with the peer group that the process of desatellization makes its first important advance. The "we-feeling" which follows from this identification constitutes a powerful ego support that permits a weakening of the dependent tie on parents. "The growing child derives a vitalizing sense of reality from the awareness that his individual way of mastering experience (his ego synthesis) is a successful variant of a group identity" [*100*]. In the peer group he also gets the chance to derive compensatory status by playing the mature roles which adult society denies him in real life.[1*] As social and sex differentiations become clearer, these roles become more and more real and specific, providing further group loyalties to bolster his ego structure.

This "we-feeling," of course, is only a variant of the satellizing process. The satellizer's relation to the group recapitulates his relation to his parents with the exception that the former rela-

*Notes for this chapter appear on page 82.

tionship is to a collective organization of which he himself is a part. But the group serves all of the satellizing ego functions of the parents: It is a prestige and approval-giving, protective body on whom the individual is dependent and from whom he derives his goals and moral values. This easily becomes apparent when we examine the non-satellizer's relation to the group. The latter cannot place himself in a position of emotional dependency on the group; the "we-feeling" is utterly beyond him. Bringing no intrinsic security or adequacy along with him when he enters the group—and with a history of parental rejection or overvaluation behind him—he can regard the group only as a potential source of compensatory security, power and prestige. Starting out with feelings of insecurity, lacking a spontaneous "we-feeling" emotional relationship with group members and concerns, and often manifesting excessive hostility and aggression, he tends to become a social isolate. Thus, feelings of inadequacy and hostility in group situations as well as exaggerated prestige motivation must be viewed primarily as causes rather than as products of group rejection, although the latter undoubtedly plays a reenforcing role.

OTHER COMPENSATIONS

The growing child's frustrated need for identification with more adult roles finds still another outlet—in fantasy life. There is an intense preoccupation with the exploits of superhuman characters in comic fiction and in movies. Hero worship of glamorous figures such as movie stars and sport figures displace the former preeminent emulatory role of the parents [*170*]. But it is not until later, in adolescence, when the former are displaced by an attractive visible adult [*170*] that the parents' influence is seriously threatened; for only then does the child have sufficient social experience and sufficient emancipation from the dependent attitude of childhood to devalue the deified stature of the parents.

THE NATURE OF THE DESATELLIZING PROCESS

As already noted, this process of emancipation from parental control and influence is not only a matter of exalting self-assertion as against conformity to others. Desatellization follows the same pattern of emotional identification with stronger prestige-giving individuals or groups as did satellization. The identifications are merely transferred from the parents to teachers, parent-surrogates and age-mates. Values, goals and attitudes are acquired from the wider community and culture outside the home; and, just as was the case with satellization, these values are acquired as a by-product of the more important personal loyalty formed in the course of emotional identification. Of the various forces displacing the parent, the peer group is the most important, since—as the source of the major portion of his status and prestige—the preadolescent and the adolescent are very responsive to its pressures.

Desatellization is facilitated if the child is given sufficient freedom to explore, to roam the neighborhood, to experiment, manipulate and learn from his own mistakes. To learn responsibility and dependability, he needs opportunities for exercising choice and practising self-direction. The ability to find sources of security outside the home also helps the child on his way toward emancipation.

Desatellization, on the other hand, is retarded by the parent's reluctance to lose the satisfactions associated with having the child completely dependent upon him. The former finds the task of relinquishing control and authority especially difficult when he is deriving some form of compensation from the child's dependence, e.g., in cases of marital discord or vocational maladjustment. The not infrequent reluctance of the child to give up his protected and sheltered position operates in the same direction. He is also hampered in his efforts toward independence by the natural feelings of guilt which arise when his identification with new values implies repudiation of parental standards. The parents in turn can intensify this guilt reaction by making conformity and adherence to their values the price of extending continued emotional support and affection.

Desatellization is, thus, a difficult and inevitably conflictful phase of ego development. The satellizer is expected to become more independent and self-assertive; and in achieving this goal he has to combat ambivalent tendencies in both himself and his parents. If he is too submissive and dependent he loses face in his own eyes and in the eyes of his peers; he might alternately feel inadequate for failing to maintain developmental progress, or hostile and resentful toward his parents for thwarting his growth. Carried too far, dependence raises the threat of a perpetually immature and inadequate personality. But if he is too independent and aggressive, he feels guilty for excessive repudiation of his parents; and in anticipation of retaliation for his hostility may experience some anxiety [*187*]. Or at other times, he may seek both to disown and to justify his hostility by projecting it onto his parents, which in turn gives rise to anxiety.

In the constantly shifting equilibrium between dependence and independence, therefore, the preadolescent child must "steer a precarious course." And (by borrowing a term from physiology) we can conceive of a homeostatic range of variability within the limits of which optimal development proceeds at a given age period from one stage to the next succeeding level.

NOTES

[1] Mowrer and Kluckhohn [*287*] do not stress the compensatory status-giving role of the peer group in explaining the increased desire for social approval at this age. They emphasize instead the burden of "unconscious guilt" derived from repressed childhood sexuality.

CHAPTER 10

Desatellization Through Adolescent Emancipation

DESPITE ITS IMPORTANCE for eventual outcome, childhood efforts at desatellization can only be preparatory, and must await adolescent emancipation for actual consummation. The sexually-immature child with no social recognition as an adult and with limited social experience is still primarily dependent upon his parents for emotional support. Before adult personality status can be attained, ego maturation must achieve a "new balance between the dichotomous needs for independence and dependence—a balance which is closer to the volitional independence and self-assertiveness of infancy than to the docility and submissiveness of childhood" [*23*]. This is largely a process of desatellization. The goal which is aimed at now is at the opposite pole of that which prevailed at the age of two and a half. In both cases there is a struggle between the child's self-assertion and repressive forces within himself and in the environment. But the battle of volitional independence lost then must be won now.

The status of satellite gives way to the acceptance of a new role in which the individual is required to evolve his own goals, make his own plans and decisions, and assume responsibility for his own destiny. "Short term goals designed to provide immediate pleasure and gratification" are replaced by long-range goals directed toward "achieving greater self-realization and social prestige" [*23*]. (This further modification of the hedonistic attitude is qualitatively different from that which transpired during satellization; it is not merely a quantitative limitation out of deference to parental wishes, but is an actual replacement by more mature goals.) "Attitudes concerned with moral values and responsibility become detached from their moorings to parental authority, and the individual becomes responsible to the moral authority of society" [*23*]. Finally, once the initial devaluation resulting from rejection by the adult world is compensated for, there is an eventual inflation of ego importance commensurate with the attainment of a more mature status.

FACTORS PRECIPITATING THE ADOLESCENT PERIOD OF PERSONALITY REORGANIZATION

The reorganization of personality status which accompanies this "re-formation of the ego" [*354*] is a product of two forces, one biological, and one social, which happen to converge at this time. The concomitant development of biological sex drive and of marked changes in outward appearance generate pressures for self-assertion and independence which make the maintenance of childhood personality status quite untenable. The child reacts to his new adult drives and appearance by striving to attain the prerogatives which they imply.

But this transition in "personality growth is not wholly spontaneous or self determined." At the same time an urgent social need is operating, a need which is derived from the fact that children can not indefinitely remain dependent upon parents, and sooner or later must assume their own share of responsibility for maintaining the culture. Thus, society reacts to the cue of adolescent bodily growth by initiating the socially-inevitable change in personality status which "his environment, and primarily the social relations of this environment demand" [*287*].

PSYCHOBIOLOGICAL EGO PROBLEMS IN ADOLESCENCE

It is frequently stated today [*90, 230*] that all of the difficulties attending the period of adolescent development can be ascribed to cultural factors which impose undue delay between the onset of biological maturation and the eventual provision of socially-sanctioned means of sexual and socio-economic expression. Hence it is implied that if this gap could somehow be closed, adolescence in our culture would be as idyllic and free from stress and strain as it is in Samoa, where no social restrictions are imposed upon adolescent sex activities.

Unfortunately, this point of view is based upon a gross oversimplification of the facts. To begin with, there is not a complete absence of adolescent conflict in Samoa [*274, 354*]. Secondly, coexistent with this promiscuous and superficial Samoan attitude toward sex is a more casual and emotionally-shallow style of life. Levels of aspiration are low, little stress is placed on "getting ahead," little confusion between moral values prevails, and the eventual attainment of status is assured. Surely all of these factors must play as important a role in producing a relatively stressless adolescence in this culture as does the mere absence of sexual repression.

Data on psychosexual development from other cultures also confirm the impression that the fact of sexual repression *per se* is not the crucial factor in determining the relationship between sexual expression and psychological conflict. The Manus girl [*274*] who practices complete sexual repression, and the Arapesh adolescent, in whose case the question of sexual repression is apparently irrelevant (since physiological sex drive seems nonexistent as such apart from affectual components), enjoy as placid an adolescence as their Samoan counterparts with very little conflict of sexual origin [*274*].

In our heterogeneous culture, on the other hand, we find considerable adolescent stress prevailing at all subcultural levels despite wide variability in the prevalence of sexual conflict. Eighty-five per cent of male adolescents in the United States accept premarital intercourse as natural and desirable, and proceed to exercise this conviction almost as freely as Samoan adolescents without developing any mental conflicts about sex [*225*]. Psychological conflict related to sex, however, is an impressive phenomenon in middle-class youths in whom sexual repression is both incomplete and ambiguous: Few of these individuals deny that they possess physiological sex urges, this belief having both deep roots in our folklore and the unqualified support of the biological science taught in our schools. But at the same time it is seriously expected on moral grounds that these physiological urges are to be repressed until marriage. Hence, it is not the sexual repression in and of itself which causes conflict, but the simultaneous acknowledgement of legitimate biological impulses and the internalization of moral standards which prohibit their adequate gratification. The damage, in other words, is caused by the fact that repression is so *incomplete* that sexual desires inundate conscious life, but at the same time fall far short of their goal. It is important to note, however, that despite the *comparative absence of sexual conflict prevailing in the lower educational strata of our society, there is no dearth of the characteristic adolescent "Sturm und Drang" typical of the culture as a whole.*

The weight of the evidence, therefore, seems to go against the current widely-held belief that there is no problem of adolescence as such, but only an adolescent problem in certain cultures. We are forced to agree with Sherif and Cantril [*354*] that "with variations in the social setting, the period of adolescence may be more or less prolonged, fraught with more or less intense problems, but that the basic psychobiological principles which operate in all of these social settings should be the same." Hence it is only to be expected that certain psychological and biological uniformities should prevail almost universally in all cultures, giving rise to a matrix of developmental probems which transcend specific influences of cultural conditioning.

We can anticipate finding such psychobiological uniformities arising from two general sources: (a) the common constellation of psychological problems reflecting on ego status which occur during any transitional period in development; and (b) the universal occurrence of certain biological changes which in turn demand various psychological readjustments.

Ego Problems Reflective of Transitional Tensions

All transitional periods in ego development are difficult since inevitably they involve a loss in established ego status and a need to acquire a new status. It is only natural to resist change, for it means giving up a secure anchorage with a stable framework of reference for an unknown quantity which has yet to be acquired. The organism is thrown into a state of developmental disequilibrium, which (as we have already seen at two and a half, four, and six) results in strained interpersonal relations until equilibrium is restored. In the meantime, a vacuum can not exist. Some sort of interim status must be provided which perforce must be makeshift and marginal in character; for always lurking in the background is the transitional anxiety which can not be set aside until the last vestige of uncertainty relative to the attainment of the new status is removed.

Transitional stress and anxiety are to be found in all cultures during the adolescent period. The intensity of their manifestations, however, seems to be a function of three factors: (a) the abruptness with which the transitional stage is inaugurated; (b) the length of time it lasts; and (c) the presence of discrepancies in rate of growth of various functions. In our culture all three factors are so arranged as to produce maximum stress and conflict.

Adolescence is ushered in with startling abruptness in Western civilization. The physiological changes responsible for the growth spurt and the sexual maturation occur as elsewhere within a relatively short space of time. And since adult status is withheld so long, the chief social recognition which these body changes receive is a sudden emotional detachment on the part of the parents. The formerly dependent child is emotionally cut adrift and allowed to flounder for himself. In addition, he finds himself suddenly precipitated from a childhood world of play into a world of adult concerns. All of a sudden "parents and teachers . . . begin to reproach the child for lack of maturity, demanding that he show some sense, use some judgment, take some responsibility . . . and stand on his own two feet" [*118*]. The trouble is that all of this is one-sided. The parents relinquish emotional support much more rapidly than they relinquish authority. They demand responsibility and concern for adult values in a child previously confined to a carefree world of play. They impose adult motivations, but postpone the reward in adult status so long that transitional anxiety is prolonged until it becomes a painful burden and the rewards themselves acquire mythical illusoriness.

It is hardly to be expected that the component aspects of any growth process should all proceed at the same rate of speed. Since physical changes precipitate the adolescent period in the first place, one might logically anticipate some gap between the onset of these changes and their social and emotional consequences. Bodily growth is dependent only upon internal hormonal rhythms. Emotional and social aspects of personality growth, on the other hand, are subject to a wide variety of cultural vicissitudes; maturation can not occur in the absence of socially-provided opportunities for relevant experience in playing mature adult roles.

Such divergences in rate of growth are bound to have adverse consequences. Since any particular behavioral capacity functions within the limits imposed by the maturational readiness of the whole organism, only two possibilities are open for earlier-maturing functions—premature utilization or postponement. The former inevitably results in some amount of dysfunction as evidenced in the sexual misadventures of emotionally immature adolescents. The latter possibility is hardly more satisfactory, for it can only result in prolonged emotional tension or developmental (e.g., psychosexual) retardation.

Ego Problems Reflective of Bodily Changes

The first problem confronting the ego as a result of bodily change is to revise the body-image which constitutes so central a part of the self-concept. Hitherto, such changes had been so gradual that the body-image was able imperceptibly to accommodate to them. However, during adolescence, growth is so rapid that a *conscious* restructuring of the body-image becomes necessary to account for changes in size, shape and contour, as well as in the primary and secondary sex characteristics. But acceptance of these changes has implications which transcend their immediate significance for body-image and self-concept. For, by accepting a new self which is cast in the physical image of an adult, one simultaneously accepts the ego roles associated with this adult image [*406*].

One of these new roles is the individual's biological sex role which sexual maturation has suddenly thrust upon him. Whether he wishes to acknowledge it or not, he is forced to cope with the reactions of others toward him as an adult sex object. Just as in middle childhood when sex first became an important factor in social grouping, this further differentiation of sexual role along biological lines has important implications for ego development. It results in an added refinement and differentiation of ego role; and the loyalties formed in the process serve as a new source of ego support. Also, acceptance of biological sex role is a crucial factor in later adjustment to the socio-economic function assigned by cultural tradition to a given sex clan.

The overwhelming importance of bodily changes during adolescence also creates universal ego problems arising out of social reactions to variability in rate of maturation and to somatic deviations.[1]* The slow maturer suffers the trauma of social rejection with a corresponding loss in ego status. Under these circumstances, "it is not surprising that in order to prove himself he sometimes resorts to behavior which is far from socially-acceptable to adults" [*344*]. Or in self-defense, he may choose to isolate himself and find solace in fantasy or in solitary pursuits. The early maturer may undergo more rapid ego maturation because of earlier and greater opportunities accorded him for assuming adult prerogatives. But, on the other hand, he may be subjected to ego trauma in failing to live up to the unrealistic expectations of adults based on considerations of outward maturity alone.

Somatic defects and deviations become important for similar reasons. Sex appropriateness and attractiveness to a large extent determine one's relative status with the opposite sex, and also with the like-sex peer group, each in turn reciprocally influencing the other.[2] These defects moreover acquire greater significance from the fact that present bodily appearance is conceived of as the *final* edition of physical form; and considering the notoriously limited time perspective of adolescents, this is a very serious matter indeed, especially since it is imagined that conformity to peer standards will *always* be as important.

The traumatic effect of somatic variations (like all other problems of adolescence) must be evaluated in terms of the fact that during adolescence the "ego lives" less in the future than is customarily its wont [*194*]. Hence it is not an easy thing to accept an ugly, unattractive body as the final physical representation of self. All sorts of ego contortions are employed "to make that reality as pleasant as possible" [*380*], even if ugliness must be made a virtue. And through the convenient mechanism of displacement, somatic defects can be made the scapegoat of all adjustive difficulties and the cause of all anxiety feelings regardless of their original source [*48*].

* Notes for this chapter appear on page 102.

Lastly, we should remember that through the medium of emergent physiological regulations and their impact on behavior and consciousness, ego development in adolescence is closer in many respects to infancy than to childhood. The newly-acquired biological sex drive and awareness (accompanied as it is by a tremendous growth spurt in affectional capacity) must be subjected to the same type of social control and canalization as were the sensuous and hedonistic impulses of early infancy.

ADOLESCENT EGO PROBLEMS OF SOCIAL ORIGIN

In the preceding section we have tried to show that there are universal psychobiological ego problems in adolescence which issue from transitional tensions and bodily change. The purpose of this exposition has been to discount the prevalent belief that *all* of the difficulties in adolescent development are primarily of social origin. However, there is no intention of minimizing the importance of social factors. In fact even while emphasizing the psychobiological aspects of transitional tensions, it has been necessary to point out that the intensity of such tensions depends upon such socially-conditioned determinants as abruptness of onset and duration of the interim period. And in the case of maturational and somatic deviations, it has been necessary to evaluate the resulting ego trauma in terms of the *social* reactions to these situations.

It is evident that "many of the distinctive problems of adolescence in our culture . . . are not the inevitable consequences of biological endowment" [*23*]. "The problems facing the adolescent vary from culture to culture, rendering the transition to adulthood more or less complicated, more or less conflicting, more or less prolonged" [*354*]. Hence we must first place "adolescent ego problems in their social settings. For significant variations and factors of social change necessarily reflect themselves in the status problems of adolescents who are themselves in a critical and unstable stage of transition . . . The adolescent strives to stabilize his ego values . . . in relation to his reference group, whatever this may be to him in his particular social milieu. He does his level best to incorporate into his ego . . . the norms of his group in his particular social setting" [*354*].

THE ACQUISITION OF ADULT EGO STATUS

That the achievement of adult status is not a direct consequence of attaining physical maturity is a discovery which comes as quite a rude shock to most adolescents. As children they fail to grasp the significant difference in status separating adults from the younger individuals who resemble them in form only. Hence while naively expecting to graduate immediately to adult status, they discover to their chagrin that they still have no standing in the adult world. In fact, in many respects they are treated exactly as children, but without enjoying the secure protected status of the latter.

The impact of this unexpected deflation results in the severest ego trauma experienced since the first crisis in ego organization which led to satellization. Not very long ago they had enjoyed the king-pin status of being the *biggest* children in the world of play. This status was reluctantly relinquished in the process of assimilating adult goals and standards of responsibility. And the climax of it all is complete rejection by the adult world, leaving them in a no-man's land of status and orientation! What follows is a gradual process of reconciliation to this prolonged deprivation of status, during which time ego anchorage is found in the new frame of reference created by the standards and rewards of an esoteric peer culture [*354*]. But until these compensatory adjustments are effected and the initial resentment wanes, hostile and aggressive reactions are the most appropriate mechanisms of defense available to the injured and threatened ego [*90*].

Factors Prolonging Adolescence

Even in relatively primitive societies, the length of the dependency period of the young is much greater than among mammals with a comparable gestation interval and life span. Culture complicates and extends the process of psychological development; and the more complex a given culture, the longer must be the period of training and education necessary to insure the continuity of the social order.

In our society, however, factors other than those concerned with transmission of cultural traditions operate to prolong adolescence. "Conditions are such as to make it extremely difficult to provide youth with the work experience so essential for normal personality development . . . So long as full employment is denied older workers, youth will stand at the threshold of occupational life baffled and frustrated" [*94*]. And even when work is available, it is frequently so monotonous and routinized that it offers no possibility for the personal satisfactions and sense of worth that comes with initiative and creative endeavor. Added to this is the alarming decrease in social mobility which inevitably follows the concentration of economic power. Nothing has a more paralyzing effect on the ambitions of youth than the fact that "in the struggle for status, inherited wealth and position are beginning to count for more than energy and capacity" [*94*].

In times of depression these conditions are exaggerated tenfold. Then it seems to the adolescent as if "the organized power of society is arrayed against" him in his legitimate quest for status [*23*]. Dependence on parents is prolonged indefinitely, marriage is impossible, education leads nowhere, and all effort seems hopelessly futile. Would it be possible to confront an ego already threatened by body changes, developmental tensions, and abrupt loss of status with anything more traumatic? Regardless of the basic strength of his intrinsic self-acceptance, there must be considerable ego deflation – at least in his extrinsic notion of ego adequacy (which is ordinarily a reflection of the value society places upon him). Even if he does blame his environment for his misfortunes, he can not avoid accepting the verdict that he is a stunted, developmental failure, a permanent sub-adult with marginal and indeterminate status. He can feel no more adequate, and mature no more rapidly than the judgments and expectations of his society permit. By governing "the availability of the experience required for personality development," socio-economic conditions are able to determine the rate of adolescent ego development and the eventual attainment of adult personality status [*23*].

Negative Reactions to Ego Threat and Status Deprivation

The simplest type of negative response induced by the lowered threshold of behavioral reactivity (resulting from chronic ego threat and prolonged status deprivation) is direct aggression against the perceived agents of frustration. Hence arise hostile and defiant attitudes towards adults and adult authority, contempt for adult goals and values, and cynical philosophies of life. Where direct expression of hostility toward the offending agent is not possible, it may be displaced to parents, teachers, siblings or society. In its most extreme form it appears as a predatory delinquency [*23*]. Where the habitual adjustive pattern leans more toward withdrawal techniques, a larger number of "escape mechanisms" are available, i.e., seclusiveness, secretiveness, ascetism, intellectualization, precipitate marriage, running away from home, and finally suicide.

Another negative way of accomodating to ego devaluation is to distort perception of reality so that the ego threat is not perceived. It is not uncommon to find adolescents who vehemently insist that adolescence presents no problems whatsoever, or at least not in relation to themselves. Superimposed on this attitude may be an affectation of cocky self-assurance. In others, the anxieties of adolescence find a displaced focus on minor somatic defects, or are reduced by flighty preoccupation with "transitory enthusiasms" [*23*].

THE ADOLESCENT PEER SOCIETY

The adolescent peer culture arises as the chief ego support of this traumatic transitional period. Its requirements provide anchorage and direction, and the acceptance and loyalty it offers bolster emotional security. Through its power to confer recognition and prestige, it provides a rich compensatory source of status which is partially capable of restoring damaged ego adequacy. Because of this central anchoring and status-giving role, it exercises undisputed control over the activities, ideals and goals of the adolescent period. It commands fanatical loyalty, and is able to exact unswerving conformity to its standards. In addition, it serves as the chief socializing influence of the adolescent period. At a time when the deterioration of adult-youth relations severely limits the emulatory role of the former in transmitting and enforcing social class standards of sexual behavior and of vocational aspirations, it successfully exerts its prestige and authority toward realizing these ends. And in the process of transferring his primary loyalties from home to the peer group, and of finding in the latter the chief source of his value-orientation and emotional support, he (the adolescent) accomplishes the major developmental task of adolescence—desatellization and emancipation from the home.

The authority of the peer group rests on one other factor apart from its power to give or withhold badly needed status. Through the force of numbers, precedent and organized resistance, it is able to protect the individual adolescent from excessive encroachments of adult authority. It provides "an organized means of rejecting . . . the accepted standards of adult society" and of clinging to "sub-adult patterns" [*394*].

It is to preserve the power which is derived from organized resistance, and from the uniformity and distinctiveness of its values that the peer society must insist on undeviating conformity from its members. Let everyone do as he pleases and the distinctiveness and solidarity of the peer culture would crumble. There could no longer be any recognizable and authoritative source of standards, or appeal to precedent and current practice ("what everyone is doing"). Split assunder by a multiplicity of ideals, the primary basis for organized resistance would vanish. Thus, whosoever by his deviant appearance or behavior threatens group identity or solidarity automatically weakens the protective and status-giving functions of the group and invites ridicule, rejection and ostracism.

For the very reason that the peer culture serves as a powerful ego support for the conforming adolescent, it constitutes another source of ego trauma for the hapless deviant. And by reference to the inflexible adolescent criteria for conformity, it does not require much in the way of individual difference to fall into that unfortunate category. It may be true, as some authors [*298*] assert, that the adolescent who manifests the least overt need for approval will receive the most acceptance. But he owes this acceptance to the emotional strength and self-sufficiency which the refusal to curry favor implies, and not to an attitude of independence in flouting group standards. Self-sufficiency, independence, competence and initiative are not outlawed by adolescents. On the contrary, they have high prestige value among these highly status-conscious individuals as long as one important qualification is observed: The urge to be unique or creative must be confined within the narrow framework of acceptability recognized by the group.

The candidates for the deviant class are partly drawn from the non-satellizing group, who find socialization difficult to begin with in childhood (see page 279). But introverts, intellectuals, somatic variants, and early and late maturers swell their ranks. If basic ego structure is strong (i.e., in secure satellizing children who are not overdependent) the ego trauma resulting from prolonged social rejection is severe but reversible. In overdependent, highly introverted and inadequate types withdrawal from reality and group living may end in "evolutionary" schizophrenia.[3] And in non-satellizers, anxiety may become so intense that reduction is sought through obsessive-compulsive, phobic, hysterical or paranoid mechanisms or in "reactive" schizophrenia.[4]

With the approach of adulthood, however, the situation becomes much more favorable for deviants. As adolescents near the threshold of adult status, the peer group having served its purpose begins to dissolve. The need for conformity to arbitrary and often inane standards disappears, and deviants along with the rest of their contemporaries become absorbed by the lower rungs of the adult vocational ladder. They assimilate the more heterogeneous adult attitudes of their respective social classes which, generally speaking, accept as normal a wider range of variability around the mean than is customary among adolescents.

EGO PROBLEMS REFLECTIVE OF SOCIAL CHANGE

In addition to the prolonged deprivation of status which customarily falls to their lot, adolescents more than any other age group experience difficulties issuing from the rapidity of social change. In times of transition, the security and status of everyone is threatened by changing requirements and the clash of values; but especially threatened are those whose status is marginal to begin with and who know no stable direction. "Not only must adolescents face conflicting and often contradictory social norms, but they must also wrestle with inconsistencies in treatment and in expectations from adults" [*23*]. Confusion prevails regarding proper levels of aspirations, proper standards of ethical and sexual behavior, and appropriate concepts of masculinity and femininity. "All of this makes the problem of finding anchorage so much more difficult" [*23*]. How is one to reconcile the "need for getting ahead" (and the aggressive self-seeking behavior it implies) with the Sermon on the Mount? In the face of diminishing social mobility, shall levels of aspiration be lowered, or shall youth "be encouraged to set their hands to the long and arduous task of so modifying the economy as to make possible the older ideal of equal opportunity in a mobile society" [*94*]?

INTENSITY OF EGO PROBLEMS IN RELATION TO CLASS AND SEX ROLES

The upper-class youth may initially face more status deprivation than his lower-class contemporary since education and training tend to prolong his period of economic dependency. However, he is secure in the knowledge that regardless of immediate delay or economic depression, his economic status is assured. The middle-class youth, however, faces the most difficult situation of all. Relative to the chances for success, his level of aspiration is set the highest and kept at that peak by "the maintenance . . . of a certain level of *anxiety* with regard to the attainment of the required behavior for his status . . . This anxiety leads to striving because only thus can anxiety be reduced to a tolerable level" [*73*]. But in his case, success is not only unassured in advance but is also frequently elusive and unobtainable despite long years of apprenticeship and privation. The resulting consequences to extrinsic ego adequacy are disastrous; and only in an individual with the sturdiest type of intrinsic self-esteem can this devaluing trauma remain peripheral to the basic core of self-acceptance.

Evidence is steadily accumulating that of the two sexes, the girl undergoes the more difficult and conflictful adolescence.[5] At one time, she definitely had an advantage in that she was not expected to effect as complete a transformation of the dependent aspects of childhood personality as her brother; but this advantage is fast disappearing and is, besides, more than counterbalanced by other considerations. To begin with, "unlike boys, girls have no core value—such as athletic prowess—which persists into the adolescent peer culture as a significant determinant of status . . . Heterosexual effectiveness . . . becomes an entirely new and solitary criterion for femininity and for feminine prestige in the emerging peer society" [*23*].

More important still is the fact that the changing status of women is creating considerable confusion as to what is the appropriate feminine sex role in society. The adolescent girl is undecided as to which concept of femininity she is to incorporate into her ego—the traditional role of homemaker and mother or the newer role fashioned on the masculine pattern. Whichever alternative she chooses, she will be subjected to violent contrary pressures at the hands of parents, school, church, peer culture and prospective husband. And along with the conflict in social sex role, another conflict related to sex is arising for the first time. All along it had been assumed that only men experience physiological sex desires apart from affectual needs. Now this situation is receiving some social acceptance as a relevant possibility in the case of women.

A great part of the difficulty girls experience in adolescence finds expression in the home because of a lag in parental attitudes which have not kept pace with these cultural changes in the status of women. Parents tend to take the emancipation of their sons for granted, and modify their attitudes accordingly. However, they appear unwilling to acknowledge the same emancipation needs in their daughters; and instead of relinquishing some control at adolescence, seek to impose more rather than less supervision and direction. Whereas in the case of boys, there is a steady increase with age in parental acceptance of their individuality and independence, the reverse is true in the case of girls. Parental attitudes of domination and interference actually tend to increase during the adolescent period.[6]

Because identifications with caste, class and sex membership groups first becomes crucially important as ego supports during adolescence, we must reckon with their negative as well as their positive attributes. The fact that a given adolescent in the United States is white, Protestant, upper-class, and can trace his ancestry back to the Pilgrims is a powerful brace to his marginal developmental status. But if he is of Negro, Jewish, Italian or Mexican descent, or lives on the wrong side of the tracks, what then? He must surely suffer an additional deflation in ego status, the traumatic potential of which must, as always, be evaluated in relation to the strength of his intrinsic self-acceptance.

THE PARENT-CHILD RELATIONSHIP DURING ADOLESCENCE

We have already stated that emancipation from home, parents, and the childhood attitude of dependency is the major developmental task of adolescence. This process of desatellization begins in middle childhood and preadolescence; and what is accomplished during this period in the way of learning responsibility and independence predetermines in large measure the later success or failure of emancipation. But until the actual onset of sexual maturation, the home is still the major source of the child's status. It is the parents' changed emotional attitude towards the sexually mature child (marked by the withdrawal of considerable emotional support of the protective kind) that precipitates the psychological process of emancipation. Status and emotional support must be sought elsewhere, and is found in school and peer society. The all-important home of childhood overshadowed by "these two more important determinants of interim status becomes reduced to a vestigeal role" [*23*].

The surprising thing about emancipation is that it is largely the outcome of positive changes in the relationships between the adolescent and *non-parents* rather than the result of any positive modification of the parent-child relationship itself. Seldom is there any planned or deliberate determination of policy. There is merely the deterioration of a relationship as it is replaced by new loyalties, new standards, and new sources of status. Parental influence and prestige wane to the point where the peer culture is even obliged to take over the functions of transmitting and enforcing class attitudes, aspirations and standards of behavior.

Along with the rest of adolescent development, emancipation is a very uneven process. The relinquishment of parental emotional support comes rather early and is quite thoroughgoing. Parents also expect greater dependability and more identification with mature goals. On the other hand, they are less disposed to recognize the adolescent's need for greater independence and to relinquish control and supervision. But it is hardly surprising that the adolescent receives such belated recognition as an adult by his parents. "Being supported tends to keep the adolescent a child in his parents' house—a child whose opinions do not count, whose judgments are overridden, who is expected to seek and follow advice" [*407*].

It is this "ambivalent and inconsistent attitude towards emancipation" which is the chief cause of parent-child difficulties during adolescence. "Parents find it especially difficult to surrender control when they derive through this domination 'a certain compensatory amount of status and affective satisfaction' " [*278*]. Adding to this difficulty is the child's ambivalence about growing up. His desire for emancipation is not "unmixed with a need for continued protection and security" [*118*]. Both this feeling and an aggressive reaction to status deprivation often make him resistive to adult standards of maturation.

Later, other reasons accumulate for the growing intensification of parent-youth conflict. Exposure to the wider cultural milieu gives the adolescent cause for dissatisfaction with the traditional practices of his home. "He becomes . . . sensitive and worried about family customs and patterns which now appear peculiar, different and embarrassing . . . and may want to conceal his family from his contemporaries as a social liability" [*118*]. He finds it necessary to proclaim his independence and even imitate the stereotyped adolescent contempt for parental dicta in order to maintain his standing in the peer group [*48, 118, 354*]. If the parent strikes an "either-or" attitude, more than likely, his child will decide in favor of his age-mates, at least covertly, since it is to them that he owes the major portion of his present status [*48, 146*]. The adolescent fears to become emotionally involved in relation to his parents since he is afraid that this attachment must inevitably assume the pattern of the only type of relationship he has ever known with them—that of the dependent child [*407*]. Hence, he feels inhibited about expressing whatever affectionate impulses he may experience toward them at this time.

On the part of the parent, considerations of rivalry stemming from the fear of being displaced are often a hidden cause of parent-child conflict. Misunderstandings also tend to arise because parents persist in interpreting their children's problems in terms of their own anxieties and conflicts at a similar age. The sex problems of her adolescent daughter may rearouse sexual fantasies and guilt feelings that the mother experienced and repressed with difficulty in her own adolescence. She now attempts to repress these uncomfortable memories by serving as a repressive influence in relation to her daughter's impulses.

Parent-youth conflict during adolescence tends to be a transitory phenomenon, disappearing in most cases with the conclusion of the adolescent period. This at least appears to be the rule in cases where a satisfactory satellizing relationship prevailed during childhood. Once the adolescent receives undisputed recognition as an adult, the main source of conflict between him and his parents is removed. The emotional ties and cordiality of the childhood era are restored, but on a new basis of equality and mutual respect. In the case of non-satellizers, special problems of emancipation may arise which engender permanent parent-child hostility (see pp. 243-244). It is obviously a matter of great importance to distinguish between the "normal" and the "pathological" varieties of this problem in child guidance work, since parents are considerably disturbed by the prospect of permanent estrangement from their children.

ADOLESCENCE AS A SOURCE OF SERIOUS PSYCHOPATHOLOGY

The combination of bodily changes, transitional tensions, and sociogenic status deprivation almost inevitably converts adolescence into a period full of threat and trauma to the ego. In addition, the satellizer must learn a new independent way of life. By forming new loyalties, he has to struggle with guilt feelings arising from the repudiation of primary allegiances to his parents. But unlike the non-satellizer, he has a basic fund of intrinsic adequacy to fall back upon. The anxiety he experiences is transitional in nature and referable to environmental stress. Although the non-satellizer is also subject to these same external threats to his ego adequacy, their capacity to inflict lasting damage on his personality is derived from the fact that intrinsic self-esteem is lacking. His ego adequacy is wholly a creature of the environmental vicissitudes which deny or gratify the hypertrophied ego demands on which he has staked his value as a human being.

Since the deprivations of adolescence fall more heavily on non-satellizers, we can anticipate greater psychiatric casualties in their ranks which are attributable to the rigors of this developmental period. However, this holds true only for anxiety disorders and disturbances referable to the need for anxiety reduction. When it comes to failure in ego maturation, i.e., failure to shed childhood attitudes of dependency and to assume adult goals and goal-seeking patterns, it is obvious that the satellizer is by far the more vulnerable. The task of desatellization does not exist for the non-satellizer. And it is only under very special circumstances that he will fail to attain adult personality status (see pp. 243-244).

But if we examine more closely the two types of psychopathology commonly appearing in the adolescent period, it becomes apparent that adolescence *per se* can hardly be called an adequate *cause* of either. It is more of a proving-ground for testing the soundness of the personality structure laid down in the earlier years. The non-satellizer would not develop anxiety states or their derivatives if originally the parent-child relationship had been so structured as to permit the acquisition of intrinsic feelings of security and adequacy; for although it is theoretically possible for unusual trauma to produce anxiety of this type in satellizers, practically it does not occur very often. And similarly, the social conditions of adolescent life which expose an individual as incapable of assuming an independent adult role in society only point up tendencies toward overdependency and passivity attributable to earlier aberrations in the parent-child relationship (or to constitutional factors [see Chapter 13]).

In succeeding sections, therefore, it will be necessary to examine in greater detail the various dimensions of the parent-child relationship, the types of aberrations that may arise in the course of this relationship, their causes, and the implications they bear for ego development and the personality disorders.

NOTES

[1] The exaggerated importance of these maturational and somatic variations are, of course, attributable to the fantastically rigid conformity requirements of the peer culture. The psychological consequences of deviation will depend on "social and individual attitudes towards non-conformity," the strength of intrinsic attitudes of self-acceptance and the possession of compensatory assets [*23, 380*].

[2] However, it is more likely for a girl unpopular with girls to be popular with boys than vice versa [*394*].

[3] See pp. 490-494.

[4] See pp. 502-503.

[5] High school girls reveal more maladjustment than boys on the Thurstone Personality Schedule [*324*].

[6] Based on unpublished data of the writer.

PART III

The Dynamics of Ego Development

CHAPTER 11

Crisis and Failure in Ego Development: I. Devaluation in Early Childhood

THE NATURE OF DEVELOPMENTAL CRISIS

IN NATURE, the rate of development is never constant. Growth consists of relatively long periods of equilibrium (during which performance is consolidated) punctuated by shorter transitional periods of disequilibrium (and seeming regression) in which new developmental directions are formulated [*149*]. In ego development, these transitional periods are times of crisis, for inevitably they arise as the biosocial status of the individual is destined to undergo significant change.

Change involves a loss of the stability and security provided by consolidated status. Gone is the familiar framework of reference which formerly gave anchorage to values and attitudes relating to self and the world. New learnings and adaptations are necessary. A new status must be forged, and in the process there are resistances to overcome and uncertainties to bear. For even if the new status is on a higher and more desirable plane, the very processes of change are inherently painful and the outcome is always in doubt.

The relative frequency of developmental regression during periods of crisis, therefore, is not at all surprising. Resistance to change and ambivalent feelings regarding it stalemate progress. Anxiety and insecurity provide an unfertile field for learning even though they may enhance motivational persistence for long-range goals. And the learning of more complex functions, while still subliminal, can never approach the efficiency of the simpler consolidated techniques which are being discarded. The creeping child moves faster through space than his contemporary who is learning to walk.

Periods of transition or crisis do not arise automatically in the course of development. There is no "morphogenic" timetable that depends solely on internal factors of maturation. Transitional periods in ego development are outcomes of dramatic changes in the organism-environment relationship which are reflective of crucial shifts in the former's biosocial status. The relevant variables are changes in capacity to cope with reality or to evaluate self, strong social pressures to conform to cultural norms and expectations, and the reciprocal influence of each of these factors on the others. For example, the crisis of devaluation (which appears as the child leaves the period of infancy and enters the stage of childhood) is precipitated by the consolidation of sufficient motor, intellectual and social skill to make possible a greater measure of self-help and conformity to parental direction. The parents in turn are motivated by a desire to gain the volitionally ascendent role in the relationship that the conditions of dependency warrant, and to rear their child in the traditions of the culture. And lastly, the child's perceptual capacity becomes sufficiently acute to appreciate more realistically his role and status. From the interaction of these variables, a crisis in ego development is produced from which new concepts of self emerge and finally become consolidated after passing through a period of instability and apparent regression.

EGO CRISES AND EROGENOUS ZONES

Significant shifts in personality development are related by psychoanalytic writers to changes in current focus of erogenous interest. The application of this doctrine to the course of ego development has already been criticized on the grounds of phylogenetic preformationism, because ego motivations are derived exclusively from psychosexual sources, and finally because infantile sensuality is uncritically equated with adult sexuality.

This does not mean, however, that the visceral, sensory and sensuous roles of these bodily areas are irrelevant for the problem of ego development. It is obvious that they must inspire important needs and serve as crucial contact points in the relationship between parent and child, frequently defining the locus of frustration and gratification. Also, differential aspects of neural and functional maturation impose a characteristic temporal sequence on the order with which each zone assumes its relative or focal importance.

However, in each case the bodily zone only serves as the instrumentality of an existing biosocial relationship and its associated ego structure. It provides an area of common concern and a channel for interpersonal communication. The specific site and mode of action involved (reception or expulsion) do not determine the nature of ego organization at any given phase but rather serve as media through which a system of values related to self become defined or seek expression. Reik [*322*] makes a significant contribution when he relates the sequence of erogenous localization to the course of ego development rather than to the Freudian scheme of psychosexual maturation. Nevertheless he follows the psychoanalytic lead by regarding the specific site and quality of activity at these zones as etiologically significant for the patterning of personality (in this case for ego structure rather than for psychosexual motivations and their characterological correlates). Such reasoning, for example, leads to the widely accepted but naive view that receptive oral activity must be correlated with personality dependency since it is physically suggestive of passive intake of materials supplied by others. Actually the prevailing evaluation of self current during the oral stage is couched in omnipotent terms despite the appreciation of executive dependency in relation to oral gratification. And even this executive dependence is not intrinsically related to the fact of oral activity *per se* but is a general outcome of biosocial incompetence.

The feeding situation is the most central and highly differentiated area of life space during infancy and the focal point of concern in the parent-child relationship. Hence it is not unreasonable to expect that it will be through this medium that the biosocial status of the infant will receive its most poignant definition and expression. The feeding situation, however, does not determine the attributes of the infant's biosocial status; it serves merely as the chief instrumentality for providing the relevant interpersonal experience in the course of which these attributes must necessarily be reflected. The actual determinants of status are the child's degree of biological competence and the parents' attitude toward and response to same. It is these general factors plus the perceptual capacity of the infant that determine his ego structure, and shape the form of the specific erogenous activity or situation which happens to be of focal significance at a particular stage of development. The status elements of motor helplessness and parental subservience, for example, predetermine the organization of any need-satisfaction sequence in the early days of infancy. They give rise to an awareness of executive dependence, but concomitantly to a notion of volitional omnipotence with its accompanying expectation of and demand for immediate gratification. Because oral activity serves as the climactic step of a sequence in which the crucial visceral need of infancy is brought to consummation, it comes to typify or become symbolic of the biosocial status and ego structure of the infant. This statement of the role of orality, however, is a far cry from the psychoanalytic view (Freud's or Reik's) that specific properties of sucking, chewing or biting bear some intrinsic relationship to psychosexual, ego or personality development.

The sensations related to bladder and bowel evacuation offer another case in point. They are not distinguished by any special properties which give rise to specific attributes of character. It just happens that these functions are subjected to training (postponement of the gratification of immediate release) during the time when parents are seeking greater control, and the ego structure is confronted with pressures toward devaluation. Sphincter regulation, thus, becomes the battleground on which the forces producing ego crisis are deployed: social pressure, increased capacity, resistance, and counter-resistance. And just as oral activity may become symbolic of volitional omnipotence, the necessity for sphincter control may symbolize the beginning of volitional dependence.

INDIVIDUAL DIFFERENCES IN RELATION TO CRISES IN EGO DEVELOPMENT

Apart from symbolizing different stages in ego development and serving as important areas in the life space of a child on which determinants of biosocial status impinge, erogenous activity is related to ego development in still another way. In considering Sheldon's data on body-typing (see page 26), it was concluded that both structural prominence and magnitude of drive associated with a particular organ system are determined in part by genetic factors. The sensuous satisfactions derived from erogenous zones constitute important components of the infantile ego attributes of hedonism and need for immediate gratification. Since there is obviously a wide range of variability in the strength of any hereditary determinant, individuals must differ markedly with respect to magnitude of a particular erogenous need. From this it follows that the attenuation of these hedonistic needs (which takes place in the course of ego maturation) will encounter more or less severe resistance in accordance with whether genetic loadings of these motivations are high or low.

Such genetically determined individual differences play an important role in ego development. That is why the progression of any developmental process can be described only in general terms. It is true that certain uniformities in biosocial status prevail from one culture to the next; that certain types of parental attitudes may be restricted to a single cultural environment while other attitudes vary more from family to family than from culture to culture; that certain regularities in the growth of perceptual capacity are observable. The identification of these variables enables us to write the general equation of ego development for a hypothetical child of a given family in a particular social setting. But for purposes of individual prediction, precise knowledge of the strength of many important personality traits is necessary. In addition to strength of hedonistic motivations, other individual differences are crucial for ego development. Notions of omnipotence and volitional independence must be related in some way to innate differences in dominance and vigorousness of response; the desire for executive independence is undoubtedly dependent to some extent upon propensity for activity and manipulation.

From these considerations it is apparent that individual differences affect the course of ego development in at least three ways: (a) They determine differentially the length of a given phase. (b) By either favoring or opposing the direction of biosocial pressures they can reduce or intensify the intensity of crises accompanying transitional periods and make more or less difficult the transition from one stage to the next. (c) They can help determine both the attitudes adopted by parents towards a child and differences in the response of the latter to the same parental attitude. Illustrations of the operation of individual differences in children in differentially affecting the outcome of ego development will be provided later.

ALTERNATIVES IN MEETING THE CRISIS OF DEVALUATION

The first crisis in ego organization arises in most households when the parents decide that the infant is mature enough to conform to their direction and to undergo training in the ways of his culture. Up to this point, his volitional fancies had been sufficiently indulged to create an illusion of omnipotence despite his actual helplessness. Now improved perceptual ability makes him reinterpret this incompetence as a damaging liability rather than as supporting evidence for his claims of volitional independence.

Instead of retaining untenable aspirations of grandiosity and omnipotence which would be destined to undergo continuous buffeting with disastrous results to self-esteem, an alternative other than complete devaluation to the extent justified by his objective capacity to cope with the environment is available to the child, namely, satellization. This involves a shift in the basis of self-evaluation from ego aspirations related to a status determined by his own capacity to control his environment, to aspirations envisaging a derived status created by the fact of relationship to and intrinsic valuation by the omnipotent parents. It has already been pointed out that although this is the most common and likely outcome of the three possible alternatives, it is not necessarily inevitable.

Implications of the Various Alternatives

Two distinct issues are involved in the choice of one of the above three alternative reactions to the initial crisis in ego organization: (1) Whether or not devaluation of ego aspirations occurs at all, and if so, to what extent. (2) Whether the basis of the status to which the child aspires is (a) *primary,* i.e., related to the child's own power aspirations in manipulating his environment or (b) *derived* from the status of other persons through a process of identification. Retention of the omnipotent ego aspirations is the only alternative requiring no devaluation whatsoever. Complete devaluation lies at the opposite pole, and satellization occupies an intermediate position.

With respect to source of status, only satellization involves change to a derived basis for self-evaluation. Both complete devaluation and the preservation of omnipotent motivations utilize the child's own power aspirations as the point of reference in determining self-esteem. In the case of the former, they are minimal in accordance with the child's actual biosocial incompetence. In the latter case, they remain at the omnipotent level regardless of whether any environmental support in terms of either competence or recognition is provided. In no individual, however, are ego aspirations solely *primary* or *derived* in nature. Various ratios between the two always prevail.

Primary ego aspirations can be gratified only by actual accomplishments of the individual, giving rise to an *extrinsic* sense of adequacy (self-esteem). *Derived* ego aspirations are satisfied both by identification with the status of others and by being accepted by the person with whom the identification (satellization) is made. They lead to *intrinsic* self-esteem, being independent of the child's own performance capacity.

In ego-involved activities, ego aspirations have a general significance the meaning of which transcends the particular task at hand. This is embodied in the level of aspiration set for any specific performance, and hence accounts for whatever generality of function is found for aspirational level involving different tasks [*250*]. From this datum one could venture to predict that within a given individual the correspondence between the levels of aspiration for any two tasks would be a function of the degree of similarity in ego-involvement which prevails. Thus, the magnitude of a child's prestige drive may be exceedingly high in task A and only negligible in task B, the discrepancy being related to intense self-involvement in the former and to indifference or dis-involvement of self in the latter [*25*].

Variables Influencing the Choice of Alternatives

Ego aspiration level, like level of aspiration in general, does not change haphazardly but lawfully. Once set, it tends to resist change, particularly lowering in the absence of impelling cause [*250*]. But if change is indicated, it will always be in the direction of preserving a maximum of self-esteem [*12*]. Abrupt changes are less likely to be acceptable than gradual ones [*23*]. One might also predict that resistance to lowering would be greater in those cases where ego aspiration levels are high and consistently reinforced. Lastly it would seem likely that an individual should be more disposed to retrench on his primary ego aspirations if his intrinsic store of self-esteem is high. Thus, while the *mean* level of aspiration in a group of subjects is invariably lowered by an experience involving defeat of expectation or disparagement of status [*250*], there are marked individual differences in the rate and extent of goal reduction. And if continued ego-involvement in the task can be assumed, it would not be unreasonable to suppose that these differences are related in some way to variability in the nature and magnitude of ego aspirations.

In addition to these variables which are involved in the general regulation of change in ego aspiration level, another class of variables is also important in determining the outcome of the initial crisis of devaluation. These are concerned with the personality of the individual child and the character of the important interpersonal relationships defining his existence. Behavioral changes that are easily conceivable in a given individual in one psychological field may be difficult or impossible of achievement in another individual inhabiting a different psychological milieu.

Satellization

In terms of the above mentioned variables, it is easy to demonstrate why the satellizing alternative usually prevails. It provides a secure and stable source of status and prevents the catastrophic loss of self-esteem that would necessarily follow from the unrealistic retention of omnipotent ego aspirations. To be sure, aspirational level is lowered, but not nearly as much nor as abruptly as would be required if the child clung to his own competence as the criterion for charting the course of his aspirations. The problem of self-esteem becomes freed of the uncertainties attending his own performance and of the vicissitudes relating to status and recognition based on his own merits. In any culture the child can not compete with adults except on a marginal basis which generates conflict and frustration. The only stable, unambiguous, non-marginal position he can adopt and still retain a reasonably high level of self-esteem and ego aspiration is a dependent and subordinate role which is built mainly upon derived ego aspirations.

However, the advantages of the subordinate status with respect to an intrinsic source of self-esteem can become operative only under certain specified conditions. Satellization implies a two-way relationship: an attitude of dependent subservience on the part of the weaker member, and an attitude of benevolent protection on the part of the dominant member in the relationship. A hostile, threatening, rejecting parent cannot serve as a figure with whom a child freely identifies in order to secure vicarious ego enhancement. Identification under such conditions can at best serve the ends of expediency or reduce anxiety by allowing the threatened child to imagine himself the possessor of the form and powers of his threatening parent.[1*] A genuine emotional acceptance of the child by the parent which cheerfully acknowledges him as a voluntarily assumed obligation, and which professes an altruistic concern for his well-being is a prerequisite for satellization. Stripped of this protection, the surrender of volitional sovereignty becomes too precarious and forbidding a prospect to constitute a realistic possibility.

* Notes for this chapter appear on page 142.

Similarly, the advantages of a derived status cannot accrue unless the parent values the child for himself and not in terms of his present competence or potential eminence. If the child has value in the parent's eyes merely as a narcissistic extension of the latter's ego or as the potential heir of his frustrated aspirations, he is required to render rather than receive ego support; he can only acquire self-esteem extrinsically by virtue of his own superior attainments. On the other hand, the omnipotent and omniscient parent who has the power arbitrarily to assign absolute values[2] to all objects in the psychological world of the child can also endow *him* with an intrinsic value which is further enhanced by the reflected glory adhering to the satellite's role.

While it is self-evident that the rejecting parent cannot extend intrinsic valuation to his child, the converse is not necessarily true. An extrinsically-valuing parent *can* be accepting—but only for ulterior motives which require that he value his child not for what the child is but for what the child can do for him (the parent).

In addition to these two crucial prerequisites for satellization, there are several other relevant variables related to personality characteristics of parent and child which merely make the process more or less difficult or prolonged, but are not important enough to exercise a crucial influence: A parent who is unduly submissive, and who by virtue of extreme permissiveness fails to impress his child with the distinction between their respective roles and prerogatives tends to extend the notion of omnipotence beyond its more usual span of duration. The child is spared the pressure of parental demands for conformity to their will and standards, and hence exhibits less need for ego devaluation. Nevertheless, the maturation of social perception eventually overcomes the autistically grounded structure of infantile ego organization; and provided that the primary prerequisites are fulfilled, he chooses satellization as the most feasible solution to the problem of maintaining childhood self-esteem in an adult dominated society. For sooner or later as his awareness of power relationships in the real world increases, he must come to realize that children can at best enjoy a marginal and dependent status, and that ego aspirations based upon his own performance capacity hold out little promise for feelings of adequacy, but extend considerable threat of frustration and anxiety.

Apart from parental attitudes there are individual personality differences among children which either facilitate or impede the course of satellization. The more dominant, tough-skinned and self-assertive a child, the greater his tendency will be to resist dependency upon the will and discretion of others; the less robust and vigorous his inclination towards dominating others, the more easily will he submit to a position of self-subordination. Differences in viscerotonia [*352*] must also be considered since one of the more important aspects of satellization involves suppression of hedonistic urges and the desire for immediate gratification. A child whose need for visceral satisfactions are relatively great will, therefore, find the burden of satellization less tolerable at first then his more cerebrotonic contemporary. But again this variability in temperament between children can not be judged crucial for the eventual outcome of satellization.

To summarize, satellization becomes the favored mode of ego organization in meeting the crisis of devaluation because it conforms best to the pattern of change which can be theoretically predicted as most probable in terms of the variables governing modification of levels of ego aspiration. It offers the advantages of (a) long-range stability, (b) maintenance of a maximal degree of self-esteem, (c) minimal and least abrupt lowering of supportable ego aspirations, and (d) an intrinsic guaranteed status, free of environmental uncertainties and vicissitudes. These advantages, however, become operative only in situations where a child is (a) emotionally accepted and (b) valued for himself by his parents. Secondary variables which may retard the rate of satellization in the child but are not crucial for outcome include (a) parental oversubmissiveness, and (b) excessive self-assertiveness or viscerotonia in the child.

Given but half a chance, therefore, in the more normal and usual family setting in this and other cultures, the typical child upon leaving behind the period of his infancy will seek to establish a satellizing relationship with his parents. The strength of this desire is frequently great enough to influence the child to interpret more favorably than objective conditions warrant the crucial aspects of parental attitude which make this re-formation in ego structure possible. He strives desperately to believe that his parents are not rejecting or valuing him extrinsically. Not until the last vestige of hope is destroyed and the evidence becomes overwhelming does he become reconciled to believing the worst. In clinical practice one not infrequently encounters children who rationalize their parents' brutality as a manifestation of love.

Non-Satellization: Complete Devaluation or Retention of Omnipotence

It has already been postulated that the rejected or extrinsically valued child is unable to satellize (in the absence of one or both of the two crucial prerequisites for satellization). Hence the shift to a derived source of status and intrinsic feelings of adequacy is blocked. As before, ego aspiration level continues to be determined in reference to the child's *own* power to influence and control his environment: His status remains a creature of his own strivings and capacities. He does not aspire to a position where he shares vicariously in the prestige of others by virtue of a dependent relationship to them.

Two possibilities now exist: Ego aspirations can still be maintained at the omnipotent level or else be drastically reduced so as to correspond to actual biosocial competence unenhanced by the borrowed status afforded by parental acceptance and prestige. The choice between these alternatives depends again on factors related to extent and abruptness of deflation in ego aspiration level, maintenance of the highest possible level of self-esteem, parental attitudes, and personality characteristics of the child. In the first instance, no devaluation of ego aspiration takes place; in the second, devaluation is complete. In neither case, however, is it possible for the child to evaluate his status as autistically as during infancy. The environment may provide more or less basis and support for the notion of omnipotence, but in any event the growth of social awareness requires that these notions be subjected more rigorously to the test of reality.

The dynamics of change in ego aspiration level operate against the choice of total devaluation which requires an overly great and abrupt depreciation of the child's ego aspirations. Furthermore, as already suggested, self-esteem depends on more than the discrepancy between aspiration and performance level. Clinical observation in vocational guidance leads to the hypothesis that the absolute magnitude of aspiration level (regardless of the discrepancy) is in itself an independent determinant of self-esteem. Instances abound where completely idle or hopelessly mediocre individuals bolster their self-esteem almost indefinitely by maintaining ridiculously high levels of aspiration which successfully block realistic and appropriate adjustments. Similarly the attainment of modest goals does not usually lead to a cessation of striving, but tends to raise the aspiration level to a point where failure is clearly risked[3] [*12*]. If high aspiration levels *per se* did not tend to enhance self-esteem these situations could not be as commonplace as they are; or stated differently, the principle that ego aspiration level resists marked or abrupt lowering is merely a corollary of the more inclusive generalization that an individual's level of aspiration tends to be shifted "in such a manner as to maintain his self-esteem at the highest possible level" [*12*]. Thus the original "discrepancy" formula for self-esteem proposed by William James and restated by the Lewinian school as accounting for subjective feelings of success and failure (level of aspiration experiments) appears to be an oversimplification of the facts.[3] In addition to the above-cited variables of absolute value and abruptness in shifting of aspiration level, self-esteem is also determined by the factors of satellization, canalization and reinforcement (to be discussed further below).

The relative frequency of various parental attitudes in non-satellizing situations also favors the retention of omnipotent aspirations rather than complete devaluation. Seldom is parental rejection so extreme in infancy as to preclude the development of ideas of omnipotence; cultural pressures generally compel even the most narcissistic parent to cater to the biological needs of his infant. It is only later when parental responsiveness to the child's emotional needs becomes more crucial, and when hostility and aggression can be expressed under the guise of socially approved training demands that the full impact of rejection is felt. Hence, although there is no underlying difference between the early and later parental attitudes of rejection, there is a profound difference from the standpoint of the perceived experience of the child: The former does not generally detract from notions of omnipotence while the latter leads to an awareness of rejection. This contrast is not received with equanimity. The hostility and aggression implied in rejection is met with counter-aggression. Excessive repression of the child's will tends to provoke an exaggerated self-assertion. Power is relished both as an instrument of revenge and as a means of reversing the negative value placed upon him. The requirements of counter-aggression, therefore, are best met by the preservation of the omnipotent infantile ego structure.

Resistance to the lowering of ego aspiration level is also increased by the absence of any possibility for acquiring intrinsic self-esteem. The acquisition of its extrinsic counterpart, therefore, becomes more of a compelling necessity. There is less disposition to compromise on the external indicators of adequacy if bankruptcy prevails with respect to its inner criteria. It should also be emphasized that once the initial tendency is set in motion it tends to perpetuate itself. Similar to what happens when any need is repeatedly satisfied by a single mechanism, the need for adequacy is also subject to canalization. Successful reinforcement, especially in the early stages of a need-satisfaction sequence, endows one of a number of potentially adequate responses with a uniquely specific capacity to serve as satisfier quite apart from its intrinsic merits or advantages.

But parents differ in the way in which they express attitudes of rejection. Where rejection takes the more passive form of prolonged neglect and disinterest (as is frequent in cases of institutionalized care) rather than aggressive hostility, the child's reaction is more likely to be in the nature of complete devaluation instead of the preservation of omnipotent aspirations. To begin with, if the neglect is thoroughgoing enough, omnipotent fancies do not develop in the first place; a serious impoverishment in the capacity for emotional response results [*155*]. Hence, in such cases there is no need for devaluation. Secondly, in the absence of overt parental aggression the maintenance of infantile omnipotence as a mechanism of counteraggression is unnecessary.

Where non-satellization is the outcome of extrinsic valuation, the picture is again markedly different. The rejected child preserves his aspirations of omnipotence in the most difficult of all possible environments. He can only anticipate unremitting frustration of his status needs in an ever-threatening, hostile home. A heavy burden of anxiety and impaired self-esteem must be borne in the present while aspirations of power and prestige are projected into the future. The need for survival also compels a humiliating outward acceptance of an authority and control which he resents. The extrinsically-valuing parent, on the other hand, not only does not apply the training pressures which create a need for devaluation, but also actively helps to perpetuate ideas of omnipotence in his offspring. It it is the function of the child to gratify the projected, grandiose ambitions of his parent, it is surely to the latter's interest to encourage aspirations of omnipotence. He, therefore, provides an environment in which such aspirations are remarkably tenable: The child is installed in the home as an absolute monarch and surrounded by adulation and obeisance. In due time, of course, increased social maturity and the quite different treatment which he receives outside the home compel a more realistic estimate of his actual status. He might then be disposed to seek the security of a derived status. But satellization in relation to his parents can not offer him an intrinsic sense of adequacy. By this time he realizes only too well that he is not valued for himself but for his role as eminent man in embryo. There is nothing left for him to do but to maintain the grandiose aspirations which if fulfilled would provide the extrinsic self-esteem which he needs and which reinforcement and canalization have taught him to crave.

The type of reaction given by the child to parental rejection is also a function of the former's personality. A dominant self-assertive child will strike back with vigorous counteraggression and stubborn negativism. At the other end of the scale, a submissive child is more apt to seek withdrawal from conflict, to comply externally, and express his aggression in fantasy. Trends toward introversion will be reinforced in the latter and trends toward extraversion will be strengthened in the former. Everything else being equal, a child with strong needs for visceral satisfaction will react more violently to the harsh regimen imposed by the rejecting parent. But despite these obvious differences in reaction, the essential pattern of response to active rejection is largely the same: In striving to attain an extrinsic sense of adequacy, ego aspirations are kept at a high level and are highly resistant to lowering. Whether expressed more or less openly, or only in fantasy behind a smokescreen of compliance, volitional independence is not surrendered. Although the acquisition of superior extrinsic status is hopefully projected into the future, chronic depreciation of self-esteem is inevitable for all during the long span of years marked by economic dependence upon parents. And for the greater majority it is a lifelong prospect.

ASPECTS AND STAGES OF EGO DEVALUATION

Satellization involves two different but interdependent and concurrent aspects of ego devaluation. The first is concerned with changing the type of status sought after and with effecting a reduction in the level of aspiration and in the desire for volitional independence. The second aspect has as its aim the attenuation of infantile hedonism, helplessness and irresponsibility. The former is a general consequence of the shift toward greater parental control in the parent-child relationship. The latter is a reflection of the training goals that underlie the new parental demands and expectations which arise in this period of development. While it is important to recognize that there is a tremendous amount of variability in the specific aims of child rearing from culture to culture, there is also a core of commonality which can be safely abstracted. Certain characteristics of ego maturation hold true in all cultures because of the operation of various general principles of individual development and interpersonal relations. Regardless of the unique set of virtues and values which each society advocates as the exclusive aim of existence, parents the world over are charged with the responsibility of rearing their young in such a fashion as to develop a mature capacity for attaining and expressing culturally approved virtues. Hence, it is to these universal aspects of ego development which are necessary for the realization of the ideal of adult maturity in any culture that parents now turn their attention in their training efforts.

The infant's motivational orientation is characteristically hedonistic with an emphasis upon immediate gratification. However, the needs for survival and adaptation and the goals of most creative activity are ill-served by this orientation. Ego maturation, therefore, requires an attenuation of hedonism: growth in the ability to develop motivations other than those involving visceral satisfactions, to plan in terms of larger and more distant goals, and to forego immediate satisfactions for the sake of making progress toward more important, long-term aspirations.

A parallel need relates to the development of a greater amount of executive independence. Growth in motor capacity for self-help is not matched by an equal willingness to assume the burdens which this entails. It is more in accord with notions of regal omnipotence just to will things accomplished and then have others carry out the necessary time-consuming manipulations. This, of course, does not rule out the possibility—and the demonstrable fact—that a child will find pleasure in doing many things for himself; activity is one of the primary sources of pleasure in childhood. (Even in adult life, the king will ask his chauffeur to move over while he takes the wheel.) Frustration of this desire for self-help is in fact one of the more important situational causes of infantile negativism. The important point, however, is that "the child's ire is not so much aroused because he is denied the opportunity for executive independence *per se* but mainly because the frustrated desire for self-help is at the time representative of the broader desire for volitional independence. In other words, he is chiefly angry because his will (as manifested by a desire for self-help) is thwarted, not merely because he is not permitted to do a particular activity *by himself* . . . The (infant) is desirous in the main of retaining the executive dependence which is associated with volitional impotence . . . He becomes more frequently aroused by an attempt to abolish his executive dependence and his habituation to 'baby ways' than by frustrating his attempts at self-help. Much of his 'conservatism' at this stage is actually a frantic effort to perpetuate by ritual the executive dependence characteristic of the earlier phase of ego organization" [*24*].

Parents, however, are unwilling to serve indefinitely as the executive arm of their offspring's will. Moreover, individual and cultural survival demands the development of skills and willingness to work in a majority of the population. Hence in accordance with the socially approved level of ambition and industriousness prevailing in a given culture, parents, more or less, will demand that their children acquire a certain measure of self-sufficiency in the ordinary routines of living.

The imposition of parental control and cultural standards of acceptable behavior would be difficult indeed if the child were to continue indefinitely in the belief that he is exempt from all responsibility and accountability. Sheer physical force and constant surveillance would then be necessary to exact conformity to norms of conduct. Child rearing, thus, becomes infinitely easier when the child recognizes the parent's right to regulate his behavior, endows these regulations with an absolute moral force superior to his own hedonistic desires, and regards himself as accountable to his parents for living up to their standards. Before this stage of development is reached, punishment and the anticipation of punishment serve to direct the child's activities into more acceptable channels; but this control is devoid of moral implications because it is only indicative of *submission* to authority rather than *acceptance* of it. When parental authority is accepted and the norms and expectations of the parents are finally internalized, inner control of behavior supersedes external regulation; guilt feelings replace threats of punishment as the chief inhibitory agents.

But the development of a sense of responsibility is no easy feat. Of all the parental training tasks it is the most difficult and delicate. In direct opposition to its realization lie not only attitudes of volitional omnipotence and independence, but also hedonistic urges and the desire for executive dependence; hence, the final outcome depends to a large extent on the attenuation of these attitudes and desires. And in turn, once conscience and the capacity for guilt feelings are firmly established, they contribute materially to the progress of this attenuation. Until this is accomplished, however, the conflict rages back and forth, the ascendency shifting first to one side and then to the other. To bolster his side in the early critical phase, the parent is required to reinforce the child's internalization of his (the parent's) dicta with his own bodily presence on the scene. He continues to resort to rewards, threats and punishments.

In the course of time, the parent acquires new sources of support and pressure in attenuating his offspring's hedonism and in inculcating feelings of moral accountability. Through the simple device of granting or withholding approval, he is able to confer or deny the benefits of derived status realizable through satellization. Because the child has no existing framework of reference for the formulation of moral values, the parent can easily impose his own frame of reference on an absolute basis by means of prestige suggestion. This prestige authority of the parent continues to grow as the child's developing self-critical faculty undermines the infantile notions of his own omnipotence, making the parent seem more omniscient in comparison. The acceptance of parental authority is also made more palatable by rationalizing the compulsory demands of the parent as elective desires of his own. Lastly it should be pointed out that the virtue of obedience to parents is upheld in the schools, sanctified by religious doctrine, and legally enforced by agencies of the state.

Stages of Ego Devaluation

Progress toward ego devaluation is not an unbroken achievement. As in any other developmental process, fluctuation in the rate and direction of change is the rule. The equilibrium keeps shifting as key variables involved in the dynamics of transition change in value and significance. Fluctuations in the course of ego devaluation reflect to a very large extent changing levels of executive competence and the child's evaluation of same.

During the infantile period of ego organization, the presence of helplessness in the larger Gestalt of apparent volitional omnipotence enhances rather than detracts from the child's estimate of his own power. The child could quite reasonably interpret this situation as follows: "It is true that I can do very little by myself. But look how successful I am when I will that my needs be satisfied! If despite my helplessness I am so powerful, I must surely be omnipotent."

The first stage of ego devaluation, therefore, requires the undermining of this attitude of volitional omnipotence which is based upon a misinterpretation of parental tolerance and solicitude. Paradoxically enough this stage is largely initiated by an increase in the child's biosocial competence which calls forth parental training demands. The pressure of these demands plus the impact of sharpened social preception shatters the illusion of omnipotence and (depending on various other factors) may or may not lead to a lowering of ego aspiration level. In the new total Gestalt of the devalued self-concept, relative executive incompetence takes on a new significance. Instead of enhancing the feeling of omnipotence, it is more realistically perceived as one of the chief reasons for his limited volitional independence. In accordance with the same logic the parents are perceived as all-powerful because they know how to do everything.

Once this first stage of ego development is completed, the child's self-estimate is appropriately depreciated; he feels relatively helpless, and hence very much dependent upon parental protection, direction and approval. In their eyes he is a "good boy," modest, obedient and manageable.

But in the fourth year, he makes rapid strides in language, motor, and social development. He establishes a certain independent status for himself outside the home in the world of his peers. The boundaries of his psychological world are extended as he learns new ways of manipulating people and social situations, while older areas in his life space take on new and richer meaning as they become more sharply differentiated. The cumulative effect of these new developments is a marked upward revision in his estimate of his own executive competence. And possessing still but a rudimentary capacity for self-criticism he tends to exaggerate his newly acquired abilities.

The tendency towards overestimation is further facilitated by several other factors: (a) the normal euphoria and intoxication greeting initial success; (b) exposure to competitive cultural pressures which provide a constant source of stimulation for the elevation of aspirational level; and (c) the presence of a convenient conceptual framework of reference in the recently abandoned concept of omnipotence. In retreating from this last position, he had left open an avenue for return: Volitional omnipotence to be sure had been previously acknowledged as untenable in the face of limited executive competence. But if one knows everything and can do everything better than anyone else, is it then not a legitimate self-estimate and aspiration? If parental help and protection are no longer required in adapting to life situations, if one can forge one's own status on a level commensurate with exaggerated aspirations, why be satisfied with the reduced derived status of satellization and its attendant disadvantages, i.e., loss of independence, attenuated hedonism and the inhibitory pressures of a sense of responsibility?

This exuberant self-assertion, however, does not remain unchecked. The ever-present reality of his dependent, biosocial status continually intrudes. The parent can always counter: "So you're big enough to run away and look after yourself, go ahead, what's stopping you?"; or, "If you can cook better than I, suppose we let you prepare supper tonight." If the child accepts the challenge, the hopelessness of his position soon brings him back to reality with a thud.

The second stage of ego devaluation, therefore, is concerned with a different type of devaluing process than the first. The ideas of omnipotence in the first instance were derived from a misinterpretation of his usual success in need-gratification despite executive helplessness (the confusion of volitional irresistability with parental altruism). In the second case, the pretensions of omnipotence are the reflection of an exaggerated estimate of the breadth of newly acquired gains in executive competence, and are largely attributable to an inadequate self-critical faculty. The second variety of omnipotence is gradually made untenable by the child's marginal biosocial position in all cultures, the growth of his self-critical faculty, the development of conscience, and by various means of coercion available to parents, e.g., rewards, threats, punishment, prestige suggestion, and the support of other cultural agencies.

RESISTANCE TO EGO DEVALUATION: NEGATIVISM

Causes

In discussing the dynamics of ego development so far, the viewpoint of automatic change, of maturational unfolding regulated by inner directional factors has been rejected. In its place has been postulated a concept of change determined by environmental pressures, shifts in biosocial competence and perceptual clarity, and factors influencing level of aspiration and self-esteem.

Implicit in any dynamic concept of behavior viewed as the product of an existing equilibrium in personality structure (produced by opposing forces), is the belief that change involves resistance. Resistance has many sources: Simple inertia; the tenacity of habitual behavior and of mechanisms enjoying a prepotent status as a result of canalization; the insecurity and loss of immediate status involved in any transition; the loss of advantages associated with present status, and the disadvantages perceived in the new status; the force of counter-aggression in response to the pressures exerted for change. All of these factors are relevant, and operative in the process of ego devaluation. They produce almost invariably periods of exaggerated resistiveness or negativism which at least in our culture may be considered normal accompaniments of ego development.

The two- or three-year-old child has been accustomed for some time to living with the advantages and immunities of his omnipotent ego organization. He is loath to part with this orientation which places him at the center of the universe and to accept instead the role of dependent satellite. The change not only involves a depreciation in present self-estimate, but also a lowering of aspirational level and of self-esteem.[4] In our culture both experiences are unpleasant and breed resistance. Only the advantages inherent in satellization make the change eventually acceptable. But the opportunity for satellization is never entirely certain, and in the meantime, until certainty is assured, the anxiety referable to increased marginality and ambiguity of status is an uninviting prospect.

Even if satellization does seem likely, it still holds out certain palpable disadvantages from the child's standpoint. To retain parental approval he must inhibit hedonistic impulses. A large measure of volitional independence must be surrendered, and accountability to alien standards of behavior must be learned.

Finally, negativism during this period (as at any time of life) may be viewed as a form of counteraggression. In pressing their training demands, parents must sometimes be aggressive and interfering. At such times, when individuality threatens to be inundated by outside forces, a common self-protective device is to become oblivious of their presence and to persist even more doggedly in the pursuit of self-initiated activity [*288, 309*]. The element of counteraggression is most prominent, of course, in the negativism displayed by the harshly rejected child. Here, parental training measures are not only rigorous and inflexible but also unsoftened by affection and solicitude. But even where parents are accepting, individual differences in resistance due to counteraggression will prevail. It will tend to be greater when either parent or child ranks high in dominance, and vice versa. In the former case, however, this increased resistance is accompanied by earlier onset of satellization than in situations where the parent is overly submissive, since the vigorousness of parental training demands is one of the crucial variables leading to ego devaluation. Hence, in cultural settings where child-rearing practices are lax and permissive [*74*], one might conceivably expect less negativism in the first stage of ego devaluation, but also later onset of satellization.

In any particular instance of developmental negativism, specific situational factors are undoubtedly important. Because of volitional immaturity, compliance may be difficult without prior or simultaneous execution of the opposite alternative of refusal [*149*]. Later, as the capacity to anticipate behavioral consequences improves, clear-cut decision is possible without advance testing of the weaker alternative. In other instances, genuine misunderstanding of requests, or requiring the child to exercise control and discrimination beyond his developmental capacity for same may stimulate negativistic behavior. Resistiveness is frequently seen in slightly older children as a means of coercing other children and adults [*363*]. At any rate, children's negativism is more blatant and impressive than adults' since they lack the latter's repertoire of polite evasions and circumlocutions in reacting to rage-producing stimuli [*17*].

Denying a child the opportunity for self-help when this desire is representative of the more inclusive wish to assert volitional independence is a common cause of negativism; but a more important excitant in the early period of ego devaluation is the parent's demand that the child help himself while the latter insists on the privilege of remaining executively dependent [*24*]. The four-year-old, on the other hand, is more eager to help himself since he sees in executive independence the path toward volitional omnipotence; and because he characteristically overestimates his executive capacity, his attempts at self-help frequently meet with parental opposition which in turn reinforces the original intention. However, as his unlimited self-confidence shows signs of diminishing at five, ambivalence about doing things for himself may set in and further aggravate the tendency towards resistive behavior.

Genetic Origins of Resistance

The core ingredients of the resistive response is the emotion of anger. The precursor of this response is the undifferentiated and unlearned reaction of emotional excitement which is adaptively elicited by any overintense stimulus from within or without. The suggestion has been offered, however (see pp. 51-52), that the differentiated response of rage results from opposition to or frustration of the child's assertion of omnipotence. Anger, thus, can be conceived of as a learned emotional response accompanying the expression of resistance to any interference with goal-directed voluntary activity. Were this not so, it would be difficult indeed to account for the relationship between frustration and rage. The latter obviously can not appear before volition is established. But why should opposition to will (frustration) provoke such a violent reaction, a differentiated variation of the original adaptive excitement elicited by potentially destructive (overintense) stimuli? Simply because volition is endowed with the characteristics of omnipotence, and omnipotence brooks no opposition. Denial is unbearably frustrating and tantamount to potential destruction only if unlimited and invariable fulfillment of volitional demands is contemplated. Chronically neglected children who are reared in institutions exhibit shallow and superficial emotionality lacking in normal intensity [*155*]. A possible explanation is that under these circumstances they fail to develop a normal quota of volitional omnipotence.

Contributing to the violence of the original rage response to frustration is the fact that early volitional goals are directed toward visceral satisfactions. Anger, therefore, is superimposed upon the undifferentiated excitement aroused by such stimuli as hunger and thirst. Later, as the volitional horizon is broadened to encompass activity, object, and relationship goals, frustration gives rise to unmixed anger which seems no less intense. Rage, therefore, not only is an indication of the gravity with which the infant regards the matter of opposition to his omnipotent pretensions, but also tends to reinforce the latter. By becoming tied to a violent emotional reaction the duration of which exceeds by far the excitation span of the responsible stimulus, frustration is converted into an issue which transcends its immediate perceptual significance as an excitant to anger. Notice is served to frustrated and frustrator alike that omnipotent pretensions will be enforced, that interference will not be viewed with tolerance, that opposition will be met with stiff resistance. After the invariability of the relationship between frustration and rage is established, a minor excitant may give rise to a major explosion—since once set off the intensity of the latter is not easily subjected to control and tends to perpetuate itself. Hence, reactions to frustration easily get out of hand and continue long after the aroused individual has ceased to be aware of the exciting cause. With increasing age, as pretensions to omnipotence decline and as children learn to react more constructively to frustration, they become better able to inhibit undifferentiated rage, i.e., their frustration tolerance increases. In part, this inhibition may reflect neurological maturation since it depends upon cortical control of lower thalamic centers [*161*].

To summarize, anger (as a distinct emotion) becomes differentiated out of primitive excitement as an expression of resistance to the frustration of an omnipotently regarded will. Because of its refractoriness to control and modulation, and its intensity, longevity and self-perpetuating properties, it reinforces the attitude of volitional omnipotence by providing excessive and often disproportionate resistance to encroachments upon its unrestricted expression. Genetically, in terms of both adequate stimulus and essential response characteristics, the negativism displayed in reaction to ego devaluation is derived from this early pattern of resistance to frustration. Ego devaluation not only involves yielding to pressures opposed to the goals of present ongoing activity, but also requires changes antagonistic to the attitude of omnipotence. The link between the frustration-rage sequence and the devaluation-negativism syndrome, thus, is clear enough with respect to the source and significance of resistance. Less self-evident because of developmental changes in the manifestation of emotion is the continuity in form which this expression of rage takes.

Varieties of Resistance

The development of the resistive response parallels the general course of emotional development. The earliest typical expression of resistance is the temper tantrum: Rage is diffuse, undirected, uninhibited. As control increases, it becomes more purposeful and adaptive; the child develops a capacity to pretend obliviousness to opposition while persisting doggedly in his self-initiated activity. This type of behavior may alternate with directed physical aggression against others.

With the growth of language, resistance adopts more verbal, subtle and symbolic forms. Threats, boasts, contentiousness, deceit, delaying and stalling tactics replace open aggression. The child learns how to "get" his parent's "goat." He deliberately flaunts forbidden words and behavior, and learns empirically how far he can stretch defiance before provoking reprisal. The technique of controlling others and perpetuating desired situations by compulsive ritualism is thoroughly mastered.

Two Stages of Resistance to Ego Devaluation

Corresponding to the two stages of ego devaluation described above are two distinct patterns of resistance. Most obvious are differences in external form of expression which are reflective of gains in emotional maturity. At two, the temper tantrum is the most characteristic type of resistive behavior. By four, temper tantrums are rare, and boisterous, "out-of-bounds" behavior becomes the chief vehicle for expressing negativism. Self-assertion ceases to remain an end in itself; spurred on by considerations of rivalry and competition, the child becomes more concerned with deliberately marking out the lines of conflict with others so that the defeat of his opponents can be more readily demonstrated. Continued progress towards his goal and eventual possession in the face of opposition is not enough. He must also demonstrate his own superiority and reveal the weakness of others. But despite his bold front, the expression of negativism begins to acquire moral implications which were previously absent. This is revealed by a growing tendency to disclaim responsibility for resistive behavior;

to ascribe it to accidental causes, to coercive agents operating on him, or to other persons; and to rationalize it as desirable or as a form of self-defense.

More important, however, than these expressive differences in form are differences in the source and significance of resistive behavior. Two-year-old negativism seeks to perpetuate a highly autistic brand of omnipotence which is reflective of a very immature grasp of the social reality in which the child lives. The basis of parental altruism is completely misinterpreted, and no incompatibility is perceived between his acknowledged executive dependence and the belief in his volitional omnipotence. At four, omnipotent pretensions are given a more legitimate and realistic basis. Executive competence is accepted as the condition for volitional independence, but because of an inadequate self-critical faculty a very minimal degree of executive ability is inflated to the point of omniscience.[5] Resistance is provoked when the exuberantly self-confident child tries to recapture volitional control from the parent but meets with restraint and rebuff. His own provocative out-of-bounds behavior is regarded as justifiable since it is obvious that he "knows better," and parental reprisals are bitterly assailed as "unfair."

THE CONSEQUENCES OF FAILURE IN DEVALUATION

The conditions under which satellization takes place have already been discussed (see pp. 113-114). It now remains to examine the consequences of non-satellization for further ego development. The importance of this task in terms of the theoretical orientation of the book as a whole is obvious; for herein lies the link between ego development and the personality disorders. The need for ego devaluation through satellization confronts the individual with the first major crisis in the history of his personality development. If he can accomplish this developmental task—and he usually can if conditions are just minimally propitious—he has won the first important round in the battle for a normal personality structure resistive to mental disease. Troublesome behavior attributable to crisis and resistance can then be truly written off as a "passing phase" that will leave no permanent residue. On the other hand, failure to undergo normal devaluation—non-satellization—can be regarded as a major developmental failure in personality growth which predisposes the individual towards acquiring certain specific personality disorders in later life. Only the general aspects of this predisposition will be touched upon here. In a later chapter the precise relationship between these predisposing factors and the symptoms of the various behavior disorders will be presented in detail.

General Consequences

Since conditions leading to non-satellization are not uniform, differences relating to parental rejection or overvaluation respectively will be reflected in the outcome. Sufficient similarity exists, however, to warrant preliminary discussion of the general consequences common to both conditions.

The acquisition of status and self-esteem continues to remain a function of the child's own ability to manipulate his environment. Although increasing capacity to perceive the social environment more realistically compels him to adopt a more modest self-estimate in the present, his ego aspirations persist on a high level. In the absence of an acceptable compromise such as satellization (which involves only moderate devaluation and guarantees a derived intrinsic status) this high level of aspiration remains exceedingly resistant to lowering. Even though a discrepancy between aspiration and accomplishment is inevitable for some time, he hopes to close the gap in the future. In the meantime, evidence points to the fact that maintenance of a high aspirational level in and of itself elevates self-esteem. Hence, regardless of their relative untenability in the present, the infantile aspirations of volitional omnipotence and independence continue to occupy a prominent and tenaciously-held place in ego structure. This condition will henceforth be referred to as ego hypertrophy.

In the struggle to attain an extrinsic sense of adequacy, hypertrophic ego aspirations necessarily lead to an intense striving for commensurate power and prestige through reality accomplishments. These are the realistic symbols of successful performance which lead to ego aggrandizement; for now in contrast to the days of infancy, omnipotence can no longer be assumed on the basis of a distorted interpretation of parental subservience to his will.

Another general consequence of non-satellization is the failure to acquire an intrinsic sense of security. Both intrinsic security and adequacy (self-esteem) are products of satellization. But whereas the adequacy feeling refers to an inner conviction of being worthwhile and important for oneself, the feeling of security refers to an attitude of confidence in facing the future with one's safety and existence protected and unthreatened. It is the outcome of a dependent personal relationship with a stronger protective individual whose concern is genuine and altruistic and who is trusted not to abuse his superior strength and status for ulterior motives. If not acquired through early satellization, the individual can only hope to acquire a partial, modified version of it by entering into a comparable type of relationship at a later stage of life. The more usual outcome is a striving for extrinsic security based on power, position, wealth and prestige.

It should be noted here that there is a very close relationship between the feelings of security and adequacy. If impairment of adequacy feelings is severe enough, the individual feels incompetent to cope with life situations; he feels fearful, alone, unprotected. His very existence seems threatened by problems of adaptation which he fears will overtax his competence and further impair his self-esteem. Hence he will overreact with fear to any minor adjustive failure. This condition, which henceforth will be referred to as neurotic anxiety, is, therefore, only a special case of insecurity in which the threat is directed especially against self-esteem and arises from a markedly damaged sense of adequacy. Insecurity is the more inclusive term connoting a fearful attitude which anticipates threat directed at more general aspects of the individual's safety. Thus, it can be stated that while an anxious person is always insecure, the converse is not necessarily true.

Nevertheless, just as feelings of adequacy enhance the sense of security, an increase in the latter will indirectly bolster the former; a general elevation of the threshold of insecurity also raises the component threshold of anxiety. If the future is safeguarded by various types of insurance against possible catastrophe, the individual feels more competent to cope with any specific problem of adjustment that might arise. And in addition, if new sources of security can be acquired in later life through belated satellizing-like relationships, the moral support of another person is also available in meeting life situations. This latter possibility also provides a source of intrinsic or derived self-esteem which makes the consequences of failure in the striving for superiority seem much less catastrophic and may eventually lead to a reduction in the level of ego aspiration.

Thus, if anxiety does arise as a consequence of the failure to establish a satellizing relationship with parents (the conditions which precipitate anxiety will be discussed in Chapter 15), hope for amelioration does not exist in either acquiring extrinsic sources of security and adequacy feelings or in deriving a modified variety of their intrinsic counterpart through a later satellizing-like relationship. Although the latter has some substitutive value, it is still a far cry from the products of early satellization, the conditions for which can never be entirely reproduced (assuming that it were desirable to do so) in view of maturational changes and the traumatic consequences of non-satellization.

Effects of Non-Devaluation on Other Attributes of Infantile Ego Structure

Concurrently with the course of devaluation of the ego aspirations relative to volitional omnipotence and independence, other changes in ego organization associated with the satellizing process have been described (see pp. 120-123). Progress in these different aspects of satellization has been conceived of as providing mutual reinforcement. But if satellization fails to take place, what is the fate of the other attributes of infantile ego organization?

It will be remembered that the goal of parental training procedures relative to these infantile ego traits is the production of a more mature personality better equipped to cope with the problem of adaptation to physical and cultural realities, and to realize the cultural ideal of desirable character and behavior. A minimal program of child-rearing geared toward this goal can, therefore, be abstracted from parent-child relationships in many different cultural settings. It includes an attenuation of hedonism, the growth of greater self-sufficiency, and the development of a sense of moral responsibility.

Progress towards these goals is achieved in the satellizing child by a process of value satellization. The child merely takes over parental goals and standards as a by-product of his more general dependent identification with them. This is done on an absolute basis without any appreciation of the issues or advantages involved. A true satellite assimilates his parent's values unreservedly since he has accepted a general position of subservience which extends to all areas. When this acceptance is complete, continued adherence to parental values is maintained by two powerful forces: (a) The benefits of derived status can only be enjoyed by a satellite as long as he remains in good-standing. Evidence of good-standing is parental approval (and absence of disapproval) which in turn demands conformity to parental standards. (b) Among the other standards assimilated by the child is the feeling of moral responsibility or accountability to conform to standards of behavior which have been given ethical implications ("good and bad," "right and wrong"). Unlike other values which are ends in themselves, moral responsibility also has this regulatory function of compelling adherence to internalized norms of behavior.

In the satellizing child the foundation of moral responsibility rests on a sense of personal loyalty to the parent. The latter continually stresses the point that disobedience or non-conformity is equivalent to disloyalty or repudiation of the satellizing bond. Finally when the child accepts the principle that *his own* non-conformity is "bad," the obligation of moral responsibility is assumed, and conscience is born. Feelings of guilt will arise when the child perceives a willful violation of this obligation on his part. The perception of a discrepancy between actual behavior and internalized standards does not (as will be shown later) automatically result in a guilt reaction. A prerequisite for the latter is acceptance of the fact that these norms also apply to *him,* and that the most important ethical value is the *personal* obligation to uphold all other values which have moral significance.

Value satellization obviously cannot occur in the non-satellizing child since a relationship of voluntary subservience does not exist. On what basis, then, can modification of the infantile ego attributes be expected? The bases are multiple, but in contrast to satellization all share the common characteristics of relativism and greater objectivity. This does not mean that prestige suggestion and authority will not operate in early value formation; in the absence of an available frame of reference, the authority of some social norm must prevail. The important distinction, however, is that this authority rests solely upon the prestige associated with superior knowledge and experience, and not upon the obligation implicit in the satellizing relationship to accept unconditionally the values of the particular person with whom the dependent identification is made. It is an objective authority of perceived superiority rather than a subjective authority derived from a relationship of subservience and an attitude of blind personal allegiance.

This prestige suggestion, however, is effective only if it is exerted in favor of certain objective considerations. These include the very same reasons which act as cultural pressures directing the goals of child-rearing. Here, however, they operate directly in relation to the needs of the child's hypertrophic ego structure; whereas in the case of the satellizing child, they have no direct influence at first, but are indirectly communicated on an absolutistic basis via the parents. That is, the non-satellizer perceives from the start (first through prestige suggestion and later through his own understanding of the social environment) that unrestricted hedonism and executive incompetence are fatal not only for survival but also for the achievement of the prominence and recognition which he craves. No other basis for appeal to change is open to him. The satellizer, on the other hand, first accepts these goals of parental training on the basis of personal loyalty and only later appreciates their relationship to reality adaptation.

With respect to the acquisition of moral responsibility there is much less basis for change in terms of the non-satellizer's ego needs. A general obligation to conform to all internalized ethical values neither exists on the basis of personal loyalty nor serves the interests of ego aggrandizement. Moral accountability, therefore, is acquired in highly selective fashion. The child will assume the moral obligations of acquiring greater executive competence and of attenuating hedonism since these obligations act as a spur and a coercive influence in keeping his motivations and performance capacity attuned to his inordinately high ego aspiration level. But other ethical norms, which serve to protect group interests (e.g., truth, honesty, cooperativeness, inhibition of aggression) may interfere with and complicate the path of ego aggrandizement. Not that he will disavow these ethical values as undesirable. Quite the contrary: They are usually accepted as quite valid and praiseworthy—but for others. The world is a safer place in which to operate if other people are moral.

If non-satellizers could acquire moral responsibility on no other basis than serviceability for ego enhancement, the prospects of their ever evolving into law-abiding citizens would be dim indeed. Fortunately, however, there exists the possibility of internalizing a concept of justice and fairness which embodies the "Golden Rule" of "Do unto others, as you would have them do unto you." This is the mature basis for moral responsibility in both satellizer and non-satellizer. In the former, however, it is superimposed upon the more primitive obligation of accountability derived from loyalty to a personal authority; hence, failure to assimilate some such norm of justice in the course of ego maturation would not leave a complete moral vacuum in this case as it would in the non-satellizer.

The last available means of curtailing unrestricted moral irresponsibility involves the use of external forms of coercion, i.e., reward, threat, and punishment. Conformity is then maintained by force, fear of reprisal and retaliation, and considerations of expediency and material advantage. This medium of control, however, is not only ineffective (since even the most stringent repression can be circumvented), but is also devoid of all ethical content. It is available also for expediting the attenuation of hedonism and the development of greater self-sufficiency, but is less necessary since the latter traits are in more complete accord with the needs of the hypertrophic ego organization.

All of these considerations point to the conclusion that the modification of infantile ego attributes is a much less thoroughgoing and stable process in non-satellizers than in satellizers, and (everything else being equal) is more likely to begin at a later date. An attitude of subservience is an extremely potent force in value assimilation. It makes possible unquestioning and unconditional acceptance before any criterion of reasonableness need be satisfied; and by the time that reasons are demanded the need to believe is so great that the flimsiest web of rationality will suffice. Resistive tendencies are effectively combatted by the child's emotional dependence upon parental approval and by an early developed capacity for guilt feelings.

In the non-satellizer, on the other hand, natural resistance is not eventually overcome by a subservient attitude. Along with the persistence of volitional independence, an attitude of resistance is maintained toward accepting the values of others. Parental approval is not a crucial need compelling conformity in non-satellizers since it does not have the significance of imparting visible evidence of good-standing in the role of satellite, entitling the latter to continued receipt of derived status. (To the rejected child, approval denotes a temporary reprieve from punishment; and the overvalued child desires—and usually receives it—as an objective confirmation of his exalted primary status). Guilt feelings come into play only much later. The most important factor influencing modification of infantile ego traits is the personality requirements of hypertrophied ego demands. But this works both ways: Where ego needs are not served by a particular ethical norm, there is no initial disposition to assume an obligation of personal conformity; and even if such obligations are acquired later through acceptance of abstract principles of justice, they stand in constant danger of being undermined by considerations of expediency relative to ego aggrandizement. In any event, indoctrination lacks the blind allegiance of satellization and must be postponed until either the objective relationship of goals and values to ego needs can be perceived, or the issues involved in ethical questions can be appreciated.

Expected Differences in Outcome between Rejected and Overvalued Children

The psychological world of the overvalued child is benevolent, accepting, adoring and deferential. His will is law. His notions of omnipotence are not only unchallenged but are also actively fostered. The ambitious parent thinks: "If he is already so willful, so dominant, so desirous of power and prominence, surely a brilliant future must be in store for him"; and in the home no efforts are spared to keep alive the illusion of grandiosity. Thus, it is possible to create for quite some time an environment in which exaggerated, infantile estimates of self-importance continue to remain quite tenable. Eventually, improved social perception as well as belated parental pressures force a shift from a belief in volitional omnipotence based on invariable parental subservience (despite executive helplessness) to the realization that power is an outgrowth of superior capacity to manipulate the environment. The child's self-estimate is consequently deflated below his aspirational level, but not catastrophically so. The continuation of considerable parental subservience and adulation, the possibility of exercising a good deal of volitional independence, and the flattering view the parent takes of his performance capacity prevent a gross discrepancy between present status and level of ego aspiration from arising. Hence, at least during the years when parental influences are the dominant factors in the child's life, feelings of adequacy (extrinsic) remain high and anxiety is effectively avoided. Insecurity feelings are also minimal since his position seems relatively impregnable and his future unthreatened.

In all of these respects the rejected child presents a contrasting picture. He lives in a hostile, threatening environment which continually emphasizes his unworthiness. A stern regimen is imposed, volitional independence is categorically denied, and an overly critical and unfair standard of judgment is applied to his behavior and accomplishments. The illusion of volitional omnipotence is therefore, swiftly swept aside. The future presents a bleak and threatening aspect, providing little basis for extrinsic feelings of security. Self-esteem is chronically depressed because of the tremendous discrepancy between current self-estimate and ego aspiration level. Moreover, the initial experience of rejection is sufficiently traumatic to result in that permanent and irreparable damage to self-esteem which is necessary for converting a predisposition to anxiety into a manifest anxiety neurosis.

In the overvalued child the predispositions for anxiety—hypertrophic ego aspirations, and relative incapacity for attaining an intrinsic sense of adequacy—are present, and an actual state of anxiety may supersede the latent condition in the event of a later catastrophic blow to self-esteem. Such a situation might arise during adolescence when the protective adulatory environment of the home gives way to the conformity-demanding culture of the peer society which pays scant heed to requests for special consideration. Or it may be precipitated even earlier by a shift in parental attitude to one of rejection.

In addition to the question of immediacy or latency of appearance, other qualitative differences exist in the type of anxiety response manifested by the two types of non-satellizers. Although the underlying damage to self-esteem is never completely reversible in either case, it is more devastating in the rejected child because it occurs at a time when ego defenses are weaker. Hence, even after the acute phases subside, enough residual anxiety remains to constitute a chronic condition which is clinically disturbing. No matter how successful he becomes, he can never really appreciate his success or believe in himself. His achievements appear unreal and impersonal to him; he cannot take either them or himself very seriously.

The overvalued satellizer, on the other hand, is able to effect a more complete recovery in periods of remission. When external circumstances are more propitious, his self-esteem is restored to its former high level; he becomes cocky, overconfident and obnoxiously self-assured. He experiences no difficulty in taking his success seriously and claiming full credit for it. However, he is apt to weather subsequent acute attacks less successfully than the rejected non-satellizer, the very chronicity of whose anxiety seems to serve as a bulwark against extreme reactions.

With respect to prognosis for genuine improvement in terms of the underlying etiological factors, the rejected non-satellizer again shows to advantage since the chances are greater that in later life he can enter into satellizing-like relationships and also reduce his ego aspiration level. Originally he would have been only too willing to satellize if not rebuffed by his parent; and later, he tends to shy away from close emotional identification with others for fear of a repetition of the original traumatic rejection. Under favorable circumstances, however, this fear can be successfully overcome.

But the overvalued child finds the feat of later satellization much more difficult. His ego hypertrophy is (at least in the beginning) less of a compensatory reaction and a form of counter-aggression than a highly tenable orientation to life which is actively promoted by his parents. The disadvantages of dependency on an extrinsic status become apparent only later; but by this time satellization becomes a highly remote possibility. He is already too completely habituated to deference, absolute independence, and a one-way flow of concern and affection. Self-subordination is painful and degrading. Conditioned to react to people in terms of their capacity for satisfying *his* ego needs, his interest in others is selfish and calculating. Protracted success in the role of omnipotence has made him obnoxiously conceited, overbearing, ruthless and insensitive in his dealings with others. Hence, even if he could experience genuine love for others, the latter, because of his unlovability, would not find it easy to reciprocate. In contrast to the rejected non-satellizer, therefore, a later source of intrinsic security and adequacy feelings is generally closed to him, and in consequence the level of ego aspirations is less likely to be lowered. Thus, both crucial factors predisposing toward anxiety states are less easily counteracted—either by deliberate therapeutic efforts or by possible spontaneous correctives in the subsequent life history of the patient.

Lastly, characteristic differences prevail in relation to the modification of the infantile ego attributes. The rejected child is under great external pressure to conform to parental demands for greater self-sufficiency, less hedonism and more moral responsibility; hence, outwardly at least, if not in terms of genuine internalization, he is further advanced than the overvalued child. The latter is especially reluctant to relinquish executive dependence since this ego trait is highly compatible with the attitude of volitional omnipotence which is nurtured so long. On the other hand, with the growth of self-consciousness, the rejected child is hindered by anxiety in the learning of new motor, social and intellectual skills; fear of failure, humiliation and further loss of self-esteem make him approach new tasks with timidity and trepidation. This factor more than nullifies his initial headstart in this area. Everything else being equal, he is also more likely to acquire a stronger sense of justice to bolster his sense of moral responsibility. Victims of injustice, unless embittered and consumed by an indiscriminate passion for revenge, are apt to be more sensitive to the demands of justice than individuals conditioned to a position of special privilege and consideration.

Within the rejected group of children, individual differences also exist. In the case of the self-assertive, dominant, "tough-skinned" or viscerotonic child, the typical response to frustration is more apt to be hostile, aggressive and defiant, resulting in chronic parent-child conflict. The less vigorous and more "tender-skinned" individual, on the other hand, is more likely to adjust by introversion, withdrawal, daydreaming, intellectualization and shyness in social groups.

NOTES

[1] This type of identification is not equivalent to satellization, and will be referred to later as incorporation.

[2] The young child's world of value judgments is largely unstructured for lack of a relevant experiential frame of reference, and is, hence, very susceptible to the influence of prestige suggestion from dominant figures in his environment.

[3] The explanation that the individual may simply be taking a calculated risk does not provide the whole answer since these aspirations are often preposterously unrealistic. Furthermore, if the factor of discrepancy were the only consideration in determining self-esteem, the achievement of self-esteem on a low level of aspiration would be just as satisfying as on a higher level; even the slightest risk of failure would be hardly worthwhile. The relative weights that must be attached to the "discrepancy" and "absolute value" variables still await determination, but it is suggested here that complete devaluation of aspirational level results in greater loss of self-esteem than would occur from a substantial discrepancy.

[4] Lowering of the aspirational level does not invariably lead to reduced self-esteem. In non-competitive cultures, self-esteem may be raised by renouncing individual ambitions and identifying oneself with group concerns. However, it is improbable that such cultural factors are relevant at this age. At four and five, however, children are highly responsive to competitive cultural pressures [*149, 150, 201, 288, 289, 291, 292*]; and hence, the negativism characteristic of this latter period may be peculiarly flavored by this situation in our culture.

[5] Four-year-old negativism seems to be less glaring in girls than in boys possibly because of the cultural expectation that girls exhibit more executive dependence than boys.

CHAPTER 12

Other Implications of Satellization

GENERAL ORIENTATION TO LIFE

SATELLIZATION (or non-satellization) is more than a developmental phase in the life history of an individual. It also represents a general orientation to life problems which defines his distinctive way of seeking status and security. Shall he adapt to the struggle for existence by becoming an independent manipulator of reality, or shall he become a dependent and devoted camp-follower of a person or group whose direction he acknowledges as intrinsically superior to his own capacity for decision and choice? The implications of this developmental phenomenon, therefore, extend to problems of perception, learning, memory and behavioral adjustment.

The satellizer's sense of security and adequacy is a reflection of a derived status based on a dependent relationship to individuals and social groups whose suzerainty is self-evident, whose right to determine goals and standards which are binding for him is absolute and unchallengable. This derived status, hence, can be enjoyed only as long as the superior powers approve of him, which in turn depends upon his degree of conformity to their demands. Therefore, in perceiving objects and events in his psychological world, and in assimilating values and objectives, a powerful need for "security" will produce an advance "set" or orientation to shape all cognitive structures in conformity with the demands and expectations of his preceptors.

In contrast, the non-satellizer's feelings of security and adequacy are related to his success in self-assertion and in achieving volitional independence and self-aggrandizement by virtue of the direct control he is able to wield over his environment. Subservience of any kind—emotional or intellectual—is a threat to his independence and is interpreted as defeat and degradation. Hence the directing need relative to cognitive set is to accept values and to "see" things in a way which will enhance his feelings of independence, importance and individuality.

Satellization is not an orientation that one decides upon consciously and deliberately. Were this the case it would be indistinguishable from the motives of self-enhancement characterizing the incorporator. The satellizer is neither critical nor selective in his loyalties. He satellizes in relation to the totality of a person for better or for worse and not merely with the aspects that are convenient or profitable. And where conditions allow, both parents are included in the process, although not necessarily simultaneously.

The tendency to satellize is not an all-or-none characteristic; all degrees of it can be represented on a continuum. Although their goals are opposite in direction, the satellizing and non-satellizing attitudes are not mutually exclusive. Superimposed on the satellizer's quest for and possession of intrinsic status is a greater or lesser striving for a subsidiary extrinsic status. Similarly non-satellizers are more or less able to form satellizing-like attachments to non-parent individuals who qualify better for this relationship. Nevertheless, the antagonism between the two trends can be seen in their tendency to be negatively correlated. Everything else being equal, the more intrinsic self-esteem an individual possesses, the less he will strive for ego aggrandizement; and conversely, the more deeply-rooted the non-satellizing orientation is, the more improbable is the later adoption of a satellizing approach.

It would also seem that the capacity for satellization is at least in part a function of hereditary endowment. Genetically determined differences in capacity probably exist between different species and between different members of the same species. For example, it is obvious that the average dog satellizes more than the average cat, that some dogs satellize more than others, and that an occasional cat is more satellizing than the average dog. In our culture at least, boys appear to satellize less readily than girls. Most wives still continue to derive the greater part of their current feelings of adequacy from the accomplishments and status of their husbands. How much of this difference in self-assertiveness is due to hormonal influences, and how much is due to cultural expectations that a woman gains status by the type of dependent relationships she forms (rather than through her own attainments) is difficult to determine. The prepotency of the latter factor, however, is indicated by the existence of cultures in which the expected sex difference is either absent or reversed in favor of the female [*274*]. The culture not only establishes appropriate sex norms for self-assertion and satellization, but also sets an acceptable standard for its members which may be very much higher or lower than the cultural ideal prevailing elsewhere.

Characteristic fluctuations in the satellizing–non-satellizing ratio also occur at various stages in the life cycle. The human being starts his career in life as a non-satellizer; an omnipotent being has no need to satellize. By the age of three, he appreciates his marginal biosocial status and the implications of his helplessness; satellization now seems more attractive. At four he exaggerates his executive competence, and believes himself capable of assuming various adult roles. Between five and eight increased capacity for self-criticism and social perception reinforces the satellizing trend. Thereafter, rapid strides in social maturity, the new source of status available in the peer group, resentment over exclusion from the adult world, the impetus of sexual maturation, and changing expectations from adults all play a role in undermining the satellizing attitude. Both attitudes are generally expressed in relation to his spouse. When his children are young, he plays the more dominant and independent role. As they mature, the relationship becomes more equal. Finally in his old age, as his powers decline, as he feels more insecure, as he becomes less competent executively and economically, the child-parent relationship may be reversed with respect to the individual doing the satellizing.

SATELLIZATION AND THE PROBLEM OF IDENTIFICATION

The distinction between the satellizing and non-satellizing orientations is frequently obscured because of the tendency to subsume both attitudes under the overinclusive concept of identification. Because of its lack of denotative specificity, this concept has now outgrown its original usefulness in describing a mechanism significant for personality development and organization. Consider, for example, G. H. Mead's well known definition: "Identification consists both in taking the attitude of others towards one's own act and in associating others' attitude towards an act or object with one's own response to the situation." On a purely descriptive level it is adequate enough; it refers to an assimilative process in attitude formation that is patently recognizable in everyday interpersonal relations. But is this assimilation an expression of independence or of dependence? Is it indicative of subservience, personal loyalty, and a quest for reflected glory, or does it betray grandiose aspirations and the objective perception of suitability for purposes of ego aggrandizement?

The inadequacy of the concept of *identification* is demonstrated by its present-day use in conveying at least three widely different meanings: (a) "to link oneself emotionally—to associate oneself in common cause with someone on whom one is or becomes dependent, (e.g., child's relation to parent) and to accept his values on the basis of personal loyalty" [*22*]. The aim here is to win a derived status by gaining approval through conformity. (b) "To accept, . . . to incorporate the values of another on the basis of their objective capacity to enhance ego-status—without forming any . . . [dependent] emotional tie to that individual" [*22*]. (c) "To make common cause emotionally with persons like oneself. This is a form of externalized narcissism (accepting someone or something like oneself as an extension of one's ego) . . . It requires no submergence or satellization of self to others, but merely incorporation of an externalized mirror image of self" [*22*]. This first meaning of identification is identical with that ascribed so far to satellization. The second type will henceforth be referred to as *incorporation*. The third variety is really a subtype of *incorporation* that commonly forms the basis of parental love in ego-hypertrophic individuals. Several examples may serve to sharpen this distinction between satellization and incorporation.

The satellizing hero-worshipper is a loyal, subservient follower of the hero who only wishes to share vicariously in the latter's pre-eminence. The assimilation of goals and values takes place blindly and automatically as a by-product of the personal relationship. He desires to be like his hero in every way because likeness is a means of demonstrating complete deference. As a follower his goal is to serve.

The non-satellizing hero worshipper, on the other hand, wishes to incorporate the capacities and prerogatives of his hero while still remaining independent of him. His role as a follower is not to serve his preceptor, but to use him as a model, to learn the attitudes and techniques that will eventually enable him to succeed to the latter's enviable and exalted position. His deference is not a form of personal subservience, but an outgrowth of the perception that deference to superior judgment is both highly expedient in a status-conscious society and exceedingly fruitful for learning the type of skills essential for self-advancement. The non-satellizer can also, of course, obtain a derived status from the position or achievements of persons whom he regards as extensions of his own ego (by virtue of kinship through family, sex, class, race, nationality, religion, etc.) without aspiring to secure similar advantages for himself. But since no subservience of self is required, this is merely a vicarious form of incorporative hero-worship not infrequently found among non-satellizers who are not too optimistic about their own chances for more direct ego enhancement.

The same distinction between satellization and incorporation can be drawn in the familiar phenomenon of a frightened child identifying with the very objects or persons which terrify him. The first child, for example, would like to be a little baby wolf; then the big bad wolf would protect him rather than eat him up. The second child would like to be an even bigger wolf and either demolish or frighten the wolf who frightens him. As he grows older the former is more disposed to be overawed by the abilities and accomplishments of his father while the latter is more apt to compete with him.

SATELLIZATION AND EXPLORATION

Both satellization and incorporation are component aspects of the mechanism of identification because of their concern with ego status. In the first case, status is gained through dependence, subservience and conformity; in the second case it is the fruit of independent achievement. There is, however, a third type of orientation in perception and learning in which the motivation is relatively free from consideration of ego status. It resembles incorporation in that emphasis is placed upon independent achievement and discovery, but the goal is oriented toward mastery of the task *per se* rather than toward mastery as an expression of ego enhancement. The fact of task-orientation, however, does not mean that ego-involvement is not present; intense absorption in any highly motivated activity presupposes strong involvement of self in that activity. But the main goal of this self-involvement is satisfaction of curiosity or successfully meeting the challenge posed by a problem rather than ego aggrandizement. For want of a better name, this approach might be called the exploratory orientation.

The exploratory orientation underlies a great deal of human activity. In every person's psychological world there is a greater or lesser sphere of value-laden, ego-involved learning experience in which the task itself and not its relation to ego status is the primary focus of concern. Where task-oriented goals or values are concerned, levels of aspiration operate, success or failure is experienced, but self-esteem is not necessarily affected since ego status is not at stake. The basis of exploratory activity lies in the active curiosity which is manifested by human beings from the earliest days of infancy. Nevertheless the tremendous need for feelings of adequacy, especially in modern competitive society has tended to reduce drastically the sphere of this orientation. In pure form it is rare indeed, being combined in most cases with various amounts of satellization and incorporation; and in terms of relative importance in the dynamics of personality organization it definitely plays a subsidiary role.

In non-satellizers, the exploratory orientation in assimilating values, goals, and interests runs into difficulty if it conflicts with the aims of ego enhancement. There may be, for example, a strong interest in carpentry, but carpenters enjoy less social prestige than bank presidents. In grappling with the problem of race relations, the weight of the objective evidence may sway them toward an attitude of tolerance; but intolerance may provide them with a potent advantage in competing with rivals whose race enjoys less social acceptance. Furthermore, the driving need for extrinsic sources of self-esteem tends to invest the greater part of highly motivated activity with considerations relative to ego status; and in anxiety states, almost every performance of the individual, regardless of how trivial or irrelevant it may be for actual social or vocational standing, is endowed with weighty implications for his self-esteem.

Because satellizers are less influenced by anxiety and considerations relative to direct ego enhancement, they are more likely than non-satellizers to pursue an exploratory orientation. They are impeded in this effort, however, by feelings of guilt for the nonconformity, and repudiation of personal loyalties which are inevitable if the independent and objective implications of this orientation are pushed to their logical conclusion.

But if there are good reasons for the "contamination" of an exploratory orientation by satellizing and incorporative attitudes, the reverse also holds true. A child may undertake a given activity in the beginning only because he is desirous of the derived or primary ego status associated with conformity to parental expectations and prestige accomplishment respectively. But after prolonged and more intimate contact with the activity in question, a more intrinsic, less ego-oriented interest may develop, illustrating the reciprocal relationship that prevails between motivation and activity.

SATELLIZATION AND COMPETITION

What relationship does each of the three learning and perceptual orientations bear to competitive urges? In what ways are they differentially affected by exposure to the pressures of a competitive society?

The satellizing orientation completely rejects the principle of outright competition; status is sought not by seeking to surpass others who are perceived as more powerful, but by becoming dependent upon them, being accepted by them, and by vicariously sharing in their status through the medium of a personal relationship thus formed.[1]* The exploratory orientation is similarly devoid of competitive implications, being concerned only with the independent and objective testing of experience. The incorporative

* Notes for this chapter appear on page 161.

orientation, on the other hand, is almost by definition competitive in nature. Ego enhancement or ego aggrandizement are relative concepts. There can be no absolute criterion for the attainment of extrinsic status; the only possible criterion is relative position in a hierarchical ranking. Success means the achievement of hierarchical superiority (i.e., prestige)—not the attainment of an objective standard of adequacy which has no reference to the performance of others.

The foregoing, of course, applies only to the more aggressive type of incorporation that is exhibited by non-satellizers. Satellizers seeking extrinsic status through their performances are frequently content with only the recognition and approval of persons whose judgment they respect even though no implications of comparative or competitive standing can possibly be present.

Despite the differential relationship of these three orientations to the competitive attitude, one is forced to agree with the universal applicability (in Western culture) of Gardner Murphy's observation that "the individual can no longer rejoice naively in elementary physical or social selfhood; he must compare the self continually with a standard set up within or with an objective standard defined by the self-gratification available to others" [*288*]. The impact of a competitive civilization on modern personality development has been such that nearly everyone, incorporator and satellizer alike, has been catapulted into the mad race for extrinsic status and the visible criteria which symbolize its attainment, i.e., wealth, power, position, and status. The satellizer, in opposition perhaps to his innermost preferences, has been forced to adopt at least in part, the incorporative orientation.

Still this does not mean, as Gardner Murphy seems to imply, that all differences have been obliterated. His generalization is valid, but is more completely applicable to non-satellizers. In the case of satellizers the incorporative orientation plays more of a subsidiary role. To be sure he is concerned with his market value; but if that is stripped from him, his self-esteem is not left bankrupt. Under such circumstances he can "rejoice naively" in his own selfhood, and at all times he can rejoice in the selves of others and derive self-esteem from their accomplishments by virtue of his relationship to them. The non-satellizer's self-esteem, however, is almost completely a creature of his extrinsic status. He can "rejoice naively" neither in his own self nor in the selves of others. The accomplishments of other people constitute a threat and a challenge to his own sense of adequacy; he can make his peace with them by either rejecting them as undesirable or by incorporating them as worthy of emulation for his own self-aggrandizement.

SATELLIZATION AND THE LEARNING PROCESS

From an historical standpoint, learning theory has been mostly concerned with structural and organizational changes in verbal material and motor skills that occur along a time dimension in relation to certain specified variables, such as amount and distribution of practice, the type of interferences and motivations, the nature of the antecedent background, etc. Later in addition to these objective aspects of the learning process, attention was given to the influence of various individual differences in learning capacity. Very little concern, however, has been felt for the effect of basic personality differences on the learning process. As long as learning tasks were restricted to mazes, conditioned reflexes, geometrical figures, motor skills, nonsense syllables and objective factual material, the neglect of personality factors was perhaps unfortunate but not calamitous since the crucial variables involved undoubtedly relate to objective conditions of the learning situation and individual differences in capacity. These latter factors, however, shed very little light on the learning of attitudes and values; for here the most important relevant variables are differences in personality organization which define the mode of concept assimilation in an interpersonal relationship. The most significant of these differences have already been identified as being related to developmental success or failure in the devaluation crisis of ego development, giving rise respectively to the satellizing and incorporative orientations.[2] By *orientation* is meant a general "set" or attitude reflective of underlying needs or motivations, which determines an individual's mode of response (e.g., acceptance or rejection, the bases for same, etc.) when confronted with new value-giving experience. Since the general characteristics of these orientations have already been discussed, only specific implications for the learning situation need be presented in this section.

Both orientations rely on prestige suggestion, especially in the beginning when the child has no relevant framework of reference for the formation of value judgments. The satellizer, however, for reasons of personal loyalty and the safeguarding of his derived status, has an absolute need to accept the suggestion of his preceptor regardless of its content. The incorporator, on the other hand, will only be disposed to accept suggestions that do not run counter to his needs for ego enhancement; and in any event, the power of his preceptor to suggest is not derived from a personal relationship but from perceived superiority in knowledge and experience.[3]

The satellizer is resistive to the acceptance of new values because such acceptance presupposes a repudiation of prior personal loyalties—a feat which cannot be accomplished without experiencing feelings of guilt. This situation arises regardless of whether the new value is accepted as a consequence of satellization with another person or as an objective product of the exploratory orientation. Because the implications of acceptance in relation to earlier allegiances are not always appreciated at first, initial resistance may be mild, only to flare up later in full force when the situation is more fully comprehended. Inevitably, many of the satellizer's childhood values are retained unchanged in adult life, but, in conformity with social expectations of greater independence and maturity of judgment, are provided with an intellectual facade of logic, reasonableness and supporting arguments. In other cases, they are reaffirmed by subsequent satellizing relationships, or more independently by genuine exploratory ventures.

Resistance to learning in the incorporator springs from an entirely different source. Guilt feelings do not enter the picture at all since values have never been accepted on the basis of personal loyalty, and hence can be replaced by others without any suggestion of disloyalty. Instead resistance is first elicited by the very fact that the source of the new idea is outside himself. He finds this situation threatening not only because it qualifies his desire for absolute volitional independence, but also because of the obvious implication that others are more adequate and competent than he is. Thus, even the mere willingness to consider an alien concept involves a loss of self-esteem, and hence gives rise to an almost "reflex" tendency to reject any new idea. But even if this initial barrier is overcome, another difficulty immediately arises: Will the new value "conflict with the present organization of values which is primarily oriented on an ego prestige basis"? Until this question is decided in the negative by finding a possibility for further ego enhancement in the new situation, resistance is apt to be continued. But just as the satellizer prefers to believe that his attitudes are based on reason rather than on personal loyalty, the incorporator also feels obliged to deny that his values reflect a need for ego enhancement and makes an effort to prettify them with a veneer of logic.

The possibility always remains, of course, that the incorporator will employ the exploratory orientation in assimilating new values. This possibility, however, is restricted by his tendency to extend the quest for extrinsic status into all ego-involved areas and to perceive in every learning situation a threat to his self-esteem. Because his self-esteem is already apt to be impaired (in cases where manifest anxiety exists), he lacks confidence in his ability to cope with new problems. Hence rather than suffer failure, humiliation and a further depression of self-esteem, he would prefer to withdraw from the field all together. If this is impossible he attempts to "forestall a new situation by making excessive advance preparations which negate the element of newness." He brings with him to every new learning situation an advance set to employ a familiar and established response pattern rather than trust to the more hazardous procedure of improvisation. Thus, forearmed and bolstered in advance against the panic which would otherwise overwhelm him, he clings desperately to this stereotyped response even if it proves persistently unadaptive; it has at least more face-saving propensities than complete paralysis of activity.

The effect of this initial failure is to confirm his worst fears, destroy all hopes of eventual success, demolish self-esteem and impair subsequent performance ability. If later success is achieved, he may be unable to enjoy it subjectively, ascribing it to accidental good fortune. Nevertheless, his general level of aspiration remains tenaciously and unrealistically high[4] (see page 372). The satellizer, on the other hand, who preserves an inner core of self-esteem and self-acceptance under most circumstances, is neither thrown into panic by new learning situations nor completely disorganized by initial experiences of failure. He can be counted upon to avail himself of whatever flexibility and improvising ability he possesses, providing, of course, that he is properly motivated.

Approval and disapproval also have quite different meanings for satellizers and incorporators. The incorporator is only concerned with approval as a form of praise, as an objective indicator of success. It enhances his self-esteem but is not vital for his sense of adequacy if other appropriate criteria of prestige acquisition (e.g., receipt of top grades, highest salary, etc.) are available. Disapproval by a person in authority, however, is an unequivocal sign of failure which lowers self-esteem, disorganizes performance and possibly leads to frank anxiety.

To the satellizer, however, the preceptor's approval is an affirmation of the fact that he is an accepted satellite in good standing and hence entitled to enjoy the derived status which goes with this role. The need for this visible manifestation of acceptance does not necessarily mean that the child actually fears the permanent loss of his acceptance and intrinsic value in the preceptor's eyes. If this were the case he would hardly risk or even court disapproval so frequently. One of the prerequisites for satellization is a reasonable assurance on his part that acceptance will be forthcoming regardless of his attitudes or behavior, that it transcends the issue of personal loyalty. Nevertheless, he finds the temporary deprivation of derived status uncomfortable; if this is prolonged too long he becomes uneasy and makes vigorous efforts to regain his former good standing. It would be difficult, however, to equate the uneasiness accompanying this temporary loss of status with true feelings of inadequacy and anxiety, since he truly believes in his unconditional acceptance regardless of transitory indications to the contrary. He knows that it lies within his power to recapture the external evidence of good standing whenever he chooses to conform.

But even if disapproval is not equivalent to loss of acceptance and is not productive of inadequacy feelings and anxiety, it is effective in another way that is far more potent than the temporary loss of status which it entails. Although the child feels certain that his eventual status with his preceptor can survive manifestations of personal disloyalty on his part, the implication from early conscience formation is still present that this type of disloyalty is "bad" and tantamount to an act of hostility against the latter which deeply wounds his feelings. The satellizer, hence, reacts with feelings of guilt rather than with feelings of inadequacy when his disloyalty elicits his preceptor's disapproval. The experience of guilt feelings, however, presupposes that the teacher's values have already been accepted; for until this occurs (while, for example, the child defends parental values against the teacher) disapproval can indicate only displeasure for failing to conform rather than for disloyalty.

The satellizer resents paternalistic and authoritarian techniques of teaching much less than the incorporator does, for in principle he has accepted this pattern of teaching from his parents. He will, however, react negatively to any attempt to ride roughshod over his basic loyalties. Paternalism works more successfully with him in the guise of suggestion and guidance. The incorporator, on the other hand, who has never accepted the paternalistic pattern of teaching, perceives in authoritarianism a frontal assault on his independence and responds with an appropriately violent brand of resistance.

Timidity in joining group discussions has quite different implications in the case of satellizers and incorporators respectively [*221*]. In the former it "is indicative of such extreme dependency on others for thought orientation that self-assertion or initiative in expressing an opinion becomes an impossibility." In the latter it is a manifestation of anxiety in the face of a competitive situation "in which he might fare badly and accordingly suffer a deflation of self-esteem in public." This is especially true because of the unstructured nature of most discussions which makes advance preparation difficult and places a premium on ability to think extemporaneously. An incorporator feels more at ease when delivering a prepared lecture, providing, of course, that his listeners are not granted the privilege of questioning him too closely. He is also less apprehensive about interpersonal communication when he is protected by the dignity and authority of a formal academic or professional title, and when he is confronted by persons of a lower academic or professional status than by his peers. In the first case, he realizes that his title enhances the intrinsic value of his opinions which, hence, are less likely to be challenged; the title also converts an intimate personal situation into a formal professional conference, gives him all of the advantages of authority and protects him from the vulnerability of a layman's opinion. In the second case he has less to fear in the way of opposition since his potential adversaries are less adequately informed and are obliged to show at least some outward deference for his views.

Incorporators generally manifest a greater will to learn than satellizers. This is, of course, just another expression of their deficiency in intrinsic self-esteem and of their compensatory striving for its extrinsic counterpart. It betrays itself by an unexpected and inconsistent indifference to knowledge which cannot be utilized for the purposes of ego enhancement, a state of affairs which often defeats the interests of genuine scholarship. Although ego-inspired drive is by no means necessary for the successful culmination of creative endeavor, it not infrequently happens that a highly talented satellizer lacks sufficient motivation to develop his abilities. Talented incorporators, on the other hand, are not held back by this difficulty but are obliged to contend with troublesome anxieties.

It should also be borne in mind that the incorporating orientation requires more active participation in the learning process than does the satellizing orientation. In its most extreme form, value satellization is a completely passive and uncritical type of assimilation, whereas incorporation must be preceded by a most searching and critical examination of the implications of the new value for the individual's ego status.

Implications for Teaching

Careful consideration of the differences in the way satellizers and incorporators approach the learning situation must inevitably lead to the formulation of a differential pedagogy adapted to the needs of each type of learner. Such a pedagogy must take into account the methods whereby new values are assimilated, the resistances raised to learning, the constructive and destructive aspects of each orientation, and the possibilities both for improvement within an existing orientation, and for modifying the learning orientation. Throughout this discussion the assumption will be implicit that neither personal loyalty nor ego enhancement are satisfactory criteria for the assimilation of values, and that the public interest as well as effective learning and sound mental hygiene would be furthered by a shift toward the exploratory orientation.

(1) In any case the essential properties of the learning orientation must be recognized and respected by the teacher. He can neither expect the satellizer to do most of his learning by incorporation nor the incorporator to learn mostly by satellization. In relation to each type of learner he must play a different role. To the satellizer he must be a warm, personal, protective, parent-like figure. Like the parent he must extend unequivocal emotional acceptance and intrinsic valuation. Regardless of the eventual type of learning orientation he would like to see established, he must be prepared to let it stem from a satellizing base.

To the incorporator, the teacher cannot attempt to be more—at least in the beginning—than a human catalyst, an impersonal vehicle for the transmission of knowledge. Any suggestion of satellization, (which is antithetical to the incorporator's goal of volitional independence) would be fiercely resented. As a long-range goal however, it would be desirable (especially in the "rejected" group of non-satellizers in whose case the plan is more feasible) to revive the latent capacity for satellization as a means of providing an intrinsic source of security and adequacy feelings. It must be realized, however, that this is an extremely difficult and delicate procedure which cannot be hazarded until sufficient rapport is established. In addition it should be attempted only by a psychologically sensitive teacher whose personality is sufficiently permissive and non-threatening to allay the pupil's "ever-present dread of repetition of emotional rejection."

(2) In order to overcome resistance to learning, the teacher must first be aware of its basis. In the case of satellizers where resistance stems from reluctance to repudiate existing personal loyalties (and to assume the associated burden of guilt), the tactful promotion of insight is often efficacious since the satellizer is usually aware only of the rationalizations he offers for his resistance and not of their actual basis.

Resistance in incorporators can be similarly combatted but with understandably greater difficulty, since the gaining of insight must inevitably be accompanied by a loss in self-esteem which is apt to prove traumatic. Other less direct methods are more feasible in overcoming the threat which new values seem to pose for the incorporator's independence and self-esteem: (a) The objectification of discussion reduces the threat to independence by divorcing it from all connotations of a personal struggle between wills [*63*]. The avoidance of paternalistic and authoritarian teaching methods accomplishes the same purpose; (b) The use of praise and the avoidance of reproof in the early stages of learning help to minimize the disorganizing effects of the panic which ensues upon confrontation with new learning situations or with initial failure. The teacher should especially refrain from taking advantage of this panic to demonstrate his own superiority or forcibly to drive home a point without fear of rebuttal. Disapproval at any time is a potentially disruptive force and should not be used to stimulate learning.

By keeping in mind that resistance in incorporators tends to be greatest in the beginning and to diminish with time (while often following the opposite course in satellizers) the instructor can guard against undue pessimism and impatience in the first case and excessive optimism in the second case.

(c) The teacher can take measures to counteract the disadvantages inherent in both learning orientations. In relation to the satellizer this means minimizing his tendency to accept new values uncritically, passively and merely on the basis of a new personal attachment. The instructor can accomplish this purpose best by carefully regulating the type of satellizing relationship he allows to develop. His acceptance of the student must be unequivocal and in no way dependent upon the latter's agreement with his views. In this way the threat of rejection for non-conformity is removed. Disagreement can also be divorced from guilt feelings by defining disloyalty as "blind identification with the instructor's values rather than as independence of thought leading to disassociation from the latter. Hence disapproval and the feelings of guilt which it elicits can be used constructively to motivate active responsibility in the learning process" [*63*]. Praise, on the other hand, should never be offered as a reward for conformity but should be reserved for evidence of genuinely active use of the exploratory orientation.

These same techniques are not applicable in combatting the criterion of ego enhancement (which is the great danger of the incorporative orientation) since approval and disapproval have meaning relative to self-esteem and anxiety rather than to feelings of guilt; hence, disapproval is potentially too disruptive for personality organization to be used as a teaching device. But the techniques described above for overcoming the incorporator's resistance are also relevant for encouraging the exploratory orientation since both tasks present the same obstacles.

(d) Even if its source is regrettable, the teacher ought to take constructive advantage of the incorporator's ego-inspired motivation and will to learn by setting his expectations at a higher level of competence, initiative and integrative effort. In the case of satellizers whose incentive for learning lacks the same spur of prestige motivation, other sources of more intrinsic drive related to the exploratory orientation (e.g., curiosity, interest) should be maximally developed.

Mental Hygiene Implications of the Various Learning Orientations

With respect to the objective criterion of learning efficiency, both satellization and incorporation offer advantages and disadvantages. Incorporators are not inhibited by personal loyalties and guilt feelings. Their will to learn is more uniformly high, and they are required to expend more active effort in the learning process. They do not have to be emancipated during adolescence from slavish adherence to the parental values, and ego maturation, therefore, less often ends in failure. On the other hand, there is excessive concern with ego enhancement which interferes with the objective pursuit of knowledge and the use of the exploratory orientation. Extrinsic prestige drives always threaten to undermine more intrinsic motives, and learning efficiency is frequently impaired by the anxiety and response rigidity which greet new learning situations and initial failure. Nevertheless, despite these weighty disadvantages, the net advantage probably lies with incorporation as the more efficacious learning orientation.

From a mental hygiene standpoint, however, it is obvious that impaired self-esteem, feelings of insecurity and predisposition to anxiety represent too high a price in happiness and behavioral stability for whatever objective advantages accrue from the incorporative method of learning. Satellization is the soundest foundation on which a healthy personality structure can be built; but concern for the process of ego maturation demands that the foundation be kept from becoming a superstructure. An appropriate personality and learning orientation at four is not necessarily appropriate at nine. Personal loyalty might be the only satisfactory and stable basis for the assimilation of moral values during the pre-school period; but as social maturity and the capacity for abstract thinking increases, developmental revision is in order. A shift to the more independent exploratory orientation is necessary if the retention of archaic developmental patterns is to be avoided. Otherwise some degree of failure in ego maturation is inevitable.

Unfortunately the educational system in our American culture is not geared to the child's growing capacities, and ego development accordingly suffers. From nursery school to the university, from early childhood to adult life, the prevailing educational milieu at home and in school is authoritarian and paternalistic. The opportunities for exercising initiative, independence and responsibility are always far behind the actual capacity for same at any stage of development. Uncritical subservience of thought to prevailing doctrines, to recognized authorities, to the printed word, to "wiser" persons in positions of power and responsibility is the ubiquitous social expectation. Deviancy is a disease, a sign of abnormality, and an invitation for ridicule and persecution. Even the highest academic degree we confer (doctor of philosophy), which is supposedly indicative of a mature capacity for independent investigation, is actually the product of a subordinate relationship between the student and his sponsor. Theoretically the latter is supposed only to offer guidance and to insure methodological and logical rigorousness of attack. Actually the academic climate in many cases is such that successful culmination of the project and receipt of the degree requires deference to the opinions and biases of the sponsor. Sometimes the need for this personal and mental genuflexion, although real enough, is subtle and only implied; but in other cases it is sufficiently explicit to elicit obvious bowing and scraping.

Until the hierarchical relationship between students and teachers is reduced to an objective difference in knowledge rather than a formal difference in degrees, titles, and academic status, students will be unable successfully to complete their studies without submitting to condescension, humiliation, and unnecessary subservience. And in such an atmosphere the capacity for genuinely independent investigation must inevitably remain stunted.

NOTES

[1] The satellizer, of course, may compete with others by seeking a more exalted derived status.

[2] It should be realized that learning *orientation* refers to the motivational aspect of learning, whereas the structural and organizational changes that take place refer to learning *process*. Both aspects of learning are, of course, concurrent and inter-related although their relative importance depends on the type of learning material involved.

The desire for identification (either satellization or incorporation) naturally represents a need of the learner for ego status, thereby supplying a motive for learning. Hence, the assimilation of values (or of other learning material) by identification enhances the particular form of ego status which the individual seeks and provides *reinforcement* in much the same manner as obtaining food at the culmination of running a maze. In addition to this self-generated, "built-in" reinforcement in relation to internal needs, extrinsic reinforcement may also be provided in the form of approval for assimilating appropriate attitudes and behavior.

[3] Imitation is a form of learning in which the behavior of one individual serves as a stimulus to elicit comparable behavior in another. The underlying learning orientation, however, is not specified in the term itself. Thus, imitation can take place in the course of either satellizing, incorporative or exploratory orientations, or on a much more mechanical basis, e.g., echolalia, learning to walk or talk. Identification, therefore, is a type of imitation in which the *interpersonal relationship* between imitator and imitatee as well as the imitated act itself is highly significant for the learning that ensues.

Mowrer [*286*] refers to the more mechanical type of imitation as "developmental identification" and to the other type as "defensive identification" (which he equates with Anna Freud's "indentification with the aggressor"). According to the distinction proposed here, however, the "interpersonal" type of imitation includes more than "defensive identification." Also, as already suggested (see paragraph 3, page 147) "identification with the aggressor" can take place on either a satellizing or incorporative basis.

[4] Hartogs' work [*168*] indicates that the level of aspiration for a specific task may be excessively lowered by persons with anxiety in order to insure future success following an initial frustrating experience. This phenomenon will be referred to later as adaptive ego-disinvolvement (see page 372).

CHAPTER 13

Crisis and Failure in Ego Development: II. Ego Maturation in Late Childhood and Adolescence

THE ROLE OF EGO MATURATION IN THE DEVELOPMENTAL CYCLE

SATELLIZATION is only a stage in ego development that best meets the needs of the young child's dependent biosocial status. In response to various pressures which make devaluation of ego aspirations and a shift to a derived source of status desirable, it effects a reorganization of infantile ego structure that is more stable, and tenable under the changed environmental and perceptual conditions of childhood. However, beginning in later childhood and extending throughout adolescence, a second major shift in biosocial status precipitates a new crisis in ego development, the *maturation* crisis, which demands a reorganization of comparable scope and significance. The issues of dependence *versus* independence, of primary *versus* derived status, of self-assertion *versus* subservience which had been laid aside for several years are now reactivated. Again violent fluctuations in these dichotomous needs are the order of the day until a new equilibrium is found. But the general trend of change is in the opposite direction. The pendulum swings closer to the infantile goals of volitional independence and mastery of the environment than to the subservient attitude of childhood. This does not mean that the young adult is back in the same place which he left at the close of infancy; for behind this shift in ego development is considerable growth in perceptual ability and executive capacity, and fundamental changes in social pressures and expectations. Thus the positions which were abandoned as untenable after the fierce resistance from three to five are given a new basis in reality which turns the tide of battle and enables them to be held permanently following the equally turbulent struggles of adolescence.

The crisis of maturation, just like the crisis of devaluation, precipitates an extended period of developmental disequilibrium. All of the difficulties attending a transitional stage of ego development must be endured again. A secure and established biosocial status is exchanged for a new status which is unsettled, marginal, conflictful and uncertain of attainment. A highly differentiated and familiar psychological field must be abandoned for one that is uncharted, ambiguous, undifferentiated and fraught with unknown implications. The quest for orientation and for a meaningful framework of reference for the assimilation of new values must be begun anew. It is no wonder then that resistance to change will come from within as well as from without.

Yet as in every evolutionary process, continuity although less striking and dramatic goes hand in hand with modification. The consequences of previous modes of ego organization leave a permanent residue in personality structure which plays an important directional role in future developments. Hence ego maturation in the satellizing child will be a very much different process from ego maturation in the non-satellizer with respect to developmental tasks, mechanisms of change, difficulties, consequences and prognosis. How reversible the effects of this previous experience are is still an open question; but it appears likely that the older the child the greater is the force required to effect a reversal of the prevailing pattern. For example, the prognosis for satellization in a five-year-old rejected child is fairly good if a basic change in parental attitudes can be effected. However, even the severest type of ego trauma in adolescence is unlikely to obliterate the inner core of self-esteem that is built up during the process of satellization and which endures thereafter.

If satellization constitutes the surest foundation upon which a healthy personality structure is built, ego maturation represents the essential ingedient of the superstructure which is the immediate functional organ of personality in adult life. The most felicitous course of personality development in our culture involves a history of early satellization followed by desatellization and the adoption of an incorporative orientation. The consequences of failure to undergo ego maturation are just as grave in terms of future mental health as those already described for failure in ego devaluation. The most serious consequence is a predesposition toward certain specific behavior disorders which will be fully discussed in later sections.

THE DEVELOPMENTAL TASKS OF EGO MATURATION

The tasks confronting ego maturation are literally herculean in scope. The aim is a complete reorganization of personality structure. The child has to become much more of an individual in his own right with ego aspirations oriented toward a status based upon his own entitlement to hierarchical standing rather than toward a passive, reflective, relationship-derived status. Hence arises a much greater concern for acquiring an extrinsic status relative to his own performance capacity to manipulate the environment. He must achieve emancipation from parental direction and attain sufficient volitional independence to make his own decisions and chart his own future. Commensurate with the ego-inflationary implications of these indications of maturity and self-assertion, his self-estimate as a person and his level of ego aspiration must rise accordingly.

Correlatively, appropriate changes in the other ego attributes are required: Further curbing of short-term, pleasure-seeking goals is necessary, and long-range objectives enhancing self-development and ego status must be encouraged. But this time the motivation for attenuating hedonistic impulses is different; it reflects a need for attaining recently internalized, more mature goals which would be frustrated by preoccupation with pleasure-seeking activities, rather than a need to gain parental approval. The difficulty of this task is increased in adolescence by the emergence of new and powerful visceral sex drives which have yet to undergo socialization, requiring an effort at suppression which is more comparable in magnitude to the situation prevailing during infancy than during childhood. Hedonism in the adolescent period is, therefore, most frequently expressed in the form of unrestricted sexuality.

Additional developmental tasks faced by ego maturation include the further expansion of executive independence and the placing of moral values and moral accountability on a more objective and wider social base than personal loyalty to parents. This latter task requires a reformulation of moral value positions in more generalized and abstract terms, greater reliance upon the exploratory orientation, and recognition of the moral authority of society.

THE FACTORS PRECIPITATING THE EGO MATURATION CRISIS

The occurrence of the ego maturation crisis provides another vivid illustration of the thesis that significant transitions in ego development are not regulated automatically by internal, "morphogenic" factors, but reflect instead crucial changes in biosocial status which are brought about by the cumulative effect of progress in perceptual and executive capacities and of altered social expectations.

The elementary school years seem unspectacular enough in their implications for human growth. But despite the fact that the rate of change is slow, the cumulative impact of steady progress is tremendous. Intellectually, the world of time and space (which at six lies within a short radius of home and the immediate present) is extended to include the globe and the universe, the historical past and the historical future [*201*]. The ability to generalize, to manipulate abstractions, to reason from the standpoint of an abstract proposition is enormously expanded [*201*]. The direction of thought relating to interpersonal issues is from the specific to the general, from the concrete to the abstract, from the personal to the impersonal [*47, 201*]. All of these changes lead the child to a clearer and more comprehensive understanding of the nature of the environment in which he lives. He feels less awed by its complexity, and more confident to navigate alone and unguided. Eventually he reaches the position where the absolutism of his moral judgments [*308*] can be modified by an appreciation of logical considerations and the use-value of rules in the regulation of interpersonal relationships.

His gains in social awareness and social competence during this period are no less important. By the time he is ready to leave the elementary school he has acquired a fairly accurate picture of the social class structure of society and of the distinguishing characteristics that make for class distinctions [*377*]. He has learned to function in a larger group, to plan more complex activities without adult direction, to participate in team activities, to play highly structured games and to abide by complicated rules [*201*]. In the course of group interaction, he has learned the meaning of team loyalty and competition, of leadership, and self-subservience in the interests of group welfare. He has acquired an intuitive grasp of group process and of the dynamics of group organization. His own role and place in relation to the group has crystallized, and he has become capable of defining it with a fair amount of precision and explicitness [*304*]. In his quest for more desirable associates he has dared to venture beyond the neighborhood backyard which at six constituted his sole arena for peer group experience.

With the help of these social accomplishments he forges a semi-independent status for himself; he becomes an entity apart from his dependent position at home, and acquires a source of extrinsic status to supplement his role as satellite in the family configuration. He now possesses a sufficient fund of social and intellectual skill and competence to qualify for a more mature and responsible role in the affairs of his culture. He feels competent enough to engage in the status-giving activities[1]* that he formerly regarded as the exclusive concern of adults. But this time, unlike the situation at four, he *really* possesses enough executive ability and independence to warrant a serious and legitimate quest for more primary status and greater volitional independence.

These gains in social and intellectual competence also have important implications for the parent-child relationship, resulting in changes which increase the need for ego maturation. Increased identification with the peer group and the attainment through membership in it of an independent status provide him with new ego supports that weaken his dependence upon parental approval.

* Notes for this chapter appear on page 246.

"By attributing the prerogatives of judgment, decision, choice and initiative to a group fashioned in his own image, he . . . effectively demolishes his exclusive association of these powers with parental figures and thus . . . paves the way for eventually assuming them himself" [*23*]. In the new light of his own maturity, his parents seem less omniscient than before; he is less content to accept their judgments on faith alone. Exposure to a diversity of social climates and more intimate knowledge of the relationships prevailing in other family constellations help to break down the deified picture which he has of his parents. Yet not until emancipation is complete is he sufficiently free of the attitude of subservience to evaluate them with critical detachment.

Hence as the ties of dependency weaken and the omnipotence of the parent declines, the latter loses his power to confer an absolute, intrinsic value on the child; as the parents' glory fades, less derived status can be reflected to the satellite. Deprived thus of a portion of his former intrinsic status, the child's need for its extrinsic counterpart (originally stimulated by his increased competence in manipulating the environment) is further enhanced. And in modern urban society the parents and the home lack status-giving activities to meet this need. The child must, therefore, look to the school and to the peer group for the satisfaction of status needs which the parents are powerless to gratify; and in this process of realignment a reallocation of loyalties and allegiances is inevitable.

Illustrative also of the new type of less dependent parent-child relationship that arises at this time, is the different response given to the birth of a sibling during this period. The older child does not necessarily regard the newcomer as a rival for the parents' protective care but may vie with his parents in seeking to extend protection to the infant. The more self-reliant and self-assertive the child is, the more he competes with the parent rather than with the sibling. Instances of such behavior can even be observed in four-and five-year-old children in our culture, and are very common among younger Iatmul children who regard themselves as executively competent from a very early age [*274*].

The Effect of Early School Attendance on Ego Maturation

This realignment in source of status takes place very gradually. An important milestone occurs when the six-year-old enters school. For the first time now he is conceded an official status in the culture which is independent of the home. He can hardly be blamed then for indulging in some self-congratulatory ego inflation: Daddy goes to work in the morning to earn money, and he goes forth to school to learn serious things like reading and writing which will eventually entitle him to membership in adult society. For several hours in each day he enjoys—at least in part—an extrinsic status which reflects his relative competence in mastering the curriculum. Mommy and Daddy have nothing to say here; another adult authority completely takes over. In that case, just how omniscient can they be if they must yield the training role to others in such vital areas? Could it possibly be that teacher knows more? As this supposition becomes articulated, serious doubts arise in the child's mind about parental infallibility; and in some cases he will openly express an opinion to the effect that his parent is the lesser authority [*378*].

Actually, the parent-child-teacher relationship is far more complicated when individual cases are considered. In the non-satellizer, for example, no readjustment in source of status is necessary since the source has always been extrinsic and just continues as such. The possibility of gaining status, however, undergoes significant change. The rejected child has a much better chance of meeting with success and recognition in school than he ever had at home. The overvalued child, on the other hand, almost inevitably suffers a loss in appreciation at the hands of his teacher and classmates. Such differences are likely to be reflected in changes related to behavioral adjustment such as overt levels of anxiety and hostility.

In the satellizing child, school attendance obviously involves greater changes in ego structure. Not only is his self-estimate boosted but also (as pointed out above) there is greater shifting in source of status, in dependence upon parents, and in the child's perception of their omnipotence. Hence, following the difficulties and conflicts associated with any transition in ego development [*354*], it is no wonder then that the net effect of early school attendance on satellizers is an improvement in those personality attributes indicative of ego maturation, e.g., independence, reliability, etc. [*378*].

But even in satellizers, the impact of initial school experience on ego development is mitigated by two important considerations: (1) In due time they react to the teacher as a parent-substitute and also form a satellizing relationship to her. It is important to point out, however, that this differs in quality from the parent-child relationship. The teacher is more concerned with the child's competence and is less disposed to offer unconditional acceptance. She tends more to dispense approval as a reward for achievement. The child feels more obliged to conform to her standards in order to retain her good will. When asked by his mother why he is not as "good" at home as he is in school, he might reply, "In school I *have* to be good." In other words, conformity in a satellizing child is partly a function of how sure he is of unconditional approval. (2) The extrinsic status which the child receives in school must be viewed within the larger framework of his total ego structure. Looked at, thus, from this hierarchical standpoint, the extrinsic status which he wins in school by virtue of his own efforts and performance ability must necessarily play a subordinate and peripheral role in relation to the derived status he receives from his parents. In the total economy of his personality adjustment, therefore, school experience can provide only a limited degree of ego enhancement and a subsidiary source of new status. The home and the parents continue to function as the major status-giving influences in the child's life during the early years of elementary school attendance.

Negativism in the six-year-old, therefore, follows the same pattern met with at age four: There is much of the same cockiness and blustering self-assurance based on an exaggerated notion of a recent gain in competence and biosocial status. But this time there is more real cause for crowing and ego inflation. The child does have some basis in reality for regarding himself as a "big shot" when he compares his present status to that which prevailed only a year ago. In addition, the authority of his parents is undermined by the tarnishing of their omniscience and the termination of their reign as sole dispensers of moral values. Hence the recently established equilibrium relative to the ascendent-submissive aspects of the parent-child relationship is disturbed once more. The limits of tolerated misbehavior become ambiguous again; and a certain amount of belligerency and aggressive self-assertion on both sides is almost inevitable until a clear understanding is reached as to the recognition which this new factor will receive in the total framework of the parent-child relationship.

THE ROLE OF CHANGING SOCIAL EXPECTATIONS DURING PREADOLESCENCE

Neither the parent nor the culture is unaware of the growth in social competence that takes place during the preadolescent years; and where opportunities are available and the economic need great enough (as in rural communities and primitive cultures) constructive use is made of these new abilities. Children are assigned responsible, status-giving tasks of considerable social and economic importance in agriculture, handicrafts, household arts, and in looking after younger siblings. The child's needs for an independent primary status and for greater executive and volitional independence are stimulated by parental and social expectations that he manifest greater maturity; and successful experience in new responsible roles further increases competence and provides the necessary experience required for ego maturation.

In modern urban cultures, however, little opportunity exists for providing children with mature role-playing experience, necessitating a "complete separation of the . . . [activity] and interest systems of child and adult . . . [Such] children . . . are given no responsibilities in the work-a-day world of adult concerns, and hence, evolve a complete set of prestige-giving values of their own" [*23*]. They are required to seek whatever compensatory extrinsic status they can find in their own peer society which allows them to play the mature roles from which they are barred in adult society. An additional source of vicarious compensation and experience is also found by incorporating the exploits of superhuman, fictional and glamorous figures. Neither compensation, however, can make up for the lack of genuine responsibility in the adult world for which the preadolescent feels himself ready and prepared. Deprived of this necessary role-playing experience and of the stimulation provided by increased social expectations of more mature behavior, his rate of ego maturation must accordingly lag behind. The character traits indicative of maturity, e.g., initiative, independence and responsibility, are learned just as any other skill, motor or intellectual, by exercise. Readiness for learning is necessary but is insufficient in the absence of adequate opportunity for practice.

Exclusion from the adult world of reality also has effects other than retardation of ego maturation and strengthening of the child's dependence on the peer group. It inaugurates a long period of estrangement between children and adults which persists until the former attain adulthood themselves. Insurmountable barriers to commonality of feeling, to mutual understanding and to ease of communication are built up. This alienation is not unaccompanied by resentment and bitterness. Although outright resistance to adult authority is usually withheld until adolescence, there is reason to believe that the preadolescent's apparent conformity is only a veneer which hides the smoldering rebellion from view. This is revealed by the often contemptuous and sneering remarks he makes about adults in his own company, and by the studied indifference to adult standards which he professes out of earshot of the latter.

Because of the preadolescent's greater concern with earning an extrinsic status and his parent's reduced power to confer intrinsic status, it should not be imagined that the latter type of status assumes negligible significance in the current economy of his ego structure. Quite the contrary, it continues to constitute the major source of status until adolescence. For the most part his parents continue to extend the same type of protective, unconditional acceptance of him as a satellite as they did in the pre-school period. It is not until adolescence that they withdraw sufficient emotional support and tolerance from the satellizing relationship to convert the latter into a minor and subsidiary source of current status. And even after this situation develops, the residual source of status available in the satellizer's inner core of self-esteem is not to be minimized.

The parent is not alone, however, in wishing to preserve the home as the major source of childhood status. The satellizing, preadolescent child despite his forays into the field of primary status still regards the latter as playing a supporting role to his position as satellite. He still feels unprepared to aspire to the prerogatives and attributes of adult ego status as long as he does not satisfy the preliminary requirement which his culture imposes as an absolute criterion of the legitimacy of such strivings, namely, physiological and sexual maturity.

PUBESCENCE AS AN IMPETUS TO EGO MATURATION

Pubescence is the crucial catalytic agent which makes it possible for the preparatory preadolescent phases of ego maturation to be converted into the consummatory adolescent stage. Up to this point, the cumulative impact of changes in the direction of desatellization has been insufficient to effect a major shift in equilibrium with respect to source of status. Such transitions in ego development require the intervention of more potent biological and social factors than have been previously available. Before they can become a relevant possibility "either an urgent social need for a change in personality status must exist, or else internal change with respect to basic drives or personality equipment must be so overwhelming that present status becomes incompatible with the changed appearance and functioning of the individual" [*23*]. Insofar as the crisis of ego maturation is concerned, the biological factor of pubescence seems to be the more crucial precipitating factor.

The pressures generated by the social needs of (a) finding new individuals to carry on the responsibility for maintaining the culture and (b) relieving parents of the burden of indefinitely supporting and rearing their offspring have already been operating for several years without effecting a transition to adult personality status. Even where "economic necessity imposes mature economic and social tasks upon pre-adolescent boys and girls," this transformation fails to occur in the absence of the anatomical and physiological changes associated with pubescence. It is also impossible to ascribe the crisis in ego development to any sudden growth in motor, intellectual or social skills, or to a spurt in capacity for self-perception. These factors which played so important a role in previous reorganizations of ego structure seem to be of negligible significance at this time. Attention must, therefore, be focused on the apparently crucial impact of pubescence on ego re-formation during this age-period.

This does not imply that changed cultural expectations are an irrelevant consideration since (as will be presently shown) the reverse is obviously true. The point is made, however, that the alteration of social pressures in this direction is not a spontaneous phenomenon but is almost universally a cultural response to the evidences of pubescence in the individual. The intrinsic effect of sexual maturation and the newly acquired capacity for reproduction in strengthening the drive toward self-assertion and independence is probably substantial enough in its own right, but defies measurement because it cannot be isolated from the social reaction which it elicits. For reasons which are apparently self-evident, most societies seem to regard physiological maturity as a mandatory indication for the consummation of ego maturation.[2]

The changed cultural expectations aroused by the appearance of pubescence would appear to operate as follows: The social value of derived status depreciates while the corresponding value of extrinsic status increases. The adolescent, thus, not only finds that he is increasingly expected to establish his status through his own efforts, but also that the latter criterion tends to displace the childhood criterion (i.e., of derived status) as the chief measure by which his social milieu tends to evaluate him. Simultaneously, social pressure is put on the parents to withdraw a large portion of the emotional support which they had hitherto been extending to him by way of conferring intrinsic status.

Other factors also contribute to the decreasing availability of derived status. As his attitude of dependency diminishes, the adolescent makes additional progress in appraising his parents objectively. Continued broadening of his social environment accelerates the process whereby the formerly omniscient parents become more and more reduced to their actual size; common experience indeed points to the fact that the reduction is carried too far. When this happens, precious little glory can be reflected, even if the satellizing relationship could be maintained; nor can a non-omnipotent being confer the same quality of derived status (merely by unqualifiedly accepting a person as a satellite) that was previously possible when his omnipotence was less tarnished.

The final stroke in dethroning the parents as a source of intrinsic status is supplied by the peer group. As the importance of this group increases in providing a source of values, standards, goals and status, while the corresponding role of the parents declines in significance, parental prestige must necessarily undergo drastic deflation.

The net result of this increased cultural valuation of extrinsic status and the curtailed availability and diminished social acceptability of derived status is a complete reversal of the relationship which formerly prevailed between these two varieties of status. In the total economy of ego organization, the major rather than the subsidiary source of current status now becomes extrinsic in nature. Concomitantly, peer group and home trade places as the chief source from which current status is available, since the peer society can actually provide the adolescent with real opportunities for gaining the extrinsic status which parents in our culture seem unable to offer. Thus, in contrast to its preadolescent counterpart, the adolescent peer culture plays a central rather than a peripheral role as an ego support, a role which is greatly enhanced by the adolescent's marginal biosocial status and the sudden evaporation of his formerly principal source of ego status.

It would be a mistake to believe, however, that this chain of events set off by the onset of pubescence is in any sense automatic or inevitably thoroughgoing in scope. Margaret Mead, for example, has pointed out that a two year interval elapses in Samoa between the occurrence of pubescence in girls and social recognition of the fact [*274*]. And in our culture the unavailability of mature social and vocational experience for adolescent boys and girls not only limits the breadth and rate of the maturational process which is realistically possible, but also lowers social expectations as to the extent and rapidity of ego development considered desirable. This latter factor further retards the rate of maturation by reducing the pressures for change operating on the adolescent.

This pegging of social expectations upon the availability of mature role-playing experience inevitably gives rise to certain discrepancies in expectancy, since the availability of such experience is by no means uniform in the different areas of interpersonal relations involving adolescents. Although the home, like society in general, offers little in the way of status-giving activities, its greater structural flexibility allows for greater modification of personal relationships than do other social institutions. Thus, the adolescent can achieve a considerable measure of emancipation from home in the way of self-assertion and independent activity even though he fails to acquire much status. His changed physical appearance makes complete perpetuation of the old parent-child relationship difficult. Society, on the other hand, is protected from the impact of individual pubescence by buffers of impersonality and emotional distance. Yet even in the home, parental demands for greater personal responsibility are apt to outdistance by far the breadth of newly granted privileges and prerogatives.

Only in the peer group is sufficient extrinsic status available for substantial progress in ego maturation to occur. Because a closer balance prevails between the demands it makes on adolescents and the privileges it extends, it can exact greater conformity to its standards.

Wherever extrinsic considerations are at stake, conformity can be gained only at a price, a price which can be defined either as a visible reward or as a reprieve from anxiety. Hence, although adult society may have fewer status rewards than the home to offer to adolescents, it wields a bigger stick and thus commands greater respect for its standards.

MECHANISMS OF DESATELLIZATION

Resatellization

In our culture, desatellization is largely an outcome of emancipation from parental influences and of increased susceptibility to pressures emanating from other adults and from the peer society. As already indicated, satellizers do not completely abandon the satellizing orientation as they mature and liberate themselves from the domination of parental standards. From the earliest beginnings of desatellization, the transference of satellizing allegiances to other persons goes hand in hand with the task of devaluing the parents. Thus, the satellizer sees in the peer group or in the school situation more than just an opportunity to gain extrinsic status. To be sure, the latter consideration is not unimportant, but the satellizing orientation continues to function, both in the learning of values and in the structuring of interpersonal relationships.

But this typical pattern of emancipation from parents followed by resatellization need not be an inevitable part of ego maturation, even for satellizers (and obviously not for non-satellizers). "In a static, tradition-bound society," as Frank [*118*] points out, "the process of emancipation does not necessarily imply a supplantation of the family 'as the principle medium through which the culture operates.' Here the family could still serve as the primary source of goals and standards while the adolescent's position in relation [to parents] merely shifts from a dependent to an independent role" [*23*]. That is, the adolescent in relatively stable rural areas could still learn most of what he needs to know as an adult from his parents, but would assimilate this knowledge for use in the role of an independent person in his own right.

In urban communities however, the situation could hardly prevail! The school rather than the home serves as the chief vehicle for transmitting culturally valuable knowledge. Parents do not know enough to educate their offspring adequately or to train them for the host of vocational possibilities which are available. Most important, however, is the fact that the modern home no longer serves as a center which provides sources of extrinsic status to all members of the household, including adolescents. Therefore, in learning the goals and values necessary for the attainment of adult maturation, the adolescent will look to persons other than his parents, persons who *can* supply status. It is these individuals then who serve satellizers as models for satellization, who provide whatever derived status exists during adolescence, and who stimulate the acceptance of ideas on the basis of personal loyalty.

Other Mechanisms

Although desatellization from *parents* (and concomitant resatellization with others) is an important method of achieving maturation in our culture, two other equally important maturational devices operate concurrently in satellizers and exclusively in non-satellizers:

(1) With the approach of adolescence, the acquisition of extrinsic status under the impact of changed cultural expectations suddenly becomes invested with a new crucial significance.[3] Hence, regardless of where he learns the new goals and skills befitting an adult member of society—whether at home, in school, or in his peer group—the adolescent is required to give greater self-reference to considerations involving his own competence and his status in the group. Accordingly, he finds it necessary to adopt much more of the incorporative orientation in the learning of more mature goals and values—because only within the framework of this learning orientation can he efficiently enhance the objectives of extrinsic status. Furthermore, the very ego attributes which constitute the object of his learning process can only be rationalized as indices of maturity if he first accepts the necessity of acquiring greater primary status, since the main justification for this change in personality organization is to provide a more formidable vehicle for effecting the changed needs of his goal structure.

Maturation, therefore, depends largely upon acquiring the motivations relevant to enhancing one's own extrinsic status; the self must be motivated to accomplish things, and not to derive vicarious status from the prowess and position of others. The transition between these two types of status is largely bridged by the child's desire to gain parental approbation for his early accomplishments. Thus, the acquisition of extrinsic status is at first only a modified manifestation of satellization. And later, once this motivation is internalized as an end in itself, appropriate maturational goals and learning methods are adopted for implementing it. In the process, maturity is achieved, since this concept can be understood only as a social norm defining the direction in which certain aspects of personality structure must change if the cultural ideal of an acceptable adult member of society is to be realized. This cultural ideal of personality maturity in turn influences prevailing expectations relative to changes in goal-structure during adolescence, the latter being inevitably fashioned in terms of enhancing the former.

For example, the enhancement of extrinsic status requires that an individual pay less attention to the immediate gratification of hedonistic needs and concern himself more with planning for long-range prestige goals; that he manifest greater independence in choosing goals and making decisions; that he acquire greater competence in implementing decisions by himself; and that he at least give the appearance of conforming to the moral standards of his social group. Granted that cultural differences exist in the extent to which this change in goal structure and the accompanying changes in maturity seem desirable. The fact remains that the direction of expected change from childhood to adult life—irrespective of its magnitude—seems almost universally to follow the above pattern.

The learning orientation employed in assimilating the new values indicative of maturity becomes more incorporative for the same reason: From the standpoint of acquiring greater extrinsic status, the criteria of blind loyalty, personal allegiance, and craving for personal approval cannot be very reliable motivations for the acceptance of new values. More efficacious and realistic in such a situation are such criteria as expediency and perceived superiority in expediting the gratification of particular status needs. The overt satellizing orientation is also frowned upon socially because it conflicts with the maturational ideal of greater volitional independence which is so crucial for the success of the new approach to status problems.

(2) A third mechanism whereby ego maturation is effected is through greater employment of the exploratory orientation. Prior to adolescence, this learning orientation can function freely only within a highly limited sphere of attitude and value formation; for as soon as the implications of independent objective investigation are pursued to their logical conclusion, the danger always exists that they will conflict with values tied to primary allegiances, and hence precipitate an avalanche of guilt feelings. That suppression of such exploratory activity will be the outcome of this conflict is a reasonable enough prediction in the heyday of the satel-

lizing era when the major source of status is found in the home. But as emancipation from parental dominance makes headway, greater opportunity for task- or value-oriented learning experience becomes possible.

The type of maturity achieved under such auspices is the most wholesome of the three: Independence and objectivity of thought and judgment are encouraged and freed from the restrictive limitations imposed by considerations relative to personal loyalty, expediency, and enhancement of ego status. Ethical values and ideas of moral accountability can be placed for the first time on an objective and rational basis. The problem of hedonism *versus* more enduring goals is approached with greater detachment; neither parental approval nor personal prestige becomes the crucial issue involved, but rather the striking of an equitable balance between personal needs and the interests of cultural survival.

Unfortunately, however, the onset of adolescence brings with it certain counter-pressures that drastically curtail the expansion of the exploratory orientation. The adolescent's marginality of status and his dependence on the peer society for same permits very little deviation from group values, and hence little opportunity for independent exploration. Similarly, the adolescent's greater concern with the achievement of extrinsic status deters him from adopting any learning orientation that might possibly interfere with its attainment.

FACTORS FACILITATING MATURATION

Maturation has been described as a gradual process of evolution in personality development in the course of which certain childhood aspects of personality become transformed into their socially acceptable adult counterparts. Broadly conceived, it also includes the progress made during the period of satellization during which time hedonism is attenuated, executive independence enhanced, and a rudimentary form of moral accountability developed. On the other hand, however, the process of satellization represents at least a temporary setback for the main goals of maturation, namely, volitional independence, and adoption of a primary source of ego status. With respect to these criteria of ultimate maturity, the satellizing child is less advanced than a non-devalued infant. Hence, even if we accept the fact that satellization represents a desirable setback in this aspect of maturation (which for other compelling reasons is necessary for the development of a secure and happy personality), it is still undeniable that it constitutes another formidable obstacle to ego maturation. It is a development which for the most part must be undone before adult personality status can be achieved; and if its dependent aspects are overemphasized it can become an insurmountable barrier or at the very least a dangerous hazard for the successful outcome of the maturational process. Even those aspects of childhood personality which undergo maturation under the aegis of satellization (e.g., excessive hedonism, moral irresponsibility) cannot attain their final form without a drastic change in orientation, although it should be reemphasized that experience with the previous orientation makes for completeness and stability in the final product.

Therefore, if we conceive of the maturational process as encompassing both the period of mixed progress during the satellizing era, and the period of gradual but steady progress through the desatellizing activities of the elementary school years, (as well as the more spectacular advances registered during adolescence), the task of evaluating factors which facilitate maturation becomes tremendously enlarged in scope. It leads to the hypothesis that "although the actual task of emancipation is accomplished under the impact of new [biological and social pressures] arising at adolescence, the question of its probable success or failure is really predetermined in childhood—depending upon the type of training for independence and responsibility which the child receives" [*23*]. The reasoning underlying this hypothesis is that much of the personality maturation occurring during pre-adolescence is actually subliminal rather than absent; and, therefore, the introduction of new biosocial determinants during the period of adolescence does not elicit changes in maturity *de novo* but from a near-threshold level.

Using this approach the factors facilitating maturation will be examined under two headings: (a) factors which facilitate desatellization and (b) status-giving factors.

Desatellizing Factors

The central developmental task of desatellization is the regaining of the volitional independence surrendered in the course of satellization. Hence desatellization can best be implemented by (a) encouraging the exploratory orientation and discouraging the satellizing orientation in the assimilation of values; (b) developing multiple sources of intrinsic security and adequacy through satellization with persons and groups outside the home; and (c) developing skills in independent planning and goal-setting by providing opportunities for practice, and appropriate conditions for learning realistic roles and goals, adequate frustration tolerance, and realistic self criticism.

Children can only feel free to pursue the exploratory orientation in the learning of values if they are absolutely sure that they are *unconditionally* accepted by their parents. "This requires that they be allowed to accept the values of our culture rather than having them crammed down their throats with withdrawal of parental emotional support as the ever-threatening penalty for disagreement" [*63*]. But even if unconditional acceptance is assured, disapproval must be used reservedly since it inevitably leads to guilt feelings in the child. Hence parental disapproval should not be administered automatically whenever the child's attitudes deviate from the parents'—as if disagreement *per se* were evil. It should be reserved for instances of serious deviancy which if left uncountered would lead to personality distortion or maladjustment. Disapproval and guilt feelings, as already indicated, can be used to discourage blind and uncritical reflection of parental viewpoints; and the praise which is usually reserved for this situation can be dispensed when evidence of independent and critical thinking is presented.

The dependent aspects of satellization can also be minimized if the child can find derived status in multiple sources rather than in his parents alone. Under such circumstances the one source is no longer so precious. He need not tread so warily to avoid arousing disapproval. Fortified by the ego support he receives from friends, grandparents, older siblings, teachers, group leaders, etc., he can afford more often to assert his independence and risk arousing parental ire. Even if these additional sources of intrinsic status play only a subsidiary role in relation to the parents, they may often spell the difference between complete subservience and occasional defiance. That some domineering and overprotective parents are not unaware of this possibility can be seen in their frantic efforts to make the child perceive all figures beyond the familial hearth as sinister and foreboding. To such children the world is populated by menacing bogeymen kept at arm's length only by the constant vigilance of devoted parents.

Desatellization is best effected, however, by developing skills that are necessary for competent exercise of volitional independence. First of all this requires provision of opportunity for exercising choice, making plans and decisions, practising self-direction, and learning from one's own mistakes. Adequate freedom for exploration, for trial-and-error learning, and for manipulating a variety of social situations is needed. Mature volitional behavior can be learned only by actual role-playing experience. Hence, overdominated children whose parents make all their decisions, and overprotected children who are never exposed to the possibility of making an independent decision lest they make a fatal error, are inestimably handicapped in the learning of volitional maturity.

Maturation of the capacity for volitional independence also depends upon increasing the child's frustration tolerance and maximizing his ability to choose realistic roles and set realistic goals for himself. To a very large extent, this aspect of maturation is a product of direct experience with frustrating and restrictive aspects of his environment. It presumes acceptance of the barriers and limitations imposed upon the free, unhampered exercise of will by the inherent structure of the social order and by the prevailing social expectations and prohibitions surrounding individual behavior. The desired outcome is for the child to acquire a realistic notion of his own capacities and status at each stage of his development; to aspire to roles that are realistically possible; to make demands on others that can be received with tolerance; to set goals that are within his grasp; to bear frustration without unduly abandoning independence, level of aspiration or legitimate self-criticism. The irreducible condition for achieving these objectives is to confront the child consistently, firmly and unambiguously (within the developmental limits of his capacity for perceiving and adjusting to same) with the unadorned realities that define his biosocial position at home and in his culture.

This condition for the development of mature behavior has been grossly violated by the present-day fetish of permissiveness[4] in child-rearing. The tremendous vogue enjoyed by this doctrine can in part be explained as a reaction to the rigid and authoritarian parental practices that were fashionable in the preceding two decades. In part it is a by-product of the recent overemphasis placed upon frustration as an etiological factor in the behavior disorders and as invariable and unqualified evil. More specifically it has been rationalized on the basis of evidence which has applicability to young infants only,[5] and by reference to the analogy of the more permissive and democratic approach to the learning of values advocated above and practiced in the more progressive schools.

However, it is one thing to advocate self-demand feeding schedules because of the low frustration tolerance of infants, and their recognized exemption from stringent social demands, and quite another matter to suggest the indefinite prolongation of this policy into the early and later years of childhood. Similarly there is no incompatability between granting children greater freedom in accepting values on the one hand, while insisting on the other that their behavior be confined within certain broad limits imposed by the social expectations and prohibitions relative to their age group.

It would seem unreasonable to expect that a child could ever orient his goal structure realistically in relation to obstacles and barriers without some direct experience with frustration. In order that he acquire sufficient frustration tolerance to persist (despite inevitable setbacks in the pursuit of long-range goals) in maintaining his essential independence and in avoiding an excessively lax and uncritical appraisal of his accomplishments, he must learn the meaning of failure and the means of grappling with it. Exposing the child to unnecessary or pointless frustration or to frustration beyond his developmental capacity for coping with same would no doubt only impede the growth of this tolerance. But the extreme permissive viewpoint embodied in the underdominating parent (who conceives of her "parental role as intended to insure the fact that her child suffers not the slightest" impediment in implementing his desires lest he become "emotionally insecure") leads to the very same result. "Purposeful and persistent avoidance of frustration creates for the child a conception of reality which is so distorted that he becomes exclusively conditioned to living in a hedonistic environment. Under these conditions, maturation, which involves adjustment to a reality fashioned in good part from the fabric of frustration, becomes an utter impossibility" [*23*].

The development of frustration tolerance, therefore, requires that a child be encouraged to solve his own problems and learn through his mistakes, that his course through life not be continually smoothed by systematic elimination of the problems which confront him. He must learn to take responsibility for the consequences of his behavior when mistakes are made and failure ensues. Parental "whitewashing" does not develop frustration tolerance but reinforces the immature tendency to cope with failure and misbehavior by rationalization, disclaiming of responsibility and abandonment of even minimal standards of self-criticism.

Another undesirable outcome of indiscriminate permissiveness is that a child finds it difficult to perceive self and self-role realistically, to deal adequately with the child-adult relationship, and to evolve goals which are realistically related to probability of success and amount of motivation at his disposal. The conditions under which self-role can be realistically learned require a clear appreciation of what can be legitimately included within the appropriate age-sex-subculture role and what must perforce be excluded from it. The attitude of unvarying permissiveness fulfills neither condition. By advocating unrestricted freedom for the child in setting his goals, by refusing to impose limitations on behavior which is socially unacceptable, and by denying the legitimacy of status differences between children and adults, the overly permissive parent or teacher makes it impossible for the child to perceive the boundaries of his role.

In some extreme cases, exposure to this variety of child-rearing leads to complete unrealism regarding the demands which an individual can legitimately make on others and their moral obligation to help him (the "Prince" or "Princess" complex). The child perceives his biosocial incompetence, and satellizes in the sense that he accepts a derived status and a dependent position in relation to his parents. But the latter cater excessively to his dependency needs, indulge his desire for executive dependence, fail to impose or enforce any demands or restrictions, and scrupulously avoid making any distinction between child and parental role. As a result of this extreme underdomination he develops the notion that he is a very precious and privileged person. His parents *have* to do things for him and *have* to help him—not because his will is omnipotent or irresistible, but because he has a special claim on their indulgence. Eventually this orientation is extended to the world at large: "The world owes me everything I need. People are obliged to help me; it is my natural due. After all they could not let *me* fend for myself or suffer pain and deprivation. In the case of other people, Yes, but not *me*. In *my* case it is different. It would be too cruel, too unfair." Such individuals approach even complete strangers with the unabashed plea, "I'm in a terrible fix, you've simply *got* to help me or I won't be responsible any longer for what I do."

In no culture can the distinction between parental and filial role be eradicated. The parent is required to be more dominant and ascendant in the relationship than the child. His judgments must be given more weight and his demands more authority. The welfare and safety of the child require that he sometimes defer completely and comply immediately with parental requests. The parent has a right to expect unconditional obedience in times of danger without offering explanations for his demands. Where differences are irreconcilable, and issues of parental responsibility or social principle are involved, the parent's view should prevail. But the adherents of unqualified permissiveness refuse to face these issues squarely because to do so would mean repudiating the theoretical basis of their child-rearing doctrines. On the other hand they cannot ignore these considerations completely—because the practical pressures of meeting everyday situations and occasional crises, and of minimally satisfying cultural demands require the adoption of more directive and authoritarian attitudes than are consistent with their underlying philosophy. What results, therefore, is an unsatisfactory compromise which only adds to the ambiguity of the learning situation.

This compromise approach is reflected in many different attitudes of the overly permissive parent. He persistently refuses to define or clarify the acceptable limits of child behavior, handling each situation as it arises according to the demands of expediency. In this way he feels that he remains true to his doctrines while still in a position to cope with special situations. But the child cannot generalize in any consistent fashion about the limits of behavioral acceptability as a result of exposure to this treatment. The parent, for example, fails to make clear that his demands upon the child have a different status than the child's demands upon him, but on occasion acts as if this were the case by using force or threats. The child who has been indoctrinated with the principle of equality of status is thereby justified in concluding that either the general principle still holds but was unfairly violated by the parent, or that he, too, can exercise the same prerogatives as the parent with respect to the employment of force and threats. The same parent may permit his child to participate in activities far beyond his developmental capacities, but if embarrassing or unfortunate consequences ensue will cut them short on some pretext rather than let him learn the fitting generalization that he is not yet equipped to handle certain situations.

The ambiguity surrounding the limits of unacceptable behavior is further enhanced by the parental tendency to avoid issues (which might arise from opposing the child's desire) by resorting to distraction. While this technique is occasionally defensible—when the child is ill, unduly fatigued, hungry, or excessively irritable—it effectually prevents him from learning what constitutes out-of-bounds behavior if used habitually as the path of least resistance. Much less objectionable is the widely accepted practice of saying, "You can't do this, but you may do this." This avoids the error of ambiguity and is a feasible method of handling many difficult situations. But if used compulsively (as implied by the popular permissive dictum, "Say 'no' to a child as infrequently as possible, but if you must, always offer him a positive alternative"), it conditions him to an environment which is highly unrealistic in terms of the social prohibitions that will inevitably limit his behavioral freedom. The restrictions imposed in most real-life situations have only a negative aspect. This does not mean that positive alternatives cannot be found or that the child should not be encouraged to search for same; but if they are available or can be applied, it should be made clear that in most cases they originate as a product of the frustrated individual's resourcefulness and are not inevitably given in the prohibition itself.

Two other favorite techniques of the overly permissive parent are self-insulation and empty verbalism when an occasion for discipline or restraint arises. Obviously, if a parent cannot see or hear anything objectionable he cannot be expected to interfere. If, on the other hand, the behavior is so flagrant that self-insulation is impossible, half-hearted verbal disapproval can be given. The parent then feels that by voicing his objections he has discharged his parental duty even if the child continues this behavior during and after the time that the reproof is being administered. Actually, however, unless he takes active measures to halt or punish the objectionable activity and to prevent its occurrence in the future, he is really condoning it. The child perceives that the disapproval is only verbal since the parent does not feel strongly enough about the matter to enforce his demands, an option which is obviously within his power were he disposed to use it. Hence, all the while that the latter stands disclaiming against the unacceptable behavior and doing nothing about it, reinforcement is continually provided by the assurance that the misbehavior is condoned and that the rewards motivating it will not be taken away. Unenforced verbal commands become in effect stated guarantees of immunity from interference and punitive action. The upshot of this situation is that the child becomes positively conditioned to verbal disapproval, and not only ignores its purported intent but also feels encouraged by it.

The conclusion is thus inescapable that the important goal of consistency in discipline cannot be achieved unless the child understands unambiguously what his environment demands and expects of him. This absence of ambiguity can be realized only if reinforcement is provided at both ends of the range of behavioral acceptability. It may be true that reward and approval are more efficacious in motivating the learning of acceptable behavior than are punishment, restraint and disapproval in discouraging undesirable behavioral patterns [*201*]. Nevertheless, neither is sufficient by itself. From a developmental standpoint it is naive and unrealistic to assume that in the early and middle years of childhood, the learning of desirable, rewarded behavior automatically endows its logical opposite with a negative valence. Each valence must be separately established in order to encourage activity at one pole and discourage activity at the opposite pole; for until such time as the negative valence is established by active measures of reproof, the unacceptable behavior has a natural positive valence in the eyes of the child which competes in attractiveness with the benefits adhering to approved behavior. He will, therefore, be constantly tempted to sample the advantages of the former; and if not discouraged by disapproval can legitimately interpret tolerance as license to continue.

In due time, of course, interaction, synthesis and mutual reinforcement ensue when only one of the reciprocal pairs described above is either rewarded or punished as the case may be. In the case of older children and adults endorsement of the "good" alternative carries with it an implied condemnation of the "bad." But this implication is never as throughgoing as the advocates of the self-consistency theory of personaliy would have us believe. Tennyson's dictum that a man must hate evil before he can love the good is true in the sense of absolute logic, but implies a level of logical consistency that is rare in the typical person's organization of values and attitudes. The temptation to test the limits of tolerance for unacceptable behavior, to see how much one can "get away with" before incurring retribution, to take advantage of laxness, certainly declines with maturity, but nevertheless is present in all of us irrespective of whether a generally wholesome conscience is operating. Hence, consistent and unambiguous discipline requires explicit definition of the limits of unacceptable behavior, reinforced by tangible evidences of disapproval, especially in the early years of life when ability to generalize values is limited.

The same need for explicit restraints holds true for similar reasons when we consider the growth of internalization of social prohibitions in relation to the problem of consistent discipline. It is true that the only effective and durable type of discipline we can hope to establish is a self-discipline based upon internalization of external restraints. The control which relies primarily upon constant supervision, force, fear or threat is certainly consistent enough in its implications but contributes little to ego maturity. This does not mean, however, that in order to promote self-discipline external prohibitions must be completely abolished. The process of internalization occurs only gradually and is never complete. Other controls, therefore, must be visible enough in the beginning, can be relaxed somewhat as maturity increases, but must always be held in readiness in the background to reorient goals which stray from the path of reality. In this sense they serve not as the chief support of realistically oriented and socially acceptable behavior but as limiting factors which restrain impulsive flights of caprice and fancy. Like policemen on the corner they are hardly responsible for the usual decorum of the law-abiding citizen, but are convenient reminders that ill-considered mischief and out-of-bounds behavior will not be passively tolerated but may lead to painful consequences.

Apart from the deleterious effects on maturation which will be described more fully in later sections, there is little reason to believe (contrary to the views expressed by indulgent parents) that excessive permissiveness makes for a happy childhood. Quite the contrary, it leads to the insecurity which follows from adhering to any unrealistic, ambiguous or inconsistent frame of reference. Unrealistic goals usually prove to be unsuccessful. Undue demands on persons other than parents ordinarily meet with a cool reception. Expectations of receiving special consideration outside the family circle are seldom realized. Ordinary frustrations cannot be borne with equanimity but lead to precipitate abandonment of goals, petulance and temper tantrums; and at this point another source of insecurity arises from the child's dependence upon his own inadequate control of aggressive impulses. In the absence of suitable external restraints he has good reason to fear the consequences which his uninhibited rage may bring upon him. He might even blame his parents: "It's your fault for making me so mad"; or, "Why didn't you stop me from doing that?" But he may also blame himself for these excesses of aggression and suffer more than his share of guilt feelings.

"Since punishment is not forthcoming from parents . . . there is not infrequently the necessity for self-punishment. Much of the wild, reckless, and unconventional behavior of the overindulged child may be attributed to his demands for punishment, and his behavior becomes so extreme only because his overindulgent parents are slow in taking him to task . . . For this reason the overindulged child may frequently be so extremely rebellious and aggressive that his behavior necessitates punishment by a somewhat hesitant parent" [*389*].

The entire complex of absent self-control, selfish unreasonableness, importunate demands for immediate gratification, unrestrained aggressiveness, rebellious self-assertion, refractoriness to routine, irresponsibility, and lack of consideration for the needs of others forms such an unattractive, unloveable portrait that social acceptance by teachers, neighbors and age-mates is difficult indeed. Thus, even this last desperate defense upon which the advocates of extreme permissiveness are thrown back—that the child is happier in such a setting—is open to serious question.

Perhaps now after a decade of overenthusiastic and uncritical endorsement of permissiveness as a panacea, as a virtue *per se,* as the epitome of the "psychological" approach to interpersonal relations, parents, teachers and clinical workers will be able to appraise its values and consequences more objectively. This will take a certain amount of courage since the prevailing climate of informed professional opinion regards opposition to "all out" permissiveness as unprogressive, reactionary and tantamount to psychological treason. But in the long run it will be rewarded by the emergence of a more rational and consistent theory of discipline than that which presently enjoys vogue as the current fad and fashion in child-rearing.

Status-Giving Factors

The acquisition of increased extrinsic status is crucial for personality development during adolescence. This becomes apparent from any cross-cultural survey of adolescent development in different times and cultures; for the outstanding conclusion that can be drawn from such comparisons is that "the prolonged deprivation of status to which adolescents are subjected in our society is one of the main causes of the greater tension, anxiety and emotional instability characterizing this transitional period in modern Western civilization" [*23*]. Contributing to the painfulness of this status deprivation are the facts that (1) the period of subadulthood—of interim status—is prolonged for such a long time (approximately eight years); (2) whatever extrinsic status is available during this extended interim period is highly marginal and divorced from the main stream of status-giving activities in the culture as a whole; and (3) the tremendous uncertainty surrounding the eventual attainment of adult status. With respect to sources of extrinsic status available to the adolescent, the peer group, the home, and society at large have been mentioned in order of importance.

It may very well be that adolescent status deprivation must become a permanent and inevitable feature of our culture because of the complexity of modern civilization which demands an extended period of education and vocational apprenticeship. To the extent that this is inevitable, we must become reconciled to the fact that adolescents can at best enjoy a marginal status derived largely from their own peer group. This peer group as the major status-giving institution of adolescence must, therefore, be regarded as one of the most important influences facilitating ego maturation in our culture. Accordingly, society has a stake in the structural organization and values of the peer culture—since the type of ego support and the quality of training it can offer adolescents in the playing of mature, responsible roles is largely dependent upon its independence and the constructiveness of its goals.

From the standpoint of individual ego maturation, it also behooves society to urge upon every adolescent as satisfactory an adjustment as possible to the demands of the peer group. The deviant "who is ostracized for so many years from the company of his fellows" can hardly be expected to emerge from his isolation without some maturational defects. He has incurred a deficit in social learning during a crucial period in ego development which may be all but impossible to rectify no matter how propitious for personality maturation his future social climate may henceforth become.

Acceptance of the crucial role of the peer culture for ego maturation, however, does not necessarily imply that no other means of reducing adolescent status deprivation are either available or possible. Cultural complexity alone cannot be blamed for the economic situation which has resulted in "an almost complete removal of opportunity for adolescent work experience . . . Undoubtedly the greatest single factor responsible for prolonging adolescence in our society is [this] unique vocational situation confronting modern generations of adolescents. In this respect they are probably grappling with a uniquely new problem in the cultural history of the race" [*23*]. But these growing pains presently characterizing our economy of abundance need not last forever; "we need not resign ourselves passively to the immutability of this social situation insofar as it affects adolescents" [*23*].

> "It is possible for society to *create* conditions under which adolescents can achieve a large measure of status, responsibility, and importance in community projects and organization. In our own times, we have seen the establishment of such projects as the National Youth Administration and the C.C.C. camps. We have also seen what youth has been able to accomplish for the war effort. There is no reason why adolescents cannot be assigned definite responsibilities in relation to community welfare projects and receive commensurate rewards and recognition. The Veterans Administration is presently revolutionizing the social basis of late adolescence. By subsidizing education and vocational training, it is accelerating the achievement of adult status by making possible early marriage and emancipation from parental economic support. Sooner or later, society will realize that the economic investment in such projects is trifling compared to the potential return in making constructive use of youthful energies, in facilitating adult maturation, and in reducing the harmful effects of emotional instability.
>
> "At the same time that the transitional period is being shortened and given more definite intermediate status, adolescents must also be given greater assurance of eventually attaining adult status. As Allison Davis states, 'In order . . . to make low-status children anxious to work hard, study hard, save their money, and accept stricter sex *mores,* our society must convince them of the *reality* of the *rewards* at the end of the anxiety-laden climb. . . . Our society cannot hope, therefore, to educate the greater mass of lower-class people in any really effective way until it has *real* rewards to offer them for learning the necessary anxiety'" [*23*].

Vocational success in our culture is central to the attainment of all other indices of extrinsic status defining the adult personality.

"On it depend the possibilities for complete emancipation, for economic independence, and for emotional, social and psychosexual maturation. Many of the anxieties of adolescents and young adults would disappear entirely or be considerably alleviated if they could achieve the proper type of job placement. Hence, in the more usual type of adolescent maladjustment, the psychotherapeutic possibilities inherent in vocational guidance greatly exceed those present in extended exploration of conflictful, emotional material. Only too frequently does the latter goal become the main preoccupation of the psychotherapeutic session, while the immediate urgency for vocational adaptation is de-emphasized so effectively that by implication it is regarded as almost irrelevant to the patient's psychological disturbance. It is hardly surprising then that, if in the course of extensive psychotherapy, substantial progress toward vocational adjustment is not simultaneously made (rather than postponed to await the solution of emotional conflicts) all the potential benefits of ventilation, catharsis, insight, and transference might be largely nullified by the patient's failure to possess the one practical instrument he needs to effect his maturation. And thus after completing several years of the treatment on which he had pinned his highest hopes, he emerges, more crushed and forlorn than before; because not only does he still have his original emotional conflicts, but also he is now several years older, still a child in his father's house, and the prospect of vocational adaptation still but a vague and intangible dream.

"It is the counselor's constant duty to emphasize and to have the adolescent accept the imperative need for vocational adjustment as the core problem of adult maturation. Without this prior acceptance, all specific suggestions are in vain. And in the event that an unsatisfying compromise must be accepted, it should be pointed out that vocational stabilization at any level of aspiration, if tangible and realistic, is preferable by far to grandiose but vaguer expectations, or to a complete absence of any adjustment. This proposition is not as self-evident as it seems, since the number of individuals with hypertrophied ego demands is legion, who, on being denied their whole-loaf ambitions, seem to prefer no loaf at all to taking many possible and proffered varieties of half-loaf solutions.

"The first task of vocational guidance, therefore, is to help establish and clarify goals. In doing this, the counselor has at his disposal various vocational interest tests. He also has to divorce vocational interest from parental desires and from glamorized notions of job duties and job prestige. But even more important is the need to reconcile and harmonize interests with objective aptitudes and with reasonable expectations of job placement. In view of the persistent trend towards reduced social mobility, a general devaluation of vocational ambitions would seem to be indicated" [*23*].

Although the modern home has less extrinsic status to offer the adolescent, it has generally proven more flexible than other social institutions in providing recognition of changing biosocial needs during adolescence. Nevertheless there is room for considerable improvement in enhancing opportunities for acquiring extrinsic status, in encouraging the child's early strivings for same by showing appropriate appreciation of his efforts, in reducing the gap between demands made on the adolescent and privileges granted him, and in according greater recognition of his needs for independence and respect.

> "The bitterest complaints which adolescents have to offer about their parents have reference to the essential lack of respect and dignity that the latter show for them. It is very humiliating for one aspiring to be an adult to be castigated like a child, to be nagged, yelled, and shouted at [*407*]. But even worse are the scorn, the ridicule, and the condescending attitude that greet physical awkwardness, faltering or confused articulation of political views, and clumsy efforts at heterosexual expression. Even if he cares little about everything else, every adolescent—just because he is first aspiring to adult status—cherishes an ideal about the essential dignity of a human being, which, if respected, would leave him decidedly less provocative and resistive to guidance. Zachry [*407*] suggests that giving the adolescent a place at the family councils would be a most constructive way both of showing respect for his developing adulthood and of adding dignity to his precarious status" [*23*].

FACTORS RETARDING MATURATION

Factors Impeding Desatellization

To a large extent these factors have already been considered in describing the conditions which are unfavorable for desatellization (see pp. 184-191). Hence only those influences need further discussion which have not already been indicated as failing to facilitate the maturational process.

The most serious factor retarding desatellization is parental ambivalence regarding adolescent emancipation. In response to cues supplied by the child's physical maturation and to pressures generated by changed social expectations, parents "wish for the independence and self-sufficiency of the child" [*278*]. On the other hand, "they fear the loss of love that removal of his dependency creates" [*278*]. They have a vested interest to protect—the satisfactions, the ego supports, the feelings of power and importance that go with having another individual dependent upon them for guidance and direction. "Emancipation requires much sacrifice by parents. They must relinquish authority" [*278*], and "learn the patience and restraint required to develop the capacity for self-direction in the child" [*23*]. This is naturally a much more difficult task for parents who are exploiting the dependent aspects of the child's attachment for them as a substitute source of status and affection in instances of vocational or marital maladjustment [*278*].

Even where parents earnestly wish to surrender the reins of control, obstacles of which they are only dimly aware often enter the picture. Children are biological and social rivals of their parents. The loss of vigor, youth, beauty, sexual prowess and vocational motivation seem ever so much more threatening when viewed in daily apposition to the boundless freshness and energy that characterize adolescents. There is an unconscious resentment which persons on the declining slope of life's curve bear toward those who are on the ascending limb; it reflects the dread of being displaced and is directed toward postponing as long as possible the day when this eventuality might conceivably occur.

But even when underlying attitudes and motivations are properly reoriented the resulting behavior may reveal unmistakable evidences of inertia. From sheer force of habit many behaviors acquire a semi-autonomous status which outlasts their supporting attitudes. Extinction, therefore, must operate on the consummatory as well as on the preparatory plane of response determination; hence, it may not infrequently take longer to establish a new pattern of behavioral responses in interpersonal relations than to acquire a new set of appropriate attitudes. And even when both aspects of change are successfully accomplished by parents, there is a perceptual lag in appreciating these changed behaviors on the part of children. Parents are perceived the same way long after their actual roles have shifted, simply because of the rigidity of perceptual expectations which force new perceptions into preconceived molds regardless of their empirical content. Thus, instead of cooperating with and being stimulated by parental expectations of greater maturity, an adolescent often rebels against his own misperceptions and withdraws from parents "for no other reason than the fact that they always are the ones to whom he has always been a helpless child. He fears to step back into the pattern of dependence . . . and thus withdraws from all adults whom he believes will not understand, and will fail to accept him for what he longs to become instead of what he feels he is" [*407*].

It is no wonder then that this parental ambivalence and inertia about reorienting attitudes and behavior toward their adolescent children results in curious inconsistencies. "Thus at one moment parents may express alarm at the rapidity with which the child is drifting away from them, and at the next moment seek to impress him with the urgency of standing on his own two feet" [*23*].

Considerable difference also exists in the relative disposition of parents to accept the emancipation claims of sons and daughters respectively. Just as girls are expected to satellize more than boys, they are expected to desatellize less. At the termination of adolescence, parents do not contemplate that their daughters will have severed the ties of dependency. Instead of showing a willingness to compromise with the latter's emancipation needs by partially relaxing control and supervision (as in the case of boys), they frequently react to the perceived threat of independence by attempting to establish a more rigorous form of discipline than was practiced during preadolescence. This parental attitude is reflective of the more sheltered vocational and sexual position accorded women in our culture. But there are indications that this cultural position has changed more radically in recent years than the supporting attitudes which it supposedly justifies. The net outcome of this attitudinal lag on the part of parents is to prolong the course of desatellization longer than would otherwise follow from the actual social roles played by modern generations of women.

"Ambivalence with respect to desatellization is also not restricted to parents. "The child's desire for emancipation is not 'unmixed with a need for continued protection and security.' He is somewhat apprehensive about his new, less dependent status and not infrequently wishes that he could somehow avoid the entire unpleasant business of growing up" [*23*]. Sometimes it appears to him that it would be so much less traumatic and anxiety-producing could he conceivably retain the derived status guaranteed by his former dependent relationship to parents rather than establish himself as an adult person in his own right.

Unfortunately, sufficient ambiguity prevails regarding the biosocial role considered appropriate for adolescents, and the period of transition is sufficiently prolonged to support frequent excursions into the realm of irreality. If the issue is so unclear and its decision interminably delayed, the fanciful goal of indefinite dependence does not seem so preposterous and incredible after all. Quite the contrary, under certain conditions it looms as a most plausible and respectable alternative which is inviting enough to merit serious consideration. The choice of dependency also avoids the disapprobation frequently dispensed for non-conformity to parental values, and the feelings of guilt which follow when affiliation with the values of others implies renunciation of primary loyalties to parents.

Personality variables related to temperament can also retard the course of maturation. The greater the child's need for comfort and visceral satisfactions the more difficult it is for him to renounce immediate hedonistic gratifications in favor of long-range goals. Self-assertion comes painfully if his habits are sedentary, if he dislikes vigorous activity, if he is timid and mild in interpersonal relations, if he shuns direct participation in social events, if his habitual adjustive techniques favor withdrawal and escape rather than attack or defense in the face of personal conflict. "Thickness of skin" now attains new significance as a personality variable, especially in determining the outcome of introversion-extraversion. As the importance of the home declines, its influence in either direction becomes minimal—either as a supportive medium favoring direct participation in experience (extraversion), or as a threatening, inimical medium predisposing toward indirect verbal contact with reality (introversion). Exposed at adolescence to the vicissitudes of the wider social arena (which operates without the prepotent intervention of either supportive or threatening home influences), his disposition to participate directly in reality largely becomes a function of how well he can withstand "the onslaughts of fortune" without recoil. The childhood tendency toward introversion or extraversion is thus forced to find a new level commensurate with the individual adolescent's "thickness of skin." The tender-skinned pseudo-extravert from a benevolent home may now find increased introversion more palatable; while the relatively thick-skinned pseudo-introverted child from a threatening home may surprise everyone at adolescence by his extraverted proclivities when given a chance to function in a more neutral environment with respect to the major source of status.

Serious discrepancies in rate of growth between various aspects of the maturational process also impede the progress of maturation.

> "In any developmental process involving several component lines of growth, discrepancies in rate of growth are inevitable. The reasons for this are self-evident. In nature, the characteristics of any growth process are uniquely determined by the special conditions relevant to its development. Thus, there is no precedent for anticipating that the physiological, physical, emotional, or social aspects of growth should proceed along parallel lines. One can only anticipate that this 'unevenness of the adolescent's development will add to his difficulties'" [*23*].

Physiological growth, for example, is mainly regulated by genetic factors which adhere quite closely to a phylogenetic pattern that has been much less influenced by recent cultural conditions than has emotional and social growth. Regardless of cultural vicissitudes in amount and quality of stimulation or expectation, there are regular changes in hormonal activity which are dependent upon such relatively constant factors as phylogenetic and individual inheritance, climate and diet. "One might also "reasonably expect physiological growth in adolescence to precede emotional and social growth since (a) the emotional changes are largely dependent upon the alteration of internal body environment; and (b) social development usually begins in response to cues supplied by physical growth" [23].

Thus, depending upon the operation of relevant genetic and environmental variables, growth in any particular area tends to proceed according to its own timetable. But the functional expression of this growth in terms of appropriate behavior is vitally affected by the nature of all other related variables.

> "Since in any particular segment of behavior the adolescent can only function as a total personality, the attainment of adult status must be postponed until *all* of the major lines of growth are completed. Thus, the first consequence of any growth discrepancy is that earlier-maturing functions, which if considered solely in terms of their own degree of maturity would be ready for earlier use, must still await the maturation of other functions before they can be effectively or fully employed; e.g., the adolescent's greater muscle mass can be fully utilized only after neuromuscular patterns of co-ordination are set up. Where new functions are associated with powerful drives, e.g., those related to sex, such postponement of function may give rise to serious frustrations and maladjustments. Complete sexual gratification demands more than physiological maturity. Also required are the emotional development and the social and economic independence that go with a total adult personality. Furthermore, not only is the effective operation of earlier-maturing functions impeded by delay in the maturation of related functions, but the former's rate of growth is also retarded. The unnatural prolongation of sub-adulthood in our society, for example, postpones complete emancipation from the home and full psychosexual development much longer than is observable in most other cultures" [*23*].

Thus, whichever alternative is chosen, serious difficulties are inevitable. Premature exercise of a relatively mature component in an immature personality yields unsatisfactory results when evaluated from either an individual or social standpoint. But if these adverse consequences are not too serious, the individual benefits from the active learning experience involved. On the other hand, postponement of function until maturity supervenes avoids the pitfalls of premature expression, but leads to tensions provoked by unmet needs and to developmental retardation for want of sufficient role-playing experience.

Status Deprivation Factors

Although it is generally appreciated that socio-economic factors are largely responsible for prolonging the course of adolescent development it is usually taken to be self-evident that these very same factors somehow manage concurrently to retard the rate of emotional and social maturation. Actually this is a rather evasive formulation since it does not explain the "precise nature of the mechanism whereby socio-economic conditions necessitating a prolongation of the transitional period of sub-adulthood become *translated* into an actual process of retardation in the sphere of psychological development. This relationship between social status on the one hand and inner ego valuation on the other hand is a fundamental problem of ego psychology" [*23*].

The intervening variables responsible for this process of translation—the level of social expectations regarding rate of maturation and the availability of mature role-playing experience—have already been mentioned. Both factors are primarily determined by prevailing socio-economic conditions. Depending on the current need for adolescent manpower, society keeps shifting its view about the optimal rate of adolescent development it regards as desirable. Logic, humanitarianism, and pedagogical philosophy have little to do with these shifts, although they do serve as institutionalized rationalizations for them and sometimes receive formal recognition in the guise of minimal schooling laws. The only essential factor involved, however, is the state of the job market—the adequacy of the supply of adult workers to meet the demand for labor, and the economic contingencies on which this depends, *i.e.*, prosperity, depression and war. Thus during times of economic depression, when all job possibilities for youth have completely evaporated, society is only too willing to promulgate the "enlightened" educational philosophy that a broad academic background is desirable for all young people "regardless of future vocation or field of specialization." But that this policy is largely a rationalized time-filler for an adolescence unnaturally prolonged by economic failure became obvious enough during World War II "when the sudden manpower shortage . . . resulted in a relaxation of the minimal schooling laws which had heretofor been uncompromisingly defended as inviolable guardians of our culture" [*23*].

The conclusion is, thus, inescapable (no matter how reluctant we are to acknowledge it) that the social expectations regarding rate of adolescent maturation are largely a reflection of the economic opportunities which society has to offer adolescents. This relationship is never a one-to-one affair, since a certain minimal level of status change is anticipated on the basis of pubescence alone, and a certain amount of time lag is inevitable between the onset of changed economic conditions and the evolution of new social attitudes. Nevertheless the correspondence is quite close; and in the more usual type of economic situation in our culture, conditions are such that little sense of social urgency is felt regarding the rapidity of maturation. Thus, although the adolescent may desire to gain status more rapidly than he is allowed to, he feels no pressure to do so—at least from the adult segment of society. The prevailing social "sets" and expectations relating to the maturational process constitute his chief frame of reference in regulating the tempo of his development. Having no other experiential criterion to rely upon, he is forced to base his aspirational level on a social norm which lays claim to widespread and virtually unchallenged acceptance.

> "In other words, his level of aspiration with respect to the proper rate of maturation generally corresponds to the relative urgency with which society regards the problem. Most adolescents would believe any other course to be virtually impossible, since like children, they tend to believe that prevailing social arrangements are absolutely given and hence immutable" [*23*].

However, level of aspiration regarding speed of maturation is itself only an intermediate variable, although admittedly closer to the psychological process of development that a socio-economic condition. "The more direct determinant of the rate of this growth process is the actual experience gained in the enactment of mature roles. One attains adult maturity by living the life of an adult" [*23*]. Hence, the retarding effect of drastically reduced aspirational levels on the rate of maturation is actually produced by making the adolescent disinclined to seek out or create mature role-playing experiences propitious for personality development.

But the availability of appropriate economic opportunities influences the rate of adolescent maturation even more directly than by merely determining in turn social expectations, level of aspiration and inclination to seek needed experience. It also provides a range within which individual differences in motivation can operate more or less effectively in modifying levels of aspiration based upon social norms (which already reflect the impact of this same economic factor). These social norms do provide a *general* frame of reference for pegging aspirations; but only in extreme cases is the influence of personality variables completely negated in the shaping of a given individual's aspiration level. Hence, if the availability of appropriate role-playing experience is only moderately curtailed, it still falls within the reach of a relatively large number of adolescents highly motivated from within (if not by social pressures) to undergo speedy maturation; whereas if access to the experience is virtually impossible, no amount of individual motivation can affect the final outcome very much.

Maturation during adolescence is also retarded by the abruptness with which the assimilation of adult, status-giving values must take place.

> "The complete separation of the value and interest systems of child and adult in our culture makes for still another type of discontinuity adding to the difficulty of adolescence. Our children—unlike those in many primitive societies—are given no responsibilities in the work-a-day world of adult concern, and, hence, evolve a discrete set of prestige-giving values of their own. At adolescence, therefore, when identification with adult values becomes necessary, there is no continuity in goal seeking. The values and status of the child world must be scrapped in entirety, and the struggle for social recognition begun again from anew. But this is not all. The adolescent, rejected by the adult world he seeks to enter, must temporarily hold in abeyance and even reject these new value-identifications for those revered in the adolescent peer society. Here he starts once more at the bottom rung of the ladder; and when, towards the close of adolescence, he reaches the top, he is sent hurtling down to the bottom again as a fledgling adult to start climbing yet another ladder of values" [*23*].

Thus, not only is there a notable absence of previous identification with value systems that suddenly become important at adolescence, but also an understandable ambivalence toward them as a result of the unanticipated failure to gain admittance to adult society. A good part of the adolescent's exaggerated quest for independence and apparent contempt for established values can be attributed to his need for rejecting the norms of the adult culture which denies him membership. He responds with the attitude that what he cannot have is not worth having in the first place. To show just how little he cares about the adult world and his exclusion from it, he joins a peer subculture which strives to make itself as recognizably distinct and separate from adult society as possible; and as a further expression of his hostility, he "takes provocative delight in fashioning norms of behavior which are shocking to adult sensibilities" [*23*]. But the ambivalence of his feelings can be seen in the very fact that he often tries to fulfill the above aims by "the deliberately premature advocacy of certain external prerogatives of adulthood such as late hours, smoking, automobiles, fur coats, make-up, drinking, etc. If adults were *really* beneath his contempt, would he strive so hard to imitate and, distort their behavior even if the object of his imitation were to express aggression and to arouse anger and grief?

Now that links have been found to bridge the gap between socioeconomic factors and rate of maturation, we are better able to wrestle with the relationship between social status and sense of ego adequacy (self-esteem) during adolescence. In satellizers, it seems probable that the inner core of intrinsic ego adequacy derived from a satisfactory satellizing relationship to parents remains fairly intact regardless of external vicissitudes. It provides ballast and stability to personality structure especially in the early years of adolescence when childhood status is precipitately removed and adult status denied, and when the intermediate status eventually forthcoming in the peer culture is still unavailable for want of adequate structure. This is a *background* function which operates despite the fact that it does not enter the conscious field of factors perceived as influencing the individual's current status.

"What does change, however, with fluctuations in external social status is the [adolescent's] corresponding extrinsic image of his ego adequacy" [*23*]. As already indicated, the important variables affecting the latter are (1) discrepancy between level of aspiration and actual status attained, and (2) the absolute magnitude of the aspirational level itself. Thus, by reference to the first criterion, a loss of self-esteem is registered by exchanging the stable, established and relatively successful role of dependent child for the insecure, frustration-laden role of pseudo-independent sub-adult. Since "in our society, the adolescent has a very marginal social status, his extrinsic ego adequacy—which is largely a reflection of the former—is correspondingly marginal" [*23*]. Because society considers him immature and grants him little extrinsic status despite his needs and aspirations for same, chronic frustration is inevitable. Whether or not social status is achieved depends upon a social verdict which the individual is more or less obliged to accept. The subjective feeling of success or failure (extrinsic ego adequacy) is then elicited by relating this verdict to level of aspiration.

But in satellizers, this loss of extrinsic ego adequacy is mitigated by possession of a basic core of intrinsic self-acceptance and by the increased self-esteem derived from closer proximity and merely aspiring to the exalted status of adulthood. In the case of non-satellizers—who are deficient in intrinsic ego adequacy—the only possible changes are in the sphere of extrinsic self-esteem. In general, these shifts are in the positive direction for the rejected group and in the negative direction for the overvalued group (since any outside environment is apt to be more benevolent than the home in the first case, while no environment could possibly be more ego-inflating than the home in the second case). In both instances, however, adolescence as a period of marginal and insecure status provides more ego trauma and damage to self-esteem than in the case of satellizers; for not only do higher aspirational levels guarantee more frustration, but also, the buffering undercoating of intrinsic self-acceptance is absent.

Social Class Differences in Status Deprivation

In the preceding section the availability of status-giving activities and the types of social expectations relative to adolescent maturation were discussed as if there were "a uniform social environment determining in the same way the growth possibilities of the transitional period for all adolescents" [*23*]. It seems rather that "the conditions under which persons have access to fundamental biological and social goals are defined by a system of privilege . . . a system of socially ranked groups with varying degrees of social movement existing between them" [*74*].

Allison Davis points to three great systems of social rank in the

United States based on socio-economic, ethnic, and color considerations and shows that

> "such status differentiations as these have the effect of defining and limiting the developmental environment of the child . . . Within each of these participation levels with their cultural environments, a child learns characteristic behavior and values concerning family members, sexual and aggressive acts, work, education and a career . . . These restricted learning environments are maintained by powerful and firmly established taboos upon participation outside of one's status level . . . [by pressures] exerted not only by those above . . . but also by persons below . . . and by those in one's particular class" [*74*].

It would not be unreasonable, therefore, to expect marked differences between classes in availability of status-giving activities and in social pressure to seek same.

> "Economic necessity may force emancipation relatively early on a working-class adolescent; on the other hand, wealth and education may prolong the period of dependency in an upper-class youth. Yet, while the former may have to seek economic independence earlier, he is in no way sure of attaining his goal; whereas the latter knows that, even if delayed longer, assured economic status will eventually be his. The position of the middle-class youth is somewhere in between; success is not assured in advance. He has to fight and struggle for it; but the greater chances of succeeding give him more incentive to strive than his lower-class contemporary. He is, thus, more highly motivated, and his behavior is more persistently oriented towards the goal of achievement than that of either of the status levels directly above and below him. In addition, each class must bear its characteristic time sequence and total load of status deprivation. Total load varies inversely with height of class standing; whereas the order in which periods of low and high load tend to follow each other is more likely to be in ascending order for the lower group and in descending order for the higher group" [*23*].

How differential social class expectations become translated into appropriately different levels of aspiration and motivation in individual adolescent members of the various social classes has been ingeniously explained by Allison Davis. This explanation also helps to further bridge the psychological gap between social expectation and level of aspiration which still remains one of the knottiest problems in the theory of maturation. In the preceding section the influence of the former on the latter was ascribed to the force of prestige or authority suggestion in an unstructured field. Davis reinforces this explanation with a motivational factor which is probably a necessary social ingredient of maturation in every culture. That is, society tends to insure the fact that adequate maturational progress is maintained by cultivating a certain amount of anxiety in the adolescent relative to the attainment of appropriate developmental goals. The tangible threat which makes this anxiety an effective motivation is the possibility of losing the status advantages otherwise accruing from successful maturation.

> "This *socialized* anxiety plays a major part in propelling him along that cultural route prescribed by his family, school, and later by adult society at his cultural level . . . [It] is derived from a long and complex series of training situations in which punishment has been invoked . . . The anxiety which middle-status people learn is effective first because it involves the threat of loss of present status [and the severe social penalties associated therewith], and second, because it leads as the individual may plainly see in 'successful persons' to the rewards of power, of social prestige, and of security for one's children" [*74*].

Anxiety is motivationally efficacious since it can only be relieved in a realistic fashion by activities directed toward the achievement of goals the threatened loss of which give rise to it in the first place. During adolescence, the status for which the adolescent is actually striving and the threat to its attainment are real enough to provoke anxiety motivation. This is perfectly apparent from a long-range point of view, but a problem of communication arises on a day-to-day basis. If adolescents are so unaccepting of adult values and authority in their daily activities and attitudes, "from whence comes the authority which is derived from threat and fear of punishment" to keep their *immediate* behavior and motivations in conformity with class standards? For "no matter how serious the youthful rebellion and restlessness may be, adult-youth conflict will in most cases be an intra-family and intracommunity affair . . . An adolescent boy was strongly and at times openly critical of everything his parent did. Nevertheless he shared the major class delineations, political views, and social-distance norms of his upper middle-class parents" [*354*]. His need was to reject his elders, and not their class aspirations and standards which he truly accepted. Hence the dilemma which he faced was this: How could he repudiate the immediate authority of his parents and still retain their social class values when such retention demanded subordination of self to this authority or its equivalent?

Long-range anxiety is an efficient taskmaster only if it is reinforced by more proximate contact with the pressures and threats which give it substance. If these are removed by virtue of a break in communication and rapport with adult society, another more acceptable source of authority for the enforcement of class norms must be found. The peer society fulfills this function admirably since the adolescent does not feel that liberation from its standards is an essential requirement for emancipation. Quite the contrary, conformity to peer standards is one of his most cherished values. He can, therefore, assign with equanimity to his peer group the proximate power to enforce class aspirations without relinquishing the rebelliousness he deems essential for his development. "And with the power of social ostracism at its disposal it sees to it that the values, associations, aspirations, and behavior patterns of its members adhere closely to the class reference group to which it owes allegiance" [*23*].

MATURATIONAL FAILURE IN SATELLIZERS

Now that the general factors facilitating or retarding maturation have been delineated, it is possible to examine the conditions under which maturational failure occurs. This outcome is the result of interaction between many variables, i.e., various dimensions of the parent-child relationship, the sex and personality of the child, social expectations relative to maturation, social opportunities for assuming mature roles, and a previous history of satellization or non-satellization. This latter factor is responsible for sufficient difference in course and prognosis of maturation to make worthwhile seperate treatment of maturational failure in satellizers and non-satellizers. Of the remaining factors, the parent-child relationship seems to be most crucial and differential in determining final outcome and will, therefore, receive major attention. Social factors have a general significance which is uniform (in terms of stimulus value) for all members of a given subculture, and hence are not apt to produce differential effects. Individual personality differences modify the impact of both parental attitudes and social factors but are too numerous and varied to categorize conveniently.

Therefore, although the following discussion of maturational failure will be organized around different aspects of the parent-child relationship, clinical prediction of individual outcomes cannot overlook either the social milieu in which this relationship takes place or the individual personality peculiarities of the principal participants. It should also be borne in mind that failure is both the terminal phase of a progressive developmental condition, and a relatively rare extreme form of a phenomenon which in varying degrees of lesser severity is a quite common occurrence.

To facilitate the examination of how different types of deviant parent-child relationships may predispose toward maturational failure, the chief ego development tasks of adolescence will first be recapitulated in Table 1.

TABLE 1.—*Ego Maturation Tasks During Adolescence*

I. The Acquisition of Greater Volitional Independence
  A. Primary Attributes
    1. Independent planning of goals and reaching of decisions.
    2. Greater use of the exploratory orientation in value assimilation.
    3. Greater reliance on non-parental sources of ego support.
  B. Secondary Attributes
    1. Aspiring to more realistic goals and roles.
    2. Increased frustration tolerance.
    3. Emergence of a balanced self-critical faculty.
    4. Abandonment of special claims on others' indulgence.

II. Reorganization of Goal Structure on a Less Devalued Basis
    1. Greater need for obtaining primary status.
    2. Increased level of ego aspirations.
    3. Increased self-estimate.

III. Replacement of Hedonistic Motivation by Long-Range Status Goals
IV. Acquisition of Increased Executive Independence
V. Acquisition of Moral Responsibility on a Societal Basis

Maturational Defects in the Overprotected Child

The overprotected child is the object of excessive parental solicitude. He may or may not be over- or under-dominated, since parental domination represents an entirely seperate dimension of the parent-child relationship. Unfortunately, however, following the lead of David Levy, the extremes of the latter aspect of parental behavior have usually been classified as inevitable subtypes of overprotection. Although such combinations are not infrequently encountered, they are by no means inevitable. Many overprotecting parents are able to maintain a proper balance of domination despite their compulsive needs for providing a completely sheltered environment for their offspring.

The dimension of parental solicitude includes overt expressions of affection and manifestations of concern for the child's health, safety and happiness. In cases of oversolicitude, these manifestations of affection and concern are unnaturally prolonged beyond the years when a child's helplessness makes them necessary for survival. The parent makes an effort to provide for his child an environment which is free of any type of hurt, disappointment, frustration or painful contact with the harsher realities of life. This goal is achieved by isolating him from all experiences which could possibly result in such consequences, preventing contact with persons who do not share his benevolent attitude to the same degree, providing a host of precautions and protective devices (including an excessive amount of personal contact and supervision), and refusing to allow him to plan or do things for himself for fear that injury or failure might result. Calculated risks that most parents regard as necessary for normal development are compulsively avoided. The child's growing capacity for greater independence, self-reliance, and self-direction in more complex situations is stubbornly ignored as the protective atmosphere of the nursery is extended indefinitely.

In most cases, this overprotective attitude is a form of projected anxiety.[6] The parent is anxious, insecure, fearful of impending disaster, and feels inadequate to cope with the ordinary adjustive problems of life. By projecting this anxiety onto his child he is able to mitigate his own anxiety in two ways: (1) Some of the perceived threat to himself is deflected, thereby making the environment seem less foreboding, and (2) he is better able to cope with the threats confronting the child than those besetting himself. He can isolate the former from painful experiences by using himself as a shield, since the frustrations facing a child are relatively concrete and avoidable; whereas he cannot insulate himself from the world and still maintain his own intense strivings. But the success he enjoys in protecting his child from danger and frustration is transferable to his own situation. By erecting an impregnable protective wall around a projected image of himself, he fancies himself immune from the sinister forces menacing his own security.

This mechanism is very similar to the conversion of anxiety into a phobia: An overwhelming threat stemming from a feeling of personal inadequacy is displaced onto an innocuous concrete cause of fear which can be readily handled by the technique of avoidance. The projection of anxiety, however, carries this maneuver a step further. Not only is the threat displaced, but also the person at whom it is directed, thereby achieving some immediate anxiety reduction by the simple device of disowning the fact that one is the real target. But for further vicarious anxiety reduction to occur from successful handling of the threat, some degree of identification with the displaced target is necessary. This is usually accomplished by identifying with an individual who can qualify as a projected mirror-image of self, e.g., one's child.

During the early period of infancy and childhood, the main effect of overprotection is to delay the appearance of satellization. Since the child is accepted and valued for his own sake, he eventually does succeed in satellizing; but since the parent tends to defer to the child's volitional omnipotence in order to avoid frustrating him, the devaluation crisis tends to be postponed. He (the child) is able to indulge his executive dependence, hedonistic impulses and irresponsibility for a longer period of time than would otherwise be possible.

The basis of this deference to the child's will is not the absence of parental self-assertiveness (although this factor might enter the picture if the parent is simultaneously underdominating), but excessive concern about the dangers of frustrating him. However, as the child becomes older, more motile, manipulative, and desirous of social activity outside the home, parental anxiety about frustrating his will becomes matched by even greater concern over the implications of this freedom for health, safety, and the possibility of failure in motor and social performance; and the urgency of forestalling the latter eventuality enjoys higher priority in terms of potential anxiety reduction. Hence, the subsequent steps which the parent takes to curb his child's range of experience are reflective of anxiety rather than of undue self-assertiveness.

From the foregoing it is clear that behavior based at either extreme along the dimension of parental domination makes it difficult for the expression of a consistently overprotective attitude. Overdomination facilitates the restriction of anxiety-producing experience, but conflicts with the overprotective tendency to avoid frustrating the child's will when issues of health, safety, and social frustration are not involved. Underdomination makes it easier for the overprotective parent to defer to the child's desires in non-anxiety situations, but makes it difficult for the latter to exercise the required firmness and self-assertion needed in limiting the child's experiences to situations which are thoroughly innocuous.

After satellization takes place, therefore, the overprotected child who accepts these restrictions which are placed upon him, fails to shed his dependency and acquire volitional independence. His experience is too limited to learn the skills required for self-direction. In facing new adjustive situations he is passive, overcautious and completely at a loss as to how to proceed next. He wants to be directed and helped in every operation. The exploratory orientation is too venturesome for him, and apart from his parents he has no adequate source of ego support.

Whatever volitional independence can develop from this parent-child relationship is also of inferior quality. Excessive parental restrictions prevent him from aspiring to overly assertive, aggressive or socially-frowned-upon roles or goals; but his isolation from the experiences and contacts usual for his age group also prevents him from learning the roles he is customarily expected to assume, and leads to a lack of realism in his expectations which is just as serious at the opposite extreme. He cannot play with his peers in a "natural give-and-take manner," but expects special consideration and protection from them as he does from parents, teachers and strangers. Having no experience in solving his own problems successfully, his goal frustration tolerance does not increase with age. He is ready to give up after the slightest setback.

But contrary to generally expressed opinion, anxiety and feelings of insecurity are not prominent in such individuals.[7] They are not "beset by feelings of inferiority, inefficiency and inadequacy" as one might reasonably imagine [*20*]. Actually the manifest inadequacy of their performances and adjustive efforts does not leave them with a sense of frustration. For feelings of failure to ensue, it is necessary that some realistic appreciation and acknowledgement of the inadequacy of a given performance be made. However, thanks to a self-protective inhibition of the self-critical faculty they usually feel eminently adequate and competent to manipulate their environment. This in addition to their intrinsic feelings of adequacy residual from satellization leaves little room for anxiety. As a consequence of this inability to recognize inadequacy of performance and to be supremely satisfied with it, no constructive attempts at modification or improvement can be initiated, providing yet another reason why acquisition of volitional independence in the mature adult sense of the term is virtually impossible.

The only type of volitional independence in the child which the overprotective parent looks upon with favor is that which increases his infantile dependency. The more dependent he becomes, the easier it is to keep him out of harm's way. For this reason, and also to avoid what he regards as unnecessary frustration (i.e., frustration which does not serve the purpose of reducing parental anxiety) the parent does not generally oppose manifestations of self-assertion in the child which are directed toward immediate hedonistic gratification or toward perpetuating executive dependence. In the latter case, there is the added incentive of preventing the possible frustration that might ensue if independent attempts to implement decisions proved unsuccessful. With such deliberate encouragement of executive dependence, the child has little incentive to seek the experience and learn the necessary skills that would make him independent in this repect. Similarly, in an atmosphere of benevolent tolerance for his hedonistic motivational orientation, and in the absence of strong parental pressures urging him to plan in terms of long-range adult goals, it is no wonder that the former goal structure is not replaced by the latter.

Confined so drastically to the social experience provided by the parent-child relationship, concepts of moral responsibility tend to remain relatively specific, concrete and limited to the ramifications of this relationship. What is learned and uncritically accepted as having moral value in a particular context associated with parental approval or disapproval stays at the same level of generality instead of yielding to more abstract principles of logic and ethics. The child (now adolescent and soon adult) still conceives of himself as morally responsible only to parents or parent surrogates, and fails to acquire the concept that he is accountable to the moral authority of the society in which he lives.

The most serious consequence of parental overprotection is its inhibitory effect on the reorganization of goal structure. Implicit in the parent's attitude is the reassurance that the child's derived status will be indefinitely available. The possibility that the latter might have to forge his own way in a hostile world and establish his own status through his own competence is a terrifying prospect which the parent strives at all costs to prevent. He is determined that his child will not suffer the fate that befell him. He tries not only to guarantee that lack of intrinsic status (which is at the root of his own anxiety) will never plague his child, but also attempts—by eliminating any need for seeking extrinsic status—to avoid frustration derived from unsuccessful quests for same.

Hence, if the offer of indefinite, intrinsic (relationship-derived) status is held out to a highly dependent, passive, hedonistically-motivated individual, poorly equipped to exercise either volitional or executive independence, it is not at all surprising that he accepts it in preference to seeking an extrinsic status for which he must struggle unassured in advance of success. It will be remembered that even the child from a normally protecting home—who is much better equipped for the latter task—is ambivalent about abandoning his derived status, and flirts with the idea of preserving it permanently.

Since this shift in aspiration to an extrinsic source of status is not made, the concomitant rise in ego aspiration level that would otherwise accompany it does not occur. There is no need to covet the exalted but hazardous prerogatives of adult personality status, and hence no need for appropriate upward revision of the aspirations directed toward its attainment. For the very same reason—since adult status is not approached—there is no basis for enhancement of self-estimate.

If failure to mature in other aspects of personality organization (e.g., volitional and executive independence, degree of hedonistic motivation) exerts an inhibitory influence on the maturation of goal structure, the reverse is no less true. In fact, one of the primary motives for effecting maturational changes in the former attributes of personality is the necessity for such changes to occur if aspirations for extrinsic status are to be seriously implemented (see pp. 178-179). If the latter goal is not internalized, what need is there to forego the advantages of childhood personality status and undergo the trauma involved in extensive reorganization? Thus, a vicious circle is established: The overly hedonistic child, poorly equipped to seek extrinsic status, is, therefore, undisposed to do so; and because of this indisposition has no need to shed the hedonism which would interfere with its attainment were he otherwise disposed. The resulting perpetuation of this hedonistic orientation is mostly a reflection of amaturation—a consequence of the failure of childhood goals to be replaced by their adult counterparts. Some degree of regression, however, does occur. It is inevitable that a number of trial forays into the field of extrinsic status will be made from time to time; and although true frustration is avoided by refusal to acknowledge inadequacy of performance (due to inhibition of the self-critical faculty), the experience is by no means productive of genuine satisfaction. Under these circumstances, retreat to the more certain childhood source of status certainly partakes of the character of regression.

The Underdominated Child

Many of the consequences of underdomination for ego maturation have already been considered in the discussion of excessive permissiveness (see pp. 184-191). The dimension of parental domination does not deal with aspects of care, affection, or solicitousness previously described as encompassed by the dimension of protection. It is reflective instead of the characteristic ascendence-submission relationship that customarily prevails between parent and child. Unlike overprotection, which can be readily explained as a projection of parental anxiety, underdomination in many cases is simply an outcome of a temperamental disparity in self-assertiveness between parent and offspring which is heavily in favor of the latter. A combination of mild, self-effacing parent and temperamentally aggressive child is not a statistical rarity.

In other cases, of course, the explanation is less simple. An underdominating parent may sometimes be patterning his behavior after his recollections of his own parents' way of dealing with him. Whether such memories are historically accurate or are the product of restrospective distortion is not too important. If, on the other hand, his parents were overdominating to a degree which he deems undesirable, he may make a deliberate effort to veer to the opposite extreme in handling his own children—as a concrete means of expressing disapproval or resentment of the former.

In overvaluing parents, underdomination is generally a projection of parental omnipotence. The parent is vicariously expressing his omnipotent ego aspirations through his child; and in order to avoid frustrating these aspirations, he must see to it that the child's will cannot be defeated, even if it means assuming a deferential role quite alien to his natural inclinations. But where this variety of underdomination is primarily an expression of overvaluation, it leads to non-satellization. Hence, it can be present only in mild degree in parents of satellizing children.

In accordance with David Levy's concept of parental underdomination as a variety of overprotection, most writers have treated it as the form of overprotection practiced by indulgent parents. For example, the following description of "parental overindulgence" by Symonds is practically identical with Levy's classical description of overprotection and with Symonds' own criteria for overprotection (which he describes as a separate attitude in a different chapter):

> "The mother separates herself from all outside interests. She devotes her entire life to her children and is with them from morning until night. At times when the average child is out playing with others, or going to school or amusing himself, the overindulged child is being played with by his mother . . . Such a parent monopolizes the child . . . and does not want him to have companionship with her husband or with other members of the family. She resents the intrusion of other children as playmates, and keeps the child from normal play experience with others. She is frequently jealous of having the child attend school . . . During the child's adolescence . . . the mother seems unable to permit the child to emancipate himself from her protective and watchful care . . . She may continue the practice . . . of having the favored child sleep with her" [*389*].

This equation of the protective with the dominating aspects of parental attitudes is very unfortunate since each relates to clearly different roles and function of parenthood. Only conceptual confusion can result when two discriminably different variables are treated as if they were synonymous in meaning. The confusion is even more regrettable when the entirely different origins and significance of overprotective and underdominating attitudes are considered.

It is true that the two attitudes apparently have an important common denominator—a great reluctance in frustrating the child.

> "The overindulgent mother seems unable to refuse the demands and requests of her child and on every occasion she gives in to his importunities. She gives him money, toys, special privileges, all out of proportion to his needs, to the appropriateness of situation, or to the economic resources of the family" [*389*].

In both cases, there is unusual tolerance for the child's hedonistic motivations and his demands for immediate gratification. But there is this important difference: The underdominating parent is not primarily concerned with shielding his child from the anxiety-laden consequences of frustration. He yields to the latter's will because he himself is excessively submissive, because he feels impelled to enact a parental role which emulates or repudiates his recollection of his own parents' behavior, or (in certain cases) because he is using his child as a vehicle for vicariously gratifying his own omnipotent ego demands in an atmosphere conveniently stripped of the exacting pressures and requirements of reality. In the latter situation, he regresses to that pleasant stage in his ego development when omnipotence could blithely be taken for granted and did not require substantiation in a real world of power, position and performance accomplishments.

The tremendous difference in the significance of the two parental attitudes is also manifested in the extent to which each is consistent in avoiding the frustration of the child's will. Because of the factors mentioned above, and because he is not primarily motivated by the need for anxiety reduction, the underdominating parent can practice almost unvarying consistency in this respect. The overprotecting parent, however, can be yielding only in situations which either increase the child's dependency, or which do not contain threats of illness, injury or failure. In these latter instances, on the other hand, the purposes of anxiety reduction are better served by opposing the child's will and protecting him from the possible dreadful consequences of his independence and courage, than by sparing him the frustration involved in blocking his self assertion. It also requires a firmness and resoluteness in limiting the child's freedom which the indulgent parent is unable to muster.

Regardless of the underlying cause of a parent's tendency to be underdominating, he usually tries to justify it by reference to certain supposedly objective criteria in his philosophy of child-rearing. To admit to the true reason would be productive of too much ego damage. Hence, as pointed out above, he will argue that any type or amount of frustration results in emotional insecurity, failure to acquire independence or self-reliance, and everlasting unhappiness. Until recently, however, these arguments would have won him scant sympathy. But the current vogue of permissiveness has put his child-rearing attitudes in a very favorable light and won him considerable applause. As a result, many parents whose natural inclinations are far removed from permissiveness or indulgence feel obliged to act the part in order to satisfy themselves and impress others that they are modern and psychologically-oriented in their parental practices. In fact, some parents seem to vie with each other for the honor of tolerating without murmur or dissent the most outrageous misbehavior on the part of their offspring.

It becomes necessary, therefore, to distinguish between two varieties of parents who preach permissiveness: (a) Those who are truly indulgent for one or a variety of personality reasons, but feel a need to rationalize their behavior; and (b) those who feel a need to conform to what they regard as the accepted model of parent behavior, but fail nevertheless in the attempt because of the absence of any real emotional convictions in this regard. The latter cannot succeed in convincing their children that they are truly permissive because their actions ultimately belie their verbalisms; but in the process they display sufficient inconsistency to confuse them thoroughly regarding the limits of acceptable behavior.

The underdominated, like the overprotected child tends to satellize late because the devaluation crisis in ego development is delayed by the parents' failure to curb the former's volitional omnipotence and to impose restrictions on his hedonistic goal structure. However, satellization does occur eventually because the child is compelled sooner or later to recognize the impossible situation facing any non-adult who attempts to steer his own course and earn an independent status in adult society; and if acceptance and intrinsic valuation by his parents present the option of acquiring a guaranteed derived status through dependent identification (satellization) with the latter, he is loath to reject it.

The satellizing relationship which results, however, is different from the usual type of dependent attachment formed under more typical ascendence-submission conditions. The child continues to manifest considerable volitional independence within the framework of his role as satellite, and uses this self-assertiveness to retain a good measure of his infantile ego attributes, e.g., executive dependence, hedonism, irresponsibility. Parental approval is forthcoming regardless of whether he surrenders these prerogatives of infancy. Hence, only limited attenuation of these ego traits occurs, creating considerable later difficulty for ego maturation.

The great paradox accounting for maturational failure in underdominated children is a super-abundance of the self-assertive aspects of volitional independence combined with a virtual absence of the personality traits that make implementation of this independence possible. The submissiveness of his parents gives him ample opportunity for practising self-direction. He is not hampered in forming strong attachments to persons other than parents, and is relatively free to pursue the exploratory orientation in value assimilation.

But because he has had such little direct experience with the limiting and restrictive features of reality, he is unable to take these factors into account in choosing roles, in setting goals, and in making demands on others which do not exceed the latter's limits of tolerance. His behavior, therefore, is typically out-of-bounds since he has never learned the limits of acceptable conduct. In his relations with other children and adults, he is aggressive, petulant and capricious. He will not defer to the judgment or interests of others, always demanding his own way upon threat of unleashing unrestrained fits of temper. Infantile techniques of aggression are employed long after the majority of neighborhood children have already abandoned them.

A very unfortunate consequence of this aspect of parental underdomination, as both Levy [*247*] and Cameron [*61*] have emphasized, is that the bullying, domineering and importunate behavior learned in relation to parents is carried over into relationships with peers and other adults. "The child whose mother has greatly indulged him, and trained him by her submission to expect submission from others, is rudely shocked and repelled by the reception his aggressive demanding gets from his neighborhood peers whose ways are very different from his mother's" [*61*]. Were he able to restrict this behavior to the home where it is not out of line with prevailing levels of tolerance, and appropriately modify it to conform to the requirements of external social situations, its implications for the outcome of ego maturation would not be so alarming. Unfortunately this is not the case. When placed in a new situation, the most natural tendency for anyone is to utilize the same types of behaviors that were acceptable and successful on previous occasions.

Granted that this initial carry-over takes place. But why, after meeting rebuff, beating, teasing and rejection from his peers, does he

> "not shift to different tactics that might gain [him] acceptance? For one thing [he] had been overtrained in but one kind of strategy and had no other method ready to which he could shift. That was the established way. And what is fully as important, he had been schooled by an [indulgent] mother to develop reciprocal needs that were equally imperious and could, unfortunately, be satisfied only by such a mother or a replica of her. No like-aged average child could possibly take her place" [*61*].

The writer is reminded in this connection of one of his child patients who persistently refused to go to school until he was eight years old. No amount of pleading, cajolery, explanation, permissiveness, catharsis, transference or reflection of attitudes had any effect. The child merely exploited the therapeutic situation and the permissive psychological approach applied to his problem to further his aim of remaining at home. He led his therapist on and complied with all of the indirect suggestions made to him, but always balked at the crucial point. Finally when the threat of overwhelming force (in the form of a truant officer) was involved, he appreciated that the game was up and yielded quite agreeably.

This child had an indulgent mother who was a slave to him in the true Oriental sense of the term. Surely he would have had to become incredibly docile and altruistic willingly to exchange this situation for the dubious privilege of becoming one of forty pupils in a classroom. Hence, he submitted only when he had no other alternative. But since the law could not compel him to play with other children, he continued to ignore them and utilize his mother as a part-time slave after school hours.

Therefore, after experiencing rejection in his peer culture because of his unacceptable behavior, the underdominated child generally makes little attempt to modify the strategy of his interpersonal relations and to learn realistic roles. In the light of his overtraining, this change would not only prove difficult, but would also fail to satisfy his "irresistible needs to dominate" [*61*].

He is willing instead to accept "ostracism and the company of younger and smaller children" [*61*], and to retreat to the privileged sanctuary of his home where frustration is unknown. Isolated, thus, from the main stream of social relations which engage his contemporaries, he never learns to exercise volitional independence in a realistic setting.

In the matter of developing frustration tolerance he is equally unfortunate. Being accustomed to meet with little resistance or frustration in goal-striving, he has not been trained to bear with temporary setbacks, while maintaining his objectives and searching for an indirect, delayed or compromise solution. When forced to set an aspirational level in an area outside the home—where he enjoys no special privilege and consideration—he tends nevertheless to transfer the expectations derived from the parent-child relationship despite their unreality. And instead of appropriately modifying these aspirations in line with recent experience—as would be natural for an individual with a more typical history of volitional development—he finds the frustration intolerable and abandons the goal completely.

Unlike the non-satellizer who has no other choice but to cling tenaciously to his exaggerated needs for extrinsic status, the underdominated child has a large fund of intrinsic adequacy. His parents also do not press him to seek a primary status of his own. In response to his imperious needs (to which they habitually defer), they continue to provide indefinitely not only derived status but also gratification of his hedonistic motivations. Thus, he can well afford to abandon his quest for extrinsic status when confronted with frustration. The set-up is perfect for amaturation as well as regression.

Feelings of inferiority and inadequacy in relation to actual incompetence of performance or adjustive effort are encountered as rarely in the underdominated as in the overprotected child. The subjective sense of failure is also avoided in the same way—by a deficiency in the self-critical faculty, preventing true appreciation of the inferior and unacceptable quality of performance. Although this serves a protective function in maintaining self-esteem, it interferes with the attainment of any satisfactory criterion of mastery or competence. The acquisition of skill in any area—including the capacity for volitional or executive independence—requires the constant comparison of existing product with a model of perfection, recognition of a discrepancy between the two, internalization of a need to close the prevailing gap, and sufficient frustration tolerance to bear discouragement until success is achieved. The underdominated child fails on all counts. He possesses neither the frustration tolerance nor the deep-seated need for superior accomplishment; and in addition, his standards of self-appraisal are so low that no room for improvement is ever perceived.

If the overprotected child feels that he has a special claim on others which obliges them to help and protect him, the underdominated child has similar feelings regarding the obligation of strangers to defer to his desires. This again is not a reflection of a feeling of omnipotence, but results from a generalization of his position of special privilege at home. As a result of being exclusively conditioned to a relationship in which all of the yielding and deference is done by the other party, he comes to think of himself as a unique person, a special kind of being to whom other people just naturally defer. If his parents recognize his unique entitlement—obviously on the basis of some predestined investment with grace, since he cannot perceive any other reason why they should extend such special consideration—why should others balk at doing the same?

The net result of this curious imbalance in volitional development, in which the desire for volitional independence is totally unmatched by capacity for same, is that the individual wills to be dependent on the will of others: This is the easier and more successful role in the light of his acual incompetence for self-direction. Unlike the non-satellizer who regards *true* volitional dependency as a sign of failure and degradation, the underdominated child does not find it basically unacceptable, since he has been able to acquiesce to the principle of satellization. Hence, as long as the outward appearance of self-assertion is preserved—a need which is too basic to be relinquished—it can actually serve the purpose of establishing and reinforcing a relationship founded on volitional dependency. Thus, what he mainly demands from others after maturational failure is well under way is that they accept responsibility for planning his future and smoothing his way.

He takes it for granted without bothering to ask in advance that relatives, friends and associates will always be available to help or fix things when needed. Never mind that they might have prior commitments, duties or responsibilities! Can't they see that he needs their assistance immediately!

The underdominated child also uses his overt self-assertiveness to perpetuate his hedonistic goal structure and executive dependency, both of which are insufficiently attenuated during childhood as a result of the parents' failure to (a) demand their curtailment, and (b) to dispense approval and disapproval on the basis of conformity to this demand. Unlike the overprotecting parent, the latter does not deliberately encourage this behavior in order to decrease the child's mobility or to avoid frustrating him unnecessarily (both of which maneuvers are intended for purposes of anxiety reduction). His attitude is more one of passive tolerance merely because he is too submissive to oppose it actively.

Failure to shift from a derived to a primary basis of ego adequacy is, thus, a negative outcome of undue parental tolerance and laxness on the one hand, and maturational failure in acquiring other adult attributes of personality development on the other hand. The laxness is manifested in the parents' inability to demand adherence to more mature criteria of goal structure, and the tolerance in allowing the child to exploit the relationship indefinitely as a source of derived status and hedonistic gratification. The child's failure to acquire the ego traits that would make the achievement of extrinsic status feasible accounts for his unwillingness to strive for same (amaturation), and his eagerness to fall back upon his childhood status when such striving is unsuccessful (regression). Contentment with his derived status, in turn, does away with much of the motivation for developing the volitional and executive independence and the internalization of long-range goals which would be necessary for successful implementation of aspirations for extrinsic status.

In this respect the underdominated child differs markedly from the non-satellizer whose infantile ego attributes are similarly unattenuated. The latter, who possesses no intrinsic store of ego adequacy, and is obliged to strive for a high order of extrinsic status, is driven by this need to develop more mature ego traits. For the same reason his (the non-satellizer's) goal frustration tolerance must be high. He can't afford to give up easily. It would be defeating his own ends to resort to the simple expedient of negating frustration by remaining unaware of inadequacies in his performance. Prominence can be achieved only if he becomes his own severest critic and taskmaster. His accomplishments can surpass the satellizer's of equal ability not only because his aspirations are higher, but also because he can see more imperfections in his work requiring revision and improvement.

The underdominated child tends to exhibit even greater maturational defects in moral responsibility than the overprotected child. Less attenuation of infantile irresponsibility takes place since the limits of unacceptable behavior are never clearly defined by punishment or disapproval. The concepts of discipline, self-control and obedience are foreign to him. Aggressive and hedonistic impulses are given free reign since compliance to external restraints is never required.

Later, when some degree of satellization takes place, parental moral values are uncritically assimilated, but without any commitment on his part to adhere to same in the regulation of his own behavior. He is convinced of the inherent rightness and wrongness of his parents' ethical positions as applied to others, but cannot see that they bear any relevance to evaluations of his own conduct. Have not his parents always behaved as if he were exempt from the usual moral restraints governing most people? True, they don't actually advocate this principle verbally; but by failing to enforce his accountability to their ethical injunctions, they provide implicit assurance that he is a specially privileged person when it comes to complying with moral values. And on the rare occasions when they do exact obedience, they do so capriciously, inconsistently and on the basis of expediency (e. g., "soft-soaping" an irate neighbor who threatens a lawsuit). Hence it becomes practically impossible for the underdominated child to abstract any consistent general rule that would indicate when a given ethical precept applies to his own conduct.

The tendency to flee from unpalatable non-indulgent relationships outside the home also has a constraining effect on the generalization of moral values and accountability beyond the family hearth. A variety of experiences is required for the abstraction of commonality. There is always the comforting possibility, however, that satellization with a firmer parent-surrogate more capable of setting unambiguous limits to unacceptable behavior might occur, thereby setting the stage for normal moral development.

From the standpoint of potential threat to society, however, moral agenesis in the underdominated satellizing child is far less ominous than in the non-satellizer. The latter's infantile moral irresponsibility is also insufficiently attenuated. His ethical values are not accepted so uncritically, but for this reason are also less stable (even if pitched on a higher plane of generality). His sense of moral accountability is more highly developed intellectually but lacks any substantial emotional basis. Most significant of all, however, are the different ends which moral irresponsibility serves in the two cases: When moral agenesis is preceded by a history of parental overindulgence, ethical license is employed for the unrestrained gratification of hedonistic impulses to the complete detriment of other responsibilities. The result is an orgy of self-indulgence leading to self-destruction rather than injury to others. The non-satellizer, on the other hand, who fails in moral development utilizes his amorality in the ruthless pursuit of ego-aggrandizement. All who stand in his path are mercilessly swept aside. The only consideration restraining him is the extent of his power to escape apprehension and retribution.

The Overdominated Child

In terms of both source and expression, parental overdomination is largely the antithesis of underdomination. But although the general consequences of both attitudes are quite similar in their impact on ego maturation, much greater possibility for heterogeneity in the child's response exists in the case of the former. This heterogeneity results from variations (a) in the brusqueness, hostility, kindliness or affection with which the overdomination is administered, and (b) in the self-assertiveness of the child. The first variable governs the acceptability of the overdomination to the child. The second variable determines the type of resistance that will be offered if overdomination is unacceptable, i. e., active (rebellion) or passive (sabotage).

Although the overdominating parent is frequently overprotecting as well, he does not necessarily have to be; and where the latter situation prevails, excessive control does not serve the purposes of anxiety reduction. In this case it actually conflicts with the need to avoid confronting the child with any unnecessary frustration (frustration which does not serve the function of mitigating parental anxiety).

The simplest explanation of the origin of overdomination in the parent-child relationship is the concomitance of inordinate dominance on the part of the parent and unusual submissiveness on the part of the child. This discrepancy can occur merely on the basis of genetic differences in temperamental endowment. More often, however, the explanation will be found in the parent's childhood or current experience. If his own upbringing had been marked by strictness and austerity, he might wish to recapitulate the same pattern if he regards it as desirable. Even if he had found it unacceptable, he might wish to inflict it on his children as a belated way of squaring accounts. On the other hand, his strictness might imply criticism and repudiation of the indulgent attitude of his parents.

With respect to more current sources of overdomination, the parent may be using his relationship with the child as a means of compensating for the lack of status, prestige or authority he enjoys vocationally or in the eyes of his spouse. He may feel a need to prove to himself that he is not the weak, ineffective or inadequate creature he suspects he really is.

Since overdomination is no longer fashionable, and does not win approval from experts in child psychology or their followers, it is not likely that the present generation of parents would simulate this attitude in order to appear modern and up-to-date. Nevertheless, parents who are genuinely overdominating usually feel a need to justify their behavior in terms of a child-rearing philosophy aspiring to the production of more responsible, mature and virtuous adults.

"Where the domineering parent's discipline is benevolent, consistent and acceptable to the child," neither rebellion nor sabotage are common [*23*]. Under these circumstances, "continued acceptance of authority on the child's part" can be maintained even into his old age [*278*]. The main feature of maturational failure, then, relates to the acquisition of the self-assertive aspects of volitional independence. The parent sees to it that all of the other aspects of adult ego maturity are developed; and since the child accepts this control, he internalizes these values without protest. He is given sufficient experience in playing mature roles, setting realistic goals, solving his own problems, overcoming frustration, and judging his own accomplishments critically. But all of this takes place too long within the framework of another's will and initiative. The parent who is much concerned with producing a mature and competent adult frowns upon hedonistic gratification, stresses self-deprivation for the sake of realizing distant goals, and sets high standards of self-help, executive competence, promptness, efficiency, methodicalness, and moral accountability. When it is time for the child to cast aside his derived status and aspire to adult ego demands of his own, the parent makes sure that archaic childhood status is no longer readily available to serve as tempting regressive bait in the event of frustration.

The resulting type of maturational failure which ensues, therefore, is only partial. The individual is well motivated, pursues long-range goals, aspires to realistic roles, has a reasonable amount of goal frustration tolerance, and is able to appraise his own efforts critically. His efforts are directed toward the attainment of a primary status for himself. He has a highly developed sense of moral duty, but may experience difficulty in generalizing and transferring this from his parents to society at large because all of his moral values are so completely dominated by the personal figures of the former.

The parent's one blind spot in this maturational program, however, is his inability to perceive that true adult personality status cannot be attained by the child without the acquisition of volitional independence; and that this in turn requires genuine opportunities for self-direction, for seeking guidance from other quarters, and for independent exploration in the matter of value assimilation. As an adult he still associates the prerogative of major volitional choice with father, mother or other adults in authority. When it comes to making an independent decision he feels himself a little boy assuming the same docile, submissive, passive, and dependent attitudes that he exhibited as a child. It is as if the capacity for volitional initiative were something far beyond him. That is the business of parents and elders. Thus, when an important decision is to be made, it seems only natural that he let others decide for him. It would be presumptuous for him to take the responsibility upon himself. Just thinking about it makes him feel very guilty, but he is often forced to do so despite himself.

Thus, at the time of decision he is overcome by perplexity, hesitancy and indecisiveness. He exhibits a complete lack of conviction, confidence and spontaneity about the choice which he makes, as if he had no right to make it in the first place. The possibility that he might have made a wrong decision terrifies him. Intellectually he recognizes that no one can be free of error, but emotionally he feels that only father has the right to make mistakes. However, unwilling to admit this, he rationalizes by asserting that he does not have enough facts upon which to base an intelligent decision. After the fateful deed is done, he is sure that he has made the wrong choice and wishes that all could be undone. Sheepishly, like a little boy caught stealing cookies, he awaits the punishment which he feels is his due.

Even as a grown man, he meekly accepts the dictates of his parents who continue to address him in the arbitrary authoritarian tone usually reserved for children. He allows them to manage his life, to rebuke him severely, and to call him uncomplimentary names without thought of protest, refusal or "talking back." Toward other adults his attitude is somewhat less submissive, but still is a diluted version of his attitude toward parents, epecially in the case of older relatives and persons in authority.

Feelings of guilt, however, go both ways. If he feels guilty for even contemplating disobedience, he also cannot escape guilt feelings for failing to gain the independence which his peers and society as a whole expect from him. Sooner or later he is forced to recognize that his relationship to his parents is a unique one, that the latter take liberties with him which his associates first regard as unthinkable and later as amusing, even if they appear perfectly natural to him. Eventually he becomes a target for ridicule if he is unsuccessful in hiding this aspect of his private life from colleagues and friends.

Because of these guilt feelings relative to his excessive submissiveness, he sometimes feels that he must make a show of self-assertion. This can be done with less attendant trauma to self if the aggressive impulses can be unleashed on persons other than parents. But sometimes he chooses to make a stand against the latter by over-reacting to a minor sign or symbol of domination, especially if it is too transparent a challenge to his nominal independence. Thus, a picayune incident is elevated into a major issue. A chalk-line is drawn beyond which he proclaims self-respect and independence cannot be further surrendered. This mark suddenly becomes a reactive barrier, a limit of tolerance, a symbol of lost opportunities for self-assertion. Endowed, thus, with this symbolic significance, it elicits a violence of reaction far out of proportion to its intrinsic importance; and the parent startled by its unexpected fury often has no other choice but to capitulate, since his rule is legally and morally unsupportable, depending solely upon an absurd degree of voluntary, internalized subservience. Moreover, he is comforted by the assurance that this retreat on his part is only strategic and temporary, that his adult child will soon be overwhelmed by guilt and remorse, and will then come begging to be restored to grace and bondage.

Such insurrections, however, are relatively rare. Provided that he is not placed in too overtly a submissive and humilitating position—if granted the formal trappings of independence and self-determination, if orders are dispensed as solicited advice rather than as commands—he prefers to play the subservient role.

There is no doubt about the fact that the overdominated child suffers from feelings of inferiority and insecurity, and from lack of self-confidence. His self-image corresponds to his parents' portrait of him as a volitionally inept individual incapable of ordering his own existence. But it would be a mistake to assume that this lack of self-esteem is in any sense generalized. For the most part it has reference only to his capacity for volitional independence. He feels sufficiently confident and adequate as long as he is in a dependent position following another's direction. Similarly, he does not experience genuine feelings of neurotic anxiety, since whatever apprehensiveness he may feel regarding the future is not related to threats directed at a chronically impaired self-esteem, but reflects instead uncertainty about the permanence of the volitional dependence he is loathe to relinquish. This manifestation of insecurity is comparable to the feelings of insecurity which the overprotected child experiences in relation to his dread of losing the indefinite iron-clad protection provided by his parents. Both individuals as a result of being conditioned to living under unique conditions have not only developed strong positive needs for the perpetuation of these conditions, but also have failed to develop the abilities which would permit adequate survival under more normal circumstances. On both counts, therefore, they have reason to be apprehensive about the possible termination of the special environments they deem indispensable to their continued existence.

Allusion has already been made to difficulties in the social development of the overdominated child. He manifests the same timid, submissive attitude toward the neighborhood children that he does at home. Soon he becomes identified as an easy mark, a child to be teased, bullied and taken advantage of, a child who cannot fight back or defend his own interests. In a dominance hierarchy depending almost entirely upon ascendant qualities of personality structure, and more or less divorced from considerations of law, justice, arbitrary criteria of status (e. g., family, wealth, vocational position), and protective benevolence, he cannot fare very well. Even nominal acceptance into the peer group becomes impossible since membership presupposes acceptance as an equal; and although different degrees of dominance are tolerated, the minimal requirement for becoming "one of the gang" is a certain amount of "spunk," initiative, self-assertion, and willingness to defend oneself against attack. Thorough-going, slavish subservience is unacceptable since the group does not possess sufficient tolerance or maturity to understand or cope with behavior that deviates so markedly from the prevailing norms governing interpersonal relations; nor can it adopt the altruistic and benevolent attitude of the parent toward the child and refrain from exploiting the situation.

Yet the overdominated child knows no other way of solving problems that confront him than by submitting completely to the direction of others. This gets him nowhere in the neighborhood group since it is hardly probable that he will find a playmate who can play the role of his parents. Moreover, by this time he has developed strong security needs based upon the continued availability of this type of authoritarian direction. Faced then with the necessity for developing new adjustive techniques and abandoning well-established security needs, he generally prefers to withdraw from the entire distasteful relationship with his peers and seek the company of parents and of adults who can play the roles his needs demand. During adolescence, as already noted, exposure to stronger internal and social pressures for manifesting independent behavior makes him feel somewhat guilty about his submissiveness, resulting in occasional acts of rebellion. But only rarely can he change sufficiently to become acceptable to the adolescent peer group which is still more intolerant of this type of deviancy.

Upon reaching adult life, he finds the subservient role more tenable socially. Group approval is no longer so important, and exaggerated expressions of independence are no longer expected by his associates. Adult society is not only more tolerant of deviancy, but also offers him many opportunities within its highly stratified organization for exercising highly respected competencies of an extremely subordinate nature. It also becomes more possible at this time to compensate for personality deficiencies in ascendancy through prominence in ability, wealth, family or social position.

If available, a domineering wife or a paternalistic boss or senior partner can substitute quite adequately for overdominating parents. Their availability may spell the difference between success and failure in vocational and marital life. Hence, a military career is very often unexpectedly successful, whereas marriage to a woman who cannot relate to him as a mother usually ends in failure. In extreme cases, where the need to be dominated remains specifically related to the parents, marriage cannot even be contemplated.

In the event that the parent's overdomination is capricious, tyrannical, harsh or inconsistent—but still accepting enough to permit satellization in the early years of childhood—the outcome is somewhat different. As the need for independence becomes greater with the onset of desatellization, parental discipline becomes more and more intolerable. Finally, instead of undergoing internalization, it is completely rejected. This revolt may take one of three forms: (a) An exaggerated display of self-assertion; (b) sabotage of the goals of maturation; and (c) a combination of both. Sabotage is the response of the less ascendant, introverted child who retreats from conflict. The more vigorous, assertive and extraverted child responds to the unwelcome threat of inundation of his will with outright aggression and defiant rebellion. This, of course, tends to facilitate rather than retard maturation. It is only when resentment is fierce enough to give rise to the desire to punish the parent by rejecting the latter's maturational aspirations for him that maturational failure occurs. In terms of eventual outcome, it differs from simple sabotage mainly in the exaggerated presence of the self-assertive aspects of volitional independence. In both cases maturational failure is relatively complete since it is implemented by design.

Sabotage is also the more likely outcome if the parents push the child beyond his motivational depth. Since the attributes of mature goal structure form so prominent a part of the parent's campaign of overdomination in this case, they are also the favored targets for counter-aggression. Where the sabotage is active, the observer is struck by the marked contrast between the violence of self-assertion and the puerility of its aims. The passively sabotaging child, on the other hand, may give the impression of eager compliance with his parent's lofty aspirations for his future despite inner repudiation of same. However, he may not find it convenient for many years—often until the death of his parent—to execute his true intentions overtly. Then, what had hitherto passed muster as a normally motivated personality seems to disintegrate suddenly and assume all of the distinctive feature of maturational failure.

The Underappreciated Child

A form of sabotage of the goals of maturation sometimes occurs in the docile, satellizing child whose parents are guilty of none of the three extreme attitudes discussed above, but who nevertheless are unusually unappreciative of their child's efforts. Such parents, in contrast to the actively hypercritical variety (who provoke the entire gamut of reactions found in overdominated children) merely take their children for granted. They never dispense praise or approval for noteworthy accomplishment, implying always that they expect nothing less and that performance could still be improved if there were only a will to do so. Hence, rather than face the continual frustration of failing to win the appreciation of the very persons whose approval furnishes the chief incentive for his strivings, the underappreciated child resorts to the self-protective device of disinvolving his ego from the aspiration of attaining adult personality status. Why bother to give up childish satisfactions, to strive for extrinsic status, to pursue long-range goals, to gain executive independence, to learn frustration tolerance and effective self-criticism, and to practice self-assertion against his natural inclinations if the reward he desires most for these efforts can never be forthcoming?

In addition to serving the self-protective purpose of avoiding subjective feelings of failure, sabotage of maturation also serves the aim of hurting his parents and providing him with the revenge he unconsciously seeks. This vindictive goal, in fact, can sometimes be accomplished without going to the lengths of complete maturational failure. For example, he may always approach the threshold of success in areas highly approved of by his parents, and then ostentatiously toss aside the fruits of victory as unworthy of his efforts. By this maneuver he demonstrates to them that he could succeed in reaching the goals they respect if he only wanted to. Another way of doing the same thing is to achieve prominence in a field that his parents regard with disdain. This implies that were he so inclined he could also have been successful in activities more to their liking. In both cases the need for obtaining revenge requires that he achieve a certain degree of adult maturity, but this is usually insufficient to result in sustained motivation over the course of a lifetime. He constantly rebels against the senselessness of achieving the visible criteria of success when they are robbed of meaningfulness and satisfaction by lack of appreciation on the part of the persons who are most important to him.

Satellizers, as already pointed out, require the emotional support they receive from the approval and appreciation of persons in relation to whom they satellite. In this respect they differ from non-satellizers who are concerned with approval only as an objective index of the attainment of extrinsic status. To satellizers also, extrinsic status is never an end in itself but a means of winning the approbation of the special individuals who are the models of his satellizing devotion. Prior to adolescent emancipation, parents generally serve this function. As the growing child acquires new sources of primary status through his accomplishments in school and peer group, he looks to his parents for approval. And if through their appreciation, he finds basic satisfaction in these activities during childhood and pre-adolescence, he is encouraged in later years to seek such status on more than a subsidiary basis (not merely as an adjunct to his derived status).

Subsequent to emancipation, the satellizing individual seeks this appreciation from teachers, peer groups, boss, spouse and others in relation to whom he satellizes as an adolescent and adult. Hence, it is possible for a child who had not been appreciated by his parents to establish satisfactory appreciative relationships at a later stage. But by this time the quest for extrinsic status has been dampened by previous let-downs at the hands of his parents. It has to be re-initiated against a background of early renunciation of the goals of maturity with the associated feelings of disappointment and resentment. Habits of indolence and irresponsibility have to be overcome, and preoccupation with hedonistic concerns must be abandoned.

Moreover, these newly found drives lack zest and spontaneity. They are assumed as burdens for the sake of others; he is never too deeply ego-involved in them himself. He feels neither the joy of success nor the sorrow of failure in relation to his efforts; success and failure are merely crucial for the welfare of persons who are important to him. Now that he has internalized the attributes of adult goal structure he feels very guilty about the consequences of his early sabotage. He must make up for the time which has been lost. As a reaction-formation to his previous attitude, he adopts the same ungenerous appraisal of his efforts that his parents formerly did. Whatever he does is insufficient, even if he exceeds by far the expectations which others set for him.

But although he manifests considerable guilt feelings about the past and heightened feelings of insecurity about the future, he can not be said to suffer from true anxiety. As an extreme satellizer, who was accepted and valued for himself, he possesses a deep inner core of intrinsic self-esteem. Hence, he does not fear the future because he feels inadequate to cope with adjustive problems, or because he fears his self-esteem will suffer as a consequence, but because of the dangers it presents to his loved ones whose welfare he is so over-conscientious in protecting, and about which he feels guilty because of past lapses. Since his ego aspirations are not primarily personal, he does not react to their possible frustration as a threat to his self-esteem. In fact, were he to be relieved of the responsibility of caring for his family, he would in all probability relapse to his former state of motivational indifference.

The reaction of maturational sabotage to underappreciation by parents is more apt to occur in the highly satellizing child for two reasons: In the first place, he is so dependent on his parents and so eager for their approval in general that he would hardly concern himself with striving for extrinsic status unless it met with positive encouragement on their part. A more independent child, less concerned with the good opinion of his parents would not be deterred to such an extent by this situation. Secondly, as the possessor of a large store of intrinsic self-esteem, he has less need for acquiring extrinsic status than a child who satellizes less. Although his parents are remiss in dispensing approval for accomplishments, they do indicate very plainly that he is valued for himself as a child quite apart from his competence.

The same type of reaction as in the underappreciated child sometimes occurs in undermotivated children who have easy-going, laissez-faire parents. The latter do not demand or expect enough, set no standards, and are indifferent to their child's scholastic or vocational success. Indifference here is tantamount to lack of appreciation, since approval which is not related to genuine concern and to a definite set of standards and expectations must perforce have an empty ring.

EGO MATURATION IN NON-SATELLIZERS

Contrast to Maturation in Satellizers

The process of ego maturation in the non-satellizing child presents a much different and easier problem than in the case of the satellizing child. The most crucial tasks of maturation—acquisition of greater volitional independence, elevation of the level of ego aspiration, and acceptance of the need to strive primarily for extrinsic status—are accomplished in advance. Volitional independence had never been really surrendered, and hence does not have to be regained. In the absence of derived status and any inner core of intrinsic security and adequacy, ego aspiration level had always been high and predicated upon the attainment of extrinsic status.

Because of his strong prestige drive for accomplishment, the non-satellizing adolescent is highly motivated to undergo maturation in other attributes of infantile personality structure, since these are ultimately recognized as obstacles to achievement. But this modification is not superimposed upon an earlier stage in which attenuation occurs merely on the basis of winning parental approval (as in the satellizing child). From the very beginning, in both overvalued and rejected children, it is influenced, mostly by the needs relating to the achievement of extrinsic status; and in the case of the latter, submission to overwhelming parental force on the basis of simple expediency is an added consideration for effecting the required personality changes.

The maturation of infantile personality attributes for purposes of implementing adult ego aspirations is neither absolute nor inevitable. It occurs only where there are no overwhelming contraindications emanating from the non-satellizing situation itself. The development of goal frustration tolerance, self-critical ability, executive independence, and long-range goals, although difficult in certain cases, is not attended by insuperable obstacles. But the imperious need for superior accomplishment and pre-eminent extrinsic status effectively prevents the setting of realistic goals in many cases. Although level of ego aspiration is uniformly high in non-satellizers and is extremely resistant to lowering in the face of frustration, there is no reason for believing that the distribution of ability in this group is significantly different from normal. Aspirational level will, therefore, be persistently and unrealistically high except in the small minority of individuals whose abilities are commensurate with their ambitions. Similarly, it is highly improbable that the self-estimate of the overvalued child will be increased during adolescence. Exchanging a highly flattering home situation for a more neutral school and peer group environment as the chief source of extrinsic status is hardly calculated to enhance his self-esteem, especially in view of the negative impact his personality tends to make on associates. The rejected child, in contrast, stands to gain in self-esteem by passing from a hostile to a more neutral environment.

The stability of these maturational changes in the unattenuated attributes of infantile ego structure is also open to question. As long as personality integration is maintained, and striving is kept within the framework of reality, there is no danger. "The insecure individual with inflated ambitions and with a driving need for self-assertion clearly recognizes that maturation is a realistic and necessary step in his struggle for power" [*23*]. But where changes are made with specific ends in view, abandonment of ends leads to reversal of change. Hence, in the event that maturation does not take place or that regression occurs, these ego attributes are ready for full-blown expression in their original unmodified form. This fact is of considerable importance in determining the symptomatology of later adult personality derangements, and the characteristics of maturational failure in non-satellizers (see below).

Most vulnerable and unstable of these changes is that which occurs in the direct transformation of infantile moral irresponsibility into moral accountability on a societal basis. The reason for this is obvious: Moral responsibility does not always advance, but frequently conflicts with plans for personal aggrandizement. Overt conformity to moral values is necessary for personal safety and freedom, and for social approval; but with respect to surreptitious immorality, the only limiting factors (in the absence of genuine emotional internalization of moral accountability) are fear of apprehension and punishment and intellectual adherence to abstract principles of justice. The latter cannot offer much resistance to temptation when the stakes are sufficiently high, and the former is an ineffective barrier since most moral breaches (e. g., double-dealing, disloyalty, malicious scheming) are not incompatible with the legal code. And where the rule of law is abrogated, as in lynchings and ruthless dictatorships, even this feeble protection is lacking. Hence, the existence of moral instability in highly ambitious individuals, whose self-esteem subsists entirely on worldly accomplishments, confronts society with a potent and ever-present danger with which it still has not learned to cope.

Some of the extreme parental attitudes predisposing toward maturational failure in satellizing children are also exhibited by parents of non-satellizers. The most frequent of these combinations is the concomitance of overdomination in the rejecting parent and underdomination in the overvaluing parent. The outcomes of these practices, however, offer only superficial resemblance to the comparable situation affecting satellizers. For the most part, the maturational process is only made more difficult by these complications in the non-satellizer. The greater need for extrinsic status, the higher ego aspirations, the relentless drive for volitional autonomy, the antipathy toward dependency, the lack of intrinsic security and adequacy, and the greater liability to anxiety are all central enough to personality organization to result in basic differences in maturational outcome.

Ego Maturation in the Rejected Child

The timid and docile rejected child, for example, never reacts to parental overdomination by accepting it as just and proper, and by relinquishing his need and desire for volitional independence. He resents domination bitterly even though he may not protest openly against it, and regards dependency of any kind as the worst type of degradation. He is willing to submit to dependency only in his outward behavior and as a temporary expedient in situations where no other alternative is possible. What is lacking, therefore, is not the desire for self-assertion but lack of opportunity and of experience in the techniques for expressing it.

Throughout childhood and adolescence he represses his feelings of resentment and hostility toward his parents. With bitterness in his heart and sub-vocal anger on his lips he complies meekly with their requests, although rejecting completely any internal attitude of dependency on his part. Inability to handle this situation directly leads to an habitual adjustive approach of withdrawal and introversion. Unable to respond emotionally as he would like to, he withdraws from conflictful situations and intellectualizes his aggression.

When he finally emerges as an adult, therefore, he is motivated by powerful needs for volitional autonomy, but finds that he has failed to master any of the customary roles necessary for adult self-assertion. This deficiency cannot be made up simply by gaining appropriate role-playing experience; for he is also lacking in the confidence and convictions that go with adult behavior in this respect. Thus, he not only ordinarily impresses others as adopting the interpersonal attitudes of a subdued little boy, but also (even if he is successful in masking this incapacity through appropriately simulated adult-like behavior) feels that he is truly incapable of *feeling* any other way.

Hence as an adult, he feels painfully inadequate about meeting persons in face-to-face relationships. He senses that in a showdown he would be unable to protect his own interests, and avoid being taken advantage of. He would rather be overcharged or cheated out of his turn than face the unpleasantness of speaking up. Subordinates immediately recognize him as a "push-over," and just about succeed in reversing the direction of supervision. If controversy cannot be completely avoided, he would rather state his case by letter or telephone than argue with his adversary in person. This inhibition against direct expression of aggression—which is a carry-over from his feeling of helplessness as a child in coping with the ruthless domination of his parents—is especially evident in relation to older persons and individuals in authority. In their presence he is overawed and subdued as a child; and if he had privately entertained the resolution to press some demand, he quickly disabuses himself of it.

Hence it is no accident that such individuals seem to be consistently on the short end of every bargain. Every action and mannerism betray them as persons unable to look out for themselves, thereby inviting aggression from others. This appearance is further enhanced by their overt and uncontrollable anxiety. What other persons usually fail to recognize, however, is that this aggression and domination are only outwardly accepted; that quite unlike the overdominated satellizer who genuinely accepts the subservience to which he is subjected, the overdominated non-satellizer gradually accumulates a reservoir of resentment and hostility which eventually overflows with such violence as to rupture existing relationships beyond repair. His vocational history is typical: In each new position, he starts out by being timid, and ambiguous, lax in enforcing his legitimate demands on others. This behavior invites domination, undue familiarity and unfair tactics on the part of the latter. Encouraged by his apparent passivity in response to their aggression, his associates become bolder and perpetrate even more brazen assaults on his dignity, until he suddenly erupts in a furious outburst of rage and indignation, or decides abruptly that his position is untenable because of the peculiar hostility of his colleagues. He remains obstinately blind to the fact that the cause of his interpersonal difficulties lies within himself (rather than in the situation), despite the monotonous repetition of this same sequence of events in every position he undertakes.

Since ordinary interpersonal relations prove so unsatisfactory—often compelling outward subjection to domination by others—the powerful drive for self-assertion and independence must seek other outlets. Under the circumstances, the most inviting and least threatening possibility is to enter a vocation which follows the same highly introverted and intellectualized path trod in previous years. For example, academic life in the university offers a respected and socially acceptable retreat from the sordid jungle of competitive existence.

In scholarly work there is ample opportunity for intellectual aggression without encountering much personal unpleasantness. The cloistered atmosphere of library and laboratory provides a welcome buffer against intruding whiffs of reality. Interpersonal relationships can be kept on a highly superficial basis. Only a minimum of personal contact is required with colleagues; and relationships with students can be ordered on an impersonal and intellectual plane. Further security in the teacher-student relationship is provided by formidable status barriers inherent in the authoritarian tradition of academic rank and discipline. But not all overdominated non-satellizers have sufficient verbal ability and good fortune to drift into academic life, although the temptation to make the attempt is almost overwhelming upon exposure because of its natural adaptive value in this situation. However, other less desirable "avoidance" vocations are also available.

The rejected child who has been overdominated is also much less prone to sabotage the goals of maturation. In view of his hypertrophic ego demands, his need for punishing his parents would have to be quite overpowering before he would sacrifice his only hope of attaining feelings of security and adequacy.

Ego Maturation in the Overvalued Child

Overvaluing parents are almost universally underdominating. In trying to re-create through their children an existence in which their projected ego aspirations can meet no frustration, they are invariably obliged to defer to the latter's will, or else shatter the fiction of omnipotence which they strive so desperately to establish and maintain. Thus, unlike the rejected child, the overvalued child has no need to repress the overt expression of volitional independence; and unlike the underdominated satellizing child, his need is for the substance rather than the form of self-assertion, and is not confined within the general framework of contentment with a derived status.

This latter difference is responsible for the relative infrequency of maturational failure in overvalued children. He who would acquire an enviable extrinsic status and has no fund of intrinsic adequacy upon which to fall back cannot afford the luxury of maturational failure. In order to implement his ego demands he must develop mature ego traits, i. e., goal frustration tolerance, self-critical ability, long range goals, executive independence, etc. These tasks are accomplished with difficulty in view of the excessively permissive environment to which he has been exposed, and his early lack of direct experience with realistic restrictions on his volitional and hedonistic impulses. His social behavior is also typically out-of-bounds, domineering, importunate, and characterized by unrestrained fits of temper and infantile aggression. But in his case, the motivation is available to modify the strategy of his interpersonal relationships and to learn more acceptable social behavior, since he recognizes the importance of good social relations in the struggle for power. Through assiduous study and intelligent application of self-control he is able to acquire an agreeable set of formal manners and a superficial veneer of good fellowship to mask his formerly offensive aggression and self-seeking. That his actions are studied, carefully planned for effect, utterly synthetic and lacking in spontaneity, few people are perceptive enough to grasp, since he lives in a cultural milieu in which such behavior is entirely compatible with social expectations. Hence, unlike the ex-rejected child, he is able to learn a highly effective form of adult self-assertion in interpersonal relationships. This enables him to more than hold his own with colleagues, superiors and subordinates except during such times as he may be disorganized by acute bouts of overt anxiety.

MATURATIONAL FAILURE IN NON-SATELLIZERS

Although maturational failure is relatively rare in non-satellizers for the reasons discussed above, there are certain typical situations in which it tends to occur. In most of these cases, the need to destroy parents is even stronger than the not inconsiderable drive for self-enhancement. Hence, such reactions are more common among overvalued than among rejected children, since the former's parents—having an important personal stake in the ego aggrandizement of their children— can be hurt more by their failure; whereas rejecting parents are either indifferent to or secretly pleased bv such failure. In a sense it almost serves to justify their rejecting attitude. They can then say, "See, he wasn't worth bothering with in the first place." For this reason even the tough-skinned, extraverted child who fights back vigorously against overdominating rejection seldom chooses this form of retaliation. He merely develops an exaggerated drive for independence once the path to freedom appears in sight, and goes out of his way to negate any form of control which reminds him of the hatefully regarded parental authority. If maturational failure does occur in the rejected child, it is more likely to take place in the docile, withdrawn, highly introverted individual whose functioning is so drastically impaired by anxiety and damaged self-esteem that all hope of making a mature adjustment within the framework of reality is abandoned.

Conditions propitious for maturational failure in the overvalued child are set in motion if the parent suddenly decides to terminate his overvaluing attitudes and bring the former under strict authoritarian control during the later years of childhood. This may happen if a more promising younger sibling appears on the scene, if the child manifests unmistakable signs of inferiority, or if the essentially domineering parent himself becomes weary of his role as "second fiddle" and desires to re-establish his pre-eminence in the household. The child who is totally unprepared for this about-face is not only incensed by the "betrayal," but is also completely incapable of accepting it in good grace. "His natural resentment in this situation is further aggravated by the fact that this is the usual time in which most children are traditionally granted more freedom" [*23*].

> "The desire for achieving absolute independence and for wreaking vengeance on the resented parent become the dominant motives in life. Both aims can be best served simultaneously by adopting an attitude of obstinate perverseness, by repudiating the entire process of adult maturation, and by choosing goals and standards of behavior which are diametrically opposite to those advocated by the parent. The final result is the development of a personality which is not unlike that already described as "inadequate," except that motivational immaturity and childish irresponsibility are combined with inflated ambitions and an exaggerated need for volitional independence (which is often in marked disparity to the individual's actual executive dependence). In extreme cases, this pathological need for independence is generalized so as to include freedom from control of any sort whatsoever. The individual then sets himself up as being above any criticism or moral censure and acknowledges no responsibility to be bound by the moral authority of society" [*23*].

OTHER DIFFERENCES IN EGO MATURATION BETWEEN SATELLIZERS AND NON-SATELLIZERS

Since greater total change in personality structure must result from ego maturation in satellizers, and since they are less motivated by the need for extrinsic status to effect this change, it is quite understandable that they will be more subject to maturational failure than non-satellizers. But in terms of resulting strain to personality structure, the reverse is true. The conflicts and insecurities experienced by the satellizer are for the most part situational and transitional in origin. It is true that his needs for primary status are not adequately met, thereby depressing his extrinsic self-esteem.

But neurotic anxiety (as defined in this book) can only arise under these circumstances if intrinsic self-esteem is also lacking. It is only the non-satellizer who possesses no intrinsic store of adequacy who, therefore, becomes a candidate for anxiety during adolescence. In the rejected child, existing anxiety is made more acute, while in the overvalued child, adolescence often furnishes the first catastrophic blow to self-esteem that is necessary to produce an overt condition of anxiety. Non-satellizers are also subject to more neurotic anxiety during adolescence because of their exalted ego demands, which are highly resistant to discouragement despite their tendency to end in frustration and lowered self-esteem.

Thus, in terms of their actual needs for extrinsic status, satellizers find adolescence loaded with much less trauma and deprivation than non-satellizers. Rejected children, nevertheless, often register an initial gain in self-esteem as a result of less exposure to their hostile home environments, while overvalued children find the greater separation from their adoring homes quite deflating. Eventually, however, the latter are better able to master a socially acceptable technique of expressing adult self-assertion in interpersonal relations.

Socialization continues to be a difficult problem for the non-satellizer during adolescence. Unable to form a satellizing relationship to the closely-knit peer group, he fails to gain the ego support and the "we-feeling" that is derived from the act of dependent identification with and self-subordination to group interests. He can not lose himself in social activities or participate with sufficient abandon and spontaneity to really experience true joy in group experience. The group to him is merely a place where one seeks extrinsic status, i.e., power, prestige, leadership, admiration and applause. The overvalued child also, still finds it difficult to gain acceptance because of his overbearing, aggressive personality, and the rejected child lacking a secure home base [*61*] tends to withdraw from group life because he is oversensitive about meeting rebuffs, and lacks experience and assurance in self-assertion. These difficulties tend to decrease in adult life, however, because of the reduced importance of group approval, and the more formal, impersonal, and less spontaneous nature of interpersonal relationships.

NOTES

[1] "The level of aspiration with its involvement of the ego does not appear genetically until the child has formed some conception of his 'self,' has developed a sense of 'pride' or of status which he feels he must maintain within a group" [*354*].

[2] An exception to this generalization occurs in Samoa, where the fact of pubescence appears to receive no cultural recognition for the first two years after it takes place [*274*].

[3] The amount of extrinsic status which an adolescent or adult is expected to achieve obviously varies from one culture to another and even within the various social class segments of a given society (see page 339). In Samoa, for example, ego aspiration levels tend to be low because of minimal cultural expectations with respect to the achievement of power and success [*274*]. Hence the possibilities for frustration of extrinsic ego needs are not very great. This is in marked contrast to the situation prevailing in our own culture.

[4] For purposes of highlighting the chief issues involved, the following critique of permissiveness is based upon the most extreme presentation of this philosophy of child rearing that can currently be found in journals and brochures concerned with parent and teacher practices. The reader should bear in mind, however, that all shades and degrees of permissiveness are possible short of authoritarianism. In fact, the author would regard his own position as a limited endorsement of permissiveness if judged against the impersonal, over-strict and rigid Watsonian criteria of child-rearing popular in the interval between World Wars I and II.

[5] Adherents of the *Cornelian Corner* school of self-demand point to the increased frustration tolerance developed in infants whose feeding needs have not been frustrated by the imposition of an arbitrary schedule (see H. Orlansky [*303*]).

[6] Overprotective parental attitudes have been more commonly interpreted (especially by psychoanalytic writers) as reaction-formations against hostile feelings toward and death wishes for the child. Although this is frequently true, it does not in the writer's experience account for the usual case of overprotection.

[7] Whatever feelings of insecurity exist usually reflect exaggerated anticipation of the physical dangers that are emphasized so greatly by parents. The child is also not too confident of the parents' capacity for protecting him since they (the parents) themselves display such fearfulness.

If these children experience anxiety it is not the neurotic anxiety attributable to impairment of intrinsic self-esteem (see page 364), but the fear of losing the derived status that is customarily withdrawn at the close of childhood.

CHAPTER 14

Dimensions of the Parent-Child Relationship in Relation to Ego Development

THE PARENT-CHILD RELATIONSHIP IN PERSONALITY DEVELOPMENT

IN THE PAST TEN YEARS, researchers and theorists in the field of personality development have paid increasing attention to the role of parent-child relationships. But although praiseworthy effort has been expended in defining [*28, 65, 235*], measuring [*28, 65, 235*] and grouping parent attitudes in naturally occurring clusters [*28*], these problems are still shrouded in considerable ambiguity. Some of the difficulty can be ascribed to confusion between popular and scientific usage, to overlapping of terms, and to lack of clarity in defining the precise aspects of the parent-child relationship to which these terms refer. In the popular literature about children, for example, "spoiled," "indulged," "overprotected," "underdominated" and "overvalued" are used almost interchangeably. Levy's linking of the protective and dominating aspects of parental behavior has also gained such widespread acceptance that the recent efforts toward systematization noted above have made comparatively few inroads into the thinking of persons who are most concerned with interpreting the role of parent-child relationships in either a clinical or theoretical setting.

Two other difficulties have still not been taken into account by current research trends. The first relates to the grouping of parental attitudes and their ordering in a hierarchy of significance. The ecological and correlational studies of Baldwin and his coworkers [*27, 28*] have done much to sharpen and objectify this problem, but still leave much to be desired from the standpoint of making significant predictions from parent-child relationships to child behavior or adult personality structure. Ecologically it is quite possible to define a given dimension of parent behavior (e. g., indulgence) in terms of a cluster or syndrome of inter-related attitudes, to scale it along a continuum, and to correlate measurements of it with certain variables relating to parent background and personality or to child behavior [*28*]. One can even rank such clusters in order of the number and magnitude of their correlations with significant personality outcomes in the child [*28*]. But how can one ever hope to fit these manifold clusters and their correlates into a meaningful picture of personality development in the absence of some comprehensive "conceptual scheme for systematizing the data"? Barker in reviewing this approach to research on parent attitudes aptly comments that it is "too empirical. Unless warmth, democracy, etc., can be better conceptualized, we will end in the same *cul-de-sac* we are in with intelligence and personality measurement: factors defined in terms of statistical operations that are so abstract that their psychological content cannot be designated" [*33*]. Similar categories of parent attitudes may have quite different outcomes depending on whether or not a given individual shares the major attributes of ego structure characterizing a particular period of development, and on the nature of the developmental tasks confronting him at a given stage of his personality development.

It would seem more fruitful and economical of effort, therefore, to start with a theoretical structure hypothesizing various stages of personality development with their component attributes and developmental tasks. One could then test various hypotheses regarding the causal antecedents of these developmental changes (e.g., different dimensions of the parent-child relationship) by relating measurements of these dimensions to developmental outcomes in children and adults. For example, according to the conceptual scheme adopted in this book, the crucial parent attitudes affecting personality development in the period of ego devaluation are acceptance and intrinsic valuation. They determine in large measure whether or not it is possible for a child to satellize; and in relation to the central changes in ego structure associated with this phenomenon, other parent practices such as overdomination, overprotection, underdomination, etc., have different consequences and assume greater or lesser significance. During ego maturation also, the fact of prior satellization is extremely important both for the outcome and the types of maturational mechanisms employed; but in satellizers, the dominating and protective aspects of parent behavior become more crucial determinants of future personality growth than the accepting and valuing aspects which formerly held the center of the stage.

A second difficulty which still results in considerable theoretical confusion has to do with the *communicability* of parent attitudes. Observers have tended to lose sight of the fact that the impact of one person's attitudes on the personality and behavior of another is less a function of their actual properties than of their properties as perceived by the latter. This does not mean that one cannot classify parent attitudes in terms of their underlying feeling tones or of the personality needs they meet in the parent. However, it does require that the consequences of these attitudes on the child's personality development be examined in the light of (a) his developmental capacity for perceiving and responding to various degrees of subtlety in attitudinal expression; (b) his own personality needs at a given stage of development; (c) his individual level of psychological acuity and sensitivity in perceiving the motivations of others; and (d) the central factors governing the nature of the parent-child relationship and their propensity to systematically influence the perceived properties of stimuli regardless of their objective content.

The young infant is protected from considerable trauma to personality structure by virtue of the primitive and undifferentiated state of his social perceptions and emotional needs. Hence while it is true that a parent's behavior is always more important than his verbalisms, his feelings—especially in their more subtle aspects and undertones—first begin to overshadow his actions when the child attains greater maturity. Parents, therefore, display needless concern and feelings of guilt and anxiety over minor deviations of their child-rearing practices and attitudes from currently acceptable norms. This process of tortuous soul-searching and merciless self-recrimination about the underlying motivations and the possible dire consequences of supposedly undesirable attitudes is not only completely unnecessary in terms of the actual dangers involved, but also robs parenthood of much joy and spontaneity.

The level of overt parent behavior is far more crucial than its underlying attitudinal substrate in early infancy, since it is only the former which is actually communicable and relevant in terms of the child's perceptual capacity and psychosocial needs at this stage of development. Infants seem to make normal developmental progress [*79, 303, 369*] and acquire ideas of ego omnipotence when provided with a certain minimal amount of care, personal attention and motherliness. The disturbances in development, health, irritability, motility, and emotional expression reported by Spitz in foundling-home infants were consequences of quantitative deprivation in these gross factors of parent behavior rather than in subtle features of attitude expression. An attitude of parental rejection, therefore, —unless extreme enough to lead to gross emotional deprivation—is much less damaging in the first year of life than in the second and third years when it rules out the possibility of satellization.

Individual differences in children's perceptiveness come into play once the *attitudes* of parents assume a more influential directional role in personality development. Attitudes can be either overt and proximate or covert and underlying. In order for the latter group to be communicable—regardless of whether they are consciously available to either parent or child—heightened psychological sensitivity is essential. Because a psychiatrist can sometimes infer that a given mother's overprotecting attitude is a reaction-formation against covert feelings of rejection and hostility, we cannot assume that hers will be a rejected child. It is more likely that he will be an accepted and overprotected child, although perhaps extrinsically- and overvalued.

It is also difficult for an observer to evaluate a parent's attitudes or behavior unless he is familiar with the child's matrix of feelings about the parent which determines how the expressed attitude will be perceived. Korner [*232*], for example, was unable to find that a child's expression of hostility was in any way correlated with judgments of parental rejection made from interview responses and observations. This is not at all surprising when one considers that the same parent attitude evaluated by an observer as rejecting may be similarly perceived by a non-satellizing child as evidence of flagrant and hostile rejection, but quite dissimilarly perceived by a satellizer as a form of benevolent and allowable domination.

Escalona [*103*] has considered some of the cultural and psychological implications of the current child-centered and permissive philosophy of child rearing with its exaggerated and self-conscious concern over the developmental implications of subtle and even abstruse distinctions between various parental practices.[1]* She suggests that this preoccupation leads to a self-recriminating, self-deprecating, apologetic attitude toward children—

> "as though we not only regretted that we have not done better by them, but also felt that we must 'make up to them' so to speak by extra indulgence and also by punishing ourselves . . . [Such] feelings of guilt are likely to lead to self-defeating action designed more to appease the individual anxiety than to remedy the situation which causes the guilt feelings."

If these feelings of guilt and insecurity are entirely without foundation in view of limitations in the communicability of attitudes during early infancy, we are imposing an unnecessary and heavy cultural burden on the function of parenthood. And if they persist into the more mature periods of childhood,

> "It is reasonable to assume that . . . children will absorb the fact that such attitudes are maintained toward them. This in turn can be expected to affect their developing concept of the self and the world about. Available clinical evidence can be interpreted in such a way, it is believed, as to show that in indirect ways children acquire a sense that something is owed them. Moreover, and related to this, the awareness of the adult's insecurity, anxiousness and guilt would seem to operate as a barrier towards developing the trust and confidence in the strength and superior judgment of adults which children require if they themselves are to feel secure and confident" [*103*].

The Stability of Parent Attitudes

The importance of parent attitudes as a determinant of personality development is largely a function of their stability and rel-

* Notes for this chapter appear on page 297.

ative continuity. Even if the effects of the same parent attitude will vary depending on the maturity and developmental needs of the child, the maintenance of relative constancy on the parent's part still adds considerably to the degree of irreversibility of the consequences of the parent-child relationships which can be expected. There is good reason to believe "that the family atmosphere in which a child is reared remains as a rule substantially the same. Through infancy, childhood and adolescence he keeps the same parents, and unless something radically alters their attitudes toward him or each other they give him essentially the same kind of treatment throughout" [*61*]. On the other hand, it is quite apparent that this statement does not hold at all for many parents, and is only relatively true for the greater majority. At the very best, a parent's child-rearing attitudes can remain no more stable than his personality structure itself.

It would seem, therefore, that most attitudes of a given parent exhibit a range of variability, within certain relatively fixed limits, the modifiability of which varies from parent to parent. Numerous opportunities for effecting changes of varying degrees of magnitude present themselves at every stage of development. The most striking change of all probably occurs in the interval between the first few months preceding and following the child's birth. The feelings that a parent will display when actually confronted with the existence of a helpless new individual for whose well-being he is responsible (at the sacrifice of much of his own freedom, comfort and leisure), may differ markedly from the preparatory set of images and emotions elicited by anticipation of the event.

> "Many unplanned and unwanted children are welcomed when they actually come, while some of those deliberately planned for are rejected. Children who are unwanted and rejected at birth may later be accepted because interparental attitudes or extraneous factors have changed meanwhile, because parenthood brings unlooked-for satisfactions, or because the child becomes more of a companion and less of a burden as he grows out of helpless infancy. Conversely, children accepted at birth may for various reasons be rejected later" [*61*].

Important changes in parent attitudes may be induced by various developmental changes in the child. Some parents can only warm up to a child after he passes out of the vegetative stage and acquires speech, locomotion, sphincter control and affectionate ways. Then these fond feelings may last as long as he remains emotionally dependent, "cute," and relatively helpless executively. They may undergo drastic revision after the child acquires some independent status of his own in the peer group, and begins to think and act independently of the parent's direction.

> "Because a parent has shown overindulgence or rejection when a child was young is no reason for thinking that this attitude is a permanent one. One must look for the effects of parental attitude on a child at the time that the attitude is expressed and not at some later time when these particular feelings have perhaps shifted and taken a different turn" [*389*].

Another major possibility for change in parent attitudes lies in significant alterations of the latter's personality structure, i.e., changes in level of ego aspiration, security, self-esteem and anxiety. Situational conditions affecting current adjustment level may also induce noteworthy change. An expectant mother preoccupied with anxieties about family finances, threatened by the loss of her husband's ego support (which would follow from induction into military service), or harassed by overwork, family discord or crowded family conditions often contemplates the birth of a child with hopelessness and dread. The latter, sensitized by maternal physiological reactions to anxiety (transmitted via the placenta from maternal to fetal circulation) may manifest from birth onward extreme hyperirritability and various somatic disturbances [*365*]. Under the circumstances it would not be unnatural for her to react to the child as an overwhelming and unwanted burden. Her extreme lack of patience compounded by his abnormally low frustration tolerance tends to elicit and perpetuate infantile rage patterns which are later expressed in the form of exaggerated negativism when he becomes fully aware of her rejecting attitude. But despite the seemingly hopeless case of rejection thus produced, an improvement in the external situation coupled with anxiety reduction, insight and a genuine desire to improve the relationship can almost reverse the prognosis providing that the parent is not hopelessly narcissistic, hostile or unconscionable, and is given (and willing to accept) skillful professional guidance.

The most common cause of variability in parent attitudes springs from the inevitable ambivalence in any parent's feelings towards his child. This hardly needs elaborate substantiation, but follows simply from the fact that

> "if the child brings satisfactions to the needs of one or both parents and gives them hopes and expectations, he also introduces problems for them which may, in turn, affect their attitudes toward him. Parenthood increases a person's responsibilities, necessitates changes in living arrangements, with perhaps a reduction in standards, and adds to whatever inconvenience and restrictions of liberty marriage may have already imposed. It modifies certain of the privileges and opportunities each parent has enjoyed inside the house as well as outside of it. It always means a division of attention, particularly on the mother's part, and a restructuring of the affectional balance" [*61*].

> "It may seem trite to state that children may be both loved and hated by their parents . . . That mothers love their children needs no proof. That they may hate them is less readily recognized and admitted, although most parents would admit that there are occasions when their children irritate them beyond measure. It would almost seem as though the parents' attitudes were an algebraic resultant of certain quantities of plus and minus feelings. When we say that a parent loves a child, we must admit that there are times when negative and hostile feelings arise but that they come less frequently or with less strength than the feelings of love . . . Conversely the mother who shows a balance of hostility toward her child will usually have periods when she feels kindly disposed toward him. However, the matter is not simply an algebraic resultant of possible forces, for the expression of love and hate intertwine in countless ways, and typically a parent's attitude is an ambivalent one which may alternate between positive and negative feelings" [*389*].

Hence, within the relational framework encompassed by generally favorable and accepting parent attitudes, there is considerable room for the expression of unfavorable practices and occasional serious mishandling without any danger of permanently dislocating personality development.

Also implied in the concept of attitude stability is a certain generality of function. For a parent to be consistently rejecting, for example, this attitude should be expressed in all or the majority of contact areas impinging upon the parent-child relationship. While such generality of attitude expression seems to be present in practically all cases coming to clinical attention, many exceptions can be found in everyday observations of parent behavior. The most obvious explanation of this discrepancy (which would square with the conclusion drawn above that "it is the net balance of love and hate that counts and not the isolated expression of either feeling" [*389*]) is that a specific parent attitude may mean one of two things: It may either be reflective of a particular idiosyncrasy or reaction sensitivity of the parent (e.g., anxiety about feeding, toilet training or autoeroticism) and entirely unrelated to the main feeling tones and personality needs underlying the relationship. Or it may be only one of a large number of vehicles through which the parent's basic emotional reactions to the child seek expression, and bear no specific relation at all to the particular function involved. In the latter case, its potential capacity for adversely influencing personality development is derived from none of the individual situations in which it appears, but from the consistency and the total impact of the central attitude on all of the important areas of interaction between parent and child.

It would stand to reason, therefore, that in serious cases of behavior disorder, disturbances of parent-child relationships would be general rather than specific in scope. This is merely another restatement of the general principle cited earlier (see page 21) that no single parental practice is crucial enough by itself to significantly shape the course of personality development.

Differences between maternal and paternal attitudes also make for considerable variability in the attitudinal matrix confronting the child. But these differences first assume importance as the child becomes older, since the father's influence on the former's personality development is extremely limited in the first few years of life [*61*]. Only later does he discard his role as sibling rival and become the model for sex role identification in boys, and the chief authority figure, representative of social morality, and punitive agent for both boys and girls. It is at this point that the attitudes of both parents interact, blend and conflict in shaping the emotional climate of the home. Fluctuations in the resulting equilibrium follow both from changes in the relative ascendency of each parent and from shifts in the strength of the child's identification with each of them.

Finally it is important to point out that

> "children growing up in the same family do not by any means have the same environment . . . When the second child comes he has not only these adults as part of his environment, but also the first child. But in a still more important way, parents are not the same parents to different children in the family . . . Usually the first-born is the one on whom are displaced the feelings around which there is the strongest conflict . . . By venting accumulated tensions on one child, these tensions are relieved, making it possible to adopt a different attitude toward another child . . . For instance, if hostility toward one's own parent has yet to be resolved, the father or mother may displace onto the newborn first child some of this hostility, but when the second child comes along the need to displace these feelings has been taken care of and the second child may be more fully the recipient of the parent's love. Children in a family may in turn be the recipients of the parent's feelings of love, hostility, guilt, anxiety, ambition, or narcissism" [*389*].

Factors Limiting the Impact of Parent Attitudes on Personality Development

Parent attitudes have been emphasized throughout this volume as the crucial variables determining the differential course of ego development. The reasons accounting for their strategic importance, the ways in which they influence ego development, and the reversibility of their effects will be reviewed in succeeding sections. The task of this section, however, is to point out that despite their prepotency, the impact of parent attitudes on children's personality development is hardly absolute or invariable but is limited in a number of important ways.

Two important limiting factors have already been discussed in considering the communicability and stability of parent attitudes. It was pointed out that the latter are effective only in so far as they can be perceived by the child, and that in this connection it is important to consider developmental and individual differences in perceptual capacity and personality needs, as well as the central theme embodied in the interpersonal relationship. With respect to the stability of parent attitudes it was emphasized that many opportunities for significant change present themselves in the course of the child's development and in relation to modifications in the parent's needs, personality characteristics, insights, and situational adjustments. Two other important limiting factors remain still to be considered: The child's own constitutional contributions to the parent-child relationship and the competing influences of the wider culture in which this relationship is imbedded.

It must be realized that from the very beginning the parent-child relationship is a two way channel of interaction in which the child always makes an active contribution. While agreeing with Symonds that "parent-child relationships are determined primarily by the attitudes of parents," we would take issue with his view that "it is only after the parents' original attitudes have had their effect in modeling even slightly the direction of a child's personality that the child emerges as an independent force in determining the parent-child relationship" [*389*].

In the first place, genetically determined differences in physique and temperament which are easily noticeable at birth play a large part in ordering the nature of the environment that will soon envelop the child. Depending on whether the child is male or female, puny or robust, ugly or attractive, responsive or phlegmatic, demanding or docile, etc., and on the interaction between these traits, parental expectations, and the traits of other members of the family, parents may respond with varying degrees of acceptance, affection, tolerance and attention. These original personality characteristics are, of course, modified in the course of later interaction with parents, but always in accordance with their innate degree of relative strength and plasticity. Shirley [*356*] cites evidence indicating the stability and consistency of childens' personality and behavior patterns during the first two years of life.[2] In addition, although close correspondence between the respective personality patterns of parents and children was not uncommon, there were several cases in which "specific training by the mother seemed to have little effect in counteracting a strongly established trait or developing one in which the child was weak" [*356*]. In another study, Shirley supplies two case histories to further illustrate her thesis that "within every newborn infant there is a core of temperamental qualities of some degree of toughness, that, coupled with the dynamic forces of growth, prevent his ever becoming a puppet of the forces that play upon him" [*355*].

This inner "core of toughness" not only plays an important initial role in selectively evoking different parent attitudes, but is also important in two other ways: (a) It determines in large measure the magnitude and kind of effect a given parent attitude will have on a child's personality development. Differences in ascendence, visceratonia, and energy level have already been described as influencing the course of satellization and maturation, the development of introversion and extraversion, and the type of response elicited by parental rejection. (b) By influencing the nature of the child's response to the parent attitude, it does much to perpetuate or modify the original basis or expression of the latter. A submissive or a rebellious reaction to rejection, for example, may either reduce or intensify the severity of the parents' attitude as the case might be. Extreme exploitation of a parent's permissiveness by a highly dominating child may pave the way for a complete reversal of attitude.

Finally, the influence of parent attitudes is limited and counteracted by other environmental variables impinging upon the child. Balancing forces are always at hand to soften extreme practices and points of view. The deviant parent must first contend with the objections of his spouse, and later with the opposition of relatives, neighbors and friends. Some effort is usually made to conform, at least outwardly, to the child-rearing norms of the subculture in which the parent holds membership. As the child grows older he is increasingly exposed to the direct influence of persons other than parents — to siblings, age-mates, teachers and other adults. Frequently these contacts can serve as a useful corrective in minimizing, if not reversing, the harmful effects induced by inappropriate parent attitudes. Children may incidentally teach each other many lessons that some parents can never hope to transmit because of resistances set up by unfortunate aspects of the parent-child relationship. And many children who never manage to identify with their parents find a satisfactory substitute in a relative, teacher or parent of a playmate.

Parents as Representatives and Interpreters of the Culture

Adding to the complexity of the parent-child relationship is the fact that parents are under obligation both to interpret the culture to the child and to serve as its official representative in dealing with him. They are under pressure to produce and deliver an individual who is a reasonable facsimile of the prevailing cultural pattern, an individual who shares particular values and traditions, who channelizes his needs in acceptable directions, who achieves certain criteria of maturity, who learns the proper restraints and inhibitions with respect to aggressive and hedonistic impulses, and who accepts institutionalized substitutes for individual needs and preferences. In fulfilling this role the parent has to think about his own reputation and be sensitive to public opinion. This requires that he exercise a certain abritrary authority in regulating the direction of his child's development. If he has himself assimilated the values and expectations of his culture with respect to the goals of child-rearing, relatively little difficulty ensues in playing the role of cultural representative. If his personal values and attitudes are at variance with cultural norms, he is often resentful and ambivalent about his role, sometimes revealing open defiance, but more often conforming verbally while covertly following his own inclinations.

Sometimes the culture itself sets up standards that are incompatible with each other. It is doubtful, for example, whether the exponents of a highly permissive home have thought through the implications of its effects in producing the type of childhood character structure that is acceptable in the more highly structured and authoritarian atmosphere prevailing in school, peer group and neighborhood homes. And how does this permissively reared child fare as an adult in our highly stratified society which places such a premium on submission to the authority derived from hierarchical status? Here the parent is caught between two fires: If he ignores the doctrines promulgated by the professional experts he must bear the guilt of irrevocably "ruining" his child's personality, and stand exposed as an ignorant, self-indulgent parent. On the other hand, if he follows their advice, he may raise a child whose personality structure is poorly adapted to meet the actual demands and requirements of the culture.

That these demands are entirely inconsistent with the reasonably expected outcomes of the very practices which are advocated is unfortunate, but nevertheless true and quite beside the point. It merely provides another example of the principle that the culture, like the individual, can tolerate considerable internal inconsistency (which is both obvious and overt) without feeling especially disturbed by it or obliged to relegate the less acceptable member of the inconsistent pair to the domain of repressed, unavailable, unmentionable, and unrecognizable beliefs and motivations. People who shudder at the exposure of inconsistency, believing it to be portentous of imminent personality breakdown, nurture a conception of human behavior that mistakenly equates the logic of behavioral organization with the logic of abstract propositions and their symbolic representations.

If we accept the view that parents play a dual role as individual agents and as representatives of the culture, what relationships might we postulate as prevailing between the contradictory demands of each role? In what ways does the child's indirect exposure to the culture through the medium of parental interpretation differ from the more direct type of exposure that he later receives at the hands of other cultural agents? Apart from individual differences in perceiving what the goals and standards of the culture actually are, the attitudes and training practices of different parents within a given culture reveal heterogeneity primarily because of differences in personality needs and structure. We can predict that regardless of the attitudes and values held by the culture at large, a parent will always express his own personality needs in the parent-child relationship. Therefore, basic categories and dimensions of attitude, such as acceptance, domination, protection, etc., will be universally distributed in all cultures although varying in form of expression according to the stereotyped idioms peculiar to a given culture.

If differences between individual preferences and culturally sanctioned practices arise, several alternatives are open to the parent. To begin with, the latter are seldom spelled out with complete absence of ambiguity and equivocation, or made explicit in specific detail with respect to finer shades of meaning and intention. The parent's behavior is not expected to conform to some single, absolute standard but to fall within a range of acceptability, the limits of which vary from culture to culture. He is ordinarily granted a certain leeway which permits him to express his difference by selective emphasis or omission of various aspects of the cultural prescription without exceeding the limits of socially approved parental behavior. If his individual needs conflict more drastically with the cultural prescription, it is likely that the former will give rise to his actual feelings and attitudes, while the latter will govern the official point of view and the overt behavior he exhibits to the world. And since parents' attitudes and feelings generally play a more important role in the parent-child relationship then their verbalisms and behavior, we can predict that parents who attempt to conform to a cultural norm of child-rearing (while having convictions in the opposite direction) will usually induce behavior in their children that more closely approximates their own needs and desires than the outcomes of the culturally favored practices to which they give lip service.

The child's experience with the version of the culture indirectly transmitted to him through his parents differs in many fundamental respects from the version he acquires himself as a result of direct contact with it. His parents always represent *specific* embodiments of cultural values rather than composite pictures or abstractions of many different examples sharing a common quality. This gives the specificity of the home models a breadth and magnitude of influence which is seldom matched by the specific attributes of any subsquent experience. For example, his conception of the appropriate male and female social sex roles is a composite of innumerable specific experiences with boys and girls and men and women. But this must compete in influence with specific portraits of mother and father, which because of their primacy and unique qualities constitute a general category in themselves despite their specificity.

In addition, the home "environment is not only a social one but . . . is also intensely personal and intimate. Rewards and punishments come with simple directness from persons, never from abstract symbols" [*61*]. Home, therefore, can never be more than a rough facsimile of what the child can anticipate at the hands of the wider culture. He can only predict that it (the culture) will treat him more objectively, casually and impersonally [*61*]. He can expect no special privileges, no special concern with his welfare and no general bias in his favor. And if he regarded his parents as unpredictable, he will find this difficulty multiplied a hundredfold on the outside as he is confronted by a much larger array of persons about whose attitudes and reaction sensitivities he knows substantially less.

WHY PARENTS CAN EXERT SO MUCH INFLUENCE ON CHILDREN'S PERSONALITY DEVELOPMENT

The strategic position enjoyed by parents in relation to their children's personality development seems at once to be so self-evident as to eliminate any need for further analysis. Surprisingly enough, however, the exploration and differentiation of a self-evident proposition often proves to be unexpectedly illuminating.

The first factor contributing to the parent's tremendous influence on the child's personality development is derived from the fact that the function of biological care and protection is from almost the very beginning exercised within the framework of an interpersonal relationship [*61*]. By the time an infant is three months old, he experiences highly important visceral satisfactions and frustrations in a psychological setting. Several months later as a functional concept of self emerges, the survival and protective values of his parents become evident to him: The child perceives the causal relationship between parents and need-satisfaction sequences, begins to appreciate his executive dependence, and derives a sense of volitional power from awareness of the frequent relationship between the vocalization of his desires and their subsequent gratification by familiar figures. As a result of all these early developments, the parents assume a position of central importance in relation to visceral satisfactions, and become associated in a benevolent and altruistic light with the crucial issues of biological care, protection and survival.

What makes this interpersonal flavoring of early infant care possible in the first place is the relatively precocious development of the social and emotional components of personality.

> "The significant part of this emotional development is that during the whole of the first year emotional discrimination is manifested approximately two months earlier than any other form of perception. The

three months smiling response, which is the infant's smiling recognition of the human partner's face, appears at an age at which no other object is recognized. Even food, the most familiar object in the baby's life, is recognized only more than two months later. The displeasure which the infant manifests at four months when left by its partner appears two months earlier than the displeasure shown by the child when its toy is taken away. The eight months anxiety shown by the child when confronted with strangers is a sign that it has achieved the capacity to discriminate between friend and stranger. This appears two months earlier than the child's capacity to differentiate toys and other objects from each other. This emotional development acts as the trail breaker for all other perceptive developments during infancy" [*369*].

Nevertheless it should be realized that a high degree of verbal and conceptual ability is not necessary to perceive the grosser factors entering into an interpersonal relationship. Even a young puppy can discriminate quite well between the dispositions and relative status positions of the various members of the household—whom it is best to obey and whom he can afford to ignore; whom he can safely approach and whom he had best avoid; whom he may nip with impunity and with whom he dare not take liberties; between the infant who pinches him out of ignorance and curiosity, the child who pulls his tail out of mischievous cruelty, and the adult who kicks him out of bad temper and malice.

As a result of the intimate relationships prevailing between interpersonal factors and visceral function, significant disturbances in the former, such as extreme emotional deprivation or separation from the mother, may give rise to dangerous loss of weight, developmental retardation and a high mortality rate [*369*].

Another obvious reason for the prepotency of the parent's influence lies in the previously mentioned fact that the parent presents a highly biased and personal picture of the culture to his child. And because this is the child's initial and most important contact with the culture, what would otherwise constitute just a special case becomes equivalent in influence to a general category; what ordinarily would only be a specific illustration of a general principle, or just one of a large number of ways of doing the same thing becomes *the only* way.

The infant's social environment is "extraordinarily restricted" for a relatively long period during which time he is exposed to no other models of behavior than his parents. The influence of these models is further enhanced by the fact that "at no later period is the development so rapid, so turbulent and so conspicuous" [*369*]. During succeeding stages of development until adolescence, the parent constitutes the most important single variable in the child's psychological field, wielding tremendous power.

> "Adults have at their disposal every means they need for enforcing their demands. They control nearly all the sources of a small child's satisfactions—food and drink, warmth, cleansing and comfort, play and protection, emotional acceptance and mothering, relief from loneliness, from restraint and pain. Adults can, therefore, reward conformity to their wishes by granting satisfactions, and punish non-conformity by withholding them. They can provide compelling motives for the resisting or disobedient child by introducing pain, confinement or immediate ostracism, accompanied by appropriate gestures, words and general manner. Later on, the gesture, word or manner alone becomes an adequate stimulus to control and coerce the child by arousing in him the anticipatory tensions that we call anxiety" [*61*].

All of the factors thus far mentioned as accounting for the parent's influence on the child's personality development—his protective and altruistic role, his association with the important bodily satisfactions of infancy, his extensive power in regulating the child's life, his primacy as a personal representative of the culture (which enhances the specificity of his role as model far beyond its intrinsic importance), the child's restricted environment and relatively rapid rate of growth—can be illustrated in the way the child acquires values and attitudes. All add directly or indirectly to the parent's capacity to influence the child's value and attitude formation by means of authority, prestige- or loyalty-suggestion, and to magnify their effect in terms of achieving a maximum degree of change with a given expenditure of training effort. These varieties of suggestion also operate maximally in a wholly unstructured and undifferentiated field as represented by attitude and value content where no other frame of reference is available.

Other explanatory principles can also be successfully applied to account for the prepotent influence of early childhood experience.

It is commonly observed "that unless behavior trends in one phase of personality development are modified deliberately or by chance, they are very likely to help determine the direction of development in a succeeding phase" [*61*]. But what appears on first sight to be a phenomenon analagous to the physical principle of inertia can be explained more satisfactorily in psychological terms by making use of the concepts of canalization [*288, 289*] and reaction-sensitivity [*61*]. Whenever a need is initially satisfied by a specific mechanism (i.e., response or goal-object), which is then repeatedly and satisfactorily reinforced by successful repetition of the need-satisfaction sequence, the particular mechanism (which originally was only one of a large number of potentially adequate responses) becomes endowed with the unique property of being the *sole* adequate satisfier of the need in question.

Once established, these

> "habitual modes of reaction . . . sensitize him to certain aspects of his experience and dull him to others. When he enters new surroundings and meets new people, he is more ready to respond in one direction than another, and this readiness itself acts selectively to bring him more of similar kinds of experience. Thus he develops his basic personality organization by a continuing process, certain behavior trends initiated early in life being reinforced and perpetuated through his similar reactions in related situations later on" [*61*].

Nowhere, as already pointed out, is this tendency to generalize attitudes and adjustive techniques originally learned in relation to parents more evident than in the sphere of interpersonal relations with other persons [*61*]. This propensity for generalizing the application of early interpersonal reaction tendencies on a social level becomes one of the more crucial channels through which parental influences continue to affect the course of later adjustment and personality development.

THE IMPACT OF PARENT-CHILD RELATIONSHIPS ON EGO DEVELOPMENT

Now that the stability, the limiting factors, the connections with the wider culture, and the channels of influence and interaction in the parent-child relationship have been explored, we are prepared to review the role of parent attitudes in bringing about significant shifts in the course of ego development. For purposes of convenience, the examination of this role can be organized under three major headings corresponding to the major stages of ego development, i.e., presatellization, satellization, and maturation, with an additional section devoted to socialization.

Presatellization

An outstanding feature of the parent-child relationship during the presatellizing period is that parents are universally more permissive, tolerant, and indulgent[3] than at any later time. This holds true for all varieties of parents. Even the parent who will subsequently prove to be rejecting seems to show some deference for the infant's extreme helplessness and for public sentiment relating to appropriate parent behavior under these circumstances. Compared to what the infant will face later on, he lives in an idyllic, child-centered world greatly concerned with his comfort and welfare while demanding little in return. But this paradisiacal situation does not last forever.

> "As a child grows in strength and general skill, more and more of his behavior is brought under regulations that govern the patterns by which his elders live. He is inducted into new rhythms of function, of need and satisfaction, of quiescence and activity. Crying and restlessness at the wrong time, for example, are deliberately ignored, whereas at first they brought him company, milk, soothing or a change. During the weaning process, a bottle and then semi-solids in a hard spoon gradually replace the warm, soft breast. Eventually, the child must learn to eliminate and evacuate at predetermined times and in arbitrarily chosen places if he is to keep the security of parental approval and win release from the toilet chair" [*61*].

It so happens that by design or otherwise this early indulgence is a very wise practice. Delay in need-gratification, by giving rise to intense visceral stimulation, originally evokes an unlearned response of displeasure. When a sense of volition and feelings of omnipotence emerge, displeasure can become differentiated into rage, for needs are then expressed in volitional form with an anticipatory set of immediate compliance. It is this volitional set plus the previous association of delay with displeasure that accounts for the invariability of the frustration-rage sequence. Frustration tolerance—the ability to bear delay without responding immediately with the primitive rage pattern—is the outcome of a learning process requiring considerable experience in a favorable setting. Before it can be acquired the infant has to learn through gradual dosing that delay does not necessarily mean denial, that the environment is not really capricious but can usually be counted on to "come through" despite initial thwarting. After he gains this sense of security in the general reliability of his surroundings, and begins to appreciate that his needs will be satisfied without vociferous and importunate demanding on his part, he gradually becomes more able to regard delay as less threatening and to endure it with greater equanimity. With maturity also come increasing opportunities for acquiring a more adequate set of responses to frustration that will have more adaptive value than uncontrolled outbursts of temper.

On the other hand, thwarting in excess of developmental capacity or readiness for same and in the absence of an established level of confidence in the benevolence of the environment, provides no opportunity for exposure to the conditions under which frustration tolerance can be learned. It can only "lead a child to develop habitual rage reactions to any frustration, restriction and criticism" [*61*].

This justification of infantile indulgence on the basis of developmental incapacity for a high order of frustration tolerance seems to be more relevant to the actual situation in infancy than the following rationale proposed by Mowrer and Kluckhohn:

> "A delayed, gradual and gentle imposition of renunciations is also the surest basis for flexibility of personality. If renunciations are hurriedly and harshly imposed, the infant's 'ego' (totality of skill habits) is likely to be so weak that repression will be his only means of resolving the conflicts thus produced. The more this occurs, the more later behavior is likely to be compulsively automatic and rigid in the face of changing reality demands"[4] [*135*].

While there may be a choice between repression and other more integrative forms of adjustment in later childhood, it is hardly likely that repression constitutes an important adjustive mechanism in early infancy. Hence, as a rationale for indulgence in the first few years of life, when the need is most imperative, this explanation is not very convincing.

Despite the very possible relationship between gradual dosing of frustration and the development of frustration tolerance, the weight of evidence goes against the hypothesis that infants are sensitive to subtle aspects of parent attitudes or that extensive defects in physical and emotional development can follow from minor forms of mishandling. Even if we concede the fact that rejecting, anxious, domineering and inflexible parents may cause "tense, unsatisfied behavior" in infants [*61*], or retard the development of frustration tolerance, such effects are in no sense crucial for ego development or irreversible. They must be evaluated in the light of the infant's relatively primitive perceptual sensitivity, and the relatively unformed and unsophisticated state of his ego, which also reduces the potentially traumatic impact of attitudes that would affect an older child quite detrimentally.

Thus, all of the major dimensions of the parent-child relationship which are so crucial for later stages of ego development seem relatively unimportant for the essential ego development tasks of infancy. Overdominating and overprotecting parents, parents who value their children only for ulterior motives, and parents who are basically rejecting despite a veneer of affection all seem to provide an adequate enough environment for the development of the omnipotent ego structure. Only gross neglect and extreme emotional deprivation such as occurs in foundling homes leads to retardation or failure in emotional, social and ego development [*155, 369*]. Even where infants are raised with only a minimum of attention, in the absence of fondling and stimulation [*79*], or "under conditions of great restraint" [*80*], evidence of developmental retardation is not apparent. The symptoms of apathy, anxiety and depression which Spitz describes in eight-month-old infants suddenly deprived of their mothers [*368*] must be interpreted with caution. It should be pointed out that these infants were not only habituated "since birth to the care and attention of their mothers" [*303*], but also had developed a sense of security exclusively in relation to a single person. We do not know if these symptoms would have arisen if the infants had been accustomed to less constant attention or to attention at the hands of several individuals. At any rate it should be appreciated that abrupt withdrawal of care and attention under any circumstances is a gross rather than a subtle condition of parent attitude, and, therefore, adds little support to the contention that infants are sensitive to the slightest variations in the emotional attitudes of parents [5] [*79*].

In commenting upon the unsatisfactory physical development and the high mortality rate in infants attributed by Ribble and Spitz to lack of sufficient "mothering," Orlansky raises the following crucial question:

> "The high death rate in foundling homes, despite satisfactory hygienic conditions, has been cited as evidence of the child's need for attention and love if it is to survive; however, it is unclear whether love or individualized care is the crucial desideratum here (any uniform institutional regime which is not adjusted to the different constitutions of its members is apt to lose those members whose constitutions can not adjust to it)" [*303*].

The supposition that the practices of anxious, rejecting, extrinsically valuing, overdominating, or inconsistent parents create anxiety and insecurity for young infants is also subject to question. The manifestations of extreme irritability and low frustration tolerance which they do exhibit cannot be equated with feelings of insecurity or anxiety; and, as already pointed out, evidence of deeper emotional disturbance in infants has only been produced by abrupt separation from the mother or by extreme and rapid fluctuations in her attitudes. Such changes as do occur may more properly be referred to as impairment of the child's sense of security in his environment rather than as manifestations of anxiety since threats to self-esteem are not involved. Disturbances of the parent-child relationship such as over- and underdomination and overprotection on the one hand, and rejection and overvaluation on the other hand, may give rise to insecurity and anxiety respectively in an older infant, but only when the structure of his ego is more firmly constituted, and when his perceptual acuity and intellectual understanding are sufficiently developed to enable him to become aware of and grasp the implications of these parent attitudes.

Satellization

New aspects of the parent-child relationship enter the picture as the child is confronted with the crisis of ego devaluation. This is not only a reflection of greater crystallization of ego structure and of gains in social and intellectual maturity, but is also indicative of selective sensitization of perception in line with the current needs of ego development. As the issue of satellization arises, new dimensions of the parent-child relationship that were formerly not very important must be perceived and evaluated, namely, acceptance-rejection, and intrinsic-extrinsic-valuation. The grosser criteria determining the adequacy of the relationship up to this point —the minimum requirements of care, attention, consistency and affection—give way to these more subtle categories of parent attitudes.

It is not implied that everything that has gone before can be forgotten or that other parent attitudes are completely irrelevant. A child made hyperirritable by an overstern and inflexible regimen is less disposed to satellize than a child whose relationship with the parent is more relaxed and cordial. Satellization tends to come later when a parent's attitudes veer toward indulgence rather than toward moderate and consistent firmness. Nevertheless the crucial determinants of satellization which enable a child to accept volitional dependency and to seek derived status are the realization that he is genuinely accepted and valued for himself; for in the absence of these two parent attitudes, the potential advantages of satellization (i. e., the acquisition of a guaranteed and stable derived status with the corollary assurance of intrinsic security and adequacy) are vitiated, making it a totally unacceptable alternative. Hence, it no longer suffices at this time for a parent to exhibit the outward manifestations of attention and affection. Evidence of an accepting attitude in the smaller and more subtle aspects of a parent's feelings and actions is required. Mere effusiveness is unsatisfactory if the child is only regarded as a "projected object of parental self-love" [*23*].

The importance of the parent attitudes of unconditional acceptance and intrinsic valuation for the child's ego development is exactly as crucial as the child's need for acquiring a derived status. There is no other stable or non-marginal status which a child can comfortably hold in our culture. Once confronted with the reality demands and the perceptual insights that make his omnipotent ego structure untenable, he must either be able to satellize or find himself caught between two other highly unsatisfactory alternatives: complete devaluation (which is too traumatic and abrupt to be acceptable) or retention of ego aspirations that are predicated upon the attainment of a primary status based upon his own performance ability. Such aspirations are not only beyond the reach of a child, but are also unrealistically and inflexibly high because of the lack of ego devaluation and the absence of any sustaining intrinsic status. Self-esteem, therefore, becomes completely dependent upon extrinsic criteria, and almost inevitably doomed to undergo chronic and drastic impairment. The consequences of non-satellization for this and other components of infantile ego structure and their implications for the development of anxiety, for maturation, conscience formation, mode of value assimilation, and socialization have already been described elsewhere in some detail.

In any satellizing relationship where the status of the subordinate individual is derived exclusively from the fact of relationship to the ascendant individual, two conditions are implicit: the latter's pre-eminence in the eyes of the former is such that he can arbitrarily (merely by willing so) confer intrinsic status on the object of his choice by endowing him with an absolute and irrefutable value that requires no substantiation or independent validation. If this is so, what he so arbitrarily gives he can also just as arbitrarily take away. Derived status, therefore, can only be enjoyed as long as the approval of the status-giving person is retained. The satellizer's need for approval thus becomes the central motivational force in his psychological field, influencing his perception of the world in such a way that its content mirrors the attitudes and the values of the preceptor whose approval he wishes to retain. Hence it is that the granting and withdrawal of approval constitutes the most effective method of control available to the parents of satellizers.

The advantages of satellization in an adult dominated world are so apparent that most children are loath to reject this alternative (once the various stages of resistiveness are overcome), even when the prerequisite conditions are barely fulfilled. They are more than willing in their eagerness to give their parents the benefit of the doubt and to interpret rejecting attitudes charitably. This in fact is one of the more hopeful factors in reversing the damage wrought by earlier rejection if the parent's attitude can be changed before it is too late. The child is generally eager to accept the change, to welcome the parent's advances, and to forget that it had ever been any different.

Maturation

Parents exercise a maturational function throughout the satellizing period even if it is placed within the framework of derived status and volitional dependency. Thus, long before the child will ever be in a position to utilize these attributes of maturity in furthering his own independent ego demands, he has made considerable progress toward the attenuation of hedonism and the acquisition of increased executive independence, moral responsibility, frustration tolerance, and self-critical ability.

It is important to realize, that these gains in maturity do not arise spontaneously and automatically out of the needs of the child. They are more than a reflection of increased readiness to undergo training as a result of increased capacity proceeding from growth, although this factor must also not be ignored. Involved in every noteworthy maturational advance relative to ego structure is some change in the expectations of the significant persons in the child's environment which is enforced by some coercive form of pressure. On both counts parents occupy a strategic position. Not only do their own expectations change as a result of altered needs and new perceptions of the child's behavioral capacity, but also channeled through them are changing cultural expectations of appropriately mature behavior at various stages of development. In both cases the parent is also the most appropriate agent for applying whatever coercive measures are necessary for effecting conformity of the child's behavior to the changed pattern of expectations.

To be sure, forces apart from those originating within or transmitted through the parent operate to stimulate and enforce maturational progress. Growth in motor, intellectual, social, emotional, or sexual capacity not only provokes new parental expectations, but aso generates new needs in the child for functioning on a more mature level. Increased capacity to perceive his own biosocial position realistically and to appreciate the adaptive value of maturation also facilitates progress during transitional phases of ego development. Pressures for maturation both originate from and are enforced by the school and the child's peer group, especially during adolescence, when they (primarily the latter) take over from parents primary responsibility for the training function. Lastly should be mentioned coercive influences coming from the child himself, i.e., internalized parental and social expectations, feelings of guilt, and anxiety pertaining to the outcome of admission to prerogatives to which he aspires but is not yet sure of attaining.

The parent's methods of compelling conformity to his expectations vary at different stages of development. Prior to satellization he chiefly utilizes physical restraint, threats, reward and punishment, while holding out the offer of derived status. During the satellizing period, he can rely upon approval and disapproval, prestige authority and the moral restraints of conscience and guilt feelings. In the early stages of desatellization when the child's quests for extrinsic status are essentially bids for parental approval, he can best encourage their continuation on a more independent basis by extending genuine appreciation of whatever efforts are made. Finally, in effecting adolescent maturation, the most effective coercive weapon at his disposal is withdrawal of the child's derived status.

In general, the individual parent (like the individual culture) exercises little influence in determining the essential direction of maturation, although he may influence some of its more specific aims. Certain general considerations which operate in every culture, namely, the needs of individual and cultural survival (see pp. 120-121), determine the criteria of personality maturity that prevail almost universally, i.e., the relative attenuation of hedonism, the growth of executive and volitional independence, greater moral responsibility, greater concern with extrinsic status, etc.; and within the framework of these general goals, particular cultures differentially weight various components, extole different patterns of personality traits, and provide specific values and rewards which its members cherish and strive for.

The parent's role in relation to the cultural goals of maturation is a complex one. In general these goals further rather than conflict with his own needs and desires. At the termination of infancy, he welcomes the increased self-sufficiency of the child since it frees him for other tasks, and approves of the shift in ascendence-submission which gives him greater control and direction of the child's activities. And during his offspring's adolescence he generally contemplates with satisfaction his own forthcoming release from the burden of support and responsibility. Nevertheless, individual personality needs of the parent which predispose him to be overprotecting, under- or overdominating usually prevail despite cultural pressures to the contrary, thereby resulting in greater or lesser deviation from the cultural ideal of maturity (see pp. 259-261).

The question of whether maturation comes about spontaneously whenever the child reaches a certain level of readiness determined by his own growth, or whether it arises in response to both changes in readiness and to pressures emanating from changed expectations is no longer an academic one. A large body of parents—largely influenced by the teachings of Gesell and the doctrines of ultra-progressive (permissive) education—now subscribes wholeheartedly to the former view in their child-rearing practices. They interpret the resistiveness (which is provoked by parental pressures to make the child move on to the next stage of ego development) as proof of their theory that external pressure of any kind is unwise, and that development unfolds in due time if left to its own devices. "Remove the pressures," they insist, "and watch the negativism disappear." This is undoubtedly true; but it still has to be demonstrated that personality maturation would also occur under these conditions. On the face of it, for reasons already discussed at length (see pp. 184-191), this possibility does not appear very likely, although it is obvious that least resistance will be provoked if pressure is applied at the time of optimal readiness. There is also no basis for believing that the parent's rapport with the child will be permanently damaged by outbursts of negativism, or that his authority role is in any way incompatible with a friendly, relaxed and cordial parent-child relationship.

Several other misconceptions are also shared by the "spontaneous maturation" school of thought. External measures of control are completely unnecessary, they argue, because *self*-discipline is both more desirable and more effective. There is no gainsaying the truth of the latter part of the propostion, but from a genetic standpoint the proposition as a whole constitutes a *non-sequitor*. The process of internalization is a very gradual one, and by definition presupposes the original existence of external controls, since obviously nothing can be internalized which does not first possess an external form. Furthermore, even after internalization is fairly well established, the presence of external controls in the background serves a salutory effect; since it is well known that in an atmosphere of complete permissiveness where no limits are set, even the most self-disciplined child (or adult) is tempted to take advantage of the situation.

Socialization

One of the most important consequences of early parent-child relationships for ego development is the pronounced tendency for the child's later socialization pattern with peers and other adults to reflect the same type of interpersonal attitudes that he originally adopted with his first socializers, his parents. That such continuity prevails is not at all surprising in view of the conclusions already reached regarding "the potentialities of early behavior trends for later personality organization" and the reasons for same (see pp. 264-265). To the child, the world of interpersonal relations is at first completely unstructured; and for the first few years of life, most of the differentiation of this unstructured field is performed by his parents. Hence, in the absence of any other framework of reference for basing his expectations of what people in the outside world are like, it is most natural for him to refer to the model provided by his parents. Also, as already indicated, the primacy of a given model in relation to an amorphous field of experience endows its specificity with disproportionate significance, making it the conceptual equivalent of the abstracted or composite content of an entire series of models (see page 263).

In terms of Gardner Murphy's canalization theory, the specific kinds of interpersonal experience provided by the parents acquire unique value as satisfiers for the child's interpersonal needs. Moreover, habituation to these particular parental responses creates needs *de novo* for them in the child, needs which can only be satisfied by the special conditions which produce them in the first place. Thus, in approaching new social situations, the child tends both to expect the same type of behavior from others as he received from his parents, and (if he found the latter satisfying) to demand it in fulfillment of his needs. He is sensitized by both experience and current needs to be on the lookout for, perceive and respond selectively to only restricted segments of his total range of social experience. And to the extent that this past experience in the home provides him with a very unreal preview of future social situations which will confront him, his interpersonal expectations will prove unrealistic; and to the extent that his parents create unique needs in him which only they are willing and able to satisfy, other social experience must perforce prove unsatisfying.

The child's willingness to face the hazards of social life are also largely determined by his interpersonal experience in the home. It doesn't take him too long to discover that strangers will generally treat him more casually and impersonally, and with less concern for his interests than he was accustomed to receive from his parents. "Every child is bound to suffer rebuffs, belittling, discrimination, mishandling and downright defeat from time to time at the hands of his associates" [*61*]. To be sure, his ability either to absorb these rebuffs and re-enter the fray, or to leave the field and withdraw within himself or within the protection of the home depends partly on the innate "thickness of his skin." But more, perhaps, depends on the nature of the parent-child relationship. His initial approach, for example, can be made without trepidation if, on the basis of friendly relations with parents, he is led in advance to expect the best from people unless given cause to believe otherwise. If on the basis of his home experience his expectations of social life are realistic, the chances are less that he will be instantly repelled by the actual situation that confronts him. Also

"if a child is to get the most out of his social operations in the wider community, he must above all have a secure and dependable home base, one that he can leave without anxiety, one he can return to confidently for supplies, repairs and reassurance. The protection of home is necessarily limited in scope. No parent can possibly spread it out over the whole neighborhood, neither can an older sibling be expected to be forever watching over a younger brother or sister. . . . If, however, he can be sure of his home, if life there provides emotional security and support when he needs them, a child can learn to absorb neighborhood reverses" [*61*].

Other reasons rooted in the parent-child relationship also exist for prompting the latter to avoid social relationships. The overprotected, underdominated, or overdominated child possesses behavioral and personality traits that make acceptance by the group difficult. Neither can the group undertake to satisfy imperious individual needs for special protection, invariable deference or continuous direction. Under the circumstances, group life must inevitably prove distasteful and unsatisfying, inviting retreat to the home. Furthermore, the overprotected child is oversensitized to the possibility of physical mishandling and unfair treatment at the hands of his age-mates, while the rejected child is especially fearful of a repetition of the rejection he experiences at home, and the overdominated child (who has never learned to protect his rights) is continually fearful of being duped and exploited. All of these reactions of avoidance and withdrawal from participation in group experience tend to drastically reduce the individual's social experience to the point where it becomes impossible for him to learn realistic social roles. And in the process of utilizing withdrawal as an adjustive technique he usually acquires an habitual introversion which further restricts the scope of his social proclivities.

A child's socialization pattern is also profoundly affected by whether or not he has undergone satellization, which in turn is an outcome of the parent-child relationship. To the satellizing child, group membership provides derived status and constitutes an intrinsic ego support. He experiences a certain spontaneous joy and enthusiasm in group activity which follows from the "we-feeling" associated with group relatedness. To the non-satellizer, on the other hand, the field of interpersonal relations is just another arena in which one contends for extrinsic status and additional ego aggrandizement. There is no identification with or self-subordination to group interests, and no possibility of deriving spontaneous satisfaction out of gregarious activity. Every social move is carefully deliberated for the possible advantages that may accrue from it, and the currency of social interchange is supplied by the synthetic manufacture of attitudes, remarks and behavior which can be construed as conventionally appropriate for the specifications of a given situation.

A similar dichotomy prevails in the type of relationship entered into with parent-surrogates. The satellizing child seeks to define it as nearly as possible in the same terms and conditions that underlie his relationship with parents. This, of course, is rarely possible since non-parents are seldom able to extend unconditional acceptance; but the fault herein cannot be ascribed to the child's lack of willingness. He is, therefore, usually required to compromise and win the adult's acceptance, at least in part, by the quality of his performance. The non-satellizer, on the other hand, does not regard the parent-surrogate as a source of derived status, but as an emulatory model strategically useful for guiding and facilitating his own candidacy for a position of comparable prestige and prominence.

REVERSIBILITY OF EFFECTS OF PARENT-CHILD RELATIONSHIP

In previous sections we have examined both the mechanisms making possible and the factors limiting the tremendous impact of parent-child relationships on the latter's personality development. Now we can profitably turn our attention to the personality and ego effects wrought by this relationship, and inquire under what conditions they will prove to be relatively reversible or irreversible. The crucial factors involved seem to be (a) the particular effect under consideration, (b) the child's age and the developmental level when subjected to a given parent attitude, and (c) the age of the child when exposed to counteracting influences.

Generally speaking, it is more possible to undo or mitigate the consequences of non-satellization than it is to reverse the effects of satellization. The hypothesis has already been offered that, barring some overwhelming ego trauma[6] in later years, the occurrence of satellization tends to leave a permanent residue in personality structure which guarantees an inner core of security and adequacy feelings regardless of environmental vicissitudes. Whatever happens to self-esteem from this point on will, so to speak, be peripheral to the intrinsic self-acceptance achieved in early childhood. Greater reversibility, on the other hand, seems possible with respect to the consequences of non-satellization, providing that it is the outcome of parental rejection rather than overvaluation. Because the rejected child is reluctant to accept the verdict of rejection in the first place, and is only too glad to welcome a change of parent attitude, almost complete reversal of the effects of rejection can be accomplished—even (in the writer's clinical experience) as late as the seventh year of life. In the case of the overvalued child, the parent attitude is more stable and less subject to change; and the child himself is less disposed to satellize because he finds his grandiose ego aspirations not too untenable in his worshipful home environment. Later also, the rejected individual is more prone to enter into satellizing-like relationships with other persons and hence to achieve some measure of derived status (and intrinsic feelings of security and adequacy) which enables him to lower his unrealistically high aspirational level. The overvalued child, on the other hand, is too accustomed to deference and homage to submit to self-subordination, and too obnoxiously overbearing to be genuinely loved for himself.

Various defects in the outcome of socialization also differ in their gravity and prognosis. Failure to learn adequate social techniques of self-defense and self-assertion because of the habit of deference to the will of others (as occurs in overdominated, rejected and overprotected children) is more permanently damaging than the excessive and obnoxious self-assertion and aggression of underdominated and overvalued children. In the course of time, the latter learn to express their aggressiveness in more socially acceptable forms, while the former find it more agreeable and less hazardous (in terms of possible exploitation by others) to curtail their interpersonal relations to a minimum. The social isolation resulting from this withdrawal further limits the possibility of learning realistic social roles.

Tendencies toward introversion-extraversion, although strongly influenced by the agreeableness of initial social contacts and by a possible genetic predisposition toward "thickness" or "thinness of skin" are probably more reversible than originally believed. Marked changes in the social climate of a child such as are likely to occur when he first enters unsupervised group play or the more autonomous, demanding and status-giving peer culture of adolescence [*23*] can bring about unexpected shifts in this dimension of personality. These shifts appear especially marked if the environmental change is favorable to the expression of original trends which have been suppressed by an unusually extreme preceding environment. The same possibility probably holds true for other habitual adjustive techniques (i.e., projection, rationalization, etc.). The reversibility of anxiety states will receive extended treatment in the next chapter.

The second major factor affecting reversibility of the effects of parent attitudes is the age of the child when exposed to a particular aspect of the parent-child relationship. Generally speaking, the pre-school period (two to five) is most vulnerable to lasting damage from unfavorable parental influences. Prior to this period, the child is largely protected by his relative insensitivity to subtle aspects of parent attitudes, and by the fact that his ego development needs are crucially affected by only very gross dimensions of parent behavior, i. e., provision or deprivation of a minimal degree of care, attention and affection. Afterwards, since so large a part of basic personality structure is already laid, and since the child's environment is no longer restricted so drastically to the home scene, the introduction of a given parent attitude is less apt to lead to irrevocable consequences. But this statement requires considerable qualification since the importance of a particular parent attitude is related to its relevance for the developmental tasks of a given age period. It must be remembered that the crucial tasks of desatellization first arise in the elementary school period and are not completed until the conclusion of adolescence. Nor does a history of successful satellization facilitate in any way the desired outcome of the succeeding phase of desatellization. Hence, parent attitudes which retard the course of desatellization, i.e., overprotection, overdomination and underdomination, tend to be most damaging when manifested during the preadolescent and early adolescent period.

The same considerations hold true, with respect to the most efficacious age periods during which counteracting conditions can reverse previously established personality trends resulting from parent attitudes. Again, the pre-school period is the crucial age in which either desirable or undesirable effects attributable to preceding aspects of the parent-child relationship can be most easily reversed by a change of parent attitudes in the opposite direction. This fact is well known to child psychiatrists who take advantage of it by directing their main therapeutic efforts toward the parent rather than toward the child.

DIMENSIONS OF PARENT ATTITUDES

The preceding discussion of the impact of parent attitudes on personality development points up the importance for theoretical and research purposes of identifying and clearly defining as many significant discriminable variables as possible that are encompassed by the parent-child relationship. In no other way will it be possible to unambiguously determine the antecedents and consequences of various parent attitudes.

Levy's two-dimensional scale (acceptance-rejection; domination-protection) obviously represented a considerable advance over previous uni-dimensional scales such as acceptance-rejection. Its weaknesses lay in failing (1) to identify other crucial dimensions in the parent-child relationship such as intrinsic-extrinsic valuation; (2) to recognize the distinction between satellization and non-satellization, and the role of this difference in modifying the impact of other parent attitudes, e. g., the difference between an "indulged" satellizer and an "indulged" nonsatellizer; (3) to perceive the essential similarity as non-satellizers between the overvalued, extrinsicaly valued child and the rejected child despite obvious differences in other dimensions of parent attitudes; (4) to distinguish between overvaluation and "indulgence" (underdomination) even though the former refers to the parent's tendency to exaggerate the child's importance, while the latter makes reference to a submissive parent's excessive deference to a child's wishes; (5) to make clear the difference between the protective aspects of a parent's role (i. e., care and solicitousness) and the relative dominance of the latter in his relations with the child. In practice, Levy makes the extreme positions on the dominance scale subsidiary to, and subtypes of an excess of parental protection. Therefore, in the schema proposed below, protection and dominance are considered as separate variables; and the confusing term "indulgence," which variously refers to underdomination, overprotection or overvaluation, is discarded completely.

At the other extreme of explicitness in identifying parent attitudes, the scales of Champney [*65*] and Baldwin [*28*] are not only too numerous for practical use in elucidating developmental sequences, but also suffer from lack of differential weighting in terms of relationship to and significance for some unified conception of personality development. They do not help us to see how the child as a whole develops an ego structure out of a matrix of parent-child relationships, but leave us instead with a galaxy of discrete abstractions of parent attitudes (each of which represents a cluster of inter-related sub-attitudes) ordered statistically on the basis of magnitude of correlation with a discrete set of measurements of child behavior and personality. For example, it is useful for some purposes to know that when parents are rated high on democratic handling (holding the factor of "control" constant), children tend to be more active, aggressive, cruel, planful, curious and disobedient [*27*]. But the significance of this type of predictability based upon an atomistic approach cannot be very great if we are concerned with the problem of why a given child acquires or fails to acquire the major attributes of ego structure characteristic of various stages of ego development.

The dimensions of the parent-child relationship included in Table 2, therefore, are not the only ones which can possibly be identified and abstracted, but comprise the major aspects of this relationship which have relevance for the developmental tasks and processes postulated in this book as constituting the essential core of ego development in our culture.

TABLE 2.—*Dimensions of the Child-Parent Relationship*

Dimension (Parent Attitude or Behavior)	*Child's Position on Scale*	
	Upper Extreme	*Lower Extreme*
1. Emotional acceptance	Accepted	Rejected
2. Valuation of child for self or in terms of parent's ego needs	Intrinsically valued	Extrinsically valued
3. Dependence of acceptance on child's conformity to parent's behavioral standards	Unconditionally accepted	Conditionally accepted
4. Magnitude of valuation of child's importance	Overvalued	Undervalued
5. Protectiveness (care, solicitude)	Overprotected	Underprotected
6. Dominance (self-assertiveness or deference to child's will)	Overdominated	Underdominated
7. Level of aspiration for child	Overmotivated	Undermotivated
8. Criticism of child (overt or implied)	Overcriticized	Undercriticized
9. Appreciation (recognition) of child's competence	Overappreciated	Underappreciated

Although these dimensions are separate variables, permitting in theory an almost infinite number of combinations and permutations, the actual number of important combinations occurring in practice is sharply limited by a tendency toward patterning. First comes the distinction between parent attitudes leading to satellization and non-satellization respectively. Satellizers are all both emotionally accepted and intrinsically valued, whereas non-satellizers are either rejected and extrinsically valued, or accepted and extrinsically valued. The rejected group of non-satellizers is almost invariably underprotected [*388*], overdominated, underappreciated and overcriticized. The extrinsically valued group of non-satellizers is almost without exception overvalued, underdominated, overmotivated, undercriticized and overappreciated. For all practical purposes, therefore, it is most convenient to refer to these two groups of non-satellizers as "rejected" and "overvalued" respectively.

Greater variability in patterning prevails among satellizing children. Except for the uniformity provided by the two prerequisite attitudes, almost any combination of the remaining parent attitudes is possible. For example, there is no good reason for believing that the overprotected child must also be either under- or overdominated although this is frequently the case. It is also important to bear in mind that there are crucial differences between the satellizing and non-satellizing child even though they may share all other parent attitudes in common except for intrinsic valuation.

THE GENESIS OF REJECTING AND OVERVALUING PARENT ATTITUDES

The importance of understanding the origin of various parent attitudes is twofold: On the one hand, it greatly enhances appreciation of the feeling tones and motivations underlying a given attitude, thereby permitting greater insight into its repercussions on the child. On the other hand, it provides significant clues regarding the modifiability of the attitude in the parent and the reversibility of its effects on the child. In this section we shall focus our attention on the genesis of rejecting and overvaluing attitudes in the parent, since the origin of overprotecting, overdominating and underdominating attitudes has already been discussed.

The expression of rejection by the parent differs in its intensity, form and impact, and sometimes in its meaning depending on the child's age and stage of development. During early infancy, the parent seldom gives vent to the full force of his rejecting tendencies. These are tempered both by the appeal of the child's extreme helplessness and the constraining influence of cultural pressures. In addition, their impact on the child is lessened by the restricted range of his perceptual sensitivity and by the primitiveness of his emotional needs in relation to the requirements of his ego development. For these reasons we are unable to accept the prevailing opinion as expressed by Symonds:

> "Rejection is more serious the earlier it occurs; if a mother rejects her daughter for the first time in adolescence, the effect on personality may hardly be noticeable, but rejection of the child under a year old has a profound effect on the child's personality. Rejection is also more serious when the child's self is weak and unstructured; the individual with

strong positive self-valuation and self-esteem is not going to be easily bowled over by threats coming from without" [*389*].

While it is probably true that a more mature and stronger ego structure is better equipped to withstand trauma from any damaging psychosocial situation, a certain minimal degree of ego consolidation is necessary before any injury can be experienced. If susceptibility to grave damage is postulated, it is certainly legitimate to inquire whether the entity concerned possesses enough structure to make distortion possible.

In the second and third years of life, the ego structure takes more definite shape. Evidence of genuine emotional acceptance and intrinsic valuation is necessary for normal ego development, and the child becomes more sensitive to subtleties of parental emotional expression. His greater biosocial competence is less apt to elicit the deference formerly shown his infantile helplessness; and rejection under the guise of training receives more tolerance and approval from relatives and neighbors than does the administration of outright cruelty and neglect to a totally incompetent infant. It is at this time, therefore, that rejection will produce the most damaging results to personality structure.

A more versatile and mature ego structure with a well-established set of defenses protects the older child from the trauma of rejection. If he is a satellizer he is bolstered by an intrinsic core of self-esteem. There are also more opportunities to form satellizing and satellizing-like relationships to other adults and the peer group. Later rejection, however, is most likely to occur in the case of previously overvalued children in which case more serious consequences are the rule. The overvaluing parent may find his child's overbearing arrogance and his own servile role no longer tolerable; or he may reluctantly come to the conclusion that his son doesn't have the ability or talent to realize the ambitions he had projected onto him, or that another sibling is a more promising candidate for this role. This abrupt about-face, as already pointed out, is so unacceptable to the child and inspires such hatred and need for revenge that complete failure in ego maturation not uncommonly results (see pp. 243-244).

FACTORS INFLUENCING THE EMERGENCE OF REJECTING AND OVERVALUING ATTITUDES

Far from being the obvious, self-evident proposition most lay people and many psychologists hold it to be, we have had good reason to conclude from the foregoing that the relationship between rejection and personality development is an exceedingly complex one. No less complicated is the interaction between the numerous variables which determine (a) the potentialities of a given parent for developing a rejecting or overvaluing attitude, (b) the probability of its actual occurrence, and (c) the form which it tends to take. Predispositions toward developing parent attitudes which lead to non-satellization in the child reflect basic personality needs that originate in the childhood of the parent. These include a history of non-satellization, the presence of unresolved hostility, incapacity for relating emotionally to others, a propensity for projection of omnipotent ego aspirations on others, self-preoccupation resulting from anxiety, and self-preoccupation resulting from excessive self-valuation or self-love (narcissism). All of the other factors merely determine whether the potentionality will be actualized as well as other aspects of form and intensity of expression. They include the following: other tangential personality traits of the parents; the particular social norms to which the parents are exposed and their sensitivity to same; the parent's child-rearing philosophy; current situational factors affecting the parent's adjustment and anxiety level; the influence of conscience; the personality characteristics of the child in relation to the parent's expectations; and finally, the type of reactions given by the child to the experience of rejection.

Basic Personality Factors

The attitudes which an adult will display as a parent go back to his own childhood and the kind of relationship he enjoyed with his parents. This applies to both the general influence of the parent-child relationship on later personality structure, and the more specific influences which parents exert as models on the child's developing concept of what parental role and function is, and on the image of what *his* role as parent shall be. In some instances the hostile attitudes of a rejecting parent seem to stem at least in part from an unresolved residue of hostility towards his own parents which in turn resulted from a situation of rejection. By identifying with the role of his own rejecting parent, he vicariously gives vent to these feelings even though they are displaced quite distantly from their original object. This reaction, paradoxical as it may seem, often exists side by side with a violent conscious repudiation of the attitudinal role of his parents, resulting in a certain amount of ambivalence. If completely suppressed, it may give rise to an attitude of overprotection, which both reflects the danger he perceives for the child in view of his own hostile intentions, and also (by overaccentuating the opposite role) serves as a form of insurance against surreptitious expression of these feelings in an unguarded moment. More often, however, the greater part of a parent's overprotecting attitude reflects identification with his child (or with himself as child *vis-a-vis* his own parents), rather than with the latter's role. It represents a displacement of the anxiety he feels for himself rather than a reaction formation against the hostility he displaces from offending parent to innocent child.

Almost without exception in the writer's experience, the parents of non-satellizing children have been non-satellizers themselves, although it is by no means true that *all* non-satellizers have non-satellizing children. A history of non-satellization predisposes an individual toward ego hypertrophy, anxiety, narcissism, and inability to relate emotionally to others. The latter two characteristics are more serious in overvalued than in rejected persons, since they result from habituation to a one-way flow of affection and interest rather than from dread of emotional involvement for fear of repetition of an experience of rejection.

To an individual overburdened and harassed by chronic anxiety, who is constantly alerted to the dangers emanating from environmental hazards (which would constitute threats to no one else), self-preoccupation is an easily understandable condition. Under these circumstances, responsibility for the care and protection of a child may seem like a such a formidable and impossibly burdensome duty that rejection becomes a very likely alternative. Other equally possible alternatives are attempts to achieve ego enhancement through projection of omnipotent ego aspirations onto the child, and efforts directed toward anxiety-reduction through the mechanism of displacing same onto the latter.

A similar degree of self-preoccupation can result from constriction of the field of interest or emotional involvement to the immediate radius of self. When this occurs, only such matters as directly affect personal welfare are capable of eliciting interest or affective response. The individual is completely unable to become ego-involved or to bestir himself in the adjustive problems of anyone but himself. The type of rejection to which this leads, therefore, does not proceed from hostility or anxiety, but from disinterest in and indifference to the needs of others, and from incapacity for relating himself emotionally to them. Whatever hostility does exist arises from the child's utilization of his nuisance value to interfere with the parent's leisure, rest, recreation or career. However, if the parent is able to project his omnipotent strivings and regard the child as a legitimate extension of his own ego structure, he can conscientiously become as intensely ego-involved in promoting the latter's fortune as he would his very own.

Subsidiary Personality Factors

Given all of these personality predispositions toward becoming an overvaluing or rejecting parent, it does not necessarily follow that the non-satellizing individual will actually become one. Much depends on various situational factors as well as on other personality traits. For example, the prevailing level of anxiety which he experiences is profoundly affected by his ability, enterprise, composure, organizational skill, astuteness in handling others, facility in disguising his lack of self-confidence, etc. If he is well-endowed in all of these faculties, he is usually able to create an environment for himself which is secure, stable and relatively free from frustration or serious threat. Under such circumstances, anxiety is kept fairly well under control, and the intensity of self-absorption can be lessened. On the other hand, an anxiety-ridden person who is poorly endowed intellectually, emotionally unstable, socially obtuse, easily flustered, highly disorganized in work habits, and overtly anxious is almost always too harassed, panic-stricken and preoccupied with his own adjustive difficulties to be anything but a rejecting parent. Similarly, the more self-indulgent and viscerotonic an individual is, the more highly motivated he will be by hedonistic considerations, and the more resentful he will be of any responsibilities relating to the needs of others which interfere with the gratification of his own imperious visceral drives.

Lastly, factors related to moral responsibility constitute an important limiting condition for the emergence of rejecting attitudes. In non-satellizers the obligation to conform personally to a set of ethical values depends largely on the strength of an abstract sense of justice. If this is high, regardless of the potency of other relevant factors, a parent can inhibit a good part of the conscious hostility and culpable negligence underlying an attitude of rejection. In the effort to highlight "unconscious" sources of aggression, many writers seem to have lost sight of the fact that a large portion of the cruelty and hostility entering into everyday interpersonal relationships is carried on at a conscious level which is subject to voluntary inhibition. The pretty, dichotomized picture of *homo psychoanalyticus* with a conscious stratum populated by noble, socially acceptable and self-edifying impulses, and an unconscious stratum seething with phylogenetic and repressed amoral and aggressive urges is tremendously overdrawn. There is a tendency towards self-consistency and self-embellishment in the organization of conscious material, but it is never complete. Individuals can live quite comfortably with a good deal of awareness of their own inconsistency and of their own unconscionable impulses; and more morally reprehensible behavior is subject to voluntary control than the proponents of the "psychological" theory of delinquency are willing to admit.

Situational Factors

The prevailing level of anxiety or hostility that becomes manifest from underlying personality trends toward same is also affected by various situational factors. Latent residual hostility toward a parent is often reactivated by an unhappy marital relationship, and then displaced onto the child. This becomes especially evident if the parent feels that he is being rejected by his spouse in favor of the child. The original trauma of rejection by his own parent, either initially or following the birth of sibling, is thereby revived, and along with it whatever affective responses were originally evoked.

The entrance of an infant into a household also creates new adjustive problems which, depending on the circumstances involved, are often highly productive of anxiety. As already indicated, pre-existing economic hardship (intensified by the expense associated with childbearing and infant care) or separation from her husband may induce an acute exacerbation of anxiety in an expectant mother which causes her to adopt an attitude of rejection that would hardly be conceivable under less trying circumstances. This extreme degree of maternal anxiety may be communicated to the fetus, sensitizing him to hyperirritability and organic dysfunction [*365*] which is further compounded by a regimen of excessive frustration. All of this only adds to the burden of caring for the child by making additional demands on the mother's time, rest, sleep, energy and ingenuity, often taxing her health. Illness in the child may, of course (and usually does), arise independently of the mother's anxiety; but in any case by adding to the difficulties of infant care and thereby eliciting a higher level of overt anxiety, the likelihood of parental rejection is greatly enhanced.

The parent's disposition to put his rejecting inclinations into effect is also influenced by various characteristics and personality traits of the child, and by the type of response the latter makes to being rejected. If the child's sex, physique or temperament is at variance with the parent's hopes and preferences, or if he is physically deformed or mentally retarded, his chances of avoiding rejection are not very bright. A docile child's reaction to rejection usually encourages a hostile or narcissistic parent to continue this treatment since the parent is not even required to placate his nuisance value. An irritable, self-assertive and rebellious child, on the other hand, is apt to destroy completely the equilibrium of an anxiety-torn parent who utilizes this response as justification for the original rejection and the subsequent counter-aggression.

Finally, the unhampered expression of rejecting tendencies is limited by the prevailing cultural norms which more or less enjoin against this variety of parent attitude. It is doubtful, however whether this factor actually exerts much influence. A parent can always find "reputable excuses for hating a child" [*389*] if he is concerned with appearances or with maintaining a relatively unblemished portrait of himself as a "decent respectable person" [*389*]. Frequently enough, however, "the same narcissistic preoc cupation with himself that causes him to neglect his child provides him with a thick skin in the face of public or private criticism. The over-valuing parent, on the other hand, poses as a model of devotion," and is usually accepted as such by uncritical observers. If he does draw criticism, it is for failing to punish or restrain the anti-social activities of his child whom he generally tends to regard as beyond reproach.

Benign and Malignant Rejection

From the standpoint of outcome, therapy and prognosis, it is useful to borrow these descriptive categories frequently employed in medicine and to apply them to two different varieties of rejection. In the benign type the predisposing personality factors are not especially prepotent; hence, if other tangential personality traits and situational conditions are favorable, it is not inconceivable that a rejecting attitude might be completely avoided, or at least considerably mitigated. The intensity and frequency of expressed rejection is extremely variable, fluctuating with changes in the above factors. In the malignant form, on the other hand, greater constancy and uniformity of expression is maintained by the overwhelming influence of underlying personality traits which are only slightly affected by situational variables.

The benign form is more likely to occur in parents who were themselves rejected rather than overvalued as children (providing that an undue amount of unresolved hostility is not residual). In such cases, rejection is an outcome of the self-preoccupation resulting from acute anxiety, although as already pointed out, overprotection (anxiety-reduction) and overvaluation (vicarious ego enhancement) are also very possible alternatives. The malignant form of rejection tends to be exhibited more frequently by parents who were overvalued as children; but recapitulation of the overvaluing pattern is also a not infrequent occurrence under these circumstances.

This discrepancy in outcome of parental attitudes between individuals who had themselves been either rejected or overvalued during childhood is easily understandable in terms of differences in capacity for relating self emotionally to others. In rejected persons, this capacity, which is ever latent but inhibited by fear of rejection, has an excellent opportunity for overt expression in the form of warm and accepting parent attitudes, since little threat of rejection can be anticipated from an infant; whereas in overvalued individuals this same capacity is largely demolished and replaced by an all-embracing affective *intro-relatedness.*[7] Other differences accounting for this discrepancy in outcome include greater moral responsibility and sensitivity to public opinion, and less hedonistic motivation in the personality structure of rejected individuals.

Practically, the difference between benign and malignant rejection is very important. While the former may lead to nonsatellization in the child if it occurs persistently during the crucial pre-school period, its consequences are never as severe as the latter form and are always more reversible. Under favorable conditions, with anxiety kept under control, especially during the period from two to five, the rejection may be mild and spasmodic enough to be quite compatible with the child's satellization. The malignant form, on the other hand, is not only relatively constant, more severe, irreversible in its effects and independent of situational factors, but is also less remediable from the standpoint of the parent's responsiveness to psychotherapy.

Active and Passive Rejection

Parent attitudes of rejection can also be characterized along a scale of activity-passivity. The passive form is typical of malignant, narcissistic rejection in which the parent is too preoccupied with self-gratification to be concerned with the needs of anyone else. Hence, it is expressed through exaggerated neglect and indifference which ordinarily would tend to arouse guilt feelings in most persons. Considerable dulling of the sense of moral responsibility is, therefore, necessary before it can be practiced with equanimity.

The parent's chief object in handling the child is to "minimize his nuisance value" by regulating the relationship in such a way that she experiences a minimum of discomfort and inconvenience with the least possible expenditure of effort on her part. She accepts the duties of child-rearing not as an interesting challenge, but as a hateful and insufferable burden. In the home she demands conformity to a regimen tailor-made to suit her own convenience so that she is "annoyed" as infrequently as possible; but in relation to others, she is completely indifferent to her child's anti-social and super-aggressive tactics—just so long as she herself is not disturbed. Her designs work most successfully in the case of a docile, unassertive child who provides little or no overt resistance and typically adjusts through withdrawal. A more self-assertive and vigorous child may be more defiant at home; or, on the other hand, may selectively channel his aggression outside the home, secure in the knowledge that he has his mother's tacit approval. This situation, as can be readily appreciated, gives rise to one of the more common forms of juvenile delinquency which are attributable to developmental defects in personality.

Active rejection is more characteristic of the benign variety during periods of acute anxiety. Because the parent generally possesses a higher order of moral responsibility than the passively rejecting parent—one which ordinarily would be sufficient to inhibit rejecting attitudes in the absence of anxiety—she cannot be passively neglectful without engendering guilt feelings. Hence, despite her desire to rid herself of the burden of caring properly for her child, she is unable to disclaim this responsibility. She therefore continues to care for him, but resentfully and with an evident hostility which she tries to rationalize as a form of counteraggression made necessary by the latter's perverseness or undeserving behavior. Thus, the more self-assertive a child is, the more he encourages this active rejection, both by exceeding his mother's lowered threshold of irritability, and by providing her with a plausible moral justification for aggression.

The Choice between Rejection and Overvaluation

Overvaluation is a parent attitude which is exhibited by both types of non-satellizing individuals. More typically, however, the more consistent form is expressed as an alternative to malignant rejection by the parent who had been overvalued himself. In the parent with a history of childhood rejection, it is an alternative to benign rejection, and hence is more subject to displacement by an accepting and intrinsically-valuing attitude during periods of reduced anxiety.

What differences can we expect to find between two parents, both non-satellizers with hypertrophic ego demands, one of whom finds the child a cumbersome and unwanted burden, a hindrance in the pursuit of his own goals and purposes, while the other is able to utilize him as an ally and substitute source of self-fulfillment in his quest for ego aggrandizement. The factors accounting for this divergence in parent attitude have not been carefully studied, but clinical observation would suggest the following hypotheses: A great deal seems to depend on the capacity to perceive another person as an extension of oneself rather than as a distinct entity, and to react to his triumphs as if they were one's own achievements. This capacity probably depends in part upon a reduction in the degree of hopefulness with which a parent regards the possibility of gratifying his ambitions through his own efforts, which in turn is related to his ability to adopt a more realistic appraisal of his prospects for the future. With ego aspirations still pegged at an exceedingly high level and with considerable life experience already behind him to serve as a criterion for the reasonableness of his expectations, a certain type of parent becomes more disposed to start anew and exploit this miraculous opportunity for self-realization by proxy.

Other factors also help determine the difference in acceptance and in the functions allotted to the child in the economy of the parent's ego organization in the two situations described above. Everything else being equal, the parent faced with the choice of either rejecting or overvaluing his child is more likely to choose the latter alternative as he is less hostile, embittered, and withdrawn, and is more sociocentric, extraverted and affectively extra-related. If adopted as an alternative to benign rejection, it is likely to be more stable than the rejecting attitude, and less easily replaced by intrinsic valuation because of its positive adjustive value to persons with hypertrophic ego demands.

WHY PARENT ATTITUDES ARE DIFFICULT TO CHANGE

Anyone who has worked with emotionally disturbed children realizes both the difficulty and the importance of changing parent attitudes. So crucial is the parent's influence on the personality development of the child that no great improvement is ever made "without some change in parental attitude or in the home situation" [*388*]. "And in view of the difficulties inherent in the latter task there is certainly no room for undue optimism" [*23*].

Why this is so should not be difficult to understand. Our inquiry into the genesis of parent attitudes had shown that "the sources of a parent's inadequacies as a parent are found in his own childhood" [*278*]. In every case they relate to potent needs which are current in the economy of the parent's personality organization. The attitudes that are evoked by these needs are sometimes adaptive in the sense that they satisfy needs for ego enhancement (e.g., overvaluation) or reduce anxiety (e.g., overprotection). When this is the case they are especially tenacious because of their adaptive value. However, attitudes often do not facilitate adjustment but are exceedingly potent nevertheless, because they either give vent to deep-seated feelings (e.g., the need to express hostility), or insulate the individual from obligations which interfere with the satisfaction of more pressing needs (e.g., rejection attributable to the self-preoccupation resulting from narcissism or anxiety).

But even where the parent does not receive some form of advantage or compensatory gratification from his errors in child-rearing, "just to admit the need for drastic revision is tantamount to indicting himself as a parent" [*23*]. A parent may be quite well aware of attitudes that put him in an unfavorable light; yet this self-awareness is far less traumatic than directly pleading guilty to these failings by open admission, or indirectly by modification of his practices. In a non-satellizer, depending on the strength of his pretensions to infallibility, any contemplation of basic change in attitudes is more or less threatening and intolerable; the connotations of self-repudiation inherent in such change are ego-deflating and suggestive of the volitional dependency which he regards as degrading. In satellizers, similar resistance to change may proceed from reluctance to repudiate primary loyalties. Change is also effected with difficulty when a parent's attitudes and practices happen to be supported by the particular fads and fashions in child-rearing which are in current vogue. Presently, this statement is just as applicable to excessive permissiveness as twenty years ago it was to an overly impersonal and highly controlled child-rearing regimen.

Another factor making for difficulty in changing parent attitudes is the complexity of the relationship between these attitudes and the formal philosophy of child-rearing to which a parent subscribes. At one extreme the philosophy may be an out-and-out rationalization of a given attitude; at the other extreme, it may have the status of an objective conviction relatively unrelated to attitudinal considerations. More commonly, however, both components are combined in various proportions. A conviction in turn may either be reached independently through empirical or logical processes or be uncritically assimilated as a result of over-responsiveness to prestige suggestion, e.g., to the opinion of "experts." On a somewhat different dimension, a parent may be evaluated in terms of whether his expressed philosophy of child-rearing is accepted on a verbal or emotional level. Purely verbal expressions of principle need not be taken seriously since they do not interfere with underlying attitudes, although they may prove quite resistant to change if they carry social prestige value. The influence and tenacity of a rationalization, on the other hand, parallels the strength of the attitude which is responsible for its evolution.

However, if there is genuine emotional identification with a point of view (apart from rationalization) even if derived on purely intellectual grounds, we may expect it to influence behavior. It may do this just by opposing contrary personality trends and mitigating their severity without necessarily being potent enough to reverse them entirely. One should, therefore, never underestimate the potentialities of intellectual convictions for effecting personality change despite present-day psychological emphasis on the irrelevancy of all except emotional factors. And while it is true that parent education (or psychotherapy for that matter) can do little to combat attitudes such as malignant rejection, a great deal can be accomplished in cases where detrimental parent attitudes stem from ignorance and misinformation rather than from severe distortions in personality structure.

Nevertheless, it should be realized that basic attitudes in human relations are reflections of personality structure that can seldom be taught to others unless some basis for their development already exists. Correct verbal expressions and even appropriate behavior can be assimilated but their counterparts in genuine feelings are still another matter. And while it is true that improvement in the former can vastly influence the parent-child relationship for the better, it cannot constitute an adequate substitute for spontaneous attitudes; for not only children are aware of the latter deficiency—parents, also, inevitably betray their negative attitudes in the smaller and less deliberate aspects of their behavior.

NOTES

[1] One correlate of this attitude is the widely prevalent assumption that *all* symptoms of behavior disorder (as well as misbehavior) are attributable to errors in child rearing (i.e., are compensatory reactions to frustration, rejection, etc.). It is necessary for parents to realize that child-rearing practices are not the only relevant variables involved in the production of behavior disorder. Genetic and constitutional factors and transitional tensions are often potent enough to result in behavioral disturbances even in an optimal home environment. Misbehavior, also, is often an experiment on the child's part to test the limits of parental tolerance or endurance.

[2] See also studies by Bayley [*39*], Gesell and Thompson [*151*], and McKinnon [*272*].

[3] *Indulgent* is used in this section in the sense of *underdominating* and deferential to the child's will rather than overprotecting. However, it is also true that parents are more protective of their offspring during this stage of life.

[4] See also L. B. Murphy [*292*] on the dangers of prematurely conferring responsibility on children.

[5] This would also apply to Spitz's observation that "periodical mood swings" in the mother are associated with coprophagia in the infant, and more rapid shifts of attitude with hyper-motility [*369*].

[6] An example of such trauma is the later occurrence of bodily disfigurement. The physical representation of self can no longer be equated with the former body image of self that had been endowed with intrinsic value. Hence arises a greater need for acquiring extrinsic status in order to make the disfigured body image more acceptable. But still the influence of prior satellization is not completely lost. The resulting ego trauma is still considerably less than would occur under comparable circumstances in the case of a non-satellizer.

[7] See note 7, page 19.

CHAPTER 15

Anxiety

THE PROBLEM OF ANXIETY provides the crucial connecting link between the two aspects of the inquiry which we have pursued so far in this book, the nature of ego development on the one hand, and the relationship between aberrant ego development and personality disorder on the other hand. In anxiety states we see at the same time both a product of disordered ego development with many characteristic signs of ego damage, and the psychopathological core of a large variety of behavior disorders which can best be understood as either complications of or defenses against underlying anxiety.

Yet in no other field of psychopathology is there quite as much conceptual confusion or as little consensus of opinion regarding fundamental problems. Is there any continuity from the fear states of animals to those of man? How does fear become differentiated out of the nameless emotional matrix present in infants? What relationships prevail between fear, phobia, anxiety and insecurity? Are there different types of anxiety that may arise in the course of ego devlopment? Can anxiety also arise in relation to situational problems unconnected with personality development or in relation to other psychopathological manifestations? In order for anxiety to develop must there first be "conflict," "repression," or "hostility"? Is there any such thing as "free-floating anxiety," or "normal" anxiety in contradistinction to "neurotic" anxiety?

In order to answer these and many other related questions, a systematic attack upon the problem of anxiety that is conceptually consistent with the theoretical framework of this book will be attempted below. Much that is arbitrary in this approach can easily be pointed out, especially in the matter of definition and classification. But in the absence of other compelling criteria, such choices must necessarily be arbitrary, and are defensible only in terms of clarity, parsimony, internal consistency, fruitfulness for research and clinical practice, and compatibility with existing empirical evidence.

DIMENSIONAL QUALITIES OF FEAR STATES

Temporal Dimensions

Fear is a differentiated emotional experience that betokens awareness of threat to some aspect of the organism's existence, integrity, safety or well-being. Involved is not only a subjective content encompassing the source of the danger, its object and possible consequences, but also a specific train of visceral and somatic reactions set in motion by this special cortical experience through the excitation of intermediate and lower brain centers. The experience of fear is then completed and given further identifying characteristics when sensation of these visceral and somatic reactions reaches consciousness via sympathetic afferent and proprioceptive fibers originating in the effector organs involved.

So much then for the definition of fear as a generic term, as a general category of experience sharing certain conditions and properties in common, whether we speak of fear in the specific sense, phobia, insecurity or anxiety. It is here, however, that commonality ends and differentiation begins as we seek to identify criteria that set apart these component derivatives of generic fear.

First of all there is a temporal distinction to be made. Every person lives in the past, present and future. That which is presently happening, or has already happened and is being re-enacted in memory is tainted by the mark of reality. It is logically and experientially distinguishable from the hypothetical quality that characterizes anticipated experience. Hence we must differentiate between fear as a current experience (or as a current re-enactment of an old experience) and fear which is experienced in contemplation of the future. Following historical usage, it will be best to refer to the former as fear in the specific sense, and to the latter as insecurity. Where the object of the threat eliciting a fear state (in the generic sense) is self-esteem, we can use the terms anxiety-fear and anxiety respectively to cover the past-present and future time relations. Fear and anxiety-fear, therefore, refer to current fear states, while insecurity and anxiety refer to anticipated fear.

In the latter situation, however, where fear is projected into the future, it is apparent that more is involved than just an emotional content. On the eve of an impending battle, a soldier may experience insecurity, i.e., an actual emotional content of fear as he anticipates the events of the morrow and contemplates the possibilities of injury or death. On the other hand, his insecurity may *not* be manifested as an emotional content evoked by a hypothetical anticipated experience pre-lived in advance of its actual occurrence, but rather as an advance "set" or exaggerated tendency to react with fear upon actual confrontation with the dreaded class of stimuli constituting the threat. In this case there is no fear content in advance of the actual event but a sensitization to react with fear at the appropriate moment, or a differential lowering of the fear threshold to a specific category of threatening events. While it will serve no useful purpose to differentiate between *content* and *tendency* by assigning separate terms to these two varieties of fear experience having reference to future events, it will be worthwhile to keep this distinction in mind in discussing anxiety and insecurity. For one thing, it should be clear that insecurity or anxiety as emotional contents are more likely to occur when the precise nature of an anticipated threat is known, whereas their counterparts as emotional tendencies are more apt to take place when the source of the danger is more nearly vague and ambiguous.

What Is Being Threatened

In the definition of generic fear, we have implied that the object against which the threat is directed must of necessity represent something that is of vital value to the organism. Fear, in other words, is no laughing matter. It is not invoked in situations of trifling import. Life, wholeness of limb, health, reputation, freedom to pursue central goals, etc., must be at stake before an individual will react with fear to a threatening situation.

Among all these values which are subject to attack, one stands out as possessing unique and central significance—self-esteem, or the individual's feeling of adequacy and competence as a person in relation to his environment. The goal of much everyday activity as well as the motivation for most adjustive mechanisms has the enhancement or defense of self-esteem as its chief object. Hence, it seems legitimate to regard threats directed against self-esteem as eliciting a special variety of fear state, which may be termed anxiety-fear when appearing as a current emotion, and anxiety when projected into the future.

It should be noted that the distinction that is made here between fear and anxiety differs from that usually cited in the literature on anxiety. Beginning with Freud [*126*], fear has been characterized as a type of emotional response to a specific identifiable source of danger, whereas anxiety has been represented as a reaction to a vague, objectless threat to a central value of personality.[1]* Fear, Goldstein holds, is differentiated out of anxiety as the individual learns to identify specific objects in his environment which formerly lead to anxiety reactions [*156*].

Our first quarrel with the traditional distinction between fear and anxiety is its inconsistency. In the same breath it appeals to two different differentiating criteria, namely the identifiability of the threat in fear, and the central importance of the value in anxiety. The use of bi-dimensional criteria in distinguishing between concepts is allowable only if contrasting positions with respect to *both* dimensions are simultaneously designated for each term. It only breeds logical confusion when one dimension is reserved for one member and a second dimension for the other member of the pair.

If anxiety is elicited only when core values are threatened, are we to believe that in fear only peripheral values are threatened? Would it be accurate to state, for example, that specific dangers like an uncaged lion, the muzzle of a gun in one's back, or an approaching locomotive when one is stalled on a railroad track represents threats to values of secondary importance? It is true that life itself rather than self-esteem is at stake in each case. But who would argue that a threat to life is any less penetrating than a

* Notes for this chapter appear on page 389.

threat to self-esteem? It would seem more consistent to hold that values of central importance are threatened in both fear and anxiety, but that the values differ in type rather than in distance from the essence of personality.

Returning to the second criterion of identifiability, we find it just as unserviceable in differentiating between fear and anxiety. Many examples of anxiety could be offered in which the victim possesses complete insight into the nature of the threat confronting his self-esteem; and not infrequently in situations involving a threat to life or health, the individual is unable to identify the source of his dread. Hence in both fear and anxiety, the source of the threat may vary considerably in identifiability; and in each case lack of identifiability adds to the severity of emotional response and to the disorganization characterizing the adjustive effort.

The classification of fear states that has emerged so far in this analysis may be depicted schematically in Table 3.

TABLE 3.—*Classification of Fear States*

Temporal Dimension	*What is Threatened*	
	Self-Esteem	*Other Central Values*
Present or Past	Anxiety fear	Fear
Future (as content or tendency)	Anxiety	Insecurity

Still within the dimension of "what is being threatened," we may distinguish two other variables of some importance. Under different conditions giving rise to fear states in the same individual (or between different individuals in the same situation), considerable variability may exist with respect to the identifiability of the particular value under attack. It may not always be apparent to the individual that the object against which the threat is directed is self-esteem, life or health as the case may be. In addition, there may be varying degrees of displacement of the value subject to threat. An example of this was given in the discussion of overprotecting parents, where it was suggested that the parent deflects anxiety from himself by perceiving that his child's safety rather than his own self-esteem is threatened (see pp. 210-211).

Source of the Threat

In addition to asking the question, "What is being threatened?", one may further delineate the characteristics of a given fear state, by posing the query, "Who or what is threatening?" A description then of the various qualities characterizing the source of the threat adds further data on the nature of the fear state being experienced. Among the chief distinctions we hope to draw from this inquiry are those between fear (or anxiety) and phobia, and between normal and neurotic anxiety.

Identifiability. That threats differ in their identifiability has already been pointed out in connection with the problem of classification. Since variability along this dimension prevails for all components of generic fear, it cannot be judiciously employed as a differentiating criterion. An identifiable threat is one which is relatively specific, unitary, and clear-cut in its implications. An unidentifiable threat, on the other hand, tends to be vague, ambiguous, generalized, and fraught with multiple implications, some of which may be contradictory. It can be readily appreciated, therefore, that unidentifiable threats produce more intense fear states and give rise to defensive behavior which is less specifically adaptive. What cannot be identified cannot be avoided; nor can specific preparatory steps be taken to contend with the threat. The organism can only place itself in a state of general alertness or mobilization, and take its chances when the dreaded situation appears on the scene. Furthermore, unidentifiable threats are less subject to experimental extinction, since it is less likely that they can be linked with innocuous consequences contiguous in time.

Accessibility. How accessible an individual's awareness is regarding the source of the threat confronting him is obviously an important dimension of his fear experience. Historically, the role assigned to repression in the production of anxiety has just about completed a full circle, beginning with Freud's earlier theory of anxiety and ending with Mowrer's latest concepts. Freud [*126*] originally held that anxiety is "general current coin for which all the affects are exchanged or can be exchanged when the corresponding ideational content is under repression." This made anxiety the common consequence of emotional (especially sexual) repression. Later, Freud modified his position considerably, demoting repression from the cause to a consequence of anxiety. In his second theory, he contended that libidinal and hostile impulses which potentially exposed the individual to danger (social reprisal) gave rise to anxiety, and that this anxiety served as a cue to repress the dangerous impulses [*135*].

Horney [*187*] and Sullivan [*387*] accepted Freud's modified version of the role of repression in anxiety. Both regarded repression as a self-protective means of coping with anxiety by relegating the anxiety-producing factors beyond the pale of consciousness. Hence, if parental rejection, hostility toward parents, or disapproval by parents are productive of anxiety in the child, he tends to dissociate awareness of these unacknowledgable phenomena from the main, accessible stream of consciousness. Repression under such conditions constitutes a maladaptive defense against anxiety rather than the chief mechanism responsible for its evolution. It does not enable the individual to deal constructively with threatening situations, since the implications of threats cannot be examined openly or critically. Despite the repression, anxiety continues to be generated; and since its cause cannot be coped with consciously, "unconscious" defenses (often of a psychosomatic nature) are elaborated. This fact explains the inverse relationship invariably found between the degree of conscious anxiety and the presence of psychosomatic symptoms. Repression, in addition, tends to become an habitual defensive mechanism which is indiscriminately overgeneralized to many inapplicable situations, leading to a generally inhibited individual devoid of spontaneous affective impulses.

Although Mowrer [*286*] rejected Freud's initial notion that *sex* repression is the cause of anxiety (since many persons who suffer from severe anxiety are characterized by no sex repression whatsoever, he re-introduced that part of Freud's discarded early theory which ascribed to repression the essential mechanism involved in producing anxiety. Mowrer starts with the individual repudiating moral urgings and transgressing against society, as a result of which he experiences guilt feelings and fear of social punishment. Then instead of acknowledging these products of his misbehavior, he represses both the fear and the guilt which, as a consequence of their repression, become transformed into anxiety.

It is the dissociation of the fear and guilt from consciousness which, according to Mowrer, is responsible for the disorganization inherent in anxiety, since when such repressed fear attempts to return to consciousness it can do so only as anxiety [*286*]. As a kind of mystical punishment to the individual for seeking to disown and deny his guilt and fear of retribution, these affects assume the more threatening and uncomfortable form of anxiety and seek to re-enter the accessible framework of personality organization from which they had been ejected.

In the writer's opinion, repression does not occupy the central role in the production of anxiety that Mowrer ascribes to it, i.e., the conversion of fear into anxiety. There is abundant clinical evidence to demonstrate that conscious anxiety can coexist with complete insight into the source and object of the threat and the relation of each to the affect experienced. More plausible is the second theory of Freud, adopted by Horney and Sullivan, which regards repression as a defensive maneuver in relation to anxiety—a means of coping with anxiety by repressing the impulses that produce it. That this maneuver is ill-adapted to obviate anxiety, and actually may operate to secondarily increase it is understandable enough. But this is a far cry from contending that repression is the mechanism originally responsible for creating the anxiety.

Displacement. Another dimension relating to the source of the threat and not unconnected with the problems of identifiability and accessibility is the question of whether the individual experiencing fear or anxiety perceives the actual threat, or projects his perception of the offending stimulus onto an intrinsically unrelated cause. Unlike inaccessibility, however, displacement has very definite adjustive value, at least of a palliative nature if not inherently constructive in terms of eliminating the cause of anxiety. It enables him to deny the real source of the threat and to substitute in its stead something which is less formidable and more easily manageable. Consequently, the displacement is always in the direction of greater specificity, concreteness and identifiability, since these factors make either complete avoidance or planned defense more feasible. In short, the description of displacement just given defines the term *phobia,* which is simply a form of fear or anxiety in which the source of the threat is displaced onto a more identifiable object.

"Free-Floating Anxiety." In contrasting anxiety to fears and phobias, it has been customary to refer to it as "free-floating" or "objectless." The writer contends that these qualities are more apparent than real, and that the entire notion of an affect which is unrelated to a stimulating object is a psychological absurdity. A person who is afraid must be afraid of something. A person who is angry must be angry at something. A person who is in love must be in love with somebody. That loose, undifferentiated pools of unattached affect (aggression, anxiety or libido) float around and are at liberty to attach themselves at various times to specific objects is a relic of Hippocratian psychology in which various affects were identified with finite quantities of various body fluids that could be poured as it were out of a central reservoir into specific vessels. The modern concept of emotion, on the other hand, is that of a capacity to react in a certain way in response to an adequate stimulus, a capacity which has no corporeal content apart from its phenomenological existence during such time as it is elicited by appropriate situations.

There are several plausible reasons, however, which may help account for the apparent "free-floating" quality of anxiety. The relative unidentifiability and inaccessibility of anxieties (which have not undergone displacement) as contrasted with fears are largely responsible for their objectless appearance. Threats which cannot be concretized or which are banished from consciousness cannot be easily perceived as the cause of a diffuse and apparently all-pervasive affect, especially when the source of the threat is internal. But because a threat cannot be identified or made accessible to consciousness is no proof that a causal relationship does not exist between it and a given affect of anxiety.

Another reason contributing to the "free-floating" appearance of anxiety is its "tendency" component which consists of a generalized lowering of the threshold to respond with fear to all potential threats to self-esteem. In the first place, the apparent generality of this threshold-lowering creates an illusion of unselectivity and independence from causally related objects. Actually, however, the individual becomes differentially more sensitive to only a limited variety of ego-involved situations impinging upon his self-esteem. Secondly, since a tendency involves no actual content but only a change in readiness to respond to a particular gradient of stimuli, it appears objectless until it is elicited by an appropriate stimulus. Nevertheless, an illusion of content is given by a subjective awareness of this increased tendency to respond with fear which takes the form of an uncomfortable and vague tension. As a result, the individual feels as if he experienced an affective content that cannot be related to any antecedent event in his psychological world.

Objective Magnitude of the Threat

Whenever a fear response is elicited which is proportionate to the objective degree of danger inherent in the threat, we have good reason to believe that we are dealing with normal fear or anxiety. Situations productive of normal fear or anxiety are common enough in anyone's experience, since life is full of hazards and unpredictable contingencies; and to respond to such situations with fear is to behave normally enough. Fear of this kind probably serves a useful adaptive purpose since it alerts the organism to danger and mobilizes the defensive faculties. It is purely situational in nature, since it can be relieved by removal of the inciting situation. Following the initial shock of confrontation, the organism is generally able to recover, avoid panic and set about constructively to cope with and contain the threat. However, it is conceivable that threats of catastrophic, objective magnitude to self-esteem can induce overwhelming anxiety tantamount to panic, which not being disproportionate to the danger involved, must still be considered as normal anxiety. The same result could also be produced by an objective incapacity on the part of the individual which renders him relatively helpless to deal with minor environmental hazards. This situation is illustrated by Goldstein's aphasic patients who, when presented with relatively simple sorting problems, responded with panic or rigid and compulsive, stereotyped patterns of problem solving.

Since the distinction between normal and neurotic anxiety hinges mainly upon the disproportionateness of the response, neurotic anxiety should be suspected in all cases where the symptoms are severe enough to result in panic, paralysis, or progressive disorganization of behavior. And if further search fails to uncover an objective threat of sufficient magnitude to account for the intensity of affect displayed, clinical investigation aimed at discovering subjective sources of anxiety is certainly warranted.

Subjective Capacity for Meeting Threat. If we turn now to instances where this same degree of anxiety appears in the absence of what seems to be an adequate external threat, we cross the boundary into neurotic anxiety. However, by adhering to our original conception of fear states as responses made to *serious* threats to an organism's integrity or well-being, we are compelled to look for an adequate excitant that is subjective in nature. Then if we find that an individual's self-esteem is impaired to the point where he no longer has confidence in his ability to cope with problems of adjustment, the degree of anxiety manifested no longer appears disproportionate despite the relative insignificance of the environmental threat which is perceived as the precipitating cause of the affect. In contrast to normal anxiety, where the occasion (i.e., the situation which cues off the anxiety) and the cause of the affect are nearly identical, the occasion of neurotic anxiety is merely the stimulus which creates the necessity for adjustment [*270*]; and the cause of the latter is the impaired self-esteem that makes the individual feel inadequate to cope with the adjustive problem, and hence fearful of the further ego-deflating impact of this failure on his already battered self-esteem. Since the main source of the threat is internal, and in addition is frequently unidentifiable and inaccessible, it is not surprising that such anxiety may often give the impression of being "free-floating."

These feelings of inadequacy are very similar to Adler's *feelings of inferiority,* which also represent a subjective attitude of weakness or a valuation of self as inferior apart from the objective capacities under consideration [*4*]. Why an individual should regard himself as more impotent and inferior than he actually is, Adler does not make too clear. Apparently, however, he originally derives these feelings from an overgeneralization which he makes as a child from his actual position of biological dependence, organic deficiency, or membership in a social or sex group enjoying a subordinate status. Overwhelmed by the implications of this inferiority stemming from an objective fact, he develops a generalized subjective attitude of inferiority regarding his adequacy. These feelings of inferiority according to Adler inspire compensatory efforts aimed at achieving security through prestige accomplishment. Then if these compensations are not successful, secondary inferiority feelings develop.

It is important to point out, however, that Adler never took the next step of identifying impaired self-esteem with anxiety states. He connected inferiority feelings with neurosis (not anxiety) only through the distorted, excessive and contradictory compensatory efforts which these feelings tend to inspire. Adler also made the error of assuming that infants perceive their objective executive incompetence as proof of weakness, whereas they actually perceive themselves as volitionally omnipotent. During the childhood period, he makes the further error of identifying the child's dependence on his parents as a source of inferiority feelings rather than as a source of intrinsic security and adequacy. Dependency on parents, as has already been pointed out, leads to feelings of worthlessness and degradation only in the case of non-satellizing children.

This distinction which Rollo May [*270*] lucidly makes between the occasion and the cause of anxiety does not imply that the two phenomena are completely unrelated. May goes on to say,

> "The occasions, no matter how insignificant they may seem to be objectively, always bear a subjectively logical relation to the particular inner conflict in the individual; that is to say, the occasions are significant for the anxiety of the subject because they, and not other occasions, cue off his particular neurotic conflict" [*270*].

While the present writer would agree that the cause and the occasion of neurotic anxiety are logically related, he would not concur in the opinion that the common denominator in this case is provided by a neurotic conflict which requires a suitable occasion for provocation. As will be further elaborated upon below, exception is taken to the position of Horney and May which assumes that intrapsychic conflict is an invariable prerequisite for the occurrence of anxiety. The presence of such conflict intensifies neurotic anxiety and can give rise to symptomatic anxiety, i.e., a type of subjectively derived anxiety related to personality disturbance apart from impaired self-esteem; but all that is required for neurotic anxiety itself is sufficient lowering of self-esteem to transform objectively insignificant adjustive problems into major threats.

How then do we account for the peculiar selectivity which enables minor adjustive situation *x* to precipitate what on objective grounds appears to be a disproportionate amount of anxiety, while another situation, *y*, comparable with respect to its objective threat value, fails to arouse the faintest trace of anxiety? The most obvious explanation is that each individual's self-esteem is predicated upon a different set of status and achievement factors. If a particular situation is relevant to an area which the individual predisposed to neurotic anxiety has staked out as providing the source of *his* extrinsic status, its threat value will be differentially enhanced. The anxiety neurotic develops a reaction sensitivity to this particular class of stimuli that makes him abnormally sensitive to the slightest suggestion of their presence, and disposes him to over-respond with fear whenever he perceives the faintest implication of a threat relating to them.

It can be readily appreciated that normal and neurotic anxiety may be frequently combined in a single situation confronting a person subject to neurotic anxiety. There is no reason for believing that the latter is immune to threats which are objectively hazardous. Such threats naturally produce even greater manifestations of panic and disorganization than threats which have no objective basis. But the casual observer is led astray in this situation since there seems to be objective justification for whatever anxiety is expressed. A definite diagnosis of situational anxiety, therefore, should never be made on the basis of observations restricted to crisis situations alone. As a matter of fact any interpretation of anxiety should be made with extreme caution. Most individuals with neurotic anxiety have learned through bitter experience that it is socially and economically disadvantageous to betray their condition to associates. Hence they develop a number of defensive devices which attempt to obviate the necessity for adjusting publicly to potential threats; and in the event that this is impossible, other techniques are mastered for concealing the panic that seizes them. Thus, many anxiety neurotics who are clever at avoiding potentially disruptive situations and at controlling the external manifestations of anxiety, and who are fortunate enough to be placed in environments propitiously structured in terms of defending them against anxiety situations, are able to escape detection indefinitely and even gain reputations for being singularly secure and anxiety-free individuals.

Expressive Characteristics of Fear States

The dimensions of fear states can be described not only temporally, and in terms of various attributes of the source and object of the threat, but also in terms of the expressive characteristics of the affect itself. Subjectively, fear or anxiety may be characterized by an acute awareness of danger, a diffuse feeling of panic, premonitions of disaster or impending doom, a conscious tension that is reflective of the lowered threshold for fear reactions (equivalent to Liddell's concept of vigilance in animals), and an awareness of the autonomic components of the fear response. The autonomic aspects of anxiety, i.e., increased pulse rate and blood pressure, irregular respiration, thirst, blanching of the skin, increased perspiration, flatulence, aerophagia, etc., are too well known to require extensive cataloguing. Similarly, we need not dwell on various motor manifestations such as tremors, tics, blocking and hyperkinesis.

More important for our purposes is the conscious accessibility of the fear affect itself and the relationship between degree of accessibility and severity of the autonomic and motor symptoms. It can be readily demonstrated in clinical practice that a sizeable proportion of patients suffering from anxiety neurosis are not only unaware of the source and object of the anxiety-producing threat, but also fail to appreciate that their somatic or psychological symptoms bear any relation to fear. That is, some persons manage to repress all or most of the subjective components of their fear reaction. Others who are less successful at doing this accomplish the same general purpose by failing to identify the subjective phenomena as indicative of fear. They complain only of vague, uncomfortable, tense, and disturbing feelings; e.g., "Something is the matter with me. I feel very strange, as if something terrible were going to happen, but I can't say what."

"You mean, you are afraid of something, you are anxious or apprehensive?"

"No, not at all. I'm not afraid of anything. I just feel strange, that's all."

It goes without saying that both types of patients—those who have no subjective symptoms of anxiety, and those who do have them but fail to recognize their relation to fear—are completely at a loss in understanding the etiology of their somatic symptoms. They are thoroughly convinced that these symptoms are simply the product of some underlying organic pathology.

The ability to admit a large amount of neurotic anxiety affect to consciousness and to manage it successfully—either through intelligent resignation (learning to live with it), creating a propitious environment, or constructively lowering ego aspiration level and increasing intrinsic self-esteem—is very important in avoiding disabling psychological or psychosomatic defenses against anxiety. It is a well established clinical fact that the greater an individual's tolerance for conscious anxiety, the less likely is he to fall prey to compulsions, obsessions, phobias, hysteria, hypochondriasis or psychosomatic syndromes such as neurocirculatory asthenia or peptic ulcer. All of these latter methods of anxiety-reduction are indicative of low tolerance for anxiety and of failure in controlling it through more constructive methods.

However, the relative rarity of pure cases of anxiety uncomplicated by one or more of the disabling defenses is a tribute to the inherent difficulty of controlling anxiety on a conscious level alone. To admit anxiety to oneself is a confession of weakness that persons with impaired self-esteem can make only by willingness to withstand considerable further ego trauma. To admit anxiety to others is to invite loss of respect, as well as various forms of aggression, and victimization in those aspects of interpersonal relations in which success is a reward for self-assurance, self-respect and self-assertion. It is true that in moments of desperation the admission of anxiety can be used as a defensive measure. The individual in effect may plead, "Please help me. I am so frightened. You have nothing to fear from such a pathetically timorous creature as I."

The danger of such appeals in our competitive society, however, is too great to permit their use under ordinary circumstances. Less traumatic and less hazardous, for example, is to express anxiety psychosomatically rather than consciously. At this level also, it affords some secondary gain, i.e., it offers a socially acceptable excuse for avoiding stressful experience, excuses failure and lack of productivity, and sometimes elicits support, solicitude and sympathy. Another advantage is in the provision of a convenient locus for the displacement of the source of the anxiety. The individual can now admit to conscious anxiety which is attributable to concern over his health. The net effect of this psychosomatic expression, therefore, is anxiety-reducing, thereby lessening the need and the possibility for its conscious management; and if conscious expression of anxiety does eventuate, it can be related to the less threatening and more acceptable cause of organic disease.

The gains thus achieved in the reduction of conscious anxiety, however, are not without their price. Of all the syndromes related to anxiety, uncomplicated conscious anxiety is the most uncomfortable, but also the least dangerous and maladaptive. As long as some habitual and rigid anxiety-reducing defense is not yet firmly established, there is hope of evolving a more constructive solution. As long as he suffers consciously, one is sure that the patient is still striving for adjustment to a world of reality on an adult level, that he has not renounced the struggle (depression), or succumbed to immature goals in an autistic setting (schizophrenia). He has not yet paid the price of achieving security by unduly limiting the scope of his operations or by rationalizing failure on the basis of illness. And lastly he avoids the situation of psychologically induced invalidism which conceivably can end in chronic illness or even death (e.g., peptic ulcer, chronic ulcerative colitis).

The distinctions that have been made in this section between various types of anxiety are summarized in Table 4. Each type will receive extended treatment in later sections.

TABLE 4.—*Classification of Anxiety States*

I. *Source of Threat Is Objectively Hazardous*

1. *Normal (Situational) Anxiety*: Source of threat lies essentially in an objective hazard or in an objective incapacity of unusual magnitude. Affective reaction is proportionate to the objective threat involved.

II. *Source of Threat Is Mainly Subjective*: An adequate objective hazard is absent, and the affective reaction is disproportionate to the precipitating objective threat:

1. *Developmental Anxiety*: Source of threat emanates from personality defects arising in the course of ego development.

a. *Neurotic (Ego Hypertrophy) Anxiety*: Source of threat is related to ego hypertrophy, i.e., a history of failure in ego devaluation with residual impairment of intrinsic self-esteem, and a predisposition toward impairment of extrinsic self-esteem.

b. *Maturational Anxiety*[2]: Source of threat is related to residual defects in ego maturation.

2. *Symptomatic Anxiety*: Source of threat not primarily related to residual defects in ego development but to other psychopathological mechanisms associated with symptom formation, e.g., repression, hostility, conflict.

III. *Source of Threat Is Both Objective and Subjective*:

1. *Transitional Anxiety*[2]: Anxiety that arises during periods of crisis in ego development, but self-limited in duration and in relation to extreme external and internal pressures for personality change, rather than in relation to residual defects in ego structure. The sources of threat come from new social expectations, loss of established biosocial status, lack of current status, uncertainty regarding the attainment of future status, and internalization of new developmental aspirations.

THE ORIGIN OF FEAR STATES

Fear in Animals

In the light of the classification of fear and anxiety states given above, how are we to interpret fear in animals? If the differential criteria are valid, they should also hold true genetically in sub-human species and illustrate biological continuity in development.

Turning first to the temporal dimension, there is certainly no question about an animal's capacity for expressing fear in response to a current threat; and if the object of the threat is restricted to life and physical integrity, it is certain that animals can experience insecurity. The experiments of Mowrer [*284*] and Liddell [*252*] have shown conclusively that animals can anticipate painful stimuli and learn responses that enable them to avoid or adjust to the pain experience. Mowrer's rats learned to avoid maze alleys associated with an electric shock, and Liddell's sheep learned to flex their legs calmly prior to experiencing a shock presaged by a warning conditioned stimulus. In relation to a more generalized threat that cannot be specifically anticipated, animals exhibit what Liddell terms "vigilance" [*254*], a general increase in alertness or a lowered threshold of responsiveness to potentially threatening situations.

Situations that threaten an animal's sense of adequacy to control or cope with his environment can also give rise to fear states. This is essentially what happens in experimental neuroses. Pavlov's dogs first learned to differentiate between perceptual cues that helped them predict when food would become available. Then the cue which signalled the coming of food was gradually made identical with the cue which indicated that no food could be expected. Thus, the perceptual landmarks which formerly gave the animal a sense of security in coping with an important adjustive problem (food-getting) were now meaningless, unstable, capricious and unreliable, having no predictive value whatsoever. Maier [*262*] made use of the same technique in precipitating experimental neurosis in rats. First he provided perceptual cues which when learned enabled the animal reliably to avoid a traumatic experience. Then these cues were robbed of predictive value by being associated sometimes with the traumatic experience and at other times with the alternative providing avoidance of same.

A somewhat different method employed by both Pavlov [*305*] and Masserman [*269*] induced experimental neurosis by endowing a single perceptual cue with contradictory connotations of harm and benefit, e.g., a flash of light that signalled the advent of both food and a fear-producing blast of air, or an electric shock that was simultaneously painful and predictive of the appearance of a food reward. Again the perceptual environment was rendered capricious and threatening in the sense that the possibility of coping with it through ordinary learning processes was completely removed.

It would be indulging in fanciful anthropomorphism, however, to assume that an animal's apprehension of being overwhelmed by a capricious environment necessarily implies appreciation of a threat to his self-esteem. Indeed, it is highly questionable whether the concept of self-esteem as we know it in humans is conceivable at the sub-human level, since it involves a degree of conceptualization that would be extremely difficult without the aid of verbal symbols. The source of the threat also does not seem to arise so much from a generalization of inadequacy relating to self (as occurs in neurotic anxiety), but appears to be analagous to the sorting situation confronting aphasic individuals who because of organic brain lesions are deficient in ability to categorize perceptions. The ability to orient self to the environment, and to achieve some measure of control over it through familiar perceptual and cognitive processes is suddenly lost; and suddenly, therefore, the environment assumes a threatening aspect. It is as if a hunter were to wake up in the forest one morning and find his eyesight gone. Certainly it is not less traumatic to be deprived of perceptual discrimination or generalizing ability. The term "experimental neurosis," therefore, is a misnomer. The animal is simply manifesting the behavioral disorganization found in extreme cases of fear and insecurity in which an adequate objective threat results in a fear response that is proportionate to the threat involved.

Threats of pain, danger to life, and loss of perceptual discrimination, therefore, induce fear and insecurity rather than anxiety in animals. There are two situations, however—both involving interpersonal relationships—in which a type of human anxiety is conceivable in infra-human mammals. It is certainly within the realm of possibility that dogs, for example, are capable of forming satellizing-like relationships to human beings from which they derive a certain amount of intrinsic status. When a dog is threatened with loss of this derived status he exhibits a type of fear response that seems qualitatively different from his reactions to other danger situations, and very much like human anxiety. Again, in the dominance hierarchy known as a "pecking order," it is not unreasonable to postulate that an animal derives some feelings of extrinsic status from his hierarchical position in the group. Might he not then experience anxiety when another animal attempts to challenge his position?

It would be rash to assume that in either case the anxiety experienced is equivalent to the anxiety manifested by human subjects who have a highly conceptualized notion of self-esteem. It should be remembered, however, that anxiety reactions are possible in infants before there is a fully conceptualized self; and significantly, just as in animals, it is elicited by threats arising in an interpersonal context. This leads to the hypothesis that interpersonal relationships provide a pre-verbal matrix from which an empirical, non-conceptual notion of self-esteem arises. Threats directed against this primitive form of self-esteem produce a rudimentary type of anxiety, which, as might be easily predicted, is richer in tendency than in content, and arises more from objectively hazardous situations than from impaired self-esteem.

Development of Fear States in Infants

In the development of the fear response, the human infant does not start where the animal's growth ends. It is true that eventually he will develop a capacity for releasing fear affects that in subtlety, sensitivity and variety of expression will overshadow by far anything achieved by his biological ancestors. But in the first year of his development, his rate of growth suffers by comparison.

The question of "original" or "instinctual" fears, the entire problem of nature vs. nurture, and the role of maturation in the development of fears, once the source of considerable controversy in genetic psychology, are all dead issues at the present time. It is generally accepted that the capacity to respond with fear to hazardous situations (which threaten the organism's integrity and continued existence as an entity) is an inherited property characteristic of at least all mammalian species. The only developmental prerequisite for fear responses is the emergence of an empirical sense of self or identity, a quality that appears relatively late in the human species. With respect to specific fears, the preponderance of research data supports the conclusion that at the human level, specific threats that give rise to fear are learned rather than inherited, that Watson's so-called two "original" fear stimuli do not elicit affects that can consistently be described as fear by unbiased observers [*353*], and that no differentiated emotional responses are present at birth [*52, 369*]. The evidence with respect to maturation is also clear. As children become older, they acquire greater perceptual and cognitive maturity which enables them to react with fear to situations, the threatening implications of which they were unable to appreciate at an earlier age [*147, 203, 208*].

We start then with the general proposition that the capacity to react with fear is part of the infant's innate endowment transmitted through phylogenetic inheritance and serving a self-preservative function. But as stated above, this capacity is only latent at birth and is differentiated out of a more primitive emotional matrix. It is extremely unlikely that there is any developmental continuity between fear and the startle response, since the latter shares all of the characteristics of a reflex and none of the properties of an emotion [*237*]. On the other hand, it is highly probable that fear is differentiated out of the amorphous and non-specific emotional response of displeasure which can be elicited in the second and third months of life by any sudden, unexpected and intense stimulus at first [*52, 203, 369*], and later by the mother's departure from the infant's presence [*52, 369*]. But apart from the startle reflex and the generalized response of displeasure, the first six months of life are singularly free from reactions to potentially harmful stimuli. Devoid of any empirical notion of self, threats can have no perceptual significance as such, but only a general noxious quality that elicits the non-specific emotion of displeasure. In addition, even if there were a pre-conceptual self that could be threatened, the large proportion of the day spent in sleep, the pervasive atmosphere of biological care, as well as perceptual and cognitive immaturity would still keep the threshold for fear reactions high.

Beginning with the second half-year of life, however, we begin to observe differentiated responses that can legitimately be classified as fear. By this time a rudimentary empirical distinction between self and the environment has been made, and a threat to the self-entity is conceivable. Because of perceptual immaturity, however, the majority of fears tend to be vague and unidentifiable (*any* intense, sudden, unexpected or unfamiliar stimulus, e.g., the approach of a stranger) rather than specific and concrete. The capacity for experiencing fear related to the future, i.e., insecurity, develops shortly thereafter. The syndrome of anaclitic depression described by Spitz [*368*] in the eight-months-old child who is abruptly separated from his mother is illustrative of such insecurity (although Spitz refers to the predominant affect as anxiety). Since the child under such circumstances tends to identify the security (which protects him from the physical consequences of his executive helplessness) with the biological care and protection supplied by a single person, namely his mother, separation from her raises a threat to physical survival which is productive of insecurity.

Anxiety cannot develop before fear, since a notion of adequacy or self-esteem must necessarily be evolved out of the less complex notion of self, and, hence, cannot be threatened before self itself. We cannot agree with Goldstein's [*156*] contention supported by

May [*270*] that fear is differentiated out of anxiety when the organism becomes perceptually mature enough to identify and evaluate the source of the threat. May holds that "some neurological maturation is presupposed before the infant can respond to threatening stimuli with undifferentiated emotion (anxiety), and greater maturation is necessary before the infant can differentiate between various stimuli, objectivate the danger, and respond to it as a fear" [*270*]. The first error in this reasoning is the reference to "undifferentiated emotion" as anxiety, when the empirical evidence indicates that it is merely displeasure. There is no evidence to support the contention that "diffuse undifferentiated apprehension (anxiety) . . . may be elicited in the early weeks of the infant's life in response to certain stimuli (e.g., falling)" [*270*].

Secondly, May's formulation (quoting Mowrer) of anxiety as "primal" rather than "derived" [*270*] springs from his use of the criterion of identifiability in distinguishing between fear and anxiety. It has already been pointed out that *both* fears and anxieties can be characterized by varying degrees of identifiability, and that anxiety can be consistently differentiated from fear only on the basis of the particular value relating to self which is threatened, i.e., self-esteem, vs. all other central values having self-reference. Anxiety, therefore, can make its first appearance only after a primitive sense of adequacy emerges, which initially reflects the infant's tendency to perceive himself as relatively omnipotent and independent volitionally (as a result of misinterpreting the reason for his parents' early deference to his needs and wishes). Threats directed against this solipsistic notion of ego grandiosity, i.e., frustration of volitional impulses, can conceivably result in anxiety if such frustration is sustained enough to challenge the assumptions upon which his sense of adequacy rests. Usually, however, occasional frustration or postponement of gratification gives rise to another specific emotion reflective of outraged ego grandiosity, i.e., rage; whereas threats directed against the continued succorance, which he perceives as essential because of his executive dependence, are productive of insecurity since the issue of physical survival is perceived to be at stake.

It requires prolonged and frequent frustration of the child's will, such as occurs during the crisis of ego devaluation, to undermine the basis of self-esteem sufficiently to produce overt anxiety. More commonly, however, the process of devaluation is carried out gradually in a general setting of affection and benevolence, thereby maintaining a high level of security which raises the threshold for anxiety responses. Hence, transitional anxiety which appears at this time tends to be overshadowed by the negativism that dominates the behavioral picture during the period of ego devaluation.

In rejected children, however, this transitional anxiety is a striking rather than an incidental accompaniment of the negativistic behavior induced by parental training efforts; terror is written all over their faces as they struggle against submission to parental demands. Ego devaluation through satellization does not result in these cases, but rather a catastrophic impairment of the extrinsic sense of adequacy which continues to operate instead of being replaced by an intrinsic self-esteem based on derived status. It is at this point then that transitional anxiety in rejected children becomes continuous with neurotic anxiety. Once the external pressures referable to the transitional period in ego development—abetted and augmented by parental rejection (which threatens security, lowers the anxiety threshold and fails to provide intrinsic adequacy)—have wrought their damage to self-esteem, the residual damage becomes the main source of threat to the individual's sense of adequacy. And since objectively adequate hazards are no longer necessary to cause anxiety, it may properly be termed neurotic rather than transitional.

Critique of Various Theories Regarding the Origin of Anxiety in Infants

In discussing various hazards connected with the emergence of a scientific psychology of ego development, we already have had occasion to comment unfavorably upon certain theoretical formulations based on the assumption that specific ego-related affects could come into being before there was any opportunity for the genetic development of an ego from the life experiences of the individual. Illustrative of such concepts is Rank's idea of the birth trauma [*314*], and Freud's conception of the birth experience as providing "a prototype for all occasions on which life is endangered, ever after to be reproduced again in us as the dread or 'anxiety' condition"

[*126*]. However, before one could logically accept the proposition that anxiety could be experienced at the moment of birth, it would be necessary to make one of two prior assumptions: (a) Either that a preformed ego already exists, or (b) that anxiety can occur without any ego reference whatsoever. Neither assumption appears very plausible in the light of modern concepts of ego development.

In contrast to Rank, Freud's interest in the birth experience was more concerned with the implications of separation from the loved person than with the degree of physical trauma involved. Freud stressed that this same phenomenon of separation was the underlying threat involved in all subsequent developmental situations productive of anxiety. He contended, for example, that the castration threat inspires anxiety because it proposes separation from a highly valued object, and because it negates in males the only possibility for physical reunion with the mother [*135*]. The weaning process similarly presents the threat of separation from the mother's breast, and the presence of a stranger induces fear because it implies the absence of the mother. For the very same reason, the child is afraid of darkness, loneliness, parental disapproval, social reprisal and finally of the prospect of death [*135*].

In terms of the general theory of ego development, the most objectionable feature of Freud's formulation is its insistence upon a fixed quantity of "primal" affect (in this case anxiety) which is the source and fountainhead of all subsequent emotional expression in later life. It relies upon the same Hippocratian reasoning that underlies the psychoanalytic concepts of sublimation and "free-floating anxiety." According to this theory, the birth experience creates a finite store of anxiety affect which constitutes for ever after the sole available reservoir from which all anxiety responses must be drawn. No new source of anxiety need ever be created; all subsequent anxiety experiences merely involve reactivation of this primal source.

Again we submit that emotions can only enjoy a phenomenological existence during such time as they are actively engaged; that they cannot be stored (as for example bile in the gall bladder) for later release; that when emotions are not undergoing active[3] expression, what remains within the organism is not a specified amount of emotional energy, but a *capacity* to express an emotional content in response to an adequate stimulus; that affect is never "reactivated" in the sense of a portion of the original fixed quantity being released, but is always generated anew in response to a current excitant. This does not imply that there is no historical continuity in the type of threats productive of anxiety in a given individual. Quite the contrary, in relation to normal anxiety, the occurrence of a given traumatic experience tends to make the individual selectively vulnerable to comparable threats that may arise in the future. But it would seem more plausible to conclude in this regard that historical continuity is provided by the interposition of a selective reaction sensitivity between the two events, rather than by the preservation of the original anxiety affect which is subsequently reactivated by a similar threat; that the expressed affect in the latter event is phenomenologically autonomous (freshly generated) rather than a "warmed-over" version of the prior affective dish.

In the case of neurotic anxiety, on the other hand, historical continuity is provided by the relative irreversibility and continued existence of ego damage induced by catastrophic impairment of self-esteem. In addition, lack of intrinsic security and adequacy, the presence of unrealistically high and extremely tenacious ego aspirations, and difficulty in relating emotionally to others constitute long-standing predispositions to anxiety that furnish considerable opportunity for commonality in the types of circumstances under which anxiety-producing situations tend to develop. It obviously adds not a whit to our theoretical or clinical understanding of fear states to speak of "the" origin of anxiety as if it were a single historical event occurring at birth which is responsible for the generation of the entire supply of the affect that will henceforth be available for expression during the remainder of the individual's lifetime. We would do better to direct our efforts toward a search for the types of residual defects in ego development that constitute adequate subjective bases for the arousal of newly generated anxiety affect when an appropriate precipitating stimulus of environmental origin appears on the perceptual scene. Viewed in this light, the classical distinction that is made between the "origin" and the "mechanism" of anxiety would become meaningless; and the elucidation of the latter phenomenon alone would provide us with all of the data that could conceivably have reference to the former as well.

As a result of his observational studies of institutionalized infants, Spitz [*370*] rejected the orthodox psychoanalytic position that recognized the prototype of all subsequent anxiety manifestations in the "concatenation of painful feelings, of discharges and excitation, and of bodily sensations" constituting the birth experience. He insists that anxiety cannot possibly appear until the third quarter of the first year since the child lacks an ego before this time [*370*].[4]

Nevertheless, Spitz still clings to the major tenets of the Freudian theory of anxiety by finding its source to lie in the traumatic separation of valued objects from the infant, and its mechanism to lie in the conflict between the ego and the id. Its primary function, he asserts, is to serve as a warning signal for the approach of danger situations created by the activation of id impulses which, if expressed, would expose the individual to social reprisals and guilt feelings. Recognition of this warning then leads to repression of the dangerous impulses [*370*]. However, we submit that the implausibility of explaining so common a phenomenon as normal infantile anxiety on the basis of highly sophisticated sexual urgings[5] (the existence of which have never been unequivocally demonstrated[6]) should be readily apparent.

More germane to the actual biosocial situation of infancy that defines the conditions under which anxiety is likely to develop is Harry Stack Sullivan's theory that the infant experiences anxiety emphatically if he senses disapproval on the part of the significant individuals in his interpersonal environment [*387*]. It is reasonable to suppose that his parent's disapprobation might loom as a threat to the child since it conceivably could lead to the withdrawal of the care and protection which he recognizes as essential to his survival in the face of his executive helplessness. However, it is a mistake to assume, as Sullivan does, that the child feels relatively impotent because of his executive dependence. Quite the contrary, as long as his needs are gratified, the latter situation enhances his feelings of volitional omnipotence by demonstrating his power *in spite of* his actual manipulative incompetence. But the threat of withdrawing biological care which is implied in disapproval may not only result in insecurity[7] (because of the physical danger involved), but also in anxiety,[7] since the basis of his adequacy feelings is undermined by the suggestion that his parents are not completely subservient to his interests.[8]

The possibility of insecurity and anxiety developing under these conditions, however, needs to be qualified by at least two important factors: (a) the actual seriousness of the threat of disapproval in most cases and (b) the child's perceptual sensitivity to such threats. During early infancy, because of obvious perceptual immaturity, such disapproval would have to take the form of gross and consistent neglect and lack of attention before giving rise to insecurity and anxiety. Granted that the child can become aware of a general interpersonal climate of care or neglect, inspiring in turn feelings of security or insecurity respectively; but this is hardly synonymous with Sullivan's conception of empathy as a process of "emotional communion" between mother and infant, especially where it is implied that subtle aspects of maternal attitudes can be transmitted in this fashion. In addition, as we have had occasion to point out previously, such severe "disapproval"[8] is a relatively rare occurrence in our culture.

After satellization takes place, the child becomes more sensitive to the implications of parental disapproval. But even then it should be realized that short of actual rejection, disapproval is a training device that is usually transitory and situational in character rather than reflective of a pervasive interpersonal climate. Despite the almost daily occurrence of parental disapproval directed at one or another of their objectionable or annoying habits, satellizing children tend to enjoy a highly secure existence devoid of deep-seated anxiety. At most we are able to detect a minor undercurrent of vague insecurity (or anxiety) that is referable to a dim awareness of the danger involved in being completely dependent on the good will of another—a danger springing from the remote possibility that the latter might conceivably prove to be capricious and unpredictable. These unidentifiable insecurities tend to be objectivated in the form of fear of highly improbable calamities, e.g., of jungle beasts, failing in school [*201*], etc., which are quite common and very persistent in children of elementary school age. Their tenacity can be ascribed both to their immunity to experimental extinction and to the longevity of the original source of fear affect from which they are displaced.

Kardiner's view of the origin of anxiety in early childhood is very similar to Sullivan's except for its greater emphasis upon the consequences of frustrating the infant's hedonistic impulses by way of parental training demands [*218*]. He sees the young infant in our culture developing a very flattering self-estimate as a result of receiving highly deferential and solicitous care. In the second and third years of life, however, the parent attempts to curb the pleasurable sensations associated with unrestricted relaxation of urethral and anal sphincters by imposing a pattern of regulated sphincter control, with relaxation permitted only under specified and arbitrary conditions. According to Kardiner this situation is productive of considerable physiological tension (blocking of pleasurable "relaxor patterns") which leads both to repressed feelings of hostility toward parents, and to feelings of uncertainty on the part of the child regarding the parent's continued willingness to provide care and protection. The most satisfactory method available for reduction of this anxiety[9] is to appease the parents by becoming increasingly dependent on them, and to conform implicitly to their desires in the hope that thus propitiated they would be less disposed to withdraw succorance.

Kardiner's formulation, however, has less logical appeal than Sullivan's because he places so much stress upon the frustration of "relaxor patterns" *per se* as the cause of the ensuing anxiety. Modern personality theorists, on the other hand, are more concerned with the total biosocial situation, in which sphincter training is only one of several instrumentalities through which the parent is at this time seeking to reverse the direction of volitional ascendency in his relationship with the child (see pp. 107-108). Also, as already pointed out, the training demands leading to satellization are generally carried out in an atmosphere that is not productive of insecurity, an interpersonal climate which, in the absence of parental rejection, results at the very worst in self-limited transitional anxiety. After satellization occurs, however, the child's level of intrinsic security and adequacy is high, significant levels of anxiety are absent, and parental authority seems to be genuinely accepted as an absolute, self-evident and unquestionable fact that does not provoke hostility in the child [*312*]. Hence, except in the case of conditionally-accepting, harshly dominating or rejecting parents, there seems to be little justification for Kardiner's generalization that exaggerated obedience represents a typical mechanism employed by children in our culture to allay significant and ever-present anxiety growing out of the parent-child relationship.

In locating the origin of anxiety in childhood, Mowrer originally [*286*] began with the same situation chosen by Sullivan, i.e., the child's genuine fear of losing his parent's love and protection (or receiving his disapproval and punishment), but attributed to repression (of this fear) the essential etiological element involved in the genesis of anxiety. The child, he held, resorts to repression of this fear because he is too dependent to flee or express hostility, too weak to evolve an objectively adequate defense, and too apprehensive of being overwhelmed by the catastrophic implications of the threat and its associated fear to admit it to consciousness. In his later publications, however, Mowrer places more emphasis on the repression of guilt feelings rather than of fear [*286*].

All of these reasons for repression are credible enough. Sullivan is especially impressed by the latter one. He writes,

> "The self comes to control awareness, to restrict one's consciousness of what is going on in one's situation very largely by the instrumentality of anxiety with, as a result, a dissociation from personal awareness of those tendencies of the personality which are not included or incorporated in the approved structure of self" [*387*].

He even goes as far as to see in this need for and experience in discriminating between approved, to-be-incorporated tendencies and disapproved (anxiety-producing) elements much of the empirical and conceptual raw material from which the notion of self is derived. The self, in other words, is organized to preserve the individual's sense of security by excluding those elements which would elicit disapproval and, hence, anxiety. In contrast to Mowrer, however, Sullivan takes the more defensible position that anxiety serves as a self-protective signal leading to repression, rather than that repression itself is the chief mechanism whereby fear is converted into anxiety.

In searching for the origin of anxiety, Horney takes the same starting point as Sullivan and Kardiner, but emphasizes a different and more indirect factor as responsible for its genesis. This common starting point, it will be remembered, is the situation in which the dependent child is confronted by parental training demands. In relating this situation to the origin of anxiety, Kardiner focuses on the consequences of frustrating the child's "relaxor patterns," Sullivan is mainly concerned with the child's affective reaction to the threatening implications of parental disapproval, and Horney concentrates on the consequences of the child's aggressive reactions. According to her formulation, it is not the threat of withdrawing protection or the undermining of the child's sense of volitional omnipotence that creates anxiety, but the fear of others that follows inevitably from an attitude of hostility towards them [*187*]. The child, in other words, is anxious only because he is hostile; and the hostility is especially dangerous in his case because of his dependency which makes him so much more vulnerable to retaliation. It, therefore, becomes essential for his safety that he repress this hostility as much as possible.

The logic of Horney's proposition that hostility leads to anxiety,[10] and that anxiety in turn may lead to repression of hostility is inescapable. Our quarrel with Horney rests upon the arguments (a) that hostility is a less general outcome of the parent-child relationship than she would have us believe; and (b) that the anxiety proceeding from hostility is, relatively speaking, only a secondary and adjunctive accompaniment of the transitional anxiety referred to above, and a minor symptomatic accompaniment of the neurotic anxiety occurring in rejected and overvalued children.

With respect to the first point, it seems that Horney commits the same error as Adler in failing to define precisely enough the conditions under which the dependency situation leads to feelings of volitional helplessness and inferiority in infants and children. But whereas Adler assumed that this relationship was an inevitable condition of human development, Horney holds that it occurs only in cases where the parent-child relationship is disturbed, more particularly when the dependency situation is such that it generates feelings of hostility in the child toward the parent. It is with the generality of criteria which she advances as productive of hostility, and her failure to differentially evaluate the possibility and significance of hostility in satellizers and non-satellizers respectively that we take issue.

No one would deny Horney's assertion that parents frequently abuse the child's physical dependency in the types of attitudes [*187*] they adopt toward him. But in evaluating the significance of these attitudes, it is first necessary to decide whether they are occasional or characteristic. If the latter, they spring from rejection and obviously result in feelings of hostility. Inasmuch as satellization cannot take place, the child can only resent parental authority but is usually required to repress this resentment out of considerations of expediency. In the event that unfavorable parent attitudes are only transitory, the general climate of dependency is not associated with hostility and does not lead to failure in satellization; however, in borderline cases, we must reckon with the possibility of ambivalence. There is also room for the development of hostile feelings in the child subsequent to satellization in relation to overdominating, undervaluing, underappreciating, and overmotivating parent attitudes. In conclusion then, we would be less disposed than Horney to associate the dependency situation with hostility without first evaluating the relative frequency of unfavorable attitudes in a given parent, the general context in which they are expressed, and their significance in relation to a given phase of ego development.

Our second major point of disagreement with Horney springs not from a denial that hostility leads to anxiety,[11] but from a difference of opinion with respect to whether hostility is a primary (basic) or secondary source of anxiety. During the crisis of ego devaluation when increased parental training demands challenge the infantile sense of adequacy, we have seen that a self-limited type of transitional anxiety develops. At the same time (especially in the second stage of negativism at four-and-one-half), the child expresses considerable hostility and aggression toward his parents. We would contend that in this situation the primary source of the threat giving rise to anxiety is the changed expectations and demands of the parents which threaten the child's self-esteem. The possible consequences of his own hostility constitute at most a secondary source of threat directed at his physical safety and, therefore, generate feelings of insecurity rather than anxiety.

Further evidence that hostility cannot be a significant source of threat at this time comes from the well-known fact that it is generally expressed overtly with little tendency toward repression. Evidences of repression become pronounced only after satellization is firmly established, and when the expression of hostility becomes associated with guilt feelings, especially in more austere and less permissive homes.

With respect to the origin of neurotic anxiety (as defined in this book) the main source of the threat lies in the catastrophic impairment of the child's self-esteem. The developmental circumstances leading to this situation invariably give rise to hostility in cases of early rejection, and in those cases of initial overvaluation followed by later rejection. But again, we submit that the threat to the child's safety posed by the presence of his hostility is relatively insignificant, and only a secondary accompaniment of the disturbed parent-child relationship which damages his sense of adequacy; and just as in the situation described above, insecurity is a better description of the affect involved than anxiety.

Conclusion. It would be helpful in summarizing our critique of theories relating to the origins of anxiety to return again to our original definition of anxiety as the emotional reaction exhibited by an individual in adjustive situations when his sense of adequacy is the major object of the threat involved. In our review of these theories we have examined several developmental situations of varying degrees of relevancy (birth trauma, disapproval, parental training efforts, etc.) which have been proposed as satisfactorily accounting for this problem of origin. Very significantly, however, none of these theories endeavors to define the precise object of the threat or to distinguish between insecurity and anxiety.

Freud and Rank derived the origin of anxiety from the birth experience without concerning themselves whether fear states could be experienced in the absence of an ego and of sufficient perceptual maturity to appreciate the implications of this experience. Freud further held that all subsequent anxiety was derived from the reactivation of this primal source. Spitz dismisses the possibility of anxiety occurring before the development of an ego, but like Freud finds the source of the threat in the potential loss of valued objects and in the activation of socially unacceptable (and, hence, dangerous) id impulses; and although he does not specifically identify the object of the threat, the presumption is that it refers to more general aspects of self than just self-esteem.

Sullivan, Kardiner, Mowrer and Horney all endeavor to identify a more credible interpersonal situation of developmental import which could give rise to anxiety. Sullivan exaggerates the prevalence and significance of disapproval as well as the child's capacity to perceive it, and erroneously describes the infant as having a low volitional self-estimate. He too does not specify the object of the threat, but it is apparent that he is referring to feelings of *insecurity* although using the term *anxiety*. Kardiner more clearly perceives the infant's high self-valuation, but overstates the significance and specific importance of frustrating "relaxor patterns" when he claims that this frustration gives rise to anxiety; however, his description of the latter affect indicates that he really means insecurity. Mowrer's earlier theory starts with the same situation and affect called anxiety by Sullivan, renames it "fear," and asserts that it is somehow converted into anxiety by its tendency to undergo repression. Later, Mowrer de-emphasizes the aspect of fear and stresses instead the repressed guilt feelings of the child.

From an historical standpoint it is interesting to note that in different ways both Kardiner and Mowrer revert to Freud's original concept of anxiety as the least common denominator resulting when any affectual impulse is subjected to frustration or repression. The difference between them is mainly in the *type* of affect considered to be most vulnerable to frustration (or repression). In the case of Freud, it was id impulses of a sexual nature. Kardiner was impressed with pleasurable affects of a hedonistic character. And Mowrer is presently convinced that guilt feelings resulting from transgressions of the moral code together with fear of parental punishment in childhood, and fear of social reprisals in later life are the chief affectual victims of repressive tendencies in personality organization.

Horney perhaps comes closer than all of the foregoing in appreciating the true developmental origins of anxiety. One of the chief virtues of her position is that she concerns herself only with neurotic anxiety, and hence traces its genesis to a disturbed parent-child relationship. Although this approach suffers from the disadvantage of making neurotic anxiety discontinuous with other types of developmental anxiety, it avoids a major theoretical difficulty common to all of the other positions—that of relating the origin of anxiety to a developmental situation general enough to include all infants. The tremendous importance of this theoretical advance is that only in relation to her formulation do we not have to ask the crucial question: "If this situation is part of the life history of *every* child, what is the differential factor that on a developmental basis accounts for the difference between transitory and universally experienced anxiety on the one hand and neurotic anxiety on the other?"

But after getting off to this good start, Horney concentrates on a relatively subsidiary aspect of the relevant developmental situation, namely, the child's hostility, as the main source of the threat, instead of giving due recognition to the latter's damaged sense of adequacy. Part of the difficulty lies in her failure to define precisely the conditions under which hostility arises in the dependency situation, with the result that she overgeneralizes both with respect to the prevalence of the hostile reaction and its tendency to generate anxiety (as evidenced by its propensity to undergo repression). Finally when we ask the question, "What is being threatened?", it becomes evident that she too fails to distinguish adequately between anxiety and insecurity, since the answer she gives refers to the child's "safety," by which she means his confidence in receiving the continued succorance that he as a highly dependent individual perceives as essential for his physical survival.

SECURITY AND ADEQUACY

Changes in Security and Adequacy as a Function of Ego Development[12]

The concepts of security and adequacy have not only achieved a prominent place in modern psychiatric literature, but also continue to receive increasingly greater attention in psychological treatises under the heading of "derived" needs or motives relating to the self concept. However, despite the glibness with which these terms are used, precious little has been accomplished in the way of rigorous definition: The two terms have been poorly differentiated from each other and are often used synonymously; their relationship to anxiety has not been spelled out precisely; and their content has not been systematically related to the various stages of ego development with their corresponding developmental tasks and levels of perceptual maturity.

In the pre-satellizing period, the infant's sense of security—his level of confidence with respect to the future beneficence of his environment insofar as his safety and the provision of his basic needs are concerned—is a reflection of the pervasive atmosphere of protective care in which he is enveloped. Security needs, of course, cannot arise until some notion of self is formed and until the infant is mature enough perceptually to appreciate his executive dependence. But by the very same token of perceptual maturity, threats to his safety must be gross and obvious before this sense of security can be undermined.

In this very same developmental period, the infant's sense of adequacy—a feeling of personal worth, importance, and ability to control and manipulate his environment to his own ends—is derived from a misinterpretation of early parental subservience to his needs and desires as a result of which he vastly exaggerates his volitional power and independence. This sense of adequacy is completely unrelated to his actual competence as evidenced by the fact that it coexists with a clear perception of executive helplessness and of dependence upon the executive competence of another; and again, threats directed at this autistic self-esteem would have to be extreme in degree and sustained in nature before resulting in feelings of inadequacy. One such possibility arises if the needs emanating from the child's awareness of his executive dependence are not satisfied, since in addition to threatening his physical safety, this situation also challenges the assumption that his parents are subservient to his volitional direction.

The crisis of ego devaluation which is precipitated by biosocial maturation, changes in parental expectations, and improved capacity to perceive self in relation to reality, results in a profound alteration of the bases of the child's security and adequacy. The gross provision of care and protection is no longer sufficient to engender feelings of security in view of the child's enhanced emotional needs and heightened perceptual sensitivity. Stunned by the sudden realization of his actual impotence—both executive and volitional—he requires greater assurance of his future safety in the new world that confronts him, a world he no longer controls by the magic power of his will, a world in which he is incompetent and marginal, a world in which all of the things he needs for his survival are controlled by powerful beings upon whose good-will he is completely dependent. Under these circumstances, he can gain real security only by feeling assured that the omnipotent ones will not abuse their superior strength, take advantage of his dependency or "use" him for their own ends; that they will accept him unconditionally and value him for his own sake. This type of security (intrinsic security) in short, can be established only in the course of a satellizing relationship in which he becomes an object endowed with a special intrinsic value and an exception to the general rule of value based on competence and power.

The need for reformulating the child's basis of adequacy at this time is just as urgent. Infantile pretensions of volitional power and independence are no longer tenable, since now they must be supported by commensurate achievements in reality—which is an obvious impossibility. Hence, an interval of transitional anxiety is inevitable; and it is to prevent the occurrence of further anxiety and damage to self-esteem that the option of acquiring intrinsic adequacy feelings (i.e., those predicated upon the derived status of satellization) is finally chosen. In fact, the entire phenomenon of satellization can be best understood as a compromise effort to maintain self-esteem at the highest and most stable level consistent with the least possible attendant ego trauma.[13] By freeing the question of adequacy from any connection with the child's own competency to manipulate his environment, it becomes a given, an absolute value derived from unchallengable authority, limited (in part) only by the duration of the relationship from which it is derived. Thus, both intrinsic security and adequacy are products of the same two prerequisite parent attitudes that are necessary for the evolution of the satellizing relationship.

However, no sooner, is the basis for intrinsic security and adequacy established when cultural influences (e.g., school, peer group) and gains in biosocial competency set the stage for still a third variety of security and adequacy (extrinsic). This type resembles the infantile (presatellizing) form more closely than it does the satellizing variety in that it too depends upon a primary rather than a derived source of status. But there is the important difference that this time ego aspirations are related in a more or less realistic fashion to actual performance ability.[14] Extrinsic adequacy becomes a reflection of the child's reputation, his scholastic ability, the approval of his teachers, his skill in sports, his sociometric status, his mastery of hobbies; and extrinsic security becomes a reflection of the feelings of safety and confidence he is able to engender for himself in relation to the future by his own efforts (i.e., independently of the parent-child relationship). It is self-evident, however, that in the general context of the child's prolonged economic dependence in our society, there is less opportunity for gaining extrinsic security than there is for gaining extrinsic adequacy; the range of competencies that are available to him, although leading to status and prestige in his child's world, count for little in protecting him from the actual vicissitudes of existence that threaten his physical safety.

It is not until after pubescence, therefore, that extrinsic adequacy can become more than a subsidiary source of the total available supply of adequacy feelings generated in the economy of ego organization. During the entire span of years covered by elementary school attendance, the sense of adequacy which the child enjoys by virtue of his derived status constitutes the central core of his self-esteem around which various adjunctive forms of extrinsic adequacy are organized. The nature of this hierarchical arrangement is clearly illustrated by the fact that many of his initial as well as later quests for performance status are primarily motivated by the desire to please his parents, "pay them back," or win their praise and approbation. Considerable evidence is at hand [*25, 107, 171*], for example, to support the view that many children, especially from middle-class homes, aspire to succeed in school mainly because of the need to retain parental approval; whereas if left to their own devices, they might be relatively indifferent about their academic standing.

Hence, what ostensibly appears to be a genuine need to acquire independent status may on further inspection prove to be only a parentally-inspired goal adopted by the child (frequently under protest) as a means of safeguarding his intrinsic status. Of course, many motives that originate in this way later take on a more voluntary and independent character; also, many ambitious attempts to win school honors are completely free of such pressures and are motivated simply by strong feelings of loyalty to parents, and by a desire to express feelings of gratitude, and earn their appreciation. However, the important thing to realize about all of the above examples is that they illustrate a mode of transition between two mechanisms of achieving feelings of adequacy: Before the acquisition of extrinsic status becomes an end in itself it serves as a means of safeguarding or enhancing intrinsic adequacy. If parents show themselves to be completely unconcerned about or unappreciative of their children's strivings to attain competence and status in their own right, the latter frequently lose interest in such pursuits and often are unable to resume them with any genuine zest or spontaneity.[15]

However, with the onset of adolescence, we note the beginning of a reversal of positions with respect to the major and subsidiary sources of *current* security and adequacy, a trend that continues and is maintained for the remainder of adult life.[16] During this period also, the attractiveness of the extrinsic sources continues to increase, since the availability of substantial and satisfactory rewards associated with competitive effort generally tends to become greater with age. By virtue of the social prestige value of his wealth, administrative authority, technical skill, professional or trade organization, family connections, etc., it becomes possible for an individual to acquire considerable extrinsic self-esteem; and through these very same media and instrumentalities plus the myriad forms of insurance available today, he can protect his safety and obtain extrinsic security. It should not be forgotten, however, that since (almost by definition) the acquisition of extrinsic adequacy in our culture depends upon social recognition and the achievement of a position of relative superiority, its availability must always be strictly limited.

Relationship between Intrinsic and Extrinsic Systems of Security and Adequacy

When the adolescent finally begins to derive the greater portion of his security and adequacy feelings from extrinsic sources, what is the fate of their intrinsic counterparts which for so many years occupied such a central position in ego organization? Two suggestions have already been offered in answer to this question: (a) the hypothesis that satellization leaves a permanent residue in personality structure, and (b) the reference to extrinsic status as the major *current* source of adequacy feelings in adult life.

These statements imply that as a consequence of experiencing feelings of intrinsic security and adequacy over a prolonged period of time, a permanent change occurs in the way in which an individual tends to value himself and to estimate the extent of the jeopardy menacing his future safety. Hence, a certain residual or underlying *quality* of security and adequacy feelings carry over into the future despite the absence of adequate current experience that could give rise to same. (Actually, of course, the adult who satellized as a child continues to form many satellizing-like relationships as an adult; and generally speaking, he tends to be loved and accepted for himself by his family and by several associates. However, experiences such as these that are productive of intrinsic feelings of security and adequacy constitute only a small fraction of the total current experience of an adult which influences these important ego-related variables.)

It would appear, therefore, that feelings of intrinsic security and adequacy constitute a fairly stable, ongoing cluster of attitudes related to self which persist into adult life and interact with current variables that influence extrinsic security and adequacy as well as their correlates. The precise relationships that prevail between these two systems are undoubtedly highly complex. The present writer, however, is inclined to the view that in an individual endowed with residual feelings of intrinsic security and adequacy, the range of fluctuation that is possible (for resultant levels of security and adequacy) in response to extrinsic factors is both narrow and peripheral. That is, his intrinsic feelings tend to remain fairly constant regardless of the environmental vicissitudes met with in later life. Even in the face of prolonged and consistent reverses in those areas of activity reflecting adversely on extrinsic security and adequacy, he stands a good chance of remaining basically secure and adequate.

Applying this principle specifically, the amount of intrinsic security possessed by an individual predetermines to a large extent his capacity to benefit from extrinsic security. The intrinsically insecure person who strives desperately to make himself secure with money, power and influence seldom impresses anyone as succeeding in this goal regardless of the enormity of his material success. The same holds true with respect to feelings of adequacy as illustrated in the following analysis of Lord Byron's triumphs by Gardner Murphy:

> "But all of these left him hungry for simple acceptance, for regard for himself as a person which no one knew how to build within him. His fundamental sickness was lack of self-acceptance, self-love, status and prestige in his own eyes. Were it not for this, the admiring majority who loved his verse would have sufficed . . . The trouble was that his inner response to himself was rejection, and those who rejected him fed that scorn of self which consumed him throughout his life. There was no quest for power as such; there was a never-satisfied quest for serenity in contemplating himself" [*288*].

Existing levels of intrinsic security and adequacy are also inversely related to the intensity of the individual's needs for their extrinsic counterparts. The reason for this is fairly self-evident: A person endowed with a reasonable level of self-acceptance has something upon which he can fall back in difficult times. He possesses a basic core of self-esteem that enjoys an absolute, market-free value; he is not obliged to justify his existence entirely on the basis of extrinsic criteria of competence and superiority. Were he to lose all of the emoluments of his extrinsic status he would still retain the basic framework of his self-esteem.

A good cultural illustration of this principle can be seen among the Arapesh, who because of heightened feelings of intrinsic self-esteem seem to be almost completely unmotivated by needs for power, competitive distinction and hierarchical status [*274*]. Similarly in working with gifted children in our own culture, the writer found a wide range in the distribution of responsiveness to an incentive of personal prestige and recognition which appeared to be negatively correlated with magnitude of intrinsic self-esteem [*25*]. On the other hand, children who seemed to enjoy greater intrinsic feelings of adequacy than their fellows were more responsive to motives such as inherent interest in the subject matter, intellectual curiosity, etc.

The fact that intrinsically secure and adequate individuals are not susceptible to catastrophic impairment of self-esteem and are not driven by ego aspirations that are unrealistically high and resistant to downward modification also makes them highly invulnerable to neurotic anxiety. In contrast to the intrinsically insecure and inadequate group, their anxiety can usually be traced to an objectively hazardous threat rather than to a subjective threat derived from a breakdown in feelings of adequacy.

Relationship between Security and Adequacy

One of the earliest and best known efforts to bring some order out of the conceptual chaos enveloping this field was Plant's attempt to differentiate between the concepts of security and adequacy [*309*]. *Security,* according to Plant, is a product of the home, consisting of the feelings that a child acquires as a result of being valued for himself. *Adequacy,* on the other hand, is Plant's term for the feelings of self-regard which a child develops as a consequence of the things he can do and the reputation he acquires for doing same. A typical source of adequacy, therefore, would be the school. Plant summed up this distinction neatly by referring to security as "who-status" and to adequacy as "what-status."

Unfortunately, Plant's choice of a differential criterion for distinguishing between security and adequacy was a most unhappy one which created more confusion that it actually dissipated. The main difficulty was that *both* concepts as he defined them referred to feelings based on a valuation of the child's worth; both, therefore, are definitions of different types of adequacy, corresponding almost identically to the definitions we have given above for intrinsic and extrinsic adequacy respectively. The present writer contends that it is less confusing to distinguish between the two types of adequacy by merely using appropriate qualifying adjectives (i.e., intrinsic and extrinsic, a distinction that would also hold true in the case of security); and to reserve the differentiation between security and adequacy for the more crucial distinction that can be made between two different categories of ego-related values, namely, the future safety of self as against its relative worth and importance.

Another difficulty inherent in Plant's position is clearly illustrated by his assertion that rural children have more security ("who-status") than urban children, and that the latter try to compensate for this lack of security by striving for greater adequacy ("what-status") [*309*]. However, it would really be more accurate to state that rural children have greater opportunities to acquire extrinsic feelings of adequacy ("what-status") by serving in economically useful roles, and that urban children must compensate for these absent opportunities by retaining as much intrinsic adequacy as long as possible.

Still another difficulty with Plant's distinction between security and adequacy is its failure to recognize the interdependence as well as the difference between the two concepts. Actually they are not nearly as distinct as Plant would have us believe. The intrinsic forms, for example, are both products of parent attitudes reflecting unconditional acceptance and intrinsic valuation of the child. In fact the most tenable hypothesis regarding the relationship prevailing between the two concepts is that each interacts with and influences the other, and that adequacy can best be understood as that component portion of security which is concerned with the *value* of self.

This latter relationship can be more readily appreciated if we approach it from its negative aspects, i.e., the relationship between inadequacy and insecurity. In our previous discussion of anxiety, we had assumed that when a threat to adequacy reaches a certain intensity, an affect of fear (anxiety) is elicited; and that frequently the source of such a threat emanates from the impairment of self-esteem itself (neurotic anxiety). We are now ready to offer a more explicit answer to the question underlying this assumption, i.e., why does a threat to self-esteem lead to an expression of fear affect?

There are two chief reasons: In the first place, a challenge to the individual's sense of adequacy raises the question of whether he is sufficiently competent to manipulate his environment for purposes of satisfactory adjustment and maintenance of biosocial position. If the threat then becomes increasingly more formidable, he feels incompetent to cope with adjustive problems and on the verge of being overwhelmed by environmental vicissitudes. It is at this point that he reacts with fear in contemplating the future. Anxiety, therefore, results primarily because of a threat to self-esteem that is serious enough in its implications to jeopardize his future safety. It can, therefore, be considered a sub-type of the more inclusive term, *insecurity,* in which the threat, instead of being projected more directly at various aspects of the individual's safety, is deviously aimed at the same target through the more indirect route of undermining his sense of adequacy in coping with his environment.

Secondly, after undergoing several experiences in which self-esteem is impaired (not necessarily in a catastrophic sense), the individual begins to realize that such states of anxiety actually interfere with problem-solving activity, and hence, potentially menace his safety. He, therefore, has still another good reason to be fearful (insecure) about threats directed against his self-esteem. On the other hand, it is evident from the foregoing that a strong sense of adequacy would provide the same two reasons (only in reverse) for enhancing his sense of security.

Looking at the relationship between security and adequacy from the other direction, we find that enhancement of security also leads to increased feelings of adequacy. It is a well-known clinical fact that the threshold for anxiety responses can be markedly raised by placing an individual in a generally secure environment. It will be recalled that one important reason for the minimal presence of transitional anxiety in the crisis of ego devaluation is the fact that the devaluing process is usually carried out in a general context of parental acceptance of the child and of genuine concern for the gratification of his dependency needs. Conversely, however, where the general climate of ego devaluation is characterized by parental rejection, hostility, and capriciousness in satisfying the child's needs, transitional anxiety is quite intense and becomes continuous with neurotic anxiety. Similarly in adult life, in the absence of any specific threat directed against self-esteem, a decrease in general security will result in a pronounced lowering of the threshold for anxiety reactions.

Security and Adequacy in Non-Satellizers

Because non-satellizing children are not unconditionally accepted and valued for themselves, they obviously cannot acquire any intrinsic feelings of security and adequacy. The best they can hope for is to achieve their extrinsic counterparts; and since complete ego devaluation represents too abrupt and traumatic an alternative for them to accept during the crisis of ego devaluation,[17] this requires the acquisition of power and prestige commensurate with the exaggerated ego aspirations residual from infancy. These hypertrophic ego demands also play a current compensatory role in that they are largely powered by the absence of intrinsic adequacy; and although they do eventually predispose the individual to frustration and further loss of self-esteem, it is still undeniable that in and of themselves they generate feelings of extrinsic adequacy.[18] Security also is sought in the same general manner—through extrinsic safeguards, although the rejected non-satellizer (within the limits imposed by his fear of further rejection) often tries to establish satellizing-like and other types of emotional relationships in which he can feel accepted for himself.

It has already been suggested that in the absence of intrinsic adequacy, the attainment of extrinsic self-esteem can only be peripheral, and, hence, not very satisfying. In addition, chronic frustration with its disrupting effect on performance efforts is more or less inevitable, inasmuch as ego aspirational level tends to be tenaciously and unrealistically resistant to lowering in the face of failure due to the individual's inability to become reconciled to a lower prestige status. A highly developed self-critical faculty also promises little in the way of ego enhancement through the technique of overvaluing the worth of his own performance.

Nevertheless, the chances for accomplishment are greater than could normally be expected from the individual's level of ability because of (1) the large amount of prestige motivation generated by hypertrophic ego demands, and (2) his very high goal frustration tolerance. This is the one bright spot in an otherwise dismal picture, since it allows for the possibility of creating environmental conditions that are relatively secure and hence propitious for the maintenance of anxiety on a tolerable level.

The absence of intrinsic security and adequacy is itself the crucial predisposing cause of neurotic anxiety; and if brought about by early parental rejection with resulting catastrophic impairment of self-esteem, the other necessary etiological factor (the precipitating cause) is concomitantly supplied. If not, either later parental rejection, or some other catastrophic blow to self-esteem will almost certainly supervene at some later date, thus making the occurrence of neurotic anxiety almost inevitable. The likelihood of this occurrence is, of course, greatly increased by the presence of exaggerated ego aspirations that set the stage for large scale deflation of self-esteem at some time or another.

A realistic therapeutic expectation in anxiety states, therefore, is to reduce anxiety to a minimum, to ward off acute attacks, and to keep the patient comfortable at as high a level of productivity as possible without developing somatic symptoms or other objectionable defenses. The restoration of security and adequacy on the same basis as can be expected in persons with a history of satellization is a forlorn hope that should never be attempted; and if the dynamics of anxiety neurosis were fully appreciated by psychotherapists, it probably never would be attempted.

NEUROTIC ANXIETY

Etiology

We have defined neurotic anxiety as a form of developmental anxiety (occurring in an individual with a history of failure in ego devaluation) in which the essential source of the threat to self-esteem arises from a catastrophically impaired sense of adequacy. It manifests itself as a tendency to over-react with fear to any stimulus which threatens to impair self-esteem further. Such stimuli generally consist of a limited group of adjustive situations having special reference to prestige areas in which there is selective ego-involvement or painful memories of an especially dismal or humiliating nature.

This definition makes explicit both the predisposing and the precipitating causes of neurotic anxiety. The condition could not occur in the absence of the particular disturbed parent-child relationship which leads to a failure in ego devaluation with its consequences of non-satellization, failure to acquire intrinsic security and adequacy, and retention of hypertrophic ego aspirations. In the first place, an individual with intrinsic security and adequacy could never suffer a sufficiently catastrophic blow to self-esteem, since such environmental debacles could result only in deflating consequences confined to the peripheral reaches of self-esteem. Secondly, in the case of rejected children, the catastrophic impairment of self-esteem inheres in the act of rejection itself. And lastly, if the catastrophic event must occur later, it is rendered almost inevitable by virtue of the individual's vulnerability to (a) core involvement of his self-esteem (in the absence of intrinsic adequacy) and (b) large scale collapse of his goal structure because of the presence of grandiose ego aspirations.

Hence, the very occurrence of neurotic anxiety becomes both a prerequisite for its further existence, and a discouraging prognostic indicator that the underlying pathological condition will be indefinitely perpetuated as a chronic disturbance punctuated perhaps by sporadic acute exacerbations. It is the writer's firm belief that the predisposing and precipitating factors mentioned above constitute the sole necessary ingredients required for initiating the mechanism of neurotic anxiety. The factors of repression, hostility and conflict which figure so prominently in other theories can either complicate and intensify existing neurotic anxiety or can occur independently in the form of symptomatic anxiety. The only other psychopathological channel that could conceivably lead to neurotic anxiety is the occurrence in mild satellizers of a particularly traumatic blow to self-esteem that has permanent implications (e.g., a disabling or disfiguring disease). But even in such cases, it is doubtful whether the anxiety is as intense or as irreversible as in the more usual sequence of etiological events.

Both DeForest [*76*] and May [*270*] deny that the child's experience of parental rejection *per se* is a cause of neurotic anxiety. According to the former, it arises in children of parents whose actions are hostile but whose words are loving. The child guides himself by the parent's actions but hopes all along that he is wrong and that the words are true. May's interpretation is almost identical, stemming from his general position that there can be no neurotic anxiety in the absence of subjective conflict. He points to several cases in which flagrant rejection did not result in anxiety states.

> "In these girls there was no cleavage, no contradiction between expectation and reality in their relations with their parents. The conflicts these girls experienced in their relations to others as well as their parents were on a conscious, objective basis. The essential point in their freedom from neurotic anxiety was that their rejection was not internalized; it was not made a source of subjective conflict, and it therefore did not psychologically disorient them in their self-appraisal or appraisal of others" [*270*].

In contrasting these individuals to others in whom rejection *was* followed by anxiety, May concludes in relation to the latter:

> "The origin of the predisposition to neurotic anxiety lies in that particular constellation in the child's relation to the parent in which the child cannot appraise the parent's attitude realistically and cannot accept the rejection objectively. Neurotic anxiety arises not out of the fact of having had a 'bad' mother . . . but out of the fact that the child

is never sure whether the mother is 'good' or 'bad'. What causes the conflict underlying neurotic anxiety, looking at the problem from the viewpoint of the parent's behavior toward the child, is rejection covered over with pretenses of love and concern" [*270*].

In the first instance what May is really describing are children rejected from the very start of infancy, children who fail to receive even the minimum of care and protection that is forthcoming to most infants who are fated to undergo rejection during the crisis of ego devaluation. Devaluation is really unnecessary in their case because ideas of omnipotence never have a chance to really develop. Hence, there is no rude shock of rejection following the omnipotent phase; and although the child enjoys no derived status and little extrinsic status, neurotic anxiety fails to develop for two main reasons: (a) there is no experience of catastrophic loss of self-esteem, and (b) large-scale frustration is improbable in view of the fact that aspirational level is low and realistic.

As for May's rejected cases who did develop anxiety, there is no denying the fact that the parental behavior emerging during the crisis of ego devaluation must have seemed unexpected and contradictory to the child. This is partly due to an actual increase in the aggressive, demanding, hostile, and unaccepting aspects of the parent's conduct, and partly to the increased perceptual sensitivity and greater emotional needs of the child. It is also true that a child is generally unwilling to accept the verdict of parental rejection until every slim hope based on possible misinterpretation or reversal of attitude is exhausted. The point at issue, however, is whether such a conflict between the child's hopes and expectations regarding his parent's behavior and the actual reality of the latter is sufficient to account for the genesis of neurotic anxiety.

In the present writer's opinion this conflict can at most intensify existing anxiety by engendering fresh sources of resentment and bitterness, and by causing the child to entertain false hopes which are subjected to continual frustration, and which divert his energies from more realistic adjustive efforts. Furthermore, except in borderline cases, doubts regarding the parent's intentions do not last forever. The essential causes of the neurotic anxiety in this situation are: (1) absence of intrinsic security and adequacy which allows a crippling blow to be struck at the heart of self-esteem; (2) the catastrophic impact on self-esteem produced by the definitive judgment on the part of the most significant figures in his interpersonal world that he is unworthy of love and acceptance; (3) the ego-deflating implications of being physically dependent on such a hated person; and (4) awareness of the difficulties and dangers involved in being completely dependent on the good-will of a hostile individual.

In the overvalued child, the same susceptibility to catastrophic impairment of self-esteem holds true, since intrinsic security and adequacy cannot be acquired as long as he realizes that he is not valued for himself but for his importance, which is intended to redound to the greater glory of the parent. Thus, like the rejected child, he is driven to seek extrinsic security and adequacy through superior achievement compatible with his hypertrophic ego demands, a fact which sets the stage for later traumatic devaluation of self-esteem. However, although he shares all of the predisposing causes of neurotic anxiety with the rejected child, he has yet to experience the catastrophic blow to self-esteem which is the essential precipitating factor, an event which may be deferred for many years or conceivably may never take place at all.

As long as the attitude of parental overvaluation is maintained, extrinsic adequacy can be kept at a reasonably high level. There is always the danger, however, that the parent might change over to a rejecting attitude as a result of growing weary of his subservient role, or of deciding that the child either does not have sufficient ability to succeed or is a less promising candidate than a younger sibling. If all of these hazards are successfully avoided, increasingly greater danger awaits him outside the home, as his parents become progressively less able to provide the extrinsic status he requires. Once he leaves the biased atmosphere of the home, he finds prejudice directed against him rather than in his favor because of his unpleasant self-centeredness and aggressiveness. Disastrous collapse of the grandiose goal structure usually tends to occur in the formative years when crucial decisions regarding educational and vocational ambitions have to be made, except perhaps in those rare cases where large-scale frustration can be prevented or delayed by unusual ability, wealth or family connections.

Anxiety as Ego Damage, Defense or Physiological Change

As a central value in personality organization, the enhancement and defense of which is one of the most powerful drives motivating human behavior, it is only to be expected that threats directed against self-esteem would provoke a wide variety of responses. These responses may be divided into three general categories: defense, escape and ego damage. Defense efforts include reactive attempts to enhance threatened self-esteem, to make the self appear strong, competent and masterful, to excuse, explain and rationalize failure, etc. Escape mechanisms provide opportunities for withdrawing the self beyond the reach of possible threats. Ego damage, on the other hand, includes current and residual reactions (to threats against self-esteem) which in and of themselves have no adjustive value, but are merely reflective of the disruptive and disorganizing effects which such threats have wrought on personality structure.

Depending on its intensity and relation to actual impairment of self-esteem, anxiety may be considered either a defense reaction or a manifestation of ego damage. When a threat to adequacy becomes sufficiently serious to challenge the safety of an individual, it elicits the affect of anxiety. Moderate amounts of this affect in a reasonably secure and adequate person have adjustive value in that they facilitate the mobilization of the individual's adaptive efforts. However, if anxiety reaches the proportions of panic, behavior becomes hopelessly disorganized and maladaptive.

If the threat is pushed still farther it may very well gain its goal, that is, an actual impairment of self-esteem may result. This may be the outcome of a humiliating defeat, a loss in biosocial status or of extreme frustration in an ego-involved area. It is clear, however, that this impairment and the accompanying anxiety can only be considered as evidence of ego damage that serves no adjustive function *per se,* although in creating a need for anxiety reduction, it gives rise to many defense and escape mechanisms.

Again, in persons who are intrinsically secure and adequate, such damage is peripheral and transitory. But in the case of neurotic anxiety, impaired self-esteem is a permanent and relatively irreversible form of ego damage, in much the same sense as the replacement of functional cardiac muscle by fibrous tissue in coronary disease of the heart.

This residual damage is severe enough to constitute the main source of threat in neurotic anxiety, since in the absence of sufficient confidence in one's ability to cope with adjustive problems, any insignificant environmental threat to self-esteem appears extremely menacing. Returning to our analogy of the heart, we could say that in persons with normal hearts, the source of the threat of cardiac failure lies in excessive environmental demands, e.g., sustained overwork, insufficient rest. However, when the heart is severely damaged, its adaptive powers to stress are seriously impaired, and any additional burden, no matter how trivial, is dangerous. And just as the main source of the threat of heart failure in organic heart cases lies *within* the damaged heart muscle, the main source of the threat of collapsed self-esteem in anxiety neurosis lies *within* the individual's impaired self-esteem. The threat of "failure brings collapse because life has been structured in terms of self-enhancement, and because the struggle to earn a favorable view of the self has been unremitting" [*288*].

If ego damage does not go beyond the stage of anxiety, however, the individual may be considered fortunate indeed. In fact, the psychopathologist working in a hospital for mental diseases rarely finds any signs of pure, uncomplicated anxiety; and when he does, he regards them as excellent prognostic indicators. Anxiety is a sign that vigorous striving for adult adjustment in a reality setting is still in progress. Besides indicating that the patient is not yet utilizing some of the more objectionable defenses, it conveys the more important assurance that he has not availed himself of the relief from anxiety which can be obtained from succumbing to further ego damage. This relief is available when the individual finally decides that he needs it badly enough to relinquish the self-esteem he has been defending at such cost. It can be gained either by accepting defeat and ceasing to strive (depression), or by ceasing to strive for adult goals on a reality level (schizophrenia). Both alternatives result in extensive ego damage and personality disorganization.

Agitation is an intermediate stage between anxiety and its two psychotic complications, more usually depression. It is indicative of the fact that anxiety bordering on panic has become so severe and continuous that even the everyday routines of living can no longer be managed successfully. All of the individual's organized defenses have broken down; and disorganization is so rampant that primitive fear of death, which ordinarily can be repressed at only minimal levels of self-esteem, stalks brazenly across the stage of consciousness. When anxiety reaches this point, the pressure for yielding to one of the two psychotic solutions promising relief from this agony becomes almost unbearable.

Teleological reasoning, however, is so ingrained in the biological and social sciences that it is very difficult for a psychopathologist to concede that a given behavioral symptom of reaction to stress could be anything but adjustive and compensatory. Even organic pathologists lapse into the same error in interpreting physical symptoms as compensatory responses of organs to physiological stress.[19] Although most psychopathologists are willing to recognize neurotic anxiety as a reflection of ego damage rather than as a compensatory form of defense, the influence of the teleological approach is still discernible in present-day theorizing about the nature of anxiety.

DeForest [*76*], for example, has recently proposed that neurotic anxiety can best be understood as a self-protective device that is highly effective in impressing others with one's helplessness, thus gaining their sympathy and protection as well as various immunities from the rigors and pressures of competitive existence. Although certain anxiety neurotics sometimes utilize their anxiety for this purpose, it would seem more credible to regard this as an incidental use to which existing damage can be put than as the primary cause for the development of the anxiety. Furthermore, considering the low esteem in which anxiety is held in our culture, and the heavy penalties which an individual must pay when it is suspected that he might be a victim of anxiety, it is extremely unlikely that anxiety would be frequently used as a defense, even in an incidental fashion.

The tremendous prestige formerly enjoyed by the James-Lange theory of emotion[20] also continues to influence modern concepts of anxiety. One expression of this point of view is the contention that anxiety is a subjective reflection of a physiological state (e.g., neuromuscular hypertension) induced by a threat to the physical integrity of the body [*89*]. Relief from anxiety, therefore, can be obtained by administering drugs which cause muscular relaxation [*89, 173*], or by desensitizing the patient to the physiological agent (epinephrine) which helps disseminate the diffuse visceral response in anxiety [*60*]. Although the present writer is willing to concede that these methods are rational, and can relieve anxiety by interrupting that particular component of conscious anxiety derived from the feedback to consciousness of visceral and muscular responses, he must insist with other critics of the James-Lange theory that the quality of an emotion is primarily determined by the nature of the perception resulting from the initiating stimulus.

We meet still another variation of this point of view in Goldstein's theory that anxiety is merely the organism's subjective awareness of being placed in a "catastrophic" adjustive situation with which it cannot cope and which, therefore, threatens its existence [*156*]. Our primary quarrel with this formulation is that it begs the question. Restated, it simply asserts (1) that when an organism is confronted with an adjustive problem which it cannot solve, it is thrown into panic and disorganization as a consequence of appreciating the possible dangerous implications of this failure; and (2) that anxiety is the subjective awareness of this behavioral panic and disorganization. Anxiety, in other words, is the affect associated with an anxiety situation, or with one of the extreme behavioral consequences of an acute anxiety state. The phenomenon and its consequences are described, and then the description is equated with the cause and mechanism of the phenomenon. Furthermore, there is the difficulty of accounting for the majority of instances in which anxiety is not manifested in the form of panic; even in neurotic anxiety, a catastrophic experience is necessary only once.

Goldstein's theory also ignores the two crucial issues involved in the mechanism and differentiation of the various types of fear states, i.e., the object and the source of the threat. At no point does Goldstein make clear what is being threatened (e.g., life, safety, orientation, self-esteem, etc.) ; hence, he can offer no suitable criterion for distinguishing between fear and anxiety.[21] He also fails to specify whether the source of the threat is primarily objective or subjective, and hence sheds no light on the differentiation between normal and neurotic anxiety. However, in the particular examples of anxiety he chooses to illustrate his position, i.e., the anxiety shown by aphasic patients who are assigned simple sorting tasks, it is quite evident that he is describing normal anxiety; since the source of threat comes from an *objective* incapacity to cope with the problem, which, phenomenologically, is equivalent to the situation in which capacity is normal but the problem prohibitively difficult. How this type of anxiety is related to neurotic anxiety, Goldstein fails to make explicit.

Anxiety in Rejected and Overvalued Individuals[22]

One of the most striking differences between rejected and overvalued children in their anxiety manifestations is the latency of the condition in the case of the latter. This is due to the postponement of the catastrophic blow to self-esteem, an event which in rejected children occurs at the close of infancy. Related to this difference is the fact that the overvalued child enjoys a superfluity of extrinsic adequacy at home, while the rejected child is enveloped in a stern, hostile environment which persistently emphasizes his worthlessness, thereby continually widening the gap between aspirations and reality. The rejected child, therefore, carries within him a greater burden of repressed hostility, bitterness and resentment. It is no wonder then that much of his motivation has a negative quality, being inspired by considerations of revenge and an "I'll show them" attitude.

The blow that results in catastrophic impairment of self-esteem is also much more devastating in the case of the rejected child because it occurs at a time when ego defenses are weaker, and because the ego has not as yet had any opportunity to be fortified by experiences productive of extrinsic adequacy; nor, in view of the child's complete dependence on his parents at this stage of his development, is there any possibility of obtaining other sources of extrinsic status. His self-esteem, therefore, is more completely shattered, and, hence, less able to be benefited by gains in extrinsic adequacy. Regardless of the objective magnitude of his success, he can never quite take himself or his accomplishments very seriously; for indelibly engraved in the innermost reaches of his self-esteem is the unshakeable conviction that he is the worthless, despicable little creature whom even his own parents could not accept.

In contrast, the overvalued individual in periods of remission from acute attacks of anxiety is buoyant, exuberant, self-confident, and full of self-assurance. He does not suffer at all from inability to take himself or his success seriously But this expansiveness which he manifests in "good times" makes him less able to weather subsequent acute attacks of anxiety than the rejected individual, the very invariability of whose depressed self-esteem protects him from the impact of violent and abrupt fluctuations in fortune.

In terms of the possibilities for improvement that depend on more than superficial situational factors, the rejected individual also shows to advantage. He still enjoys the option of establishing satellizing-like relationships with others, and is generally capable of being loved for himself. The resulting feelings of intrinsic security and adequacy which he gains from such experiences not only reduce his current load of anxiety, but also make it possible for him to lower his ego aspiration level. The overvalued individual, on the other hand, finds satellization too degrading, and is usually too obnoxiously selfish to inspire genuine feelings of love for him in other persons.

Because of his extended training in the ways of infantile omnipotence, the overvalued child is also more reluctant to surrender the prerogative of executive dependence. However, when he realizes the expediency of acquiring executive independence, he is not hampered as is the rejected child by overt anxiety in the learning of new motor, social and intellectual skills. Nevertheless in periods of acute anxiety in later life, he is more apt to regress to the position of demanding assistance from others.

We have also seen that the rejected individual, trained in the habit of repressing self-assertive and aggressive feelings, develops introverted and withdrawing tendencies, tends to avoid situations involving conflict, and intellectualizes his aggression. As a result he fails to master effective social techniques of expressing aggression, a circumstance which makes him vulnerable to exploitation by others and generates more hostility that requires repression. This seething internal reservoir of repressed hostility in turn intensifies existing anxiety (see pp. 357-359). The overvalued individual, on the other hand, has had abundant experience in giving vent to hostile feelings. His problem is to learn how to make his aggressive tactics seem less offensive and ruthless than they really are.

SYMPTOMATIC ANXIETY

We have chosen to identify the term "neurotic anxiety" with the principal type of anxiety induced by a subjective threat. This is the traditional anxiety neurosis, the origin of which we have related to a primary defect in ego devaluation that predisposes an individual to catastrophic impairment of self-esteem. It is this damage to self-esteem which then constitutes the subjective threat. Apart from *situational* (normal) anxiety, however, there are still three types of anxiety induced by subjective threats that we have yet to consider. When the source of the threat is related to defects in ego maturation, it may be called *maturational.* When it is related to normal developmental pressures found in transitional (crisis) periods of ego development it may be termed *transitional.* And lastly, there is *symptomatic* anxiety that is associated neither with normal developmental pressures nor with residual developmental defects but with other psychopathological mechanisms. This may be discussed under the sub-headings of repression, hostility, conflict and guilt.

Repression

From an historical standpoint, two issues have become associated with the problem of repression in relation to anxiety: (1) To what extent does repression of impulses, drives, emotions, attitudes, etc., generate anxiety? and (2) the role of repression as a defense mechanism in suppressing impulses that give rise to anxiety. It is clear that in the second instance it is not repression which is the source of symptomatic anxiety, but the nature of the impulses involved which require repression. Nevertheless, because of historical usage, it will be convenient to consider the two problems together.

It was Freud who originally claimed that repression (frustration) of libidinal impulses lead to anxiety [*126*]. Horney [*187*] reinterpreted this to mean that it was not frustration of sexual urges *per se,* but the threat which such frustration poses to security, adequacy and independence (values associated with sex activity in our culture) which causes the anxiety. Kardiner [*218*] invoked the same principle as Freud, but was more concerned with the frustration of "relaxor patterns" than with sexual impulses. Mowrer [*286*] like Horney tried to place the problem of repression in relation to anxiety on a more psychological (rather than biological) level by asserting that it was the repression of guilt and fear of social reprisal that was mainly responsible for generating anxiety.

In Horney's sense, frustration of sex urges is really a form of *situational* anxiety, since the source of the threat to self-esteem is an objective form of status threat. Also, it is only legitimate to refer to the affect resulting from the frustration of needs as anxiety when such frustration reflects adversely on the individual's sense of adequacy. This is not to say that the frustration of biological needs (i.e., those mentioned by Freud and Kardiner) does not give rise to any affectual change whatsoever. We have already indicated (see pp. 85-86) that frustration of *acknowledged* physiological sex drives (partial repression) induces a state of altered behavioral reactivity with resultant feelings of emotional tension. The interaction between these sex urges and various moral restraints also produces psychological conflict. But neither emotional tension nor conflict can be equated with anxiety.

It is, therefore, only in Mowrer's position that the question of *symptomatic* anxiety first becomes relevant. Mowrer goes beyond the biological frame of reference implicit in Freud's original theory, but clings essentially to the same psychological formulation, i.e., that it is the mechanism of repression *per se* which is chiefly responsible for producing anxiety. We would not attempt to deny that repression is related to anxiety. Our point is simply that repression is only a minor and secondary source of anxiety that sometimes coexists with the situation giving rise to neurotic anxiety. Neurotic anxiety occurs in the absence of repression (in cases where insight is complete); and the mere acquisition of insight or the reincorporation of repressed guilt into conscious personality structure cannot reconstitute damaged self-esteem. In fact, in many cases where the source of the anxiety is overwhelmingly obvious, e.g., unambiguous parental rejection, complete repression of this fact is practically impossible despite its unpalatibility.

Symptomatically, however, repression intensifies existing anxiety by interfering with the evolution of constructive solutions and facilitating the development of objectionable defenses. If the source of threat cannot be admitted to consciousness, rational defenses cannot be worked out, and "unconscious" solutions will be evolved. If the individual cannot acknowledge his anxiety consciously, he will do so deviously in the form of psychological and somatic symptoms.

Another source of symptomatic "anxiety" arises when an individual discovers within himself attitudes, motivations, etc., which are personally or socially unacceptable. Anxiety originates in this case from the existence of internal impulses which if expressed would expose the individual to loss of self-esteem. Since in most cases, however, the individual's safety (rather than his self-esteem) is involved, it would be more accurate to refer to the resulting affect as symptomatic *insecurity*. Repression plays no part in generating this anxiety, but is merely employed as a defensive measure to protect the individual from the consequences of executing his dangerous impulses.

It is in connection with this particular function of repression that anxiety is often referred to as a "danger signal" [*268*]. It enables an individual to avoid danger situations that arise from dissident elements within himself which are at odds with cultural standards and their internalized counterparts. As long as man remains dependent upon his culture he can neither flee nor express himself with complete disregard for social conventions. Hence, it is likely that repression will continue to play the highly important role of enabling the individual "to avoid the danger situation of which anxiety sounds the alarm" [*135*]. Other defenses are both possible and undoubtedly more desirable, but none perhaps is so easily available.

Hostility

Hostile feelings offer an excellent example of internal impulses which place the individual in jeopardy by inviting social reprisal. But for other reasons as well, it is productive of symptomatic insecurity and anxiety. In all instances of dependency, a condition which prevails to a greater or lesser degree throughout the lifetime of every individual, feelings of hostility arouse the danger of alienating the person on whom the individual is dependent for his safety, support, security, livelihood, etc. [*187*]. The rejected child, for example, feels tremendously hostile toward his parents, but at the same time fears his hostility because he cannot risk alienating them further on account of his dependency. The satellizing child is also made insecure by his hostile impulses since his parent's approval of him as well as his derived status is thereby endangered.

Feelings of hostility also generate insecurity (in situations where there is no dependency also) because of the expectation that it will lead to retaliation or counter-aggression. This fear of retaliation (as evidenced by a sharp increase in the repression of hostility) becomes much more pronounced after the development of conscience, a fact which suggests the hypothesis that the child might feel less threatened by corporal punishment, deprivation, and loss of succorance than by the shame and discomfort associated with guilt feelings. Because of the self-reproach implied in attitudes of guilt, the pretty, unsullied picture of self is threatened; and since self-esteem is now involved, the affect elicited is anxiety as well as insecurity. For the same reason the child also feels that such parental reprisals are justifiable and deserved rather than the mere reflection of superior force [*312*].

Hence, because hostile impulses endanger the individual's safety and derived status as well as expose him to counter-aggression and the trauma of guilt, the need for their repression is strong. However, other self-protective measures are also available. The provocation for hostility can be obviated if no cause for anger or affront is ever perceived. Some children, for example, are able to interpret all parental aggression as not only justifiable but also as a disguised form of benevolence. Many adults in our culture are also unable to perceive any malevolence, especially in people of superior status; and if this becomes too obvious to deny, they always have a ready excuse at hand or some basis for claiming the other's "good intentions." Another method of securing safety under such conditions, as Horney [*187*] points out, is to hedge in one's hostility by various neurotic trends such as exaggerated compliancy, unobtrusiveness, or dependence. A quite different approach is to seek safety in power and independence, i.e., to become so powerful and independent of others that safety is possible *despite* one's hostility.

If repression is chosen, all of the same reasons discussed above which explain why repression is productive of symptomatic anxiety would also apply here. In addition, repression tends to become overgeneralized as a defensive device because of its easy availability, and to be applied indiscriminately in all situations where hostility might arise. Hence, even in situations which require aggressive behavior and in which hostility is not particularly dangerous, it is still repressed. This results in the production of the familiar overinhibited individual who represses all hostile feelings lest their expression on even one occasion might expose him to danger. He may not even permit himself to develop feelings of hostility by selectively failing to perceive actions in other persons which normally would elicit a hostile response. The rejected child, as indicated previously, is so overtrained in repressing hostility that he often fails to learn socially effective techniques of self-assertion. An unfortunate by-product of this passive, compliant attitude toward aggression by others is that it encourages the latter to continue their ruthless, exploitative actions.

Since hostile impulses are productive of guilt feelings in satellizers (and sometimes in rejected individuals), strong efforts are usually made to disown or justify them. Both aims can be simultaneously accomplished by projecting the hostility onto others. If this mechanism is successful, one either rids oneself of hostility by planting it elsewhere or justifies its presence on the grounds of self-defense. However, although guilt-engendered anxiety can be obviated in this fashion, a new source of anxiety is created in the form of a hostile, threatening environment.

We wish to emphasize, however, that anxiety arising from hostility is only symptomatic anxiety, which in terms of origin, intensity, expressive characteristics and prognosis is quite distantly removed from neurotic anxiety. Hostility, to be sure, arises almost invariably in situations leading to the development or expression of neurotic anxiety. But the primary threat responsible for the neurotic anxiety is not derived from hostile impulses, but from gross impairment of the individual's self-esteem. Also in such cases where satellizing loyalties are not implicated, hostility does not arouse guilt but fear of reprisal; hence, insecurity would be a more appropriate term for the secondary affect engendered by the hostility.

If we turn now to the other side of this relationship, it becomes evident that Horney was also correct in her proposition that anxiety causes hostility [*187*]. It is extremely plausible to suppose that an anxious individual will feel hostile toward persons who are in some way responsible for his anxiety; and this is confirmed by clinical observation. However, as already indicated, we cannot go as far as Horney in believing that hostility inevitably inheres in the fact of dependency (see pp. 328-329).

Anxiety may also lead to hostility in order to provide the anxiety neurotic with a more self-consistent orientation toward life. Hence, in order to justify his anxiety, he is motivated to perceive the world as hostile, which requires that he in turn develop feelings of hostility. This reaction may also be interpreted as a form of displacement of the source of the anxiety from a subjective to an objective focus. The latter form is obviously more acceptable and more manageable.

We must also examine the occurrence and value of aggression as a defensive technique in anxiety states. As an occasional device designed to enhance self-esteem on a relative basis by deflating the status of others, it is a very common phenomenon. As a permanent form of defense against anxiety it is more rare because it tends to generate too much anxiety and leads to extreme social unpopularity. A more likely defense against anxiety is repression of hostility, and the assumption of a sympathetic, uncritical attitude toward others in the hope that they will reciprocate and thus create a situation propitious for anxiety reduction. Hostility is more apt to be exhibited by anxiety-ridden individuals after they become more secure in a given situation [*290*].

In any event we can be sure that the anxiety neurotic is unable objectively to evaluate the merits or faults of individuals who either threaten or enhance his precarious security. His perception of the former is ten times as black as reality, and his perception of the latter is equally fallacious in the opposite direction. This is confirmed by empirical evidence which indicates that the better adjusted, more successful and self-accepting individual, as well as the individual who is ranked high in a given trait is more prone to estimate his own and others' abilities realistically and in accord with group ratings [*69, 196, 306, 351, 398*]. Level of aspiration also tends to be more realistic after an experience of success than after an experience of failure [*251, 345*].

Conflict

Not long after Horney had declared that the danger inhering in hostile impulses and their repression constituted the source of "basic anxiety" [*187*], she modified her position considerably to place greater emphasis upon conflict between "neurotic trends" as the important etiological factor [*189*]. Such conflict, according to Horney, arises between contradictory personality trends through which the individual seeks safety. The reason for conflict is that on one hand he seeks feelings of adequacy through self-enhancement, i.e., through self-assertive, independent, aggressive, and power-seeking measures; and on the other hand, he is fearful of the consequences to self-esteem if such efforts should fail, and seeks security through dependence, conformity, and the hedging in of his hostile impulses. These two approaches to acquiring security and adequacy are obviously mutually exclusive. A decision to "play it safe" by behaving in a compliant, passive, and dependent fashion poses a threat to his hopes for ego enhancement through independence and aggressive action; whereas a decision in favor of the latter undermines security by threatening a trend which guards against the expression of hostile, aggressive impulses. Whichever choice he makes, therefore, leads either to insecurity or inadequacy. The same conflict is present in the choice between strivings for prestige and fear of failure; desire to be loved and fear of rejection; need for the expression of hostility and independence and fear of alienating persons on whom one is dependent; desire for material success at any cost and the inhibitions stemming from moral considerations.

Besides the insecurity or inadequacy that follows from choosing an adjustive mechanism which automatically threatens an alternative device through which safety or self-enhancement is sought, conflict tends to increase helplessness by fostering confusion, indecision, stalemate, and hence failure to take any action whatsoever. This Horney maintains is especially true since these "neurotic trends" tend to be compulsive in nature [*187*]. It is quite understandable, therefore, that any factor inducing paralysis of decision or action would undermine an individual's confidence in his capacity to cope with his environment, and hence be productive of anxiety.

It is important, however, to distinguish the aspect of conflict which threatens security and adequacy from the aspect which merely results in neurophysiological and psychological tension as a consequence of frustrating needs. We have met this problem before in examining the relationship between frustration and anxiety. Conflict frequently leads to frustration of needs when two needs are incompatible. If one is chosen, the other must either be denied or repressed. If a stalemate ensues, both needs are frustrated.

We can summarize this discussion by reiterating what has already been said in relation to repression and hostility as etiological factors in anxiety: Conflict is a secondary and symptomatic form of anxiety that can either occur independently, or can intensify existing neurotic anxiety. In individuals who are basically secure and adequate, conflict cannot produce more than transitory and peripheral anxiety; and in cases of anxiety neurosis, conflict would be unable to precipitate serious bouts of anxiety if the patient were not already rendered especially vulnerable by virtue of his impaired sense of adequacy. It is the latter factor, therefore, which must be accounted the major source of the threat in neurotic anxiety.

This overvaluation of the etiological role of conflict in producing neurotic anxiety can be seen in the following statement by May:

"In neurotic anxiety, the cleavage between expectations and reality is in the form of a *contradiction;* expectation and reality cannot be brought together, and since nobody can bear a constant experience of such a cleavage, the individual engages in a neurotic distortion of reality. Though this distortion is undertaken for the purpose of protecting the individual from neurotic anxiety, in the long run it makes the contradiction between the individual's expectations and reality more rigid and hence sets the stage for greater neurotic anxiety" [*270*].

In the light of the theoretical framework adopted in this chapter, however, we would insist that the disparity between expectations and reality (exaggerated ego aspirations) is a consequence of the individual's failure to acquire intrinsic feelings of security and adequacy, a failure which predisposes him to neurotic anxiety. It (the disparity), therefore, is primarily a *symptom* of neurotic anxiety, and only a secondary *cause* of the additional symptomatic anxiety which ensues from the resulting frustration and associated hostility to which he is exposed by virtue of his unrealistic expectations. In addition, the lack of extrinsic security and adequacy which he fails to obtain by passing over realistic possibilities for same (and aiming instead for the stars) might be considered a further source of symptomatic anxiety arising out of this situation.

Guilt

Feelings of guilt arise when an individual perceives that his behavior is not in harmony with internalized moral values. They are especially intense and painful when the moral values concerned are the product of deep emotional loyalties typically formed in the course of a satellizing relationship. Hence, just as neurotic anxiety tends to be characteristic of intrinsically insecure and inadequate individuals, severe guilt reactions are more commonly found in persons with a history of childhood satellization. Nevertheless, guilt is found frequently enough in non-satellizers, and anxiety in satellizers. Guilt feelings are a very common cause of symptomatic anxiety in intrinsically adequate individuals.

We have already seen that one important reason why hostile impulses inspire anxiety is the fact that they also give rise to guilt feelings which in turn are responsible for the resulting anxiety. The relationship between guilt and anxiety is simply this: The condition for experiencing guilt is a perception of one's behavior that is incongruous with the pretty, idealized picture of self that we all nurture. The resulting necessity for acknowledging the culpability and debasement of self is the cause of the shame and discomfort of guilt, feelings that are feared more than physical punishment.

Guilt feelings also greatly intensify the fear of punishment or reprisal for misbehavior. If there were no guilt feelings involved, the individual would merely be apprehensive on the basis of his objective chances of being caught and punished. But if he feels guilty, he also believes that he deserves punishment and *should* be punished. The threat of punishment is thus removed from the sphere of objective probability alone, and becomes fraught with moral implications. When punishment is felt to be justified it tends to be perceived as inevitable, since the individual fears that if he is not caught he might very well give himself up in order to be at peace with himself again. It is a well known fact that guilty persons frequently seek punishment, since punishment is the one sure method of reducing guilt feelings in our society. Repression, therefore, intensifies anxiety derived from guilt feelings because it tends to diminish the inevitability of punishment. This explanation is offered as an alternative to Mowrer's assumption that repression of guilt *per se* results in anxiety.

It should also be apparent by this time that, contrary to Mowrer's theory, guilt alone cannot cause neurotic anxiety. Like repression, hostility and conflict, it only gives rise to symptomatic anxiety, which is transitory, self-limited and peripheral in persons who are intrinsically secure and adequate. Feelings of guilt cannot destroy basic self-acceptance unless it is already undermined. And in the case of more serious guilt reactions, there is always the safeguard of confession and willingness to accept punishment as a means of guilt reduction.

MATURATIONAL ANXIETY

By maturational anxiety is meant the anxiety which is experienced by certain individuals in relation to various residual maturational defects in their personality development. Such individuals have satellized normally, possess intrinsic feelings of security and adequacy, but have failed to undergo complete ego maturation because of exposure to unfortunate parental practices. Their anxiety, therefore, is referable to difficulties associated with relinquishing derived status and striving for an extrinsic sense of adequacy, and, hence, is on a different plane of centrality and intensity than neurotic anxiety. Furthermore, in many cases, a poorly developed self-critical faculty forms part of the picture of faulty maturation, with the result that the individual's self-esteem is protected from deflation by an incapacity for perceiving his own incompetence.

The overprotected individual feels threatened at adolescence by the prospect of losing parental protection and the adequacy of his derived status. But even during childhood his sense of security had been somewhat undermined by lack of confidence in his parents' ability to protect him because of the latter's overt fearfulness. As a consequence of their exaggerated apprehensiveness in viewing the environment, he becomes overtrained in anticipating physical danger from the most innocuous situations. He tends to lack confidence in his ability to handle himself adequately since he assimilates parental doubts about his competency. However, as already pointed out, deficiencies in his self-critical faculty minimize the possibility of his feeling threatened by his own incompetence. His outlook on life is usually much more sanguine than is warranted by the objective circumstances confronting him.

The underdominated individual is similarly protected by an immature self-critical faculty from experiencing threats to self-esteem that ordinarily would arise from rebuffs and frustration attending his unrealistic goals and expectations. More serious, therefore, is the threat to his security and adequacy arising from the absence of effective internal and external controls over his aggressive impulses (see pp. 190-191).

The overdominated individual experiences a limited type of anxiety related principally to his feelings of incapacity for volitional independence. He accepts his parent's view of himself as incapable of directing his own affairs. His sense of insecurity is derived from fear of losing the volitional direction of the person on whom he is dependent. However, because his parents are generally hypercritical of him, he does not gain the protection of an impaired self-critical faculty. Yet, his possession of intrinsic security and adequacy, as well as the possibility of becoming volitionally dependent on others after leaving the parental home, protects him from severe (neurotic) anxiety.

It sometimes happens that a satellizing child has hypercritical and perfectionistic parents who are not particularly overdominating but who erect impossibly high standards despite the fact that they accept and value him for himself. Such children, although feeling intrinsically adequate, never manage to attain unqualified feelings of extrinsic adequacy. They do not suffer from neurotic anxiety, but always seem to carry with them lingering doubts as to their capacity for adequately meeting external criteria of competency. Thus, the extrinsic picture of ego adequacy which starts in early childhood from the comments of parents tends to have a pervasive influence. Since this holds true in the case of an intrinsically adequate child, how much more traumatic must it not be in the case of a rejected child whose very existence is negatively accepted by his parents!

A form of maturational anxiety is also found in individuals whose quests for extrinsic status were not sufficiently appreciated by their parents. Having failed to obtain the approbation of the most significant persons in their interpersonal environment, they are unable ever to feel completely satisfied with their achievements. Success, recognition, and acclaim all tend to have a hollow ring. The same result occurs also in the case of individuals with laissez-faire parents who adopt an attitude of complete indifference toward the accomplishments of their children.

TRANSITIONAL ANXIETY

Transitional anxiety arises during periods of crisis in ego development. Its source lies in pressures that are inherent in the very nature of developmental transition. Hence it occurs universally in all individuals and at every age when rapid personality change is required. The relevant factors entering into the threat are new social expectations regarding the abandonment of an old and the gaining of a new biosocial status; the need to accomplish new developmental tasks; an intermediate period of disorientation and lack of definite status; and uncertainty whether the new status will ever be attained. In addition to these objective pressures, there is also a subjective component of the threat that is derived from internalization of the developmental tasks imposed by the culture.

Transitional anxiety, therefore, first arises during the crisis of ego devaluation. In an atmosphere of benevolent parental acceptance, it tends to be minimal, self-limited, and overshadowed by the more spectacular evidences of negativism. The threat to the child of losing his volitional omnipotence is dampened by his high level of security. Hence, with fear of loss of succorance at a minimum, and uninhibited by feelings of guilt, aggression is the most natural emotional reaction to frustration of his omnipotent pretensions.

The next important crisis inducing transitional anxiety occurs during adolescence. On the one hand, as both Rank [*316*] and Fromm [*141*] stress, there is fear of losing protection, dependence and derived status, and the parallel fears of individuation, freedom, autonomy and responsibility. On the other hand, failure to gain independence and release from his dependent security leads to feelings of inadequacy and guilt, and to social disapproval [*316*]. Rank also points out that the adolescent becomes so jealous of his hard earned autonomy that he becomes reluctant to part with any of it by forming genuine love attachments requiring emotional relatedness to others [*316*].

Transitional anxiety during adolescence, therefore, comes from three diverse sources. In the first place there are various temporal pressures inhering in the nature of adolescent transition, especially in our culture, i.e., abruptness of onset, prolonged status deprivation, discrepancies in the rate of growth of various component aspects, etc. (see pp. 86-88). Secondly, there is fear of autonomy and the loss of a sheltered protected existence. Fromm [*141*] points out that this anxiety can be alleviated by forming new emotional relationships with others or by escaping from the new possibilities for freedom. The former tendency, however, is combatted by the fear of surrendering newly gained autonomy. Lastly, and most important is the anxiety that is derived from the myriad factors which threaten the adolescent's acquisition of adult status —the cultural conditions which prolong his dependency and deny him opportunity for playing mature and responsible roles.

These unusual social conditions in our culture intensify the normal dread and uncertainty regarding the attainment of adult prerogatives which all cultures inculcate in adolescents to keep maturation moving in the appropriate direction. This is what Allison Davis means by "socially-adaptive anxiety" [*73*]. Implicit in this dread is the fear of social disapproval if failure should occur, and the fear of losing the advantages pertaining to the new status. And in our complex, heterogeneous culture, all adolescents do not share the same transitional anxiety, but experience dread in relation to the hazards associated with attaining the specific goals appropriate to their social class membership.

SITUATIONAL ANXIETY

Situational anxiety is the normal type of anxiety that arises in relation to objective threats to an individual's self-esteem. It is a self-protective reaction which is limited to the duration of the situation that elicits it, and is proportionate to the objective magnitude of the threat involved. Three types of situational anxiety will be considered: (1) that which is derived from the cultural situation; (2) that which follows from special individual incapacities; and (3) that which inheres in all constructive, problem-solving activity.

Cultural Factors

Cultural factors produce or alleviate anxiety in many different ways. In the first place, just as a child may be intrinsically valued for himself by his parents, an adult may be more or less valued for himself by his society. The intrinsic worth of a human being can be extremely high, as in the Arapesh culture, or it can be almost nil, as in our society, where a man's value is mostly a reflection of the price he fetches in the market place [*142*]. This distinction by Fromm is an exceedingly valuable one, but makes a serious error in assuming that the self-esteem of all men will be similarly affected by its dependence on market value. Actually, the impact of this situation on the individual's self-esteem will be peripheral in the case of satellizers and central in the case of non-satellizers.

Nevertheless, if we bear the latter difference in mind, it would be legitimate to say that the level of extrinsic status toward which a person feels impelled to strive is inversely related to the intrinsic cultural valuation of man (or directly related to the emphasis placed upon his market value). In our society, maximum value is placed upon the goals of social prestige and hierarchical status; and it is in the struggle for these goals that an individual either attains or fails to attain extrinsic adequacy [*219*]. The more violent the competition for these individual goals, the greater the amount of intra-social hostility which is generated [*219*], the less ego support an individual can derive from group relatedness, and the greater his psychological isolation [*142*].

Thus, although "no society has the power to give absolute security and protect the child or the adult completely against the loss of love" [*288*], in our particular culture the vicious circle of "competitive striving, intra-social hostility, interpersonal isolation, anxiety, and increased competitive striving" [*270*] is exceptionally acute. It was this situation which Horney had in mind when referring to "basic anxiety as a reaction to living in a basically hostile and chaotic society" [*187*].

Another cultural factor influencing the level of situational anxiety has to do with the *availability* of the degree of extrinsic status for which a particular culture motivates its members to strive. If, for example, as in our culture, adolescents and adults are drawn into a mad race for competitive status, and the possibility of many individuals acquiring such status is greatly limited, it stands to reason that situational anxiety will be relatively intense and widespread. This is especially true in periods of economic depression when youth spend many years of apprenticeship, education, training and self-subordination only to find unemployment at the end of the arduous and anxiety-laden trail. But even in normal times, adolescents must tolerate prolonged status deprivation; and the bitter pill is not made any easier to swallow when it is compounded by an apparent capriciousness in the cultural distribution of rewards. The theory that success is the inevitable reward for conscientious work, self-denial, and superior ability bogs down as adolescents begin to see rewards monopolized by individuals whose sole entitlement to same springs from wealth, inherited position, family connection, or a highly developed capacity for double dealing and sycophancy.

Kardiner gives us an example of the same type of cultural situation leading to situational anxiety in a relatively primitive culture.

> "The ego attitudes of this situation can be seen in the Tanala culture. Submission and ingratiation are ego-acceptable roles as long as basic needs are not frustrated and protection is guaranteed, and as long as the smart of being the underdog is soothed by the absence of ostentation. An ego-organization built up by basic disciplines to expect reward for submission can do only a few things if this need for protection is frustrated; it becomes both anxious and aggressive" [*220*].

In addition to the situational anxiety that can be attributed to general status deprivation, economic depression, and differences in the accessibility of cultural rewards on the basis of social class membership, special groups of adolescents and adults in our culture experience further cause for anxiety in social and economic discrimination related to their sex, race, religion, and ethnic and national origin. Furthermore, situational anxiety tends to be accentuated during periods of rapid social change, war, international tension, political upheaval, and deterioration in public and private morality. Orderly social organization ordinarily provides the individual with many safeguards and forms of security, e.g., protection against violence, tyranny and chaotic disorganization. If this organization should collapse, the individual would be required to erect his own defenses against these dangers.

It not infrequently happens that when situational anxiety is prolonged and intense, it also acquires some subjective components. The threat to self-esteem finally leads to an actual impairment of the sense of adequacy which is peripheral in the case of satellizers and central in the case of non-satellizers. This in turn becomes a further source of threat, especially when the individual unwarrantedly attributes the failure he experiences on the basis of cultural factors to his own ineptitude. These feelings of inadequacy must be differentiated from the anxiety which is derived from objective organic or intellectual deficiences which constitute a threat to self-esteem insofar as they expose the individual to ridicule, and ostracism, or predispose him to failure in various adjustive situations. We have seen, however, that adolescents often tend to exaggerate the importance of such defects; and as a result of this overvaluation, the greater part of the source of threat may become subjective rather than objective. Except in cases of permanent crippling or disfigurement, however, organic defects are seldom severe enough to produce neurotic anxiety.

"Constructive" Anxiety

Many writers (Freud, Goldstein, May, etc.) on the subject of anxiety point out that anxiety inheres inevitably in all constructive activity leading toward self-actualization. The development of any individual's capacities depends on his willingness to experience frustration, solve new problems, risk the possibility of failure, face unpleasant, threatening situations, and to abandon established positions of security for exploration in uncharted fields. This means that individual as well as group progress can only take place if there is a positive disposition to accept and "move through" the burden of anxiety inherent in each new learning situation.

ANXIETY AND MOTIVATION

We have already referred to evidence from the animal experiments of Mowrer [*284*] and Liddell [*252*] which indicates conclusively that anxiety reduction can be a potent motivating factor in learning. In laboratory experiments with humans, punishment has not proven to be a very effective incentive for learning, but the weight of the evidence shows that it is more efficacious than a neutral motivational environment [*177*]. The present writer submits, however, that the relative efficacy of reward and punishment as determined for a short-term laboratory task, might easily be reversed were we to consider real life situations over an extended period of time.

In our particular culture at any rate, it is quite evident that whether desirable or not, anxiety is one of the most common motivating devices employed by parents, teachers, employers, etc. It is undoubtedly true that positive motivations such as job satisfaction, joy in craftsmanship and creative effort, and desire to be socially useful are much more wholesome than anxiety reduction, but few motivations *today* are as compelling as the fear of losing one's job. The source of anxiety motivation lies not only in various natural contingencies (e.g., sickness, death, starvation) that threaten existence, but also in a series of cultural derivatives arising from fear of physical punishment, guilt, disapproval, social reprisal, ostracism, and loss of status. "Socially-adaptive" anxiety, for example, helps provide the adolescent with motivation to attain the general developmental goals appropriate for his age group and the more specific goals appropriate for his social class membership; it is powered by the threat of failure to acquire the status prerogatives associated with successful maturation.

However, to acknowledge the potency of anxiety motivation is not to assert that it is the only or the chief source of motivation. This would be committing the same error as Freud, who failed to see any motivation arising except in a negative fashion—as the product of sublimation or reaction-formation. Motivation can be derived from many positive sources such as curiosity, interest, ability, etc. And even if the original source does happen to be related to anxiety reduction, it is possible that in the course of pursuing the activity which it inspires, other more positive motivations might develop which in time may assume the more dominant energizing role.

It is in non-satellizers, however, that anxiety reduction really occupies the central position in the motivational picture. There is a relentless drive for extrinsic adequacy and ego enhancement to fill the void of absent intrinsic self-esteem and to allay the anxiety that arises from its impairment The tremendous amount of prestige motivation generated by hypertrophic and tenacious ego demands leads to greater accomplishment than could otherwise be expected from a given level of ability despite the tendency toward disruption of performance efforts because of anxiety and over-reaction to frustration. In non-satellizers, goal frustration tolerance is extremely high, and performance as well as self-esteem frustration tolerance are relatively low; while in satellizers exactly the reverse situation prevails.

The more realistic and intelligent non-satellizer spares himself continual frustration by refusing to expend his prestige motivation indiscriminately in all directions, including those areas in which his natural endowment is poor. By selectively disinvolving his ego from prestige aspirations in such activities and channelizing his drive into areas where he is apt to face little competition [*25*], he manages to maintain extrinsic self-esteem at a higher level and anxiety at a lower level than the non-satellizer who sees a threat to himself in anyone's accomplishments and feels obliged to compete with every individual who crosses his path. Hartogs [*168*] found that in simple paper and pencil tests, anxiety patients "showed an unduly high initial level of aspiration with the following goal-levels kept intentionally low." His results can easily be interpreted as evidence of the high level of ego aspiration prevailing in anxiety neurotics before they are fully aware of the nature of the task and the threat it entails, which is followed by protective ego disinvolvement once frustration is experienced.

ANXIETY AND LEARNING

Apart from its role as a motivating agent, anxiety exerts a profound influence on the learning process. In the first place, anxiety is one of the more compelling emotions, and intense emotion is generally conceded to have a disruptive effect on the individual's capacity for adjustive responses in situations calling for more complex adaptations than mere "fight or flight." This belief generally corresponds to everyday experience. Experimental corroboration of this fact has been found in the animal work of Pavlov [*305*], Liddell [*253*], Hamilton [*162*], and Masserman [*268*]. In every case, strong emotional reactions—whether evoked by induced frustration and conflict, or by forcing an animal to exceed his discriminative capacities—produced an altered state of behavioral reactivity which included among other things an impairment of ability to learn or to make successful adjustive responses. At the simplest level of reaction, as in the Pavlovian experiments, this was manifested by an incapacity to discriminate between the positive and negative response value of conditioned stimuli which had previously been established on a very stable and predictable level [*305*].

On a much higher level, both experimentally induced emotional disturbance and that elicited by the experience of repeated frustration were found to be effective in producing non-adjustive behavior. Hamilton [*162*] was able to show for both animal and human subjects that the disorganizing effect of emotion operates primarily by reducing the variability of response and by favoring the perseveration of previously acquired reactions that were non-adaptive for novel problem situations. From a clinical standpoint, however, efforts to demonstrate a relationship between existing emotional disturbance and learning capacity have not been so successful. Despert and Pierce [*82*] made the latest of several attempts to demonstrate that the I. Q. (as determined by several retestings over a period of years) fluctuates in accordance with the emotional stability of the subject. These fluctuations, however, were not greater than could be expected in terms of the standard error of measurement [*165*]. It still remains to be proven, therefore, that the functional expression of intelligence—as measured by our conventional intelligence test—is adversely affected by emotional disturbance.

However, a more promising attack on this problem was made by Weidensall [*397*] as long ago as 1916. Instead of using the intelligence test—which essentially requires the exercise of conventional and familiar patterns of response to more or less stereotyped learning situations—she employed the mirror tracing test as a means of bringing out a subject's emotional disturbance. This learning problem represents a new and different type of learning task quite alien to the everyday experience of most individuals. In this type of situation, the past experience which an individual brings to the problem instead of being an asset is actually a hindrance. In fact, ability eventually to master this learning task depends on the subject's capacity to ignore and inhibit his customary modes of response which obviously lead him to make false moves. The subject must be willing to abandon habitual patterns of eye-hand coordination in favor of an improvised trial-and-error technique. It may be noted that in this respect the mirror-tracing test is comparable to Hamilton's puzzle box situation which had been successfully used in animal and human experiments to demonstrate a negative relationship between emotional disturbance and learning. Furthermore, within the normal range of intelligence there is no correlation between mirror-tracing ability and intelligence.

In terms of this latter approach, the clinical aspect of the problem assumes an entirely different orientation. The issue is no longer whether emotional disturbance affects learning capacity as such—but *what component* of learning capacity it affects. Where conventional learning tasks are involved, no deleterious influence has been demonstrated; where novel, extemporaneous learning is at stake, such an effect is demonstrable. Weidensall's finding that emotionally-disturbed reformatory girls achieved poorer scores than normal controls on the mirror-tracing test has been confirmed by Holsopple [*186*] on a similar population; by Loutitt [*258*] using naval psychiatric patients and reformatory inmates; and by Peters [*307*] with psychotics, juvenile delinquents, and criminals. When Peters classified his socially maladjusted patients as either emotionally stable or unstable, he found that the latter's performance was reliably inferior to the former's. Using maze material and the Kohs block test, Diethelm and Jones [*87*] found reliable differences in the attention, learning, retention and thinking ability of the same anxiety patients between two series of performances, each characterized by different levels of clinical anxiety. Ammons [*16*] has reported that all ten subjects (out of a total of 174) who became too disturbed to finish a mirror drawing task showed evidence of insecurity on the Rorschach test.

Quantitative evidence is available, therefore, which indicates that anxiety impairs the efficiency of the learning process. From the standpoint of behavior theory, the next questions are: Why? In what way? In all areas or selectively? Do anxiety sufferers approach learning situations differently? Are their techniques of learning unique?

Clues to the answers of these questions come both from (1) the empirical evidence quoted above which indicates that anxiety influences learning adversely in the case of novel adjustive tasks rather than in situations which are relatively familiar; and (2) from our definition of neurotic anxiety as a tendency in individuals suffering from impaired self-esteem to over-react with fear to any anticipated adjustive situation that contains a further threat to self-esteem.

It is important to bear in mind, however, that although the real basis for the anxiety comes from an internal lack of self-esteem, the actual reaction of anxiety is not elicited *in vacuo,* but in response to a real adjustive problem. And by definition, an adjustive problem is one which requires the evolution of a new organization of responses. This does not mean that the problem must necessarily be a uniquely new experience for an individual; in fact, many anxiety-producing adjustive situations represent recurrent problems for which the individual has been unable to ever evolve satisfactory enough solutions that would remove the problems in question from the adjustive category. In other words, for a problem to be adjustive, it must involve more than pulling a well-established, familiar, or routine response pattern out of one's behavior repertory.

If anxiety will be elicited only in response to an adjustive situation, it follows that the anxiety sufferer will strive as far as possible to remove the adjustive element from situations which confront him. He might conceivably do this in two ways: (a) by "priming" himself in advance of meeting the adjustive situation so that he can prepare a mode of attack beforehand; (b) if this is impossible, by searching his available response repertory for an appropriate solution that would not involve any reorganization of existing patterns. The advance "set" would, thus, rule out the threatening necessity for improvisation and would provide the individual with the security he finds in having available a prepared solution for a given problem.

It is postulated, therefore, that anxiety inhibits the learning of a new problem because of (a) a rigid, inflexible learning set which resists displacement due to a feeling of inadequacy with respect to making new adjustive responses; reliance upon stereotyped response patterns as a learning "crutch" and source of security; and a "face-saving" attempt to produce a "visible" response when panic would otherwise result in blocking or utter confusion; (b) the panic that results from initial over-reaction with fear to a frustrating new situation which inhibits the learning process as any intense emotional experience would; and (c) the panic resulting from progressive accumulation of frustration as the unsuccessful performance is prolonged or repeated. Having no confidence in the ultimate outcome, the anxiety sufferer exaggerates his failures, becomes unduly disorganized, and as a measure of self-protection disinvolves himself from the task, lowering his level of aspiration to the point where success is assured.

It is not implied that learning is disrupted in only the neurotic type of anxiety. In normal anxiety, as represented by the experiments of Hamilton as well as in Goldstein's cases of aphasia, panic also ensued. But this panic arose either from the objective difficulty of the problem or from an objective incapacity, and not from a subjective impairment of self-esteem. Hence in instances of normal anxiety, the subject does not initially confront a new problem with fear and a rigid learning set related to this fear,[23] and does not over-react so catastrophically to initial frustration. The disruption of his performance is almost completely a function of the panic arising from the cumulative impact of prolonged frustration. And while it is true that a new task presents a threat to him also, it only leads to the normal anxiety that inheres in the acceptance of any challenge involving constructive activity. Initial failure is taken in stride because of his attitude of self-confidence in believing that with time and patience all problems that are not insuperable can be successfully met; and if there does happen to be some initial disorganization, recovery tends to be rapid.

THE SELF-CRITICAL FACULTY

Another important factor affecting the individual's extrinsic sense of adequacy, the probability of his being frustrated, and the level of anxiety he manifests is the state of his self-critical faculty. This refers to his tendency to evaluate with varying degrees of severity or lenience the acceptability of his behavior, the degree of status he has acquired, and the quality of his productions. It reflects in part the influence of maturational factors and various parent attitudes, and in part the level of his self-esteem and the critical standards which prevail in his environment. Although tending to remain fairly stable and consistent in line with long-range personality trends, it also retains a certain adaptive flexibility. In persons who are intrinsically secure and adequate, it tends to be more lenient and to fluctuate less than among non-satellizers, in whom it is ordinarily not only more severe but also more variable.

We first meet the self-critical faculty (or the lack of it) in the pre-satellizing period when the infant is able to entertain grandiose conceptions of his volitional power *partly* because of his very limited capacity to perceive his status realistically. Afterwards, improvement in this ability becomes one of the precipitating causes of the crisis of ego devaluation. Nevertheless, self-critical ability is still rudimentary as evidenced by the child's tendency to overvalue the extent of his executive competency in the second stage of negativism (see pp. 130-131). It is only when the self-critical faculty becomes a more important determinant of daily behavior (at approximately five years of age in Gesell's population [*149*]) that this type of negativism really begins to subside and give way to a more consolidated and homogeneous form of satellization.

During the succeeding years, the further development of the self-critical faculty becomes a progressively more crucial aspect of personality maturation. This growth is facilitated by parental practices which require the child to take responsibility for the consequences of his inappropriate behavior or inadequate performances. Undue laxity in excusing misbehavior or in evaluating inferior performance favors the emergence of an impaired self-critical faculty. The acquisition of greater volitional independence on an adult and realistic level presupposes the ability to recognize imperfections in performance; otherwise the individual feels completely satisfied with a highly inferior product, aspires to nothing better, and initiates no efforts looking toward improvement.

Because of overly uncritical parental attitudes, insufficient drive for adequate performance, and low goal frustration tolerance, both the overprotected and the underdominated child are unable to acquire sufficient self-critical ability (see pp. 222-223); and since this failure in turn has adjustive value in minimizing the possibility of frustration and protecting against the loss of self-esteem that would otherwise result in view of the individual's objective incompetence, additional motivation is provided for the arrested development of this function.

With respect to overdominated and overcriticized children, just the opposite situation prevails. Such children are required to live up to a high standard of excellence in order to meet with full parental approval. Because of their strong internalized needs to turn out high quality performance and their reasonably high goal frustration tolerance, they are able to learn adequate self-appraisal; in fact, in the light of these needs, the development of a superior self-critical faculty becomes a definite asset. In non-satellizers with exaggerated needs for prestige accomplishment, a severe self-critical faculty is even more expedient and imperative, but operates selectively in relation to performance; where moral behavior is involved, leniency of self-judgment is the more expedient alternative (see pp. 136-137).

The non-satellizer's impaired self-esteem and lack of intrinsic self-acceptance also tend to make him adopt a harsh view toward himself. The same is true of the underappreciated child who assimilates his parent's tendency to regard his achievements with lack of enthusiasm.

We have already cited evidence which shows that self-estimate tends to be disturbed in the poorly adjusted individual, and after experiences of frustration. It is also less accurate with respect to abilities which are rated low by other persons, and in areas marked by conflict or insecurity (see pp. 359-360). The precise interpretation of an overly severe self-critical faculty offers many difficulties, since in various cases it can be indicative of a disturbed parent-child relationship, situational tensions, excessive ego demands, perfectionism, vanity, or impaired self-esteem.

The experience of a decade in the pharmacological, neurosurgical, and electro-shock treatment of psychopathological conditions in which the self-critical faculty is exaggeratedly severe, i.e., anxiety, agitation, and depression, has provided us with considerable information about the neuroanatomical substrate of the self-critical faculty. The most drastic of these measures, prefrontal leucotomy, which almost invariably relieves anxiety, depression, and agitation after other less radical forms of intervention fail, seems to exert an almost specific inhibitory effect on the self-critical faculty by interrupting thalamo-cortical fibers which connect the orbital quadrant of the thalamus to the frontal cortex [*20, 259*]. Electro-shock therapy which has a similar effect results in cortical damage; but the exact locus of this damage has not yet been definitely determined.

Neurophysiological evidence from animal experimentation also suggests that the pharmacological locus of the euphorogenous action of narcotic drugs is the thalamo-cortical tract. The adjustive value of narcotic drug addiction probably depends at least in part on the inhibition of the self-critical faculty, which permits the inadequate psychopath to retain extrinsic feelings of adequacy despite his manifest incompetency [*20*].

The above-cited evidence has been brought forward to show that it is possible to change the psychological expression of the self-critical faculty by bringing physical influences to bear on its anatomical substrate. It is realized, however, that such change is normally effected on a psychological plane alone—in the course of ego defense measures or as the outcome of ego damage. Defensively, enhancement of adequacy feelings can be obtained by inhibiting the self-critical faculty as in manic states, inadequate psychopathy, and certain forms of moral delinquency. Exaggeration of the self-critical faculty, on the other hand, is usually a manifestation of ego damage, e.g., anxiety, agitation and depression. Under certain conditions (to be described below), however, it may serve a defensive function, for example, in compulsive perfectionism, and in the "self-frustration" mechanism.

DEPERSONALIZATION AND FEAR OF DEATH

One of the most mysterious phenomena that psychology is obliged to explain is the apparent indifference which the individual as well as his culture displays to the certainty of death. In the entire animal kingdom, man alone has such a highly conceptualized sense of personal identity, man alone can contemplate the implications of death, and man alone is capable of resenting the fact that his personal identity is purely a function of his physical integrity. Why is it that an individual in our culture, knowing or suspecting that his ego identity will vanish at death, can absorb himself so completely in the affairs of the world as if he were settling matters of ego status for all eternity? Here is a man of seventy sitting in his business office maneuvering with intense application and consummate shrewdness to outwit a rival in a business deal that might bring him several thousand dollars profit. How can he concern himself with such trivia when tomorrow he himself for whom all this frantic competitive activity is expended might pass into nothingness? If psychologists explain his efforts as mechanisms of ego defense and enhancement, how can they explain his indifference to this, the greatest danger of all, which not only threatens to obliterate all previous efforts but also the ego itself?

The most plausible answer to this enigma that we can offer at the present time is that normal feelings of insecurity about the prospect of death (apart from immediate tangible threats) are repressed below the threshold of awareness providing that a certain minimal level of self-esteem is maintained. When neurotic anxiety becomes acute, fear of death tends to become a troublesome symptom. At this point the patient is usually in a state of agitation. However, once he is resigned to failure and the defeat of his ego aspirations, and renounces all striving (depression), he even looks forward to death and becomes suicidal. Death fears, therefore, are a good prognostic sign in psychotic depressions as well as in reactive schizophrenia, where the ego, by virtue of regression to infantile concepts of self and of removal from the arena of reality, is removed beyond the reach of the threat of death.

Definite developmental trends can be seen in the ideas of death held by children in our culture. At first the notion of death is completely incomprehensible and unacceptable, and the possibility of death is usually denied in the four- and five-year-old [*64, 295*]. Then comes a period when the cessation of corporeal existence can be accepted, but only in a symbolic sense [*295*]. Finally in the middle and late years of childhood the concept of death in the adult sense of the term can be appreciated [*259*]. In anxiety-ridden, rejected children, fear of death may induce nightmares having to do with death themes; in some cases, this fear is so intense that insomnia might result, since sleep is symbolic of death, and since people may die suddenly in sleep without awareness or opportunity for struggle against it. In children as well as in adults, therefore, it can be confidently stated that morbid preoccupation with the idea of death does not cause anxiety but occurs rather as a symptomatic reflection of it.

An example of morbid concern with problems of death can be found in present-day devotees of spiritualism. This cult reflects a positive protest against and a denial of human mortality and the dependence of ego on a neuroanatomical substrate. Beneath this attempt to remove personal identity from any relationship with biological processes lies a haunting fear of death and a severely damaged self-esteem. Religious doctrines of the hereafter, on the other hand, are reflective of extreme cultural anxiety which afterwards becomes institutionalized. Hence, normal individuals who believe in the hereafter espouse such beliefs as articles of faith in a formal sense or as matters of genuine conviction rather than as a defensive measure against overt and obsessive fears of death.

Depersonalization

Depersonalization refers to a breakdown in personal identity or awareness of self that occurs under conditions of extreme stress, and quite frequently in relation to anxiety states. However, considerable confusion has arisen about the interpretation of this phenomenon because of (1) failure to identify the quality of self-awareness preceding the onset of symptoms of depersonalization; and (2) failure to differentiate between the adjustive and ego damage aspects of depersonalization.

Goldstein [*156*] contends that anxiety, as experienced by an individual in the catastrophic situation, leads to a disintegration of self-awareness and of the relationship between self and the outside world. This in turn makes him unable to evaluate his environment realistically and to identify the source of the threat.

While we would tend to agree that this type of depersonalization is symptomatic of acute panic, we would insist that the phenomenon occurs quite late in the course of anxiety states, either as a desperate defense measure or as an indication that considerable ego damage had already taken place. Initially at least, an accentuation of self-awareness is generally the rule in severe anxiety states. We have seen that self-preoccupation is one of the pathognomonic signs of acute anxiety[24] and one of the main factors responsible for inducing an attitude of rejection in parents (see pp. 291-292). Under such conditions, the individual *is* unable to evaluate his status objectively, but this is a consequence of impaired self-esteem, excessive self-criticism and over-reaction to environmental threats rather than a reflection of self-dissolution.

In describing the initial effects of imprisonment in concentration camps, Bettelheim confirms the above point of view:

> "It seems that most, if not all prisoners tried to react against the initial shock by mustering forces which might prove helpful in supporting their badly shaken self-esteem. Those groups which found in their past life some basis for the erection of such a buttress to their endangered egos seemed to succeed . . . Even the smallest change in their former private world attained tremendous importance . . . Their desire to return exactly the person who had left was so great that they feared any change, however trifling, in the situation they had left" [*44*].

The same viewpoint that anxiety helps to consolidate the ego before it leads to ego deterioration is implicit in Sullivan's concept that in the experience of having to distinguish between those impulses which generate approval and those which are productive of disapproval (and, hence, anxiety), the self is more clearly delineated [*387*].

Under conditions of increasingly greater stress or more devastating anxiety, depersonalization may develop either as an adjustive device or as a sign of extreme ego damage. Personal identity becomes detached from extremely degrading experiences as a means of protecting the individual from a damaging loss of self-esteem. For example, an unwilling prostitute might try to divorce her ego from any connection with the experiences relative to prostitution [*354*]. Bettelheim employed the same mechanism as a concentration camp prisoner. He states that his one main problem in camp

> "was to safeguard his ego in such a way that if by any good luck he should regain liberty, he would be approximately the same person he was when deprived of liberty. He has no doubt that he was able to endure the transportation, and all that followed, because right from the beginning he became convinced that these terrible and degrading

experiences somehow did not happen to 'him' as a subject but only to 'him' as an object" [*44*].

Amnesic conditions, fugues and "multiple personality" states also illustrate the adjustive value of depersonalization. In such cases, however, the individual does more than feel that a given experience is unreal or is not happening to him. He represses or dissociates an entire body of inter-related experience from the main current of his self-awareness. Thus, he is able to eat his cake and have it too: He can express a host of unacceptable impulses, and at the same time escape any connection of them with his sense of personal identity.

The adjustive value of this type of depersonalization becomes clear when under the strain of even greater stress, the other variety of depersonalization appears. Here ego damage is so great that the old self is depersonalized and replaced by a new. The individual no longer regards degrading, regressive or infantile behavior as unreal or apart from himself, but accepts it as a characteristic product of his "new self" operating in a new framework of "reality." This acceptance of the regressive self as his new personal identity, as indicative of what he really *wants* to be is a sign of the extreme ego deterioration which takes place during the transition between the acute and chronic forms of reactive schizophrenia. It is also illustrated in Bettelheim's account of the last stage of ego disintegration exhibited by concentration camp victims:

> "No longer was there a split between one to whom things happened and the one who observed them . . . everything that happened to them, even the worst atrocity, was 'real' to them . . . [And] once this stage was reached of taking everything that happened in the camp as 'real', there was every indication that the prisoners who had reached it were afraid of returning to the outer world . . . A prisoner had reached the final stage of adjustment to the camp situation when he had changed his personality so as to accept as his own the values of the Gestapo" [*44*].

Hence, we have to distinguish between (1) depersonalization as an adjustive mechanism which consists primarily of a dissociation of personal identity from humiliating and unacceptable experiences happening to self, and (2) depersonalization as a symptom of ego damage in which marked changes in personality occur; i.e., the individual becomes depersonalized in the sense of acquiring a new and different personal identity, but accepts this new identity (with all of its regressive and unacceptable features) as his "real" self. The former is illustrated by the depersonalization occurring in certain cases of acute anxiety (after accentuation of self-awareness); in conditions of involuntary or ambivalent participation in degrading experiences, and in amnesias, fugues, and in cases of "multiple personality." The latter type is illustrated by the depersonalization occurring in chronic cases of reactive schizophrenia when the regressive picture of self is accepted as real. "Adjustive" depersonalization, therefore, is a hopeful prognostic sign in early cases of such schizophrenia. Although there is some adjustive value (escape) in the extreme personality regression and the complete withdrawal from reality found in this entity, such a fabulous price is paid in terms of personality disorganization that it would be more appropriate to regard it as a form of ego damage complicating neurotic anxiety.

DEFENSES AGAINST ANXIETY

The basis of many defense mechanisms lies in the need for anxiety-reduction. Defense efforts are elicited even before anxiety appears—when self-esteem is threatened; and when the threat becomes intense enough to evoke the affect of anxiety, the original need for defense becomes even more imperative. As a means of bringing together some of the scattered material in this chapter relating to defenses against anxiety, a brief cataloguing of the various defenses will be attempted below. More extensive discussion will be provided in Chapter 17.

Four types of defenses will be distinguished: (1) direct forms of ego enhancement of an aggressive, compensatory and independent character; (2) conciliatory, submissive and dependent forms of defense; (3) various indirect and devious means of ego enhancement, which attain their goal without primary reliance on either aggressive or submissive tactics; and (4) mechanisms which provide escape from anxiety situations.

Direct means of ego enhancement include: (a) strong prestige drives for money, success, power, superior status, etc.; (b) the affectation of boastful, blustering, supercilious, and belligerent attitudes, or the simulation of tremendous calm, poise, nonchalance and indifference to social conventions; (c) aggressive attacks on the opinions, behavior or reputations of other persons in the hope of showing to advantage in relation to the deflation of their stature; (d) the unleashing of destructive tendencies as a means of demonstrating one's power in influencing the course of events; (e) finding substitutive gratification in the achievements of other individuals who are regarded as ego extensions of self, e.g., the overvaluing parent.

Conciliatory forms of defense are illustrated by the following types of behavior: (a) a sympathetic, charitable and tolerant attitude toward others as a means of soliciting comparable lenient treatment from them; (b) stressing one's anxiety and helplessness as a bid for sympathy and immunity from aggression; (c) repression of hostile impulses in order to insure one's safety; (d) failure to perceive the hostility of others lest one feel obliged to retaliate and hence risk one's security; (e) justifying the hostility of others for the same reason; (f) a need to be liked by *everyone* in order to feel secure; entering into friendly relationships indiscriminately with all-comers; (g) exaggerated conformity to social demands; excessive compliancy to authority; (h) complete surrender of individuality in group activity; (i) abandonment of individual initiative and the prerogatives of independent action; (j) endeavoring to form satellizing-like relationships with others; (k) suppression of self-assertive and hostile tendencies by reaction-formation.

Indirect and devious defenses against anxiety are legion in number: (a) rationalization of failure and escape from competitive striving through psychosomatic symptoms of anxiety, hypochondriasis, fatigue states, and hysterical conditions; (b) displacement of the source of the threat to a more concrete, identifiable, and manageable danger (phobia); (c) monopolization of consciousness by a displaced and innocuous source of threat (obsession); (d) displacement of the object or target of the threat to another person, e.g., the anxious parent who overprotects his child; (e) minimization of frustration and loss of self-esteem through ego-disinvolvement, depersonalization, and impairment of the self-critical faculty (e.g., mania); (f) delusional distortion of the environment (ideas of grandeur and persecution); (g) disowning and justifying unacceptable impulses (projection); (h) achieving compensatory ego gratification through regression in goal maturity; (i) compensatory ego satisfaction through compulsive eating, activity or sexuality; (j) finding security through compulsive rituals; (k) compulsive rigidity, inflexibility, and perfectionism in performing tasks in order to eliminate excessive fear of uncertainty, tentativeness and improvisation; (l) undue advance preparation in meeting new situations; (m) reliance on familiar and stereotyped methods of problem-solving.

Escape mechanisms include: (a) avoidance of new, potential anxiety situations; (b) repression of or denial of anxiety; (c) adopting an impersonal, third-person reference to problems productive of anxiety; (d) withdrawal from social situations which generate anxiety, e.g., asceticism, intellectualization, absorption in fantasy; (e) self-insulation from emotional involvement in interpersonal relations to avoid the possibility of rejection; (f) finding a part-time escape from reality, e.g., alcoholism; (g) constriction of the field of activity to limit the magnitude of area from which threats can arise; (h) self-frustration to avoid anxiety situations or the necessity for accepting a realistic half-loaf solution to grandiose ego aspirations.

PROGNOSIS OF ANXIETY

The development and nature of neurotic anxiety is such that predictions regarding prognosis must be made separately for young children, on the one hand, and all other age-groups on the other. Only in terms of the former is the question of reversibility (cure) relevant. The very best the latter can look forward to is palliation. With respect to the possibility of reversibility, the issue in essence is whether or not and under what conditions the effects of parental rejection or overvaluation can be reversed.

Since the child is almost always reluctant to accept the verdict of rejection, and is more than receptive to any change for the better in the parent's attitudes (see page 272), it is the variables affecting the probability of such change that are crucial in deciding the prognosis of childhood anxiety caused by rejection. This brings us to the distinction already made between (1) benign parental rejection, which is not strongly predetermined by personality factors in the parent and, hence, fluctuates greatly with situational conditions, and (2) malignant rejection, which exhibits greater constancy of expression because of prepotent personality predispositions (see page 291). The hypothesis has already been offered that the former type of rejection is manifested most frequently by parents who were themselves rejected as children, while the latter type is manifested most commonly by parents who were themselves exposed to overvaluation (pp. 291-292).

Parents who were rejected themselves tend to retain a capacity for relating themselves to others (especially their own children), which can be fulfilled under favorable conditions, i.e., minimal anxiety; whereas overvalued parents tend never to acquire this capacity (see page 291). The rejected parent is also influenced more by moral considerations, is more sensitive to public opinion, and tends to be less self-indulgent. Hence, the possibility of sufficient change occurring in the latter's attitudes to enable the child to satellize, acquire intrinsic security and adequacy, and be purged of neurotic anxiety is good providing that it does not come too late; in the writer's experience, almost complete elimination of anxiety has been accomplished with child patients until the age of seven. In cases of malignant rejection, however, the writer has never succeeded in effecting comparable results except in instances where a substitute parent (usually an interested relative) could be provided; it is futile for the therapist himself to attempt this role since he cannot provide sufficient sustained ego support to induce satellization.

The therapist's task of changing parent attitudes is lightened considerably if the parent is intelligent, has insight into the meaning of his attitudes and their effects upon the child, feels guilty about them, and is sincerely desirous of improving the parent-child relationship. Even more important, however, are those situational factors which regulate the current level of parental anxiety. A harassed, panic-stricken, self-preoccupied parent cannot benefit sufficiently from therapy to change the quality of the parent-child relationship. The relevant situational factors, in turn, are largely dependent upon other personality traits of the parent, such as ability, capacity for disguising anxiety, etc. (see page 294).

Parental overvaluation—including the variety practiced by parents who had been rejected themselves—is a much more difficult attitude to change. In the first place, it has more adjustive value for the parent and tends to become a fixed, canalized defense against his anxiety. Secondly, overvalued children do not generally exhibit overt anxiety and are less likely to be brought to the attention of a therapist. Thirdly, the overvalued child finds his grandiose ego aspirations quite tenable in his environment and is not disposed to satellize.

Prognosis for Palliation of Anxiety

If cure cannot be effected in early childhood, the therapist can still attempt palliation. The value of such a goal should not be deprecated since success often means the difference between psychological invalidism on the one hand, and sufficient freedom from anxiety to do creative work and experience some personal happiness on the other. The important errors to guard against are unrealistic expectations of cure in adult cases of neurotic anxiety, and failure to take sufficient cognizance of the important role of situational factors. The first error is quite universal among psychotherapists, and the second error is committed in different ways by psychoanalytic and non-directive therapists. The former tend to ignore the current situation until insight is secured, and then attempt to have the patient apply this insight toward the solution of his everyday problems. But all along, an unfavorable environmental situation is operating to increase the anxiety and prevent the patient from acquiring and utilizing the potential benefits of insight. If at the end of a two year period of therapy, an adult patient is still economically and volitionally dependent on his parents, has no way of earning a living, and has not even made a start in the direction of formulating his vocational goals, he is psychologically in a worse position than he was before beginning therapy.

Non-directive therapists, on the other hand, are too rigid and fanatical (in practice if not in theory) about the necessity for self-direction, about avoiding transference and dependence on the therapist, and about avoiding any manipulation of the environment. While these latter goals might be desirable on a long-term basis, they cannot be striven for in the early stages of treatment when the disorganized, anxiety-ridden patient requires some active ego support and directive guidance. Furthermore, (a) the acquisition of insight is seldom possible without employing a developmental approach, and (b) the patient's avoidance of a realistic adjustment is encouraged by an attitude of complete permissiveness (e.g., the therapist expressing no judgments whatsoever, letting the client set his own limits in the relationship, etc.).

The following important good prognostic signs should be looked for by the psychotherapist: (1) a history of parental rejection rather than overvaluation (see page 139); (2) the absence of psychosomatic symptoms and the presence of high tolerance for conscious anxiety; (3) the absence of fixed defensive techniques such as phobia, hysteria, compulsions, etc.; (4) lack of excessive repressed hostility and resentment; (5) realistic ego-disinvolvement without undue constriction of the individual's psychological world; (6) insight into the nature of the threat and the meaning of symptoms, as well as ability to recognize the special factors which precipitate bouts of anxiety; (7) an attitude of "learning to live with" unavoidable anxiety, avoiding insoluble situations, and making advance preparations (within reason) for threatening situations that are manageable; (8) hopeful situational factors such as secure employment, opportunity for creative expression, and wholesome interpersonal relationships; and (9) the possession of other personality traits and abilities which help an individual create a secure environment for himself (see pp. 288-289).

Unfavorable prognostic indicators include agitation, depersonalization, and overt fear of death. The most fateful of all unfavorable prognostic signs is evidence that the patient is ceasing to strive or is striving for regressive goals in an unrealistic setting.

NOTES

[1] See Rollo May's historical summary of the distinction between fear and anxiety [*270*].

[2] *Maturational* and *situational* anxiety have not been specifically mentioned in this section but have been referred to in previous chapters.

[3] It is not implied that such active expression must necessarily be conscious.

[4] We would agree that anxiety first makes its appearance at this time, but not because of the concomitant emergence of the ego, but because of the development of the first rudimentary sense of adequacy. According to the schema proposed above, fear (which presupposes the existence of an empirical notion of self) develops three months earlier.

[5] For a discussion of the issue of infantile sexuality, see pp. 21-23.

[6] The inadequacies of this theory in accounting for neurotic anxiety are discussed on pp. 355-356.

[7] Sullivan does not distinguish between the insecurity and anxiety components of this reaction, thereby weakening his theoretical position considerably.

[8] In discussing Sullivan's concept of disapproval, we are omitting reference to the parent's challenge of the child's volitional independence which occurs during the crisis of ego devaluation. This challenge leads both to negativism and transitional anxiety (see pp. 365-366).

[9] Kardiner uses the term *anxiety* here, whereas according to the definitions adopted in this chapter, *insecurity* would be more appropriate.

[10] We are using the term *anxiety* here in the more general sense as representative of all fear states. Actually as will be pointed out later, *insecurity* is the more appropriate term.

[11] For a discussion of this relationship see pp. 357-360.

[12] Since the material in this section recapitulates and reorganizes concepts already familiar in other contexts, it is presented in bare outline only.

[13] For a full discussion of the dynamics of this choice see pp. 110-112.

[14] We are omitting from this discussion the second stage of negativism which occurs between the ages of four and five when the child overestimates his biosocial competence (see pp. 130-131).

[15] This parental attitude sometimes leads to various defects in ego maturation (see pp. 233-236).

[16] A possible exception to this trend is found in the dependency of old age.

[17] See pp. 110-112 for a discussion of the dynamics of this situation.

[18] See pp. 116-117.

[19] For example, most pathologists and internists still believe that polyuria is a compensatory mechanism in chronic nephritis that makes possible the excretion of nitrogenous wastes through the elimination of a greater volume

of urine. Actually, there is no possibility for further excretion after the glomerular filtrate is formed. The polyuria, therefore, is not a compensatory mechanism but the outcome of tubular damage with impairment of water resorption. The net effect is the production of a greater volume of urine with a lower specific gravity and no change in the quantity of nitrogenous wastes excreted.

[20] According to this theory the subjective quality of an emotion is a retroactive reflection of the unique pattern of visceral and motor responses initiated by the responsible stimulus.

[21] Goldstein more or less accepts the classical distinction by asserting that in fear, specific threats (which potentially could produce anxiety if not managed successfully) can be identified, whereas in anxiety the source of the threat is objectless and unidentifiable.

[22] The material presented in this section is also discussed on pp. 139-140.

[23] It is true that Goldstein's aphasics developed fixed defensive methods ("sets") of approaching problems in categorization; but these "crutches" were related to an actual incapacity and not to subjective impairment of self-esteem.

[24] Horney [*187*] draws particular attention to the defensive role of compulsive narcissism during bouts of acute anxiety.

CHAPTER 16

The Development of Conscience

MODERN PSYCHOLOGY and psychiatry have tended to drift away from concern with problems of ethics and moral values. The moralizing orientation in psychotherapy is treated with scorn in present-day textbooks of psychology; and if the directive and non-directive schools of thought agree on any one thing it is that there is no room for moral judgment in the therapeutic situation. The focus is on adjustment. The therapist, we are told, cannot say that behavior is good or bad; he can only express an opinion on the quality and efficacy of an adjustive mechanism. When he can divorce himself completely from ethical judgments, and can concern himself only with understanding the psychopathological origins and adjustive significance of deviant behavior, it is alleged that he has attained the ideal therapeutic attitude. The thesis that will be presented below—which in many ways parallels the position of Fromm [*142*]—is that not only is it impossible for a psychotherapist to ignore the question of moral judgment but also that it is undesirable and artificial for him to attempt to do so.

BEHAVIOR AND ETHICS

Far from being unrelated, the problems of behavior and ethics are inextricably bound together. To appraise a man's personality and ignore his moral character is equivalent in many respects to evaluating the setting of a ring while overlooking the diamond. True, the psychologist has a ready explanation for this apparent paradox. Moral values, he contends, are subjective and unverifiable. Every man to his taste and to his opinion; no objective psychological criterion is possible. We can only describe a man's personality traits with the aid of existing measuring instruments, hazard a guess as to how they developed, try to evaluate their adjustive value, and provide a plausible explanation for their anti-social components.

If you press him further by saying, "Yes, but what I really want to know is whether Mr. X is a decent and trustworthy man? Is he intellectually honest? Would he take unfair advantage of me? Is he able to control his unconscionable impulses? These factors are more important in getting along with him than knowing that he is introverted, tends to think in abstract terms, possesses an I.Q. of 120, has superior computational ability and a compulsive father." At this point the psychologist usually becomes defensive, and insists that moral judgments are not only beyond the pale of science, but would also irreparably impair his objective findings. "If you are interested in those subjective aspects of personality," he concludes, "why don't you ask his former employer. He can tell you. He is not a scientist."

The same psychological abhorrence of ethical judgment can be seen in our modern orientation toward anti-social conduct, crime and delinquency. Criminality is regarded as either a psychological or a social disease. There are no delinquent individuals, only delinquent parents or delinquent social systems. When one really understands why a criminal behaves as he does, the psychological evaluation is complete. Whether he is good or bad or whether he is morally accountable are arbitrary value judgments, matters of social policy or legal philosophy which do not concern the psychologist. To the latter, the delinquent is a product of his heredity and environment, an individual who had no other choice but to act as he did; and in the light of this psychological determinism moral responsibility and retribution are necessarily irrelevant, inconsistent and illogical. Behavior can be appraised as unfortunate or antisocial but never as evil. As long as it can be explained in psychological terms, it cannot be perceived as evil, since such an evaluation implies a value judgment which lies beyond the scope of behavioral assessment.

In the history of psychology, as Fromm [*142*] points out, this moral relativism is a comparatively recent development. Aristotle, Spinoza and Dewey, for example, all held that ethics can only be based on a science of behavior, and that "objectively valid value propositions can be arrived at by human reason" [*142*]. And whether the psychologist chooses to recognize it or not, most purposeful human behavior has a moral aspect, the psychological reality of which cannot be ignored.

Two problems are paramount in all ethical systems: (1) What shall man live for? Toward what goals shall he strive? What is involved in true self-realization? What is mature behavior? (2) Is man morally accountable for his behavior? Under what circumstances can he be exempted from moral accountability? Can antisocial behavior be reduced to psychological terms alone? If so, does psychological understanding obviate the necessity for moral judgment? In both instances, no valid or realistic ethical principles can be predicated apart from what is known about the behavioral capacities of human beings. It is futile to speak about life goals which are motivationally insupportable. The meaning of self-realization can be understood only in terms of purposeful strivings that can be related to the biosocial matrix from which human behavior emerges. The degree of maturity that man may conceivably attain cannot possibly exceed the maximum level which is defined by optimal interaction of the relevant variables involved in his personality development. The question of moral accountability can only be answered in relation to the problem of moral development or conscience formation, which in turn is an important facet of ego development.

These two core problems of ethics, therefore, are not beyond the domain of psychological investigation. As a matter of fact, they can and will be solved only as quickly as the science of human behavior itself advances. And if we admit the possibility of discovering objectively valid and verifiable principles of behavior, we must likewise be committed to the proposition that value judgments "built upon the science of man" have an equal claim to objective validity.

We do not mean to imply by this that all value judgments are empirically verifiable in terms of the laws of behavior. Relative to what is known about moral development, we may hold a man more or less accountable for his misbehavior and feel reasonably certain that such a value judgment is comparable to any scientific deduction derived from naturalistic data. The same holds true for judgments of the goodness or badness of behavior in so far as ultimate goals are concerned. Once we empirically determine what is "best for man" in terms of his nature and capacities, we have a yardstick for ethical measurement and a basis for psychological value judgments. If, for example, we were to discover that self-realization was the highest goal toward which man could strive in terms of enhancing his nature, we would have an objective dimensions along which to rate the ethical quality of purposeful behavior. In the sense then that a given act facilitates an outcome that has thus been empirically determined as an "ultimate" goal for man, it can be termed "good." However, to state that the original criterion for selecting "ultimate" goals—the enhancement of man's nature—is "good" is to express a philosophical value judgment for which no phenomenological validation is possible. Such judgments must stand or fall on their logical or metaphysical merits. Fromm's dictum that " 'good' is what is good for man and 'evil' what is detrimental to man, the sole criterion of ethical value being man's welfare" [*142*], fails to distinguish between these two kinds of value judgments.

Two other sources of ambiguity and confusion also exist in Fromm's epochal attempt to effect a rapprochement between psychology and ethics: (1) Although making a tremendous contribution by simply reasserting the position of other humanistic philosophers that ethics must be based upon the science of man—a position that has fallen into complete disrepute among present-day psychologists—he fails to go much beyond this in a psychological sense by discovering relevant principles of human behavior upon which an objectively valid system of ethics could be built. He revives Spinoza's concept of self-interest—behaving in such a way as to lead to "full development of [one's] potentialities" [*142*]—and rightly contends that this concept is "objectivistic inasmuch as 'interest' is not conceived in terms of the subjective feeling of what one's interest is but in terms of what the nature of man is" [*142*]. But whereas Spinoza as a philosopher was content to advance this concept as an objectivistic *hypothesis,* Fromm as a psychologist (without producing any additional empirical proof) asserts it as psychological *fact.* Instead of providing naturalistic evidence for an hypothesis advanced by a philosopher untrained in psychological research methods, he reiterates it in more psychological terms, and believes that through this verbal translation the gap between hypothesis and fact is satisfactorily bridged. Actually what had always been a philosophical desideratum based upon a hopeful view of human nature still remains as such; and we are no closer than before to a psychology of ethics that deals with the proposed goals of man's strivings.

(2) Fromm's failure to differentiate clearly between philosophical and psychological value judgments and to provide an empirical foundation for the latter in terms of behavioral data led him into a still more serious error. Dealing as he does with philosophical desiderata instead of with the raw material of human nature, his psychological theory strays far from the conditions of human moral development. His postulates, therefore, lack psychological validity since they assume the existence of fully-developed capacities for moral behavior and ignore preparatory learning processes and developmental phases. Surely a man cannot hope to learn what his true self-interest is without first following innumerable false leads. And although a humanistic conscience—in which a rational responsibility to abstract principles of justice can supersede uncritical submission to authority—is conceivable in an adult as a final stage of a developmental sequence, it cannot be reasonably expected in a young child, even in a non-authoritarian society, since it is not consonant with known empirical data regarding moral development.

In ignoring the conditions of moral development, therefore, Fromm dismisses the ontogenesis of ethical behavior, a mistake that is fatal for any psychological theory of ethics. The choice between humanistic or authoritarian ethics[1]* insofar as the individual human being is concerned is largely a function of his personal history and developmental capacities; it is not merely the outcome of a struggle between conflicting philosophies or cultural trends as Fromm implies. The feelings of moral obligation which an adult acknowledges in relation to an authoritarian social institution is not comparable to the authoritarian conscience which emerges from a satellizing parent-child relationship. The former might very plausibly be indicted as undesirable, while the latter

* Notes for this chapter appear on page 471.

can be accepted as a developmental precondition for the evolution of a stable humanistic conscience.

THE PHILOSOPHY AND PSYCHOLOGY OF VIRTUE

After assuming that self-realization is the true ultimate goal of human existence, Fromm goes on brilliantly to relate the traditional problems of humanistic ethics to this proposition.[2] The central principle again is Spinoza's dictum that self-interest (behavior facilitating self-realization) is "identical with virtue." However, if man "is ignorant of his self and its real needs," he can "deceive himself about his real self-interest" [*142*]. Hence, Fromm asserts,

> "Modern man *lives* according to the principles of self-denial and *thinks* in terms of self-interest. He thinks that he is acting in behalf of his interest when actually his paramount concern is money and success; he deceives himself about the fact that his most important human potentialities remain unfulfilled and that he loses himself in the process of seeking what is supposed to be best for him" [*142*].

If selfishness (greed for money, power, success) is incompatible with man's self-interest, are we to assume that man should not love himself if he wishes to be virtuous? Fromm answers in the negative:

> "Selfishness and self-love, far from being identical, are actually opposites. The selfish person does not love himself too much but too little; in fact he hates himself . . . It is true that selfish persons are incapable of loving others, but they are not capable of loving themselves either" [*142*].

True self-love implies concern with fulfilling one's potentialities, a concern which does not influence the selfish person. Hence,

> "The attitudes toward others and toward ourselves, far from being contradictory are basically conjunctive . . . Love of others and love of ourselves are not alternatives. On the contrary, an attitude of love toward themselves will be found in all those who are capable of loving others" [*142*].

This point of view takes issue with Freud's position that only a fixed quantity of libido is available to an individual, so that the more love he expresses for others, the less he has left for himself. Actually, the selfish person who has no intrinsic self-esteem is too concerned with extrinsic criteria of success to be able to love others. However, neither does he have his own self-interest or self-love at heart, but merely self-aggrandizement. The same preoccupation which hinders him from loving others prevents him from loving himself. On the other hand, an individual who intrinsically accepts himself is both able to relate himself emotionally to others, and to evince concern for self-realization (self-love) rather than self-aggrandizement.

Fromm makes a genuine contribution to the psychology of ethics by explaining the not uncommon paradox of the highly "unselfish" person who constantly seems to be advancing the interests of others to his own detriment—the person who apparently loves everyone but himself. He proposes that such individuals *really* do not love others either. They are persons who essentially have contempt for themselves and either hate others behind a reaction-formation of over-solicitude, or use this "martyrdom" as a rationalization for their failures and as a compensatory source of ego-enhancement.

Using the same Spinozoan concept of virtue, Fromm offers a simple Spinozoan answer to the old ethical problems of pleasure and happiness. He discards pleasure as too subjective and unreliable a criterion of value.

> "The word 'pleasure' without qualification seems to be most appropriate to denote the kind of good feeling that results from relaxation . . . Just because Spencer is right in proposing that every socially useful activity can become a source of pleasure, he is wrong in assuming that therefore the pleasure connected with such activities proves their moral value . . . Happiness and joy although, in a sense, subjective experiences, are the outcome of interactions with and depend on, *objective* conditions and must not be confused with the merely subjective pleasure experience. These objective conditions can be summarized comprehensively as productiveness" [*142*].

> "Happiness as well as unhappiness is more than a state of mind. In fact happiness and unhappiness are expressions of the state of the entire organism, of the total personality . . . The subjective feeling of

being happy, when it is not a quality of the state of well-being of the whole person, is nothing more than an illusory thought about a feeling and is completely unrelated to genuine happiness" [*142*].

It is obvious that the transition between pleasure and happiness as motivational stimuli represents an important step in ego maturation which we have already traced from infancy through childhood, adolescence and adult life. In satellizers we have noted the difference between the childhood modification of hedonistic impulses because of a genuine internal need to conform to parental values, and their later replacement by long-range goals for purposes of prestige or self-realization. In non-satellizers, on the other hand, the latter purposes are predominant, and deference to parental non-hedonistic standards occurs only as involuntary submission to superior force.

Fromm makes a significant break with psychoanalytic theory and an important contribution to the psychology of ethics when he insists that "man has an inherent drive for growth and integration" and that "the proper conditions for the development of the good [need not] comprise rewards and punishment . . . It follows from the very nature of man . . . that the power to act creates a need to use this power and that the failure to use it results in dysfunction and unhappiness" [*142*]. Acceptance of this principle, however, does not negate the fact that prestige and anxiety-reduction are also highly efficacious motives.

Just as happiness is a reflection of progress toward self-realization, destructiveness according to Fromm is an indication of "blocked productive energy." Here, however, he falls victim to his own enthusiasm and indulges in excessive overgeneralization, since we know that destructiveness can also serve as a source of ego enhancement, a primitive reaction to thwarting of any kind, and as a defense against anxiety. Fromm carries this reasoning a step further by claiming that the conditions leading to destructiveness are the same conditions which create a predisposition to neurosis:

"Every neurosis is the result of a conflict between man's inherent powers and those forces which block their development. Neurotic symptoms, like the symptoms of a physical sickness, are the expression of the fight which the healthy part of the personality puts up against the crippling influences directed against its unfolding" [*142*].

Where lack of "maturity, spontaneity and a genuine experience of self" are general failings in a particular culture, Fromm speaks of a "socially-patterned *defect*" which the individual shares with others and which usually saves him "from the outbreak of neurosis." This concept of the etiology of neurosis and "defect" is obviously highly overgeneralized, applies essentially to non-satellizers, and can more readily be understood as a symptom rather than as a "cause" of behavior disorder, i.e., as a common outcome of ego hypertrophy.

Finally, Fromm asks whether faith is compatible with humanistic ethics. Can man deny the existence of a moral authority which transcends his reason and experience and still have faith? It all depends on what one means by faith. By "irrational faith," Fromm means "the belief in a person, idea, or symbol which does not result from one's own experience, thought or feeling, but which is based on one's emotional submission to irrational authority" [*142*]. By "rational faith," he means the harboring of a conviction that objectively valid truths can be found through the employment of scientific method, that man can discover empirically verifiable moral values, and that he can conform to a rational moral authority which possesses no dogmatic, omniscient, or predetermined claim to absolute validity, and exercises no coercive control apart from the force of reason.

A CRITIQUE OF MORAL RELATIVISM[3]

The proponents of moral relativism, who hold that man cannot through observation, experiment and reason discover ethical values that are comparable to other scientific truths, base their contention on four main arguments: (1) that a concept of absolute truth is incompatible with the philosophy of science; (2) that "good" and "evil" are relative to the circumstances under which an act is committed, e.g., the analogy of the "white lie"; (3) that moral values cannot be universal or objectively valid since they are conditioned by historical and social factors; and (4) that even if it were possible to base an ethical system on the facts of "human nature," a separate system would have to be devised for every culture and subculture since human nature is primarily a function of cultural environment.

The first argument with respect to absolute truth merely confuses the issue. To be objectively valid, ethical values have to be no more "absolutely," "unquestionably and eternally true," and unrevisable than any other scientific proposition [*142*]. Implicit in the modern concept of scientific truth is the assumption that any empirically derived formulation in science is tentative and approximate, i.e., the truest statement that can be made in the light of available knowledge. The achievement of "absolute truth" is a theoretical not a phenomenological reality. For every event that happens there *is* a true or "absolute" explanation, the discovery of which must always remain a goal to be striven for rather than a goal which is attainable. After an infinite series of revisions and refinements this goal can be approached but never reached.

Secondly, if the alleged dependence of ethical judgment upon situational factors is examined critically, it will be found that the illustrations used in support of this argument represent instances in which a conflict exists between alternative moral principles. It is wrong to tell a lie, but it is conceivable that circumstances exist in which a more compelling moral duty takes precedence. However, to admit that ethical principles can operate antagonistically in the same field is not to negate the objective validity of the individual principles. Most complex physico-chemical, biological and social phenomena represent just such equilibria between opposing forces. The outcome or resultant in these cases reflects the relative strength of the competing variables.

The third objection posed by the opponents of a psychological theory of ethics—that moral values can only have meaning in a specific cultural framework or historical epoch—also has the characteristic markings of a pseudo-issue. Fromm elucidates this problem by referring to the latter concept as "socially immanent ethics," by which he means "such norms as are necessary for the functioning of a specific kind of society and of the people living in it" [*142*]. He contrasts this notion to "universal ethics," or those "norms of conduct the aim of which is the growth and unfolding of man" [*142*]. The socially immanent ethics of a given society may conceivably embody none of the principles of universal ethics, and may even violently conflict with same, e.g., the ethics of totalitarian nations. On the other hand, the specific ethical code of a given culture may represent the application of universal ethical principles to prevailing social and historical conditions.

In neither instance is the case for an objectively verifiable system of ethics invalidated. The fact that a ruthless segment of society can give its destructive ethical code the sanction of law does not rule out the possibility of a science of ethics any more than Hitler's racial edicts eliminated the possibility of a science of anthropology. And the fact that the same ethical principle may find expression in different ways depending on the social climate does not in any way vitiate its universality. Universal moral values can only be stated in general terms. Their implementation in a given cultural setting is a matter of social engineering. We make use of the same principle of steam pressure regardless of whether we use it to run a locomotive, power a ship, or operate a sewing machine.

The last argument advanced by the proponents of moral relativism is that if we try to tie ethical values to human nature, we can have no universal system of ethics, since there are no aspects of human nature which follow from behavioral properties and capacities of the organism that are universal in distribution. In previous sections we have discounted this notion by pointing to the inevitable psychological commonality that must exist among individuals in different cultures on the basis of neuroanatomical, neurophysiological and endrocrinological similarity, on the basis of common genetic factors that limit psychological development or predetermine its sequential course in terms of process, and on the basis of exposure to similar types of interpersonal experiences.

> "Man is not a blank sheet of paper on which culture can write its text; he is an entity charged with energy and structured in specific ways, which, while adapting itself, reacts in specific and ascertainable ways to external conditions . . . In opposing the erroneous assumption that certain historical cultural patterns are the expression of a fixed and eternal human nature, the adherents of the theory of infinite malleability of human nature arrived at an equally untenable position . . . If man were infinitely malleable [he] . . . would be only the puppet

of social arrangements and not—as he has proved to be in history—an agent whose intrinsic properties react strenuously against the powerful pressure of unfavorable social and cultural patterns . . . Human nature is not fixed, and culture, thus, is not to be explained as the result of fixed human instincts; nor is culture a fixed factor to which human nature adapts itself passively and completely. It is true that man can adapt himself even to unsatisfactory conditions, but in this process of adaptation, he develops definite mental and emotional reactions which follow from the specific properties of his own nature" [*142*].

PROBLEMS OF MORAL DEVELOPMENT

The investigation of the moral development of the human being provides one of the main cornerstones for an empirically verifiable psychology of ethics. It enables us to go beyond the contributions of the humanistic philosophers who were content to assert their belief in the possibility of an objectively valid system of ethics based upon the science of man, but who never did more than propose philosophical desiderata for ethical behavior that were neither based upon nor substantiated by scientific data. But although genetic psychologists have provided us with considerable empirical data about moral development we have failed to utilize it in a constructive way in building a science of ethics. Psychoanalysts have ignored this data in favor of untestable hypotheses of their own derived from retrospective clinical material relating to behaviorally deviant individuals drawn from a highly selected segment of the population; and in common with their non-psychoanalytic psychological colleagues, who are familiar with the developmental evidence, they have taken a relativistic position in relation to moral value judgments. Fromm, while rejecting the relativistic viewpoint, has for the most part merely integrated and translated into psychological language the same ethical propositions and desiderata advanced by the humanistic philosophers.

By means of a developmental approach it becomes possible (1) to determine the limits that define man's capacity for acquiring moral behavior and the sequential steps involved in moral growth; (2) to predict the various types of delinquent behavior that may arise as a consequence of aberrant moral development; and (3) to determine under what conditions individuals shall be held morally accountable for their misdeeds.

Looked at in this light the learning of moral values is only a component aspect of ego development. It obeys all of the principles regulating the assimiliation of any ego-related value, except for the understanding that an issue of good or evil is involved. When in addition, a notion of obligation and the possibility of inhibitory control arise, and a self-evaluative attitude is adopted towards one's own behavior in areas which impinge upon moral values, the collective term, "conscience" is employed. It should be realized, however, that "conscience" refers to a class of ego-related value judgments and possesses no more substantive properties than a generalization such as "ego." An illusion of substantive identity, however, is provided by the association of conscience with the highly specific and identifiable self-reaction of guilt with its familiar psycho-physiological response pattern.

From a developmental standpoint, therefore, we can see no theoretical advantage in separating moral development from any other aspect of ego development involving the learning and assimilation of values. It only confuses the issue to postulate a separate layer of personality as embodying in a reified fashion the properties associated with conscience reactions, and arising in an inevitably predetermined manner in relation to a single aspect of psychosexual development.[4] In our analysis of the development of conscience, therefore, we shall be concerned with the same type of variables that determine the outcome of other aspects of ego development, namely, the biosocial competence of the individual, the demands of his social environment, his capacity to perceive himself and his environment realistically, the various dimensions of the parent-child relationship, and other personality characteristics of parent and child (e.g., dominance, strength of hedonistic motivation, introversion-extraversion).

Havighurst's Conception of Moral Development

The most significant recent investigation of character development that illustrates the empirical approach is Havighurst's and Taba's study of adolescent character and personality in a midwestern town. Relevant data from this study will be cited later to illustrate certain aspects of moral development. Here, however, we shall be concerned only with presenting some of the basic assumptions regarding the development of character which these workers started out with in planning the investigation.

> "An individual's behavior is a product both of the social environment in which he has lived and of his own personal make-up. The social environment—home, school, neighborhood, age group, community—establishes a code for good conduct. Through these agencies the code is communicated to individuals and in a sense is forced upon them; through these channels a person learns what is expected of him; and through them he is rewarded or punished to the degree to which he lives up to expectations.
>
> "The make-up of the individual—his personal characteristics, intelligence, goals, drives, interests, adjustment patterns—constitutes the second general influence upon his character development. Although to some extent personal make-up is determined by heredity, to a very great extent, these personal qualities are the results of earlier social experiences.
>
> "The moral character of the individual is always the result of what he already is as a person combined with the play of social forces upon him.
>
> "It is important to note that there is no clear demarcation between that which lies within the person and that which lies in the social context around him. Values and codes which were first imposed by society are eventually adopted by an individual as his own" [*171*].

After defining the major component factors entering into character formation, Havighurst and Taba postulate that "character to a great extent is learned behavior" [*171*]. They describe three chief modes of learning moral values: (1) through explicit reward and punishment; (2) through "unconscious imitation" of prestigeful persons in the hope of being rewarded at a later date; and (3) through "reflective thinking." These methods of learning, however, leave little room for the operation of personality make-up. The second method also does not differentiate between the simple mechanisms of prestige suggestion and reinforcement on the one hand, and the more complex emotional process of identification on the other. Neither is any distinction made between the two separate varieties of identification, namely, satellization and incorporation, or between these two ego status orientations in the learning of values and the exploratory orientation (e.g., "reflective thinking"), which focuses more on objective considerations.

However, in analyzing their data, the authors go far beyond this limited frame of reference which they set for themselves initially, and relate character development in very meaningful ways to differences in personality and motivation. Thus, the original, rather primitive classification of modes of learning moral values is abandoned in favor of a more significant motivational classification which includes such categories as "(1) ambition and social mobility, (2) affectional responsiveness, (3) submission to authority, (4) impulses and emotionality, (5) negativism, and (6) rationality and reflection" [*171*]. These motivational categories can very easily be subsumed under the three learning orientations (i.e., satellizing, incorporative, and exploratory) discussed in Chapter 12 (see pp. 151-156). Havighurst and Taba also interpret them in relation to "the over-all personality of the individual." They state:

> "Good character means one thing in one type of personality and something quite different in another type; character is formed differently in different personalities" [*171*].

Hence "adaptive persons" are mostly influenced by ambition and social mobility, and conform easily to prevailing patterns in their social milieu. "Self-directive persons" are highly reflective in their moral choices; and although they too may be largely motivated by prestige considerations are more critical and independent in reaching ethical decisions.

> "Submissive persons, too, are very self-critical concerning their moral behavior, but their doubt springs from a very different source. Unlike self-directive persons they are worried, not by the problem of whether or not they are living up to their own principles and whether or not those principles are the correct ones to follow, but by whether or not they are living up to the expectations of persons who are in authority over them.

> "The defiant persons have rejected the generally approved moral beliefs and principles. They have not experienced satisfaction and social approval for good behavior to a degree sufficient to learn the beliefs and principles which lie behind good behavior. They are ruled by selfishness and aggressive impulses" [*171*].

These relationships between personality, motivation, and character development have been presented as illustrative of the assumptions underlying a particular empirical approach to the investigation of conscience formation. Before discussing the actual findings in greater detail and relating same to the theoretical framework of the present volume, a brief summary of methodological techniques and problems in these areas would be in order.

The Measurement of Moral Character[5]

The problem of moral development need no longer remain a matter of conjecture and hypothesis as in the philosophical era of psychology. A number of empirical methods are available, each possessing certain advantages and limitations, and a variable degree of reliability and validity, which, however, is satisfactory enough for research purposes. These measuring instruments may be roughly classified into three general categories: measures of moral behavior, measures of moral reputation, and measures of moral belief. They are especially valuable when used conjunctively and in relation to other measures of personality study. Of the three most definitive investigations of moral development, those of Piaget [*308*], Hartshorne and May [*169*], and Havighurst and Taba [*171*], the last mentioned is perhaps the most significant, since a real effort was made "to understand how variables combine in any one individual to produce his character and reputation" [*171*]. This study, in the words of the investigators is

> "similar to recent studies in personality which focus attention upon the dynamic patterning of traits within individuals. The attention here is upon those traits of personality which are subject to the moral sanctions of society, in other words, upon traits of character."

The work of Hartshorne and May [*169*] has focused attention upon the organization of moral traits, and has led to a rather general acceptance of the situational nature of moral behavior. This conclusion, based upon the low correlation between different performance measures of the same character trait (e.g., honesty) needs reinterpretation in the light of more recent concepts. In the first place, there is reason to believe that in the age period of ten to fourteen studied by these investigators there is lack of generality in moral concepts. In Havighurst's and Taba's study, for example, correlations between measuring instruments were much higher partly at least because all of the subjects were sixteen years of age. Secondly, Hartshorne and May studied moral behavior phenotypically. If the different behavior manifestations, on the other hand, had been examined from the standpoint of significance in the total personality configuration (i.e., genotypically), apparently contradictory phenotypes might have been reduced to similar genotypes. Lastly, no allowance was made for degree of ego-involvement in the various performance tasks measuring character; and degree of ego-involvement has been shown to account for a large part of the apparent specificity in the organization and expression of motivational traits [*25*].

In terms of meaningfulness, there is perhaps no superior measure of moral behavior than that derived through ecological observation of a longitudinal nature. Such observations, obviously, are exceedingly time-consuming since a large number of samples of a given moral trait are required to establish reliability and generality. A recent modification of this method which requires less time, effort and expense involves the use of standardized experimental situations in which group behavior is observed behind a one-way screen while verbal responses are recorded by mechanical transcription devices. The great advantage of both methods is that behavior is observed in situ. A possible disadvantage is that the children are more or less aware of the fact that their behavior is being observed. However, this disadvantage is less serious than one might imagine since experience has shown that children soon become oblivious to the presence of an observer; also, the one-way screen and mechanical recording devices enable observations to be made without the knowledge of the subject.

An ingenious short-cut to the method of observation was devised by Hartshorne and May [*169*] in the form of objective performance tests of character traits (e.g., cheating in games and on tests, stealing money). By means of these tests it was possible to sample moral behavior unbeknown to the subject in a highly reliable and standardized fashion. The obvious disadvantage of this method is that such test situations cannot possibly evoke the spontaneous type of behavior which takes place under real life conditions. However, this is only a limiting factor which by no means destroys their value or usefulness as a measuring instrument. Unfortunately, the situational specificity of test scores has led to the virtual abandonment of this method. But if a sufficient number of different tests of the same trait which intercorrelate reasonably well are employed, an additive total score is justifiable since absolute moral consistency is only a theoretical abstraction. Furthermore, if measures of ego-involvement are available, the component scores can be weighted on this basis and hence rendered more comparable.

Reputation can also be used as a measure of moral character as long as one realizes that it is not synonymous with character, but is a reflection of same as perceived through the eyes of an individual's associates. Such judgments are necessarily subjective, distorted by social class and other types of bias, and vitiated by the distinction between private and public aspects of personality; and since reputation is largely based upon the latter aspects, it mirrors to an unknown extent the ability of an individual to accurately perceive and simulate the behavioral traits expected of him. Havighurst and Taba, however, were able to obtain reliable measures of reputation by pooling a number of ratings made from a wide "variety of points of observation" [*171*]. Correlation coefficients between the different measures of measuring reputation (check list, character sketches, guess-who test) ranged from 0.36 to 0.77.

A third method of ascertaining the moral character of an individual is to obtain verbal expressions of his values and to ask judges to rate same for various categories of ethical content. Data can be obtained through interviews in which the subject is asked to explain the moral basis for some of his own observed behavior, or is asked to choose one of a number of possible alternatives in hypothetical situations having moral significance. A more indirect variant of the latter method is use of projective techniques (e.g., story completion, picture-story, sentence completion, etc.) which rely on identification with third persons rather than on direct interrogation. Although this device encourages the subject to respond with greater sincerity and honesty, it is difficult to interpret the significance of findings, since the degree of personal identification with the characters in a given picture or story is unknown. Havighurst and Taba [*171*] obtained data on moral beliefs through the use of such devices as a paper-and-pencil inventory; essays on "The Person I Would Like to Be Like" and "My Heroes," and a Life Problems Test.

The value of expressed beliefs as an index of character is, of course, vitiated by the obvious fact that they are colored to an unknown extent by insincerity and desire to favorably impress the observer. The same criticism, however, may also be levelled at behavior despite widespread acceptance of the adage that "actions speak louder than words." Are not most persons highly motivated to obtain "good" reputations, which means that they frequently will behave in accordance with perceived expectations rather than with their own moral values? As a matter of fact, many individuals will often express their true feelings verbally, whereas in situations calling for translation of same into action, they are constrained by fear of reprisal. There is no doubt but that in some situations a verbal expression is a franker and more revealing index of moral character than its behavioral counterpart.

Moral Beliefs and Moral Character

A widely prevalent opinion consonant with the moral confusion and cynicism of our times is that there is little or no relation between moral beliefs on the one hand and moral behavior on the other. This view is in accord with current psychological emphasis upon drives, motivations and emotions as causes of behavior with a correlative devaluation of the significance of cognitive processes. In part, it is also a reflection of moral relativism, since it proceeds from the assumption that moral behavior is simply a matter of passive adaptation to and assimilation of prevailing group norms. It is presumed that an individual will believe as the social class to which he owes allegiance believes, and that he will act in accordance with the behavioral expectations of this same group; and if there is little correspondence between social class expectations regarding belief and behavior, he will presumably manifest the same type of discrepancy. Although this view is quite plausible in some respects and is supported by several empirical studies, it obviously oversimplifies the issues involved.

It is our contention that there is a very high correlation between *true* moral beliefs on the one hand and moral behavior on the other. The apparent discrepancy between the two can be largely explained on the following grounds: (1) It is often assumed that moral belief is synonymous with moral knowledge; (2) *expressed* beliefs are confused with true beliefs; (3) much of the discrepancy is an outcome of genuine moral confusion, inconsistency and conflict rather than of deliberate or "unconscious" insincerity.

Moral knowledge is only one aspect, and a relatively minor aspect of moral belief. It is true that a certain minimal amount of intelligence and social experience is required to learn acceptable moral values. The latter however, become transformed into moral beliefs only when they are invested with sufficient emotional and intellectual conviction to constitute genuine dispositions to behave in a certain way. Immoral behavior in persons of normal intelligence who are exposed to acceptable moral beliefs is not an outcome of insufficient moral knowledge but either of (a) lack of a feeling of obligation to conform to these values, or (b) selective impairment of the self-critical faculty in relation to ethical aspects of their own behavior.

The negligible significance of moral knowledge as a variable in moral behavior is borne out by the low correlations which Hartshorne and May found between moral knowledge and performance [*169*]. There is also little difference between delinquent and nondelinquent boys in ability to identify the correct ethical alternative in hypothetical moral problems [*35*]. Curiously enough, intelligence correlates much more highly with moral conduct [*169*] than it does with moral knowledge. This can be interpreted to mean that intelligence influences moral behavior not (as might be expected) through determining moral beliefs, but in an extraneous manner, i.e., intelligent children have less reason to cheat in order to do well in school work and are more apt to perceive the conditions when cheating might prove dangerous. One difference between the delinquent and the non-delinquent youth (within a given socio-economic class) is that the latter's greater mean intelligence enables him to avoid participation in illegal activities where the chances of apprehension are great.

A second reason for the seeming disparity between beliefs and behavior is that expressed beliefs are not necessarily *actual* beliefs. Avowal of conventional and socially acceptable beliefs is considered to be judicious in any society, although during adolescence, youths often delight in expressing cynical and antisocial viewpoints which exceed by far their actual behavioral manifestations in this direction. On the other hand, in relation to peer group activities, adolescents tend to be highly conforming in their beliefs.

Discrepancy between belief and behavior may also be brought about by insincerity in behavior—behavior that is expedient and primarily designed by the individual to earn a good reputation despite its inconsistency with his true beliefs. This possibility raises a very difficult problem of interpretation, since it would be legitimate at this point to ask the following question: In the light of our definition of belief as a genuine conviction, as a disposition to behave in a certain way that is consonant with underlying thought and feeling, is not such expediency an indication that it is essentially the purported belief which is insincere rather than the behavior which actually reflects the individual's true belief?

A simple unqualified answer cannot be given to this question. Certainly behavior in choice situations has to be regarded as a test of the sincerity of belief. A belief cannot possibly be genuine unless an individual is willing to undergo suffering, if need be, for it. However, common sense argues that some concessions to social expectations—if only in the external manifestations of behavior—are necessary for normal adjustment. It is impossible for any individual continually to buck the stone wall of convention and steer his own moral course independently of the norms that prevail in his social group. Thus, depending on the nature and extent of the compromise, the intention (e.g., legitimate self protection or ruthless disregard of the rights of others), the degree of coercion involved, etc., it is possible for a true moral belief to eventuate both in contradictory expressed belief and behavior which are therefore insincere but for understandable and justifiable reasons. However, in some other cases of discrepancy between belief and behavior, where such extenuating circumstances do not exist, it would be necessary to conclude that the expressed belief is insincere (i.e., not reflective of true belief) in the light of its behavioral counterpart.

A third possibility—in which neither belief nor behavior is insincere—can also account for this discrepancy. A moral belief may be sincerely held and still give rise to incompatible behavior which cannot be excused on the grounds of self-protective conformity. A genuine belief exists in this case which is accurately reflected in expressed belief but is not translated into compatible behavior because of the greater strength of competing motives, namely, considerations of self-aggrandizement.

In summary, then, disparity between moral belief and behavior arising from apparent insincerity may exist under three different conditions: (a) Expressed belief is insincere, being inconsistent with both true belief and behavior, but no real gap exists between the latter two phenomena. (b) Expressed belief and behavior are both insincere and inconsistent with true belief for reasons of legitimate conformity to social norms. Hence in this instance, the disparity between true belief and behavior is mostly phenotypic. (c) Neither expressed belief nor behavior are insincere in the sense that a genuine true belief does not exist, but are inconsistent with the latter only because of the prepotency of a competing motive. In all three cases, therefore, it is necessary to conclude that belief exerts a profound influence on behavior if by belief we mean actual cognitive and emotional content as opposed to expressed verbal characteristics.

Finally we come to the third main reason why there appears to be so much discrepancy between moral belief and behavior, namely, lack of consistency, insufficient generality and confusion between moral beliefs. Here the issue is not that a genuine moral belief does not exist and is represented by an insincere verbal expression, or that a true moral belief is present but leads to inconsistent behavior for reasons of justifiable expediency or the greater strength of a competing motive. The apparent discrepancy rather is an indication of cognitive limitations in logic and consistency. Granting as we must that a very large portion of the moral inconsistency manifested by any individual has to be ascribed to the two reasons discussed above, an irreducible minimum still remains which can only be explained on the basis of the lack of complete logical consistency that to a greater or lesser extent characterizes human intellectual organization. It is just as fallacious to ascribe *all* moral inconsistency to conflicts between motives as it is to ascribe *all* forgetting to purposeful repression.

In early childhood we see evidence of such inconsistency on the basis of developmental immaturity in ability to generalize; and although improvement in this ability continues until adult life, it always falls short of complete perfection. In connection with their test of Student Beliefs administered to a population of sixteen-year-olds, Havighurst and Taba found

> "marked inconsistencies. For example . . . there is high agreement with the statement that members of clubs and communities should expect help from non-members; yet a large number of subjects maintain that a person has a right to refuse a job for a club when it does not benefit him personally . . . Inspection of test items suggests that sixteen-year-olds assent to generalized statements and statements which conform to accepted stereotypes, but reject others which express the value in connection with an unusual detail or take a less-familiar approach to it.
>
> "The main impression derived from studying the cases of extreme discrepancies was that the students who were high on Student Beliefs and low on Life Problems were those who had accepted certain stereotyped slogans but who had not thought through the meaning or implications of these slogans. There was little relationship between what these individuals expressed as their general beliefs and the values which determined their particular decisions" [*171*].

Much of this inconsistency, however, should not be ascribed to inevitable cognitive limitations in logical process. There are at least two other contributing factors here: (a) the method of moral education, and (b) the objective moral confusion prevailing in our culture. Many times there are conflicts between moral values when differences between alternatives cannot be clearly discriminated. However, in a very real sense as Havighurst and Taba point out, this outcome is conditioned by the type of moral education given in our culture.

"Moral beliefs are formed by accumulating reactions to immediate situations, not by a conscious formulation of a generalized code of conduct. This reflects the fact that the teaching of what is right and wrong is done with reference to isolated, concrete acts of behavior; relatively little effort is made to help young people generalize from these situations or to help them develop a coherent moral philosophy. The development of a personal and rational code, when it does take place, grows out of the accidents of personal make-up and patterns of adjustment. Under these circumstances, maladjustment rather than adjustment tends to be the stimulating force toward reflection, criticism and personal orientation" [*171*].

This relative inability to generalize moral values which follows from our educational system is especially apparent in the application of moral beliefs to life problems. Havighurst and Taba found the degree of relationship between these two variables to be "very low" because

"in Life Problems several acceptable values were set into conflict with each other, while on Student Beliefs each item represented a single value. Making decisions which involved conflicts of values requires compromises which are not faced when each of these values is considered separately . . . The ability to apply moral beliefs to an increasing range of conflicting life situations is quite undeveloped at the age of sixteen. These subjects see the more obvious lines of action but seem at a loss whenever a subtle weighting of values is called for. They find conflicts hard to face; they tend to solve conflicts by using slogans rather than by using concepts of the relative significance of values" [*171*].

The other extenuating factor contributing to this apparent cognitive deficiency in moral consistency is the widespread moral confusion permeating modern society. This situation which is illustrated by the formal cultural endorsement of humility, kindliness and helpfulness, with a simultaneous overvaluation of prestige, aggressiveness, and success, has deteriorated rapidly since the onset of World War II. The current generation of youth, therefore, has developed an extremely high tolerance for moral ambiguity and confusion. Because of the prestige suggestion inherent in the operation of social norms, they are assimilable by many individuals in such a way that their incompatibility is never perceived; it is presumed by the perceiver that inconsistency in cultural values is inconceivable, and, therefore, an advance "set" exists to perceive such values as consistent regardless of manifest content—even if logic-tight compartments must be constructed to prevent critical comparisons from being made. Hence, while it should be realized that assimilation of cultural norms is never a completely thorough-going or passive process, a basis for uncritical acceptance does exist.

Another type of evidence that is advanced to support the thesis that moral beliefs do not influence behavior comes from studies pointing to the fact that Sunday School attendance and degree of religious observance are correlated negligibly with moral conduct [*45, 169, 184, 384*]. Havighurst's and Taba's data also support this proposition:

> "When social position is kept constant, there is a reliable tendency for those subjects rated high on religious observance to have higher character reputations than those rated low on religious observance . . . Those subjects with no church affiliation tend to have a lower character reputation than those who are affiliated with a church" [*171*].

This means that religious observance forms part of the total pattern of formal, socially approved behavior which is important in determining an individual's reputation.

> "Church membership itself is not an independently powerful influence in the development of character, but . . . is often associated with other factors or constellations of factors that tend to produce good or bad character reputations. It . . . is one of the things that communities like Prairie City expect of their 'good, respectable people' . . . Most people who value their status in the community do not treat it lightly" [*171*]

The important thing to bear in mind is that evidence such as this only proves that formal religious *observance* makes for good character *reputation* but is indifferently related to moral conduct. It does *not* prove that religious *belief* itself is unrelated to moral behavior. In fact, evidence to the contrary is available. In Havighurst's and Taba's study there is a suggestion that members of the closely-knit Lutheran community have extremely high reputations for honesty and responsibility. That such reputation is more reflective of actual behavior than is usually the case with reputation is borne out by the fact that in Prairie City "the Lutheran subjects rank lowest among the four Protestant churches in social status" [*171*]. On the basis of these findings the authors conclude that "the true role of any church in the character formation of its members should probably be sought in an intensive study of individuals rather than of groups" [*171*].

Recent studies in personality theory also suggest that religious beliefs may be related to character structure and cognitive phenomena. Orthodoxy of religious belief was found to be related to tendency toward ethnocentrism and anti-Semitism [*6*]. Research is going forward at the present time to test the hypothesis that religious orthodoxy is associated with rigidity of thought. In terms of personality maturation, too, it might be reasonable to suggest that orthodoxy inhibits the rate of adolescent emancipation, since one of the important mechanisms of ego maturation in our culture involves replacement of the satellizing by the exploratory orientation in the assimilation of values. As we shall see later, this shift in orientation facilitates the development of a functional and reciprocal sense of moral obligation.

DEVELOPMENTAL STAGES IN CONSCIENCE FORMATION

The investigation of conscience development offers us considerable encouragement for establishing an empirical and objectively valid psychology of ethics because of the implications which such knowledge holds for the understanding of delinquency and for the assessment of moral accountability. But we can only hope to understand the development of conscience as an integral component of ego development. It shifts with changes in the parent-child relationship, in social expectations, perceptual ability, and cognitive organization, and with maturational advances in biosocial competence and goal structure; and in turn it has an important influence on all of the latter aspects of ego development.

We shall also regard conscience as a composite concept embodying many component growth processes which do not necessarily develop at the same time or at the same rate. On the one hand, the same factors are at work which are implicated in the assimilation of any value, except, of course, that they operate in the context of a moral judgment of good or bad. On the other hand, numerous other variables enter into the total configuration—the idea of personal moral obligation, self-evaluative attitudes, inhibitory control of behavior, and a complex psycho-physiological reaction known as guilt. In using the term, *conscience,* therefore, it should be understood that what is meant is the entire complex of variables entering into the moral behavior of a particular individual, even if all of the possible components are not represented at any given time.

The Presatellizing Stage

Needless to say, the infant enters the world completely irresponsible in a moral sense and remains this way for the first few years of his life. This does not mean that his moral future is wholly uncharted. By virtue of his latent capacity for assimilating ethical values, acquiring a feeling of obligation, evaluating his own behavior, carrying on cognitive processes, etc., the broad sequential outlines of conscience formation are already predetermined in terms of process, but not in terms of specific content.

Presatellizing "conscience," for the most part, involves little more than the development of inhibitory control on the basis of learning to anticipate and avoid punishment. Previous experience with a given type of unacceptable behavior leads the child to expect pain, deprivation, isolation, or disapproval if such behavior is repeated, and hence leads to feelings of insecurity in contemplating same. Inhibition of such behavior, therefore, is rewarding since it reduces insecurity. If this latter term were substituted for "anxiety," we would be in complete agreement with Mowrer and Kluckhohn [*287*] that "conscience" during this age period

> "is a form of anxiety, but the danger signals which set it off are cue-stimuli resulting from the individual's own behavior, behavior which if 'found out' is likely to be followed by chastisement."

Thus, in the presatellizing era the child is aware of his parents' demands, standards and values, but does not truly internalize them. He is primarily concerned with satisfying his own immediate needs and asserting his volitional independence. The parent can compel conformity only by arousing feelings of insecurity in relation to forbidden acts, which means associating the latter with pain, restraint, threat of isolation, etc. Such control, however, is stripped of any moral implications since it only indicates submission to authority on a need-reduction basis rather than any genuine acceptance. Before guilt can be experienced not only must moral values be internalized, but also a feeling of obligation to conform to them, as well as sufficient self-critical ability to recognize disparity between standards and behavior.

However, in viewing such inhibitory behavior in young children resulting from insecurity and anticipation of punishment, adults tend to superimpose their own frame of reference. Because they would bring more sophisticated conscience reactions such as guilt to the situation, they assume that these responses also hold true for the child. Mere perception of parental disapproval does not evoke guilt at this stage of the game. The parents' disapprobation rather is productive of insecurity in the infant since it sometimes carries the threat of withdrawal of succorance. Also the fact that hostile feelings toward parents can be expressed so openly at this time argues against the possibility that guilt feelings are implicated.

Early Satellizing Conscience

When the needs of the parents and the culture coincide with sufficient growth in the child's biosocial competence to make him responsive to training demands, a new stage in conscience development is reached. As the child perceives his actual volitional impotence and his dependence upon parents for volitional direction, and agrees to accept a satellizing role in relation to them, ego devaluation is accomplished; and with satellization comes a need to assimilate parental values and the gradual emergence of a feeling of obligation to conform to them. True conscience appears for the first time, since inhibitory control becomes predicated upon an acceptance of the satellizing situation (with its concurrent need for maintaining the conditions under which derived status can be enjoyed) rather than upon anticipation and avoidance of punishment and the reduction of feelings of insecurity.

The development of a satellizing conscience, however, is a very gradual matter. It does not unfold spontaneously but in response to the parents' new authority role and training demands. Before internalization and self-discipline can be acquired, external forms of control must be maintained, especially in the initial phases. The self-evidentness of this proposition is especially apparent in the first period of negativism which accompanies the crisis of ego devaluation. Resistiveness at this stage is directed against the changes in ego organization that are required if devaluation is to be effected. The child is understandably reluctant about surrendering notions of volitional independence, relinquishing his privileged position of executive dependence, foregoing immediate hedonistic gratification, and assimilating alien moral values.

As parental training demands become insistent and threatening enough to the prevailing ego organization to elicit negativistic behavior, the child's grandiose self-esteem is challenged. Anxiety responses appear in addition to the presatellizing reaction of insecurity to parents' disapproval. A common, face-saving, anxiety-reducing device at this time is the "sweet lemon" mechanism. After the child is required to renounce his immediate goal and submit to parental desires, he may assert that he voluntarily chose the alternative which he was forced to adopt because he really liked it better in the first place.

Gradually, however, under propitious conditions, negativism becomes supplanted by a satellizing attitude which carries over into the sphere of value assimilation. Typically this assimilation occurs as a by-product of the general attitude of subservience, and hence takes place on a highly uncritical level. It is reinforced (a) by the child's need to retain his derived status which, therefore, causes him to react with anxiety whenever it is threatened by parental disapproval; and (b) by his acceptance of the moral obligation to abide by the standards which he has internalized. This latter step is accomplished by acquiescing to the proposition that disobedience or personal non-conformity to parental standards is "evil," disloyal, and hurtful to the supreme authority figures whom he has accepted as his models. At this point a basis for guilt reactions is established. When the child perceives disparity between his own behavior and his internalized standards, this complex psycho-physiological response is set into motion. It consists of the subjective elements of shame, anxiety, remorse and self-disgust, and the autonomic reactions of vasomotor instability, sweating, visceral giddiness and inhibition of ordinary vegetative functions.

As soon as guilt feelings can occur, another powerful motive arises for interiorizing and abiding by parental values, namely, the need for guilt-avoidance. The possibility of experiencing guilt makes punishment inevitable, since in addition to the anxiety which it evokes by threatening self-esteem, the intense reactions of self-condemnation and reproach, shame, self-disgust and remorse are generally more punishing and inescapable than external punitive agents.

This level of conscience behavior, however, is more of an end-product of satellization than a realistic description of what to expect in the early stages. Reinforcement of parental values at this time is provided primarily by the following factors: (1) the prestige authority of the parent who takes over the mantle of omnipotence which the child abandons after the crisis of ego devaluation. In the absence of any prior or competing moral frame of reference, prestige suggestion exerts considerable influence in attitude formation; (2) the use of rewards, threats and punishment, bolstered by the parents' physical presence on the scene until compliance is effected; and (3) the child's physical dependence upon the parent for purposes of survival (in contradistinction to dependency needs based upon status considerations).

The interplay of factors leading to early conscience formation is also dependent upon various other aspects of the parent-child relationship and upon other personality characteristics of the two principals. Unconditional acceptance and intrinsic valuation of the child by the parent (following upon an initial history of parental altruism) are necessary preconditions for the development of a satellizing conscience. The firmer and more consistent a parent's discipline is, the more easily are his standards assimilated. If there is marital discord, the child can identify with either parent only at the risk of alienating the other [*287*]. Children of both sexes find it more difficult to accept the father's authority because of the negligible male influence in the ordering of home and school life. Finally, where parents belong to a subcultural group of low social status, children tend to resist identification with them, and to be unduly attracted by the values of the dominant class [*68*].

With respect to personality variables in the child which influence the course of conscience formation, ascendence and viscerotonia are perhaps the most crucial. The more self-assertive a child, the more likely will he be to resist the imposition of parental standards upon his behavior. Similarly, the greater his need for visceral satisfactions the more reluctant will he be to accept the obligation of conforming to standards aimed at minimizing these satisfactions.

The interaction between conscience development and other aspects of personality maturation, i.e., attenuation of hedonism, growth of executive independence, etc., is evidenced by the fact that while hedonistic impulses retard the acceptance of a satellizing conscience, the latter once formed, greatly facilitates the further course of personality maturation. No amount of external coercion is as effective in curbing infantile personality trends as the child's own acceptance of moral accountability in relation to the parent.

But the instability of early satellizing conscience is as great as the instability of early satellization itself. When in the fourth year of life the child acquires still greater biosocial competence, and (because of a rudimentary self-critical faculty) exaggerates his qualifications for volitional independence, he tends to become dissatisfied with his position of subservience to parental authority. This leads to the second stage of negativism which is brought to a close by an increase in self-critical ability that finally enables him to accept with equanimity his marginal status in the culture.

Despite the boistrous, aggressive, and competitive characteristics of four-year-old negativism, the effects of early satellization are not completely lost. Evidences of guilt feelings are present, and the influence of conscience is discernible if only in the elaborate efforts made to justify violations of the accepted code of behavior. Neither moral values nor moral obligation are rejected outright. Instead, exemption from moral accountability is claimed on the grounds of highly implausible extenuating circumstances which can only be seriously advanced because of the child's extremely limited self-critical ability. Misdeeds are attributed to real or imaginary playmates, to accident and chance occurrence. When reproached for making excessive noise, he may claim to be a wild animal or an inanimate noise-making machine like a phonograph or fire engine. At other times he invokes the excuse of involuntary reflexes such coughing, denies hearing a command, or claims that he "forgot," or "tried hard" to refrain from doing something, but nevertheless was unsuccessful. When confronted with a demand to give an account of a previous escapade, he may blandly assert that he doesn't remember, or defiantly state that he "isn't talking" or "can't tell," or that others are "also bad." Sometimes he will appeal to the fact that a specific negative command was not issued prior to the misdeed or that similar behavior was tolerated on a previous occasion; at other times he may feign inability to apply a general injunction to a specific situation, claiming that the former alone is insufficient if not explicitly related by the parent to every situation to which it is applicable.

Numerous other examples can be given to illustrate the incomplete acceptance of satellizing conscience at this stage of development: (1) the belief that a misdeed "doesn't matter" if no one sees it; (2) the concept that only the injured parent can dispense punishment, and only in relation to the immediate present; that parents can only punish misbehavior occurring on their own property; (3) willingness to forego the long-range benefits of keeping a promise to gain the advantage of an immediate pleasure; (4) the belief that misbehavior is legitimized if it is accompanied by willingness to accept the consequences; (5) threatening reprisals against the parent (e.g., to "beat up" the latter when he grows up); (6) projecting blame onto the parent; (7) the use of promises as a convenient technique for evading immediate parental pressures; (8) the tendency for remorse to last just as long as approval is withheld or deprivation is threatened; (9) the general futility of parables and fables as ways of subtly indicating to a child that he has undesirable moral traits. What usually happens is that the child grasps the moral of the story quite easily but fails to see that it has any relevance whatsoever for his own behavior; (10) the belief that if a behavior, formerly the recipient of parental disapproval, can be repeated at a later date without criticism, absolution is provided for the original wrong and guilt. Hence, the common tendency for children to repeat forbidden behavior may reflect the hope that *someday* the parents' reaction might conceivably be neutral or approving.

In conclusion, then, it appears that in the early satellizing period moral values are fairly well internalized, but that a sense of moral obligation is still quite rudimentary. The child will cheerfully agree that other children must not do certain things before he is willing to apply the prohibition to his own behavior. Nevertheless, sufficient sense of moral obligation is present to prevent him from repudiating outright his feeling of moral accountability to his parents. This much is made clear by the elaborate rationalizations he invents to justify his misbehavior. Moral principles tend to be highly specific; but exaggerated specificity is often feigned as a means of justifying misconduct. Self-critical ability is still at a low level as demonstrated by the implausibility of the rationalizations he devises. External and visible controls, reward and punishment, and prestige suggestion are still very important in compelling conformity to parental standards, whereas feelings of guilt and remorse are rudimentary and seldom more than transitory in duration. In general if the four-year-old is allowed to choose between enhancing his moral reputation (in order to make future benefits possible) and deriving immediate enjoyment out of a situation, he will elect the latter alternative.

Late Satellizing Conscience

The cardinal feature of this stage of conscience development is the stabilization and internalization of the sense of moral obligation as a result of gains in self-critical ability. As long as the child can uncritically view himself as capable of managing his own affairs and as entitled to volitional independence, feelings of moral obligation are bound to be unstable, since he finds the authority role of the parent distasteful and provocative of hostility and resentment. However, after he learns to appraise himself and his situation realistically enough to accept the dependent biosocial status that is inevitably his in any culture, he is able to make a satisfactory satellizing adjustment to parental authority, which he can now regard as self-evident and unquestionable.

Evidence of genuine internalization of the moral obligation to conform to parental standards is abundant at this stage of development. There is a marked increase in sensitivity to reproof and in the intensity and duration of remorse reactions [*150*]. Conscience to a large extent becomes its own taskmaster and functions in the absence of external coercive agents. The child appears concerned with the spirit as well as the letter of moral duty. Threats of reprisal for punishment are less frequently uttered, and expressions such as, "I like you even if you hit me," are not uncommonly heard. Unlike the earlier periods of conscience development when parental disapproval gave rise to insecurity, anxiety and hostility, the more usual reaction at this time is guilt. Such guilt reactions are elicited almost automatically—even before the child can perceive the discrepancy between deed and standard, since he tends to proceed on the assumption that such a discrepancy must exist if he is reproved by his parents.

In the late satellizing stage, reinforcement of the sense of moral obligation is provided primarily by guilt feelings. These become a powerful deterrent to unacceptable behavior which is much more anxiety-producing than external punitive agents. In the first place, remorse is more perseverating and recriminating than pain or deprivation. Secondly, it is more inevitable since detection cannot possibly be avoided. Lastly, and most important, the punishment dispensed by one's own conscience does not reduce guilt or confer absolution. In contrast, punishment by parents (because of continual occurrence in the sequence of misbehavior, guilt, punishment, forgiveness and reacceptance), acquires highly important guilt-reducing properties for the child.

As a symptomatic variety of anxiety, guilt is unmatched in its potential disruptive influence on self-esteem. Hence, both guilt-avoidance and guilt-reduction serve as extremely potent motivators of human behavior. Fear of guilt reprisals plays the central role in the moral inhibitory control characteristic of this age period, and for that matter, as we shall see later, of all subsequent periods as well.

Nevertheless, the satellizing conscience (or "the authoritarian conscience" as Fromm prefers to call it) still shows some resemblances to non-internalized, expediential pre-conscience which is

> "regulated by fear of punishment and hope for reward, always dependent on the presence of . . . authorities, on their knowledge of what one is doing, and their alleged or real ability to punish and reward. . . . The most important point of similarity is the fact that the prescriptions of authoritarian conscience are not determined by one's own value judgments but exclusively by the fact that its commands and tabus are pronounced by authorities" [*142*].

Satellizing moral values are accepted in a completely uncritical fashion; their self-evident rightness is unquestionable. The satellizer

> "has found inner security by becoming, symbiotically, part of an authority felt to be greater and more powerful than himself. As long as he is part of that authority—at the expense of his own integrity—he feels that he is participating in the authority's strength. His feeling of certainty and identity depends on this symbiosis; to be rejected by the authority means to be thrown into a void, to face the horror of nothingness. . . . To be sure the love and approval of the authority give him the greatest satisfaction; but even punishment is better than rejection. The punishing authority is still with him, and if he has 'sinned,' the punishment is at least proof that the authority still cares. By his acceptance of the punishment his sin is wiped out and the security of belonging is restored.
>
> "The prime offense in the authoritarian situation is rebellion against the authority's rule. . . . Obedience implies the recognition of the authority's superior power and wisdom; his right to command, to reward, and to punish according to his own fiats. . . . The respect due the authority carries with it the tabu on questioning it. The authority may deign to give explanations for his commands and prohibitions, his rewards and punishments or he may refrain from doing so; but never has the individual the right to question or to criticize. If there seem to be any reasons for criticizing the authority, it is the individual subject to the authority who must be at fault; and the mere fact that such an individual dares to criticize is *ipso facto* proof that he is guilty" [*142*].

Implicit in the acceptance of "the authority's superiority" is renunciation of the desire to acquire the latter's unique prerogative to determine moral values or to "become *like* the authority, for this would contradict [*his*] unqualified superiority and uniqueness" [*142*]. Hence, independence in assimilating values—either by accepting the values of another or determining one's own through reason and reflection—is tantamount to repudiating the authority and is productive of guilt feelings. These feelings are rooted in the "child's authoritarian conviction that the exercise of his own will and creative power is a rebellion against the authority's prerogatives to be the sole creator, and that the subject's duty is to be his 'things'" [*142*].

It is important to realize, as Fromm points out, that not only does acceptance of dependence lead to guilt feelings for independent behavior, but also that the latter in turn reinforces the original dependence by creating a need for forgiveness. Hence "the most effective method for weakening a child's will is to arouse his sense of guilt" [*142*].

A second type of continuity that prevails between preconscience and satellizing conscience is the fact that "even though the relationship to authority becomes internalized, this internalization must not be imagined to be so complete as to divorce conscience from the external authorities" [*142*]. Even in adults, Dollard claims, "the inhibition of any act of aggression varies directly with the strength of the punishment anticipated for the expression of that act" [*90*]. However, while accepting this statement, we cannot agree with Fromm that

> "the presence of external authorities by whom a person is awed is the source which continually nourishes the internalized authority. If the authorities did not exist in reality, that is, if the person had no reason to be afraid of them, then the authoritarian conscience would weaken and lose power" [*142*].

As already pointed out, external force is not the chief support of a genuinely satellizing conscience, but a restraining factor which tends to inhibit occasional impulsive acts and experimental testing of the limits of a situation.

Between the ages of five and seven the concepts of *good* and *bad* tend to be related to specific situations which elicit parental approval or disapproval, and first begin to acquire some real generality of meaning by the age of eight [*150*]. This requires that parents use specific prohibitions and punishment as well as reward and approval in teaching acceptable moral conduct. It would be unrealistic to assume that merely by giving approval to acceptable behavior, its negative counterpart is thereby automatically discouraged. Not only does such logical consistency fail to prevail, but also the positive attraction which the undesirable behavior holds for the child remains undiminished, even though the valence of its opposite alternative may be enhanced by reward.

Piaget [*308*] stresses the "absolutism" of the child's moral judgments during this period of development. By this he means two things: first, that the concept of moral obligation is unilateral rather than reciprocal; and secondly, that rules are perceived as having a self-evident rightness, a "sacred and traditional reality" rather than the functional purpose of facilitating interpersonal relationships on the basis of equity and mutual agreement. Both of these characteristics are in harmony with the description we have given thus far of satellizing conscience. Fromm contends with validity that they apply to overtly permissive parent-child and teacher-child relationships as well as to the more traditional authoritarian forms.

"Instead of overt we find anonymous authority, expressed in terms of emotionally highly charged expectations instead of explicit commands. Moreover, the parents do not feel themselves to be authorities, but nevertheless they are the representatives of the anonymous authority of the market, and they expect the children to live up to standards to which both—the parents and the children—submit.

"Liberal and 'progressive' systems of education have not changed this situation as much as one would like to think. Overt authority has been replaced by anonymous authority; . . . 'don't do this' by 'you will not like to do this'. In fact in many ways, this anonymous authority may be even more oppressive than the overt one. The child is no longer aware of being bossed (nor are the parents of giving orders), and he cannot fight back and thus develop a sense of independence. He is coaxed and persuaded in the name of science, common sense and cooperation—and who can fight against such objective principles" [*142*]?

We may also apply Piaget's analysis to the problem of moral law in the peer group. To the young satellizer, the moral authority of the peer society is analagous to the moral authority of the parents; it is a given, a fixed and immutable reality, a state of affairs that could not have developed in any other conceivable fashion, a law rooted in unilateral moral obligation. This attitude is derived from the fact that the satellizing child's relation to the peer group parallels his relation to the parent. At this stage of the game, the main function of the group is to provide a supplementary source of derived status; and the child accepts its authority on the same unilateral and absolutistic basis as he does the parent's. On the other hand, the non-satellizer passes directly from a condition of preconscience to a social situation in which his main concern is with the acquisition of extrinsic status. His approach to moral law, therefore, is necessarily functional and based on mutual obligation, even if his particular point of view may be jaundiced by considerations of ego aggrandizement.

Other reasons also exist for the "moral absolutism" of the child during the period from five to eight: (1) Generally, he operates in small, single and isolated groups. Hence he only has experience with one set of rules [*308*], the self-evidentness of which is enhanced both by the absence of alternatives and the prepotent specificity of the initial model (see page 263). (2) The peer society at this age level may be characterized as an "informal, unorganized group." Not only are the roles of the members toward each other poorly defined in a formal sense, but there is also a lack of individuation or functional division of labor. In such a situation it would be difficult indeed to define moral law in terms of functional and mutual relationships between individuals. If only by default then, the child tends to revert to the only concept of moral law he knows, the unilateral concept that governs the most significant interpersonal relationship in his psychological world, i.e., the parent-child relationship.

As we shall see in subsequent sections, changes in the heterogeneity and differentiation of peer group organization and in its status functions make possible a reformulation of the concept of moral law on a more reciprocal, functional and exploratory basis.

Conscience in the Desatellizing Period

As the satellizing orientation begins to wane in the middle and preadolescent years of childhood—until it becomes but a subsidiary source of current status in the adolescent period—marked changes in a corresponding direction occur in the organization of conscience. Nevertheless, in the same way that the impact of childhood satellization leaves a permanent residue in adult personality structure, the satellizing conscience becomes the only firm substructure upon which a stable, rational conscience can be built.

Five main lines of development in conscience formation can be noted at this time: (1) There is a decline in moral absolutism. The self-evident rightness of moral propositions tends to be replaced by a more empirical, exploratory, and rational approach based upon functional needs in interpersonal relationships [*308*]. (2) Conscience becomes less authoritarian and more reciprocal in nature. "Constraint and unilateral respect" give way to "mutual respect and cooperation" [*308*]. (3) Moral principles acquire greater generality and abstractness. (4) The child's moral viewpoint becomes less egocentric [*308*]. (5) The sense of moral accountability (the feeling of obligation or responsibility to abide by internalized ethical values) is placed on a societal basis instead of remaining a function of the child-parent relationship. These changes are produced by modifications in the parent-child relationship, shifts in the child's needs for and source of status, alterations in his group experience, and maturation of his perceptual and cognitive processes.

The first break in the authoritarian conscience occurs when the child enters school. A new source of moral authority enters the picture challenging the omniscience and infallibility of the parents. And the mere fact that he becomes aware of the existence of alternative ethical values—even if he does not accept them—undermines his parents' claim to uniqueness as the sole law givers. As long as more than one alternative exists, as long as he is required to exercise choice and discrimination, a given set of values can no longer be completely accepted as self-evidently true. With increasing age, more and more of the child's store of axiomatic truth acquires the status of hypotheses needing external verification.

As the child escapes from the constraining uniformity of the family hearth into the more variable practices of the culture at large, the prepotent influence of the specificity of his initial models begins to decline. Parental values and ways of doing things can then be viewed in perspective as specific hypotheses to be tested rather than as invariable imperatives having the same validity as propositions derived from inductive logic or from rational discrimination between alternative value judgments. Not only is he confronted by many conflicting value systems, all of which dispute the parents' early monopoly on moral authority, but eventually he also becomes part of a peer group which sets itself up as a moral authority in its own right. He becomes less awed by adults and older children and more inclined to search for moral values that reflect the principles of cooperation and reciprocal obligation and serve a functional purpose in regulating group life [*308*]. According to Piaget's findings, this desire for equality and reciprocity in interpersonal relationships increases with age [*308*].

Various changes in the organization of the peer society also facilitate the transition to a more functional and reciprocal moral law. Groups become larger, less isolated and more stable. Children experience membership in several different groups exhibiting a varety of rules, practices and values. As formal hierarchical relationships are established and individual roles differentiated, the need for cooperation and mutual obligation increases, as illustrated by the development of "certain features of solidarity such as not cheating or not lying between children" [*308*]. The child's attitude toward the group also changes in terms of his status needs. The older he becomes the more he looks to the group as a source of extrinsic status rather than as an adjunctive source of intrinsic security and adequacy. It is for this reason and also because the group is never dignified by the same halo of sanctity surrounding his parents that the child can adopt the exploratory orientation in his peer group long before he dares to do so at home. It is not until adolescence that the omniscience of parents becomes sufficiently devalued to permit full and objective criticism of their practices.

Growth in ability to generalize, to think more in terms of abstractions, and to reach logical conclusions in more complex types of problems also tends to promote the development of a more consistent and rational moral code divorced from situational rules and regulations. When to this cognitive equipment is added emotional and attitudinal liberation from parental values and a higher level of self-criticism [*88, 196*] (which enables one's own behavior to be judged in the same perceptual framework as the behavior of others) all of the essential elements of a rational conscience are present. The child is then ready to adopt the exploratory orientation in relation to moral problems, and transfer his feeling of moral accountability from parents to the moral authority of society.

By the exploratory orientation (see page 147) we have meant an approach to the learning situation which is task-oriented and relatively free from considerations of ego status. The ego is involved in the sense that there is strong identification of self with performing the task and following it through to a successful conclusion or to its logical implications. However, the outcome remains an end in itself which provides feelings of success or failure but not in relation to ego status or self-esteem. Whether or not the problem is solved according to the objective considerations involved rather than whether derived or extrinsic status is achieved is the main focus of concern and the primary motivating factor; and under such motivational auspices there is obviously much less opportunity for distortion of the process and product of the learning effort.

However by egocentricity of moral thinking, Piaget not only includes this meaning but two others as well: (1) inability to "dissociate what belongs to objective laws from what is bound up with the sum of subjective conditions;" and (2) inability to perceive, pay sustained attention to, and take into account the needs, feelings and viewpoints of others. Although other investigators have neither found the same sharp break nor the same qualitative differences between age groups in logicality and egocentricity of thought, there is no dispute about the fact that real differences in degree do exist. The decline in all three aspects of egocentricity facilitates to a great extent the emergence of a functional and rational moral conscience based upon mutual obligation.

Although the child does make some progress away from egocentricity in adopting the satellizing orientation, in that "the mind stops affirming what it likes to affirm and falls in with the opinions of those about it" [*148*], Piaget rightly claims that true liberation from egocentricity requires mutual respect and freedom to criticize in a climate of equality.

"Just as, if left to himself, the child believes every idea that enters his head instead of regarding it as a hypothesis to be verified, so the child who is submissive to the word of his parents believes without question everything he is told, instead of perceiving the element of uncertainty and search in adult thought. The self's good pleasure is simply replaced by the good pleasure of a supreme authority. There is progress here, no doubt, since such a transference accustoms the mind to look for a common truth, but this progress is big with danger if the supreme authority be not in its turn criticized in the name of reason" [*148*].

Conscience During Adolescence

Most of the material in the previous section applies here too, since adolescence must be regarded as a period of desatellization. The main differences between preadolescence and adolescence are in terms of the intensity and completeness of the underlying desatellizing processes, which bear the relationship of preparatory and consummatory stages to each other.

For many reasons, the adolescent is both more strongly disposed and in a better position than the preadolescent to employ the incorporative and exploratory orientations. The parents by this time are devalued to the stature of ordinary mortals and are unable to extend derived status by fiat. Furthermore their disposition—which reflects the expectations of the culture—is to withdraw derived status and compel the adolescent to seek a greater measure of extrinsic status; but since they themselves cannot provide what they advocate, they must yield authority and allegiance to the peer group which can.

A reshuffling of loyalties takes place on the basis of this shift in status-giving power. The adolescent looks to his peer group primarily as a source of feelings of extrinsic adequacy; but the group as the chief moral authority of adolescence also becomes the major object of his residual satellizing attitudes in value formation. The increased importance of the incorporative orientation is a reflection of his greater concern with achieving extrinsic status; and the greater prominence of the exploratory orientation reflects his enhanced needs for independence, equality and self-assertion that lead to emancipation from parents. In making this transition, feelings of guilt are inevitable, since repudiation of loyalties to parents is necessary in accepting new value systems; on the other hand, failure to complete internalized developmental goals expected by the culture is equally productive of guilt feelings.

Adolescence in our culture also provides an extended period of time during which experimentation with a functional morality is possible. As Piaget [*148*] points out, our culture is unique in that the adolescent is not absorbed soon after the termination of childhood into an adult world of absolutistic moral standards. Strict conformity to the adult culture is not demanded, although this does tend to occur anyway, since despite overt rebelliousness, the moral values of adolescents resemble those of adults more and more closely as they grow older [*204*].

Adolescents do take an active role in elaborating new moral standards to fit the needs of their group, although in this they are not uninfluenced by the prevailing standards of the socio-economic class to which they owe allegiance. We have already seen that adolescents tend to share the major values of their class reference groups, and that the peer culture itself takes the responsibility of enforcing these standards. Furthermore, despite greater flexibility in the group evolution of new values, once these are determined more complete conformity is demanded than in the adult culture. In conclusion, it must be admitted that the freedom to choose between moral alternatives in adolescence is present but is much more apparent than real.

Piaget [*148*] also contends that the modern adolescent by virtue of living in a heterogeneous society has the opportunity of choosing between a multiplicity of alternative moral standards in contrast to the single code confronting the adolescent in primitive cultures. It is undeniable that the availability of alternatives greatly facilitates the development of a rational and functional conscience; it is problematical, however, whether it can be regarded as a *sine qua non.*[6]

Nichols, for example, describes a relatively static and primitive society in which moral standards are learned informally by adolescents through incidental experince in association with adults. Despite the availability of only a single moral standard, "they developed a rational morality based on its connections with actual human needs and social relationships" [*299*]. It would seem, therefore, that for a functional and reciprocal morality to develop, one does not necessarily require a complex, heterogeneous society with many alternative value systems.[6] It suffices to have an exploratory and problem-solving approach unencumbered by rigid adherance to a traditional code which has lost contact with actual needs in interpersonal situations and relies instead upon the self-evident rightness of a sacred authority. In addition to the realistic limitations noted above upon the adolescent's freedom to choose between moral alternatives, it is important to realize that the very complexity and multiplicity of different value systems which can seldom be explored definitively may only make for confusion and inability to appreciate the issues involved in arriving at standards with functional value.[6]

Moral beliefs of adolescents show several interesting trends when compared to pre-adolescent beliefs: There is a trend toward expediency and conformity which reflects the greater concern with extrinsic status; a trend in the direction of cynicism which is indicative of the same factor plus aggression toward adults; and a trend toward greater tolerance and flexibility. The latter is revealed by the fact that the number of things "thought wrong" [*310, 381*] as well as unconditional and absolute moral standards (i.e., unqualified condemnation of lying and stealing under any circumstances) decline with age [*395*]. More account is taken of extenuating circumstances. Two-thirds of the junior high-school students in Stendler's study condoned stealing under such conditions, whereas only ten per cent adhered to an absolute standard [*376*]. On the other hand, expediency and cynicism are revealed by the decreasing percentage of "moral" reasons and the increasing percentage of "practical" reasons given for the disapproval of lying [*395*], and by the fact that almost one-quarter of eighth- and ninth-graders offered "amoral" reasons for not stealing, e.g., possibility of apprehension [*376*]. The same tendency toward cynicism is shown by the large percentage of college students who justify the "double standards of sexual morality" [*224*].

The trend toward increased expediency and conformity is illustrated most vividly in Havighurst's and Taba's study of adolescent beliefs in Prairie City.

"Accepting familiar stereotypes is one outstanding characteristic of these beliefs. . . . Individual positions deviating from the generally accepted code are feared and shunned. This is shown by hesitancy in expressing opinions contrary to common beliefs, and by approving wrong behavior if most of one's associates are involved in the act. There is a marked tendency to subordinate individually held positions to both adult and peer-group opinion, even when one's own positions are considered morally right. . . . A third characteristic is lack of readiness to face conflict of choices. The predominant reaction to conflict situations is uncertainty or an attempt at a compromise solution. For example there is hesitancy in taking positions when loyalty to friends and schoolwork conflict" [*171*].

An apparently contradictory phenomenon met with in many adolescents especially of the ascetic and overintellectual type is a variety of moral perfectionism. In some cases it is indicative of the naivete, inexperience and impulsiveness of adolescents, and of the initial reaction to the shock of disenchantment upon being initiated into the corruption existing in certain areas of public life formerly believed to be sacrosanct. In other cases, however, it has the same significance as exaggerated cynicism, namely, as a form of aggression against adult society, in which a strong motivational "set" exists to perceive all adult behavior in an unfavorable light. The cynical adolescent then proceeds to emulate and outdo the behavior he purports to perceive in adults, while the perfectionist in an orgy of self-righteousness sets himself up as a champion of truth and virtue against a hopelessly wicked world. Not infrequently, however, the same individual oscillates between the two reactions and manifests each alternately.

Cultural Factors in Moral Development

We have already observed that differential cultural environment exerts a profound influence on various aspects of ego development. Hence, it would certainly be legitimate to inquire to what extent the development of conscience is

"influenced by the value systems of the social groups to which the individual belongs, or to which he relates himself positively or negatively. The values held by the family, by the dominant groups and institutions in the community, and by persons in positions of authority and high status constitute the 'moral climate' in which a young person grows up. These groups and persons are in a position to punish undesirable conduct and reward desirable conduct, and their expectations have much to do with the standards of behavior developed by the individual" [*171*].

Within a given social class environment not only are there distinctive educational and vocational aspirations and accepted forms of social participation for adolescents, but also characteristic moral values relating to sex, aggression, honesty, community responsibility, thrift, loyalty, etc. [*171*]. These value systems parallel for the most part the value systems espoused by the adult members of the subculture despite the refractoriness of adolescents to adult direction; the peer culture takes over the task of enforcing this conformity since adolescents can accept its authority without resentment.

This differentiation of moral value systems on the basis of social class does not mean that complete homogeneity prevails within a given class. Actually, considerable communication and interaction occur, with the lines of influence generally proceeding in a downward direction. Where a single institution such as the high-school becomes the common meeting ground of a number of subcultural groups, the moral standards of the resulting adolescent peer society reflect the morality of the middle-class which controls it. Adolescents from other social class backgrounds must either adapt to these standards or choose to remain on the periphery of social acceptance. In the light of these considerations, therefore, the proposition that a given individual must *inevitably* assimilate the particular values of his own social class is absurd, although it is true that this phenomenon is facilitated by the presence of segregation and "disorganized areas" in large urban centers [*171*]. Equally implausible, on the other hand, is the notion advanced in some quarters that modern forms of communication have *completely* broken down class differences in moral beliefs and behavior.

It is also necessary to distinguish between official and actual moral ideologies.

"The differences in moral values among the various social classes are probably greater in practice than in words. People all up and down the social scale in Prairie City tend to agree verbally with an official moral ideology, from which their actual moral behavior departs in various ways" [*171*].

The gap is perhaps most marked in lower-class children since their parents do not consistently enforce middle-class standards despite verbal affirmation of same. Furthermore, the teachings of middle-class parents are reinforced by other cultural agencies such as school, church and community organizations. The lower-class child, on the other hand, experiences considerable "conflict between the standards of his home and the expectations of his teachers, Sunday School and club leaders . . . but usually resolves it by participating in few activities outside the home" [*171*].

However, the discrepancy between verbal and behavioral morality is one which transcends social class differences and constitutes an almost universal phenomenon in our culture. It is a sign of moral disintegration and confusion that is symptomatic of a rate of social, political and economic change that has by far outstripped its ideological substrate. Concern for moral values has been swept aside in the struggle for power. As traditional moral restraints continue to be abandoned at an alarming rate, the exponents of expediency are able to attract ever more converts on the basis of a bandwagon psychology. Anything goes as long as it can be provided with a veneer of legitimacy which protects the individual from legal reprisal. The form rather than the content and intention of behavior has become the chief criterion which governs the social operation of moral judgment in our society.

What it means for a child or adolescent to grow up in such a moral climate is something which still requires considerable investigation. We can only predict that it will bring out the worst aspects of the incorporative orientation in moral behavior, encouraging expediency, lack of principle, and cynical acceptance of moral depravity. We can expect children to grow up unconcerned with human values and the welfare of others, indifferent to the existence of injustice, and sold on the attitude of getting the most out of people and valuing them solely on the basis of their market price. The character traits that will impress them most will be duplicity, hypocrisy, insincerity, chicanery and double-dealing. With justice they will feel that they in turn will be valued by others solely for what the latter can get out of them. At the very best it can lead to ethical confusion and inconsistency and some effort to remain inside the framework of a selective moral code which grants a clean bill of health to individuals who manage to operate within the letter of the law.

On the non-satellizer, this situation works no particular hardship, since his own moral proclivities are inclined in this direction in the first place. The satellizer, on the other hand, is unable to make the required adaptations without experiencing feelings of conflict, guilt, self-reproach, and resentment toward a culture that requires such moral compromises for the sake of survival and legitimate ego enhancement. He feels impelled to crush all vestiges of moral feeling in himself because he perceives this as a handicap in a jungle existence, in a "dog-eat-dog" society in which one "does" others or is "done in" by them. To reach the top, he fears that he must think of himself alone or others will climb to success on his shoulders. But try as he may, he cannot stifle his conscience completely. In desperation he may adopt a double moral code: one for his friends and family, another for his colleagues and competitors. But in any case guilt feelings exercise considerable restraint over his behavior so that his violations of the moral code are generally less flagrant and more defensible than the non-satellizer's. His immorality more usually serves the interests of survival rather than catering to the predatory needs of aggressive ego aggrandizement.

Havighurst and Taba found a moderately high positive relationship between social class and reputation in Prairie City which could not be explained on the basis of prevailing stereotypes about social class [*171*]. It seemed more likely that the determining factor in the relationship was conformity to school requirements which in turn meant acceptance of middle-class values. This interpretation was "substantiated by the fact that there was a high relationship between school achievement and character reputation and a comparatively low relationship between school achievement and social class" [*171*]. This situation is analagous to the positive correlation found between church attendance and character reputation, since religious observance like conformity to school requirements is a good index of middle-class morality which is distributed in ever diminishing amounts as one descends the social scale [*171*].

Critique of Fromm's Humanistic Conscience

In formulating his concept of conscience, Fromm commits the same general error as in defining what he means by virtue, i.e., he equates a philosophical desideratum (e.g., self-realization as the proper goal of man's existence) with a psychological (motivational) reality. In the case of conscience, however, this deficiency is even more serious since any tenable conception of conscience must be related to known empirical evidence bearing on moral development. Fromm solves this problem in a typically psychoanalytic fashion—by blithely ignoring all of the evidence, and hypothecating the existence of a reified personality structure (the humanistic conscience), the origin of which he does not bother to explain but which by inference appears to be an axiomatic correlate of human consciousness. This is how he describes it:

> "Humanistic conscience is not the internalized voice of an authority whom we are eager to please and afraid of displeasing; it is our own voice, present in every human being and independent of external sanctions and rewards. . . . [It] is the reaction of our total personality to its proper functioning or dysfunctioning. . . . Actions, thoughts, and feelings which are conducive to the proper functioning and unfolding of our total personality produce a feeling of inner approval, of 'rightness' characteristic of the humanistic 'good conscience.' On the other hand, acts, thoughts and feelings injurious to our total personality produce a feeling of uneasiness and discomfort characteristic of the 'guilty conscience'. Conscience is thus a re-action of ourselves to ourselves. It is the voice of our true selves which summons us back to ourselves, to live productively, to develop fully and harmoniously—that is, to become what we potentially are" [*142*].

In other words, after assuming that self-realization is the true goal of life, Fromm invents a mystical guardian or inner voice that chirps happily whenever the realization of this goal is furthered, and rings like a burglar alarm whenever it is ignored in favor of more mundane considerations. The psychological naivete of such a formulation of conscience is quite reminiscent of the theological approach and is highly unacceptable in the light of modern concepts of internalized moral values, feelings of obligation, self-criticism, and inhibitory control.

Fromm's lack of a developmental approach becomes especially glaring in his discussion of the "authoritarian conscience." The young child, he claims, fights against the irrational authority represented by his parents but feels guilty because of it [*142*]. Actually, the three-year-old, who can hardly be classified as a rationalist, does not object to parental irrationality or arbitrariness, but to the aggressive infringement by his parents upon his prerogative of volitional omnipotence; and his expressions of hostility are not accompanied by guilt feelings until moral obligation is internalized at a much later date. Similarly Fromm's objection to the authoritarian conscience on the grounds that it is invariably predicated upon the needs and interests of the authority is only convincing in an historical sense and in relation to social institutions. From a developmental standpoint it is difficult to grant Fromm's premise that parents regard children as "good" only when they are docile and obedient. Furthermore, this "obedience" serves not only the parents' convenience but is also necessary for personality development, adaptation to the culture, and cultural survival.

Fromm finally carries his condemnation of the authoritarian conscience to its logical conclusion by denying that it "has to exist as a precondition for the formation of humanistic conscience," and by insisting that the satellizing conscience is unstable unless constantly reinforced by external pressures [*142*]. Apart from the many developmental reasons already given to demonstrate that a wholly rational conscience is a psychological absurdity in the early years of childhood, there are many practical reasons which militate against the use of reason as the sole basis of child training: (a) few parents would have sufficient time and patience for instituting such a regimen and abiding by it consistently; (b) cognitive limitations would make it impossible to make many "reasons" intelligible to the child; (c) many parental requests cannot be justified on the basis of reason but are nevertheless essential on the grounds of conformity to cultural expectations; (d) many emergency situations in childhood require implicit, unquestioning obedience; (e) rationalism would not eliminate negativistic behavior in the child since it is caused not by parental arbitrariness but by developmental delusions of volitional omnipotence or of executive competence; (g) the stage of satellization is necessary for normal personality development.

This by no means implies an unqualified endorsement of authoritarianism in child-rearing. The intention is merely to point out the developmental limitations inherent in the child's capacity for acquiring a rational conscience. While disagreeing with extreme positions such as Fromm's, the writer has already indicated that authoritarian training techniques are employed long after they are developmentally obsolete, and has suggested several methods of minimizing the undesirable aspects of the satellizing orientation in value assimilation (see page 158).

Conscience and Superego

It is customary for many psychiatrists and clinical psychologists —even those who are not psychoanalytically oriented—to use the Freudian term "superego" as if it were synonymous with conscience. This practice is not only exceedingly unprecise but is also highly misleading, since superego does not refer to the developmental conscience described above as a part of the ego, but to a separate, reified layer of personality derived from a specific, inevitable, and universal event in psychosexual development.

Throughout our discussion of conscience development we have stressed Sherif and Cantril's proposition that

> "there is for the individual no psychological difference either in the genesis of or the function of 'moral' codes (which psychoanalysts separate out as the 'superego') and other norms of behavior the individual learns. The emerging developing ego is in large part composed of *all* these interiorized social values" [*354*].

The values subsumed under conscience are merely internalized in an ethical context and are more closely related to such factors as self-criticism, obligation, self-control and guilt feelings.

The rationale for the superego as something special and apart from the rest of the ego is poorly conceptualized in psychoanalytic literature. It is not clear whether the ego or the superego has the function of testing reality and of clearing the way for the expression of id impulses. The distinctions between ego, superego and ego-ideal are also obscure and are defined differently by various analysts [*354*]. Confusion exists as to whether the superego is a product resulting "from the repression of the Oedipus complex [or] is itself the mechanism which effected the repression" [*354*].

The superego according to Freud arises in relation to the child's task of repressing Oedipal wishes, namely sexual desires for the parent of the opposite sex and hostility toward the rival parent of the same sex. In order to effect this repression, the child identifies with the moral standards of the father, a task made easier by the fact that this event "takes place in the prehistory of every person" [*134*]. The final outcome of this repression and of the incorporation of the father's moral tabus against sexual expression leads to the formation of the superego, which in effect becomes the "heir to the Oedipus complex" [*134*].

Evidence for the existence of an Oedipus complex is entirely impressionistic and is based upon retrospective clinical material. No unequivocal empirical findings are available which indicate that hostility toward parents of the opposite sex is derived from sexual rivalry; in fact, studies of preference for parents in young children invariably show that the mother is preferred by both boys and girls [*362*]. The alleged universality of the Oedipal complex has been undermined by Malinowski's findings which suggest that hostility between father and son is not present in a culture where the maternal uncle happens to be the authority figure [*265*]. The phylogenicity of such complex and specific urges and identifications is also highly untenable on theoretical grounds (see pp. 5-6).

The concept of superego, lastly, ignores all of the developmental evidence available on the growth of conscience—from complete infantile amorality to a sense of moral responsibility based first on fear of punishment, later on uncritical satellization, and finally on rational notions of moral reciprocity and functionalism. It is a static concept which makes no allowances for the fact that the nature of conscience keeps on shifting as

> "the original frames derived from the parents sooner or later prove themselves inadequate for any satisfactory adjustment to the group

situation. These frames are, then, at least in part, discarded in favor of new standards imposed on the individual by his relationship to others in the group. . . . Moral codes can and do arise spontaneously in children's social groups. . . . These results of Piaget together with the data from cultural anthropology which show the extreme variation of the Oedipus complex even within a single culture indicate that the psychoanalytic concept of the universal development of a 'superego' in human beings has no basis in fact as a special part of the ego with a special function" [*354*].

Mowrer's Formulation of Conscience[7]

Although Mowrer still uses the terms *conscience* and *superego* interchangeably, his concept of conscience is much closer to the developmental picture we have sketched above than to the psychoanalytic formula. He breaks decisively with the Freudian doctrine that the superego is the "heir of the Oedipus complex," and relates conscience formation to that aspect of the parent-child relationship implicated in the child's acceptance of the parents' authority role. He postulates no phylogenetic impulses of sex desire for one parent and a combination of hostility for and identification with the other parent.

> "There is no doubt that in many cultures most of the content of conscience in the effectively socialized person is formed by the internalization of parental demands. . . . [However] in some cultures the value standards of grandparents or of age mates seem to be absorbed at least equally with those of parents" [*287*].

Mowrer, however, overvalues the importance of the "authority crisis" in psychosocial development that occurs between the first and second years of life, equating it to the more inclusive crisis of ego devaluation. At this time much more happens in terms of ego development than the fact that the parents suddenly become demanding, punitive and authoritarian. These changes in the quality of the parent-child relationship can be subsumed under the more general transformations that occur in the child's source of ego status and in his notions of volitional omnipotence and independence. Hence to regard the child's problem of coping with parental authority as the crucial fulcrum upon which the fate of his later personality development rests is to view the significance of conscience development out of context and out of perspective. The only correlative aspects of ego development which Mowrer considers at this time are various psychomotor, imitative and identification functions related to the acquisition of executive independence.

The same criticism applies to Mowrer's conception of the resolution of this initial crisis in ego development. Acceptance of parental moral values is only a component part of the entire series of personality changes that occur as a result of satellization. The process of resolution does not occur suddenly as Mowrer implies, but in the course of two distinct stages. The first involves the correction of a misperception of volitional omnipotence (based upon a misinterpretation of parental altruism) and the second involves the acquisition of a more realistic self-perception of executive competence. Also, contrary to Mowrer's assumption, in the case of satellizers, the acceptance of parental authority and discipline usually does not produce much anxiety because of the child's underlying feeling of security; the symptoms of anxiety are overshadowed by those of rage and negativism.

By thus overemphasizing the significance of the "authority crisis," Mowrer is led to the position that problems of conscience and guilt and the repression of same are central for the pathogenesis of neurosis (see page 327). The normal child, he holds, resolves the authority crisis by internalizing the standards of the parent and integrating them with his ego. The potential psychopath, on the other hand, rejects or reverses the moral standards of his parents; while the future neurotic internalizes parental moral authority but is unable to assimilate and integrate it with his ego, i.e., he tends to repress too much of the guilt and fear of punishment resulting from his own hostility and misconduct. As a consequence of such repression, guilt and fear become transformed into anxiety, which in turn inspires a host of symptoms concerned with anxiety reduction.

A critique of this "guilt theory" of anxiety has been presented elsewhere (see page 363). However, two points mentioned previously but not in this particular context, bear repetition here: (1) There is little empirical evidence to substantiate the belief that genuine and sustained feelings of guilt and remorse occur in the age period from two to four; and (2) largely for this reason, repression is not an important adjustive mechanism at this time.[8] Hence the satellizing child's feelings of hostility toward parents neither give rise to serious remorse nor appear to undergo much repression, as can be easily observed in most normal households. Such repression is more common in non-satellizers—not because of guilt feelings, but because reprisal is feared. And if both guilt and repression are not particularly significant for personality development during this age period, the developmental basis of Mowrer's concept of neurosis in conscience formation cannot be very tenable.

CONSCIENCE AND GUILT

Summary of Psychological Processes Underlying Conscience

We have employed the term "conscience" in a generic sense as referring to that aspect of ego structure concerned with the cognitive-emotional organization of moral values. As the outcome of an elaborate developmental process, a set of internalized moral standards is built up in relation to the interpersonal relationships of the child's life. In this process of conscience acquisition, the child is more than a passive recipient. It is true that he accepts values from those who discipline him; but in the process of internalization, the norms he adopts are modified by his own individuality and are endowed with qualities which they originally did not possess. Functionally, therefore, the rules and the role of the disciplinarian do not operate as the latter sees them, but as they appear in the eyes of the child who projects them into reality.

Considered in this non-reified light, the operation of conscience can be seen to depend upon a number of underlying psychological processes. Since these component processes mature at different rates and vary in relevance and importance during the various developmental stages of conscience formation—even failing to evolve at all in certain cases of aberrant development—it is not possible to regard all of them as indispensable for the functioning of conscience. Also, as Cameron emphasizes, "conscience is rarely a completely consistent and coherent system of behavior" [*61*].

To begin with, the operation of conscience presupposes a capacity to anticipate unpleasant consequences. Regardless of whether the deterrent is punishment, insecurity, anxiety or guilt it could not lead to inhibitory control of behavior if the child were not able to project the consequences of his actions into imagination in advance of their execution. However, once this power to anticipate is acquired, it cannot become very effective in the functioning of conscience until self-restraint becomes possible. The acquisition of inhibitory self-control is a very gradual process which parallels the growth of the ability to endure postponement of immediate hedonistic gratification. Implicit in the development of self-control is the proposition that there is a counter-need potent enough to enable learning to occur in a direction opposite to the motivational influence exerted by hedonistic needs. In the course of ego development the nature of this need varies from avoidance of pain and disapproval to insuring the continued basis of derived status and the avoidance of guilt feelings.

Conscience formation also implies the ability to internalize values, by which is meant the capacity to assimilate external standards, or to evolve new standards which in either case exert a relatively stable *internal* directional influence on behavior. Such internalization can occur either through the satellizing, incorporative or exploratory orientations. The process of internalization in relation to conscience development differs from the internalization of any other value only in the fact that a moral issue is involved.

The assimilation of moral values, however, does not necessarily mean that these values will influence behavior in any stable and systematic fashion until a sense of obligation or "oughtness" evolves [*185*]. The sense of obligation refers to the individual's feeling of duty or responsibility to conform to or abide by his internalized code of moral values in his own personal behavior. Developmentally this step appears after the internalization of other values. The child believes that certain actions are good or bad before he feels that he "ought" not do them himself. As Hollingworth so succinctly puts it, "the key to morals or ethics is the feeling of obligation, the recognition of imperatives in thought and action. It is the sense of obligation that transforms mere behavior into conduct" [*185*].

The basis of the sense of obligation also changes with age and personality development. In the satellizing era, it is a component function of a generally subservient attitude of sharing in and desiring to retain derived status, of loyalty, unilateral accountability and a need for approval. Thereafter these aspects of obligation acquire a residual substrate function, and more abstract cognitive factors divorced from the parent-child relationship become more prominent, i.e., concepts of justice, equity and reciprocal duty; responsibility to group, social class, and society. Like every other moral value, the sense of obligation also acquires more or less stability and effectiveness in regulating behavior in accordance with the degree of internalization it undergoes.

The feeling of obligation provides the central cognitive-emotional strand of the fabric of conscience. It is the unifying factor welding together the various moral values of the individual into an organized system of behavior. It gives generality and genotypic consistency to moral conduct by entering into every moral decision he makes. Whether or not he refrains from committing an immoral act depends on more than the relative strengths of the positive valence of the latter and the deterrent influence of the relevant moral principle involved. The *total* inhibitory control that can be employed in this situation is rather the strength of the particular moral value multiplied by a general factor represented by the effectiveness and stability of the sense of obligation. It is the association of inhibitory control with this general feeling of moral obligation that gives to conscience its apparent substantive properties, and provides the individual with a powerful regulatory mechanism over his behavior that is very similar to the philosophical concept of "free will" in the moral sense of the term. We shall return to this theme later in our discussion of moral accountability and culpability.

The final psychological process involved in the operation of conscience is the self-critical faculty. Without this capacity for realistically appraising one's own intentions and behavior in the light of internalized moral principles, it is neither possible to inhibit immoral actions nor to experience guilt after they are executed. The importance of the self-critical faculty in the development of conscience can be seen in the fact that the latter remains in a rudimentary state until the former is reasonably well advanced (age five to eight). When self-criticism can be employed, guilt feelings become possible since these are a reaction to the perception of a discrepancy between one's own behavior and the moral standards in relation to which a sense of obligation exists.

Guilt, hence, is less of a psychological process underlying or necessary for the operation of conscience than it is a cognitive-emotional reaction of the individual to the actual functioning of conscience in a situation where perceived disparity exists between behavior and obligation. The core ingredient of guilt is the feeling of shame, which Gardner Murphy describes as a "collapse in the usual mechanism of adequate self-portraiture and an immobilization in helplessness with or without an appeal for renewal of status" [*288*]. In addition to shame, guilt includes the feelings of self-reproach, self-disgust, self-contempt, remorse and various characteristic visceral and vasomotor responses. Phylogenetically, shame is not a distinctively human response since it undoubtedly occurs in animals such as dogs who are able to enter into satellizing-like relationships with human beings. This means that on an emotional plane at least, it is possible to think of conscience in animals providing that the level of abstraction is kept sufficiently low.

Through the processes of retrospective association and anticipation guilt tends to be incorporated into the behavioral system of conscience, providing it with some of its most distinctive identifying features and substantive qualities. Behavior leading to guilt evokes the anticipation that retribution will be inevitable either through the suffering inherent in guilt feelings, the seeking out of social punishment as means of guilt-reduction, or through the medium of a supernatural agency. The inevitability of punishment, therefore, is one of the characteristic properties of conscience reactions [*287*].

Guilt-Reduction as Motivation

Guilt feelings have already been discussed as a cause of symptomatic anxiety (see page 362). In the everyday behavior of human beings it is perfectly apparent that self-justification constitutes an impelling and ubiquitous motivation. The picture of self as shameful and contemptuous is highly threatening to self-esteem and is productive of considerable anxiety. Hence we can expect that guilt-reduction mechanisms will for the most part parallel those we have already catalogued for anxiety-reduction (see pp. 384-386).

The most commonly used mechanism of guilt-reduction is repression. Contrary to Mowrer's assumption, however, repression of guilt is not the primary cause of even symptomatic anxiety, but is mainly a consequence of it. Conscious guilt is repressed because it is anxiety-producing. This repression in turn intensifies the anxiety not because of some mysterious reason associated with "the return of the repressed," as Mowrer claims, but because repression obviates the possibility of punishment, confession, expiation and other guilt-reduction mechanisms. It is true that repression can never be complete, as demonstrated, for example, by the appearance of repressed guilt feelings in dreams. This incompleteness of repression, however, does not provide a convincing explanation for the conversion of guilt into anxiety since we know (a) that conscious guilt can be productive of anxiety, and (b) that repression interferes with the evolution of guilt reduction mechanisms.

Projection of guilt is a more effective means of guilt reduction, since in this fashion accountability is not merely repressed but is actually disowned by perceiving the blame elsewhere. This, of course, involves distortion of evidence similar to what happens in rationalization. Through depersonalization, amnesic states, and states of multiple personality it is possible to divorce segments of behavior from the sense of personal identity and thereby to disown all connection with the associated guilt. Obsessions displace concern away from the genuine source of guilt feelings and monopolize the field of consciousness with relatively innocuous material, whereas compulsions may often symbolize a form of expiation. In another type of displacement noted by Fromm, "a person may feel consciously guilty for not pleasing authorities, while 'unconsciously' he feels guilty for not living up to his own expectations of himself" [*142*].

More direct forms of guilt reduction include punishment, confession and expiation, all of which are extensively employed by various religions. Social punishment, i.e., that form which is imposed from without or made known to others, can confer almost complete absolution. Confession involves the preliminary phase of punishment: Self-culpability is exposed to others so that their condemnation can be secured in place of self-condemnation which has less guilt-reducing properties. A variant of this mechanism is found in the self-accusatory auditory hallucination. It is more guilt-reducing for a latent homosexual to hear external voices accusing him of being a "loathesome fairy" than to accuse himself of the same tendency. A patient of the writer's ceased hearing such voices after gaining insight into this mechanism, but soon began to hear motors humming. When in turn this symbolic substitution was understood, the motors vanished only to be replaced by overt symptoms of anxiety. Expiation is a form of punishment emphasizing restitution or exaggeration of the particular moral trait or virtue in relation to which a sense of guilt is experienced. A typical example of the latter variety is the adjustive mechanism known as reaction-formation, e.g., the mother who feels excessively guilty for rejecting tendencies may become inflexibly oversolicitous toward her child.

Various formal and culturally-stereotyped varieties of guilt- reduction are also available, such as verbal magic, pseudo-remorse, and hypocritical religious observance. Thus, many persons tend to believe that if they make a formal, verbalistic show of remorse, confession, and self-castigation, their guilt is absolved. The insincerity of this maneuver is revealed by the fact that their remarks are offered as a preface to the actual execution of the behavior that is verbally condemned.

The more morally bankrupt certain people become—the more incapable of experiencing genuine feelings of guilt—the more they seek out the formal moral respectability that comes with ritualistic religious observances. They wish to continue their immoral practices and still enjoy a reputation for righteousness. Sometimes, of course, they must suffer continuous chastisement by hearing their hypocrisy berated by the minister. But even this does not phase them. Furthest from their thoughts is a desire for genuine reform, and at the same time they are too shameless to be offended by moral reproach. What happens, therefore, is a sentimental orgy in which tears of pseudo-remorse and self-pity are shed as their calumny is exposed; and once having shed these tears they are convinced that they are morally acquitted and entitled to pursue the same unprincipled path.

It is not necessary to believe, however, that all guilt feelings are intolerable and must somehow be repressed, disowned, rationalized, confessed, expiated for, etc. In the same sense that there is tolerance for conscious anxiety, there is tolerance for conscious guilt, the degree of tolerance, of course, being subject to wide individual differences. Man's portrait of himself need not be free of all moral blemishes. Hence, a good deal of ordinary guilt can be acknowledged on a conscious level and taken in stride without any efforts made toward guilt reduction. There is reason to believe that the intrinsically secure person who is moderately self-sufficient possesses more guilt tolerance than either the insecure or the overly dependent individual.

In our culture we tend to underestimate man's capacity for moral depravity.[9] We tend to assume that people could not conceivably be guilty of certain immoral intentions and practices because if they were, "how could they possibly live with themselves?" And if we do admit such a possibility, we reveal the impact of psychoanalytic doctrine and moral relativism on our thinking by blaming "unconscious motives," and by absolving the individual from moral accountability on the grounds that he is the innocent product (victim) of his heredity and environment and could not possibly have acted in any other way.

Several alternative explanations, however, should be considered. In the first place, most people can tolerate more conscious guilt than we are willing to concede; we have exaggerated man's need for perceiving himself as completely untainted in a moral sense. Secondly, many times when we think that a person should be experiencing guilt feelings he really is not for one or both of two good reasons: (1) No real internalization of moral obligation has taken place; or (2) self-criticism is inhibited to the point where no discrepancy can be perceived between behavior and obligation, regardless of how flagrant the disparity may appear to others. It is necessary to differentiate this latter situation from instances in which (a) guilt is actually experienced but wrong-doing is still denied because of pride, inability to admit being in the wrong, and outright intellectual dishonesty; and (b) guilt occurs but is rationalized away without conscious awareness of distortion or misrepresentation of facts.

The mental hygiene value of keeping guilt on a conscious level parallels the advantages of dealing with anxiety on the same basis:

The possibilities of evolving constructive solutions are greatly enhanced. In the case of the former, this means learning to bear and live with one's quota of guilt while taking such realistic preventitive and restitutive measures as are indicated. Where legitimate compromises with moral principle are clearly necessary, the reasons for same should be unambiguously perceived and acknowledged as such rather than rationalized on a more acceptable basis. In this way it is possible to retain one's moral code intact under the most trying of circumstances. Unless the reasons for unavoidable moral expediency are kept clearly in mind, habituation to and corruption by same tend to occur; and what starts out as a reluctant maneuver under duress ends up by becoming the individual's characteristic mode of ethical behavior.

Children generally in contradistinction to adults are not capable of making this type of adjustment. Being unable to appreciate or evaluate the issues involved in making inescapable moral compromises, they are more likely to actually assimilate rather than simulate acceptance of the inferior ethical alternative represented by the compromise. We are witnessing just such a situation today in Germany. Many adults were able to survive the Hitlerian years morally unscathed, whereas the children who grew up at the time remain completely indoctrinated.

In our present moral climate where expediency enjoys such vogue, the practitioners thereof try to rationalize its use by exaggerating the cultural necessity for conformity, deference to authority, and unprincipled opportunism if one is to "get ahead." Granted that this situation is largely as pictured, much depends on how *far* "ahead" one wishes to get if "hunting with the hounds" and currying favor with those who push others around seem to be preconditions for same. At any rate there is more cultural tolerance for independence and non-conformity than these persons are willing to concede, and even some chance of winning admiration in the process.

When this is pointed out, the last defense that will usually be offered is insecurity. Although this may be ostensibly true, it is not the sole reason. Unprincipled ambition is the main motivation, as proved by the fact that the attainment of security usually does not put an end to but rather intensifies moral expediency.

ABERRANT CONSCIENCE DEVELOPMENT IN SATELLIZERS

Satellizing abnormalities in conscience development are most serious in the underdominated child. Three mutually reinforcing conditions make it very difficult for him to acquire a concept of personal moral obligation. In the first place, an overly permissive and lax atmosphere encourages perpetuation of the infantile need for immediate hedonistic gratification. No experience is acquired in postponing the satisfaction of such needs or in controlling agressive reactions to frustration. Inadequate external supports are provided for the internalization of moral standards. Hence the acquisition of a sense of obligation is retarded both by the existence of strong counter-needs and by the absence of any outer controls to temper these needs. Secondly, implicit in the underdominating parent's attitude is the suggestion that the child is a specially privileged person immune from the obligations that apply to ordinary people. Thirdly, the underdominated child is not encouraged to develop a realistic self-critical faculty and hence fails to appraise his behavioral deviations with adequate severity.

Langdon and Stout's study of well-adjusted children shows that the parents of such children tend to be reasonably firm and consistent in their discipline, to stress cooperative and reciprocal principles of moral obligation, and to demand responsible conduct in accordance with the child's developmental capacities. In addition these parents uniformly provide positive moral instruction in the child's dealings with others [*238*]. Supportive evidence in the same direction is the finding by Sheldon and Eleanor Glueck that laxity and inconsistency in paternal discipline are more commonly found in delinquent than in matched non-delinquent youths drawn from the same social environment[10] [*154*].

The advantages of firm, consistent and realistic parental discipline are quite apparent: The child acquires a sense of security in his value orientation. He knows what is expected of him and how far he can go. Undue temptation to "test the limits" is not present. He is not required to bear a heavy burden of guilt for unrestrained aggression, guilt that cannot even be absolved because of parental reluctance to punish. He is able to apply moral standards to the special requirements of specific situations without being rigid and absolutistic. This is not true, for example, in the case of lower-class children, who tend to be trained inconsistently in middle-class values. Such children are more authoritarian and inflexible than their contemporaries from upper socio-economic groups in their moral judgments of lying, stealing and obedience [*166*]. This points to the conclusion that values which are accepted only half-heartedly and under inconsistent circumstances must be adhered to rigidly if they are to be maintained at all.

In the moral development of underdominated children some comfort can be gained from the fact that in the middle and late years of childhood there is a possibility of their satellizing in relation to parent surrogates who can provide more satisfactory conditions for the assimilation of moral obligation. There is in addition the mitigating factor that the goal of immoral behavior is usually directed toward hedonistic self-indulgence rather than toward ruthless self-aggrandizement at the expense of others.

In overprotected and overdominated children, defects in conscience development are apt to be less serious. A sense of moral obligation develops but tends to remain at the level of loyalty to parents instead of being replaced by feelings of obligation to society as a whole and to rationally derived principles of ethics. Moral values also tend to remain relatively specific because of insufficiently diversified experience to allow for the abstraction of general concepts. Excessive subservience and loyalty to parents may completely inhibit the influence of rational considerations. On the other hand, allegiance to parental values may be somewhat limited to the latter's physical presence. Not infrequently in such a situation, the death of the parent leads to sudden moral collapse in the child. But at the very worst, the ensuing delinquency consists of self-indulgent, immature behavior. Because infantile moral irresponsibility is largely attenuated in the course of acquiring a satellizing sense of obligation, misbehavior is seldom viciously or aggressively antisocial.

DEVELOPMENT OF CONSCIENCE IN NON-SATELLIZERS

Conscience development in non-satellizers differs both in process and outcome from the picture we have drawn thus far for satellizers. This much is obvious: If two main component phases of the phenomenon in the latter are characterized as "satellizing" and "desatellizing" respectively, the mechanisms of conscience formation must certainly be radically different if satellization does not occur in the first place. The abnormalities in growth of conscience that accompany non-satellization are merely part of the total picture of ego hypertrophy that characterizes such cases. On the positive side, the importance of parental affection, understanding and patience for good adjustment in children is brought out in such studies as Langdon and Stout's [*238*]. On the other hand, a common attitude in narcissistic, rejecting parents is extreme tolerance for and condoning of antisocial behavior in their children as long as such behavior does not cause annoyance to them. Also on the negative side there is evidence that delinquency occurs more frequently when parents are neglectful and make children feel unloved and unwanted, and when home life is unintegrated [*154*]. Delinquent girls judge their fathers as lacking in solicitude, affection and concern for their futures, and as harsh, rejecting disciplinarians. [*400*].

Prior to the period when satellization normally occurs, the non-satellizer's moral development is not distinguished in any way from the satellizer's. In the presatellizing stage, infantile irresponsibility is curbed on the basis of avoiding pain, deprivation and insecurity. However, in the early and later satellizing stages, instead of a sense of obligation developing in relation to a general attitude of value subservience, loyalty, and need for approval and retention of derived status, the non-satellizer continues to conform to parental standards for the same expediential reasons as during infancy. He is sensitive to prestige suggestion at the hands of parents, but only because he recognizes the latter's objectively greater knowledge and competence—not because he is motivated by a strong need to unconditionally reflect their value judgments. Fear of deprivation and loss of succorance rather than guilt avoidance keep him in line and check the overt expression of his hostility and aggression. Moral obligations are assimilated on a selective basis only, that is, if they are perceived as leading to ego enhancement.

In his interpersonal and peer-group relationships, the non-satellizing child is more eager for and more disposed to demand reciprocal moral obligation and the application of functional concepts of ethical law. This leads to the use of the exploratory orientation in the discovery of principles of justice and equity which are then internalized as moral obligations. This internalization, however, is highly precarious since (a) infantile irresponsibility has never been attenuated by strong, emotionally charged feelings of obligation in relation to significant individuals in the child's interpersonal world; and (b) powerful needs for ego enhancement are often in conflict with the content and goals of ethical norms. Under the pressure of such conditions, moral obligation stands a good chance of collapsing. When this occurs, ethical values as such are not repudiated since the demands of expediency require at least external conformity to group norms. Also, it is in his interest for other persons to behave morally since this adds to his feeling of security.

The needs of ego aggrandizement rather are served in this conflict situation by one of two devices: (a) selective inhibition of the self-critical faculty with resulting inability to perceive obvious disparity between principles and behavior where it is convenient to be blind to same; and (b) acceptance of the unique status of being such an unusual person that one is *above* the law which holds for *ordinary* people. This latter process is facilitated by pre-existing ego hypertrophy. A famous exposition of this philosophical position is given by Dostoievsky's character Raskolnikov in the well-known novel, "Crime and Punishment." Institutionally it has been expressed in the National Socialist doctrine of the "Herrenvolk."

Sometimes, however, where the non-satellizing sense of obligation (acquired through the exploratory orientation) is unusually strong, the conflict is resolved in the other direction through the mechanism of reaction-formation. The component aspects of this mechanism include conscious realization of the existence of motives and attitudes which are at variance with internalized moral beliefs, shocked abhorrence at this discovery, violent repudiation of these unacceptable feelings, and a strong conscious determination to foster behavior which is completely antithetical in character.

There is no doubt but that reaction-formation can alter considerably both the goal and content of a good part of any individual's moral conduct. Nevertheless, because of the absence of a satellizing foundation, and complete reliance on whatever emotional supports can be garnered for moral values derived on rational grounds, it presents many elements of instability: (1) The original antisocial and morally irresponsible tendencies are not wholly rejected but merely suppressed. (2) Acceptance of the antithetical values tends to be ambivalent because of strong competing prestige needs associated with ego hypertrophy. (3) Incomplete acceptance of the moral alternative may lead to disguised sabotage with surreptitious expression of antisocial trends under the guise of uncompromising virtue, e.g., expressing ruthlessness and cruelty under the banner of patriotism, religion, devotion to duty, etc. (4) Awareness of the underlying strength of the unacceptable attitudes encourages the erection of exaggerated defenses. Afraid to trust himself at all, iron-clad security is sought in rigid tabus instituted against the undesirable behavior, accompanied by a self-conscious over-emphasis of the antithetical moral trait.

Behavior thus becomes unspontaneous, stereotyped and unduly circumscribed. Moral judgment passed on others' conduct tends to be formal and absolutistic rather than related to the relevant situational and personality context in which the genotypic aspects of the behavior could be more fairly evaluated for ethical content. There is no notion of relativity, of extenuating circumstances, of intermediate points between good and evil, or of summation and fusion of parallel and antagonistic tendencies into a resultant vector. Only two antithetical alternatives can be conceived of in the solution of a moral problem. As will be seen later, the operation of reaction-formation in relation to the functioning of the self-critical faculty plays a role in the abrupt shifts in self-evaluation that occur in the manic-depressive psychoses.

In adolescent and adult life, this rational conscience buttressed by the mechanism of reaction-formation constitutes the chief mainspring for moral behavior in non-satellizers. Arrayed against it are the exaggerated demands of ego aggrandizement, the absence of real attenuation of infantile irresponsibility through the formation of satellizing loyalties, the selective operation of moral obligation and of the self-critical faculty, and habituation to and corruption by the practice of expediency (with resultant inability to distinguish between circumstances which make its use inexcusable and conditions under which it is legitimately necessary and even desirable).

This description of the non-satellizing conscience must be qualified somewhat by the differences which exist between rejected and overvalued individuals. In many respects the moral development of the latter is similar to that of underdominated children (see page 454). There is the same lack of pressure for conformity and the same parental implication that the child is immune from ordinary moral obligations. However, the overvalued child is unable to form satellizing relationships outside the home, and the goal of his immoral behavior is more likely to be self-aggrandizingly and aggressively antisocial rather than impulsively hedonistic.

The rejected child, on the other hand, is under greater pressure to conform to parental control which tends to be harsh, severe and demanding. Hence there is greater likelihood that he will either be more conforming outwardly on the basis of expediency, or that he will be openly rebellious and aggressively repudiate the entire parental code of moral values. Even in the first case, there may be covert repudiation of the parents' standards. In instances where the rejecting parent is narcissistic and neglectful, tacit approval is often given to the child's antisocial behavior since the parent is too self-preoccupied to curb it as long as it does not disturb him. Hence in such cases the child displaces the hostility he feels toward the parent to his relationships with other individuals. On the positive side, however, the rejected child possesses a latent capacity for forming satellizing-like relationships which enable him to experience the type of guilt feelings that occur in normally satellizing children.

DELINQUENCY

Approaches to Delinquency

The history of social attitudes toward delinquency, including the various competing philosophies current today, reflects the dilemma society finds itself in when it is forced to make moral judgments regarding guilt, culpability and punishment without any adequate criteria of moral accountability. For most people, delinquency is still a matter of unethical behavior based on inherited moral weakness, an indication that the individual has voluntarily succumbed to the temptation of illegitimately benefiting himself or giving vent to aggressive impulses at the expense of his fellow citizens. However, more sophisticated points of view, namely the legal, psychological and sociological prevail at the level of expert opinion.

The law is primarily concerned with protecting the interests and safety of individuals, groups and society. With this end in view, the most practical assumption to make is that in the absence of evidence to the contrary, unlawful acts are willfully committed and render the offending individual liable to punishment. The strict legal test for responsibility only requires that the accused person know right from wrong and be able to appreciate the nature and quality of his act [*174*]. However, in deference to the recognized contribution of emotional factors to the commission of crime by mentally disordered individuals, certifiable "insanity" itself is often accepted by the judiciary as proof of irresponsibility, and "uncontrollable impulse" as at least a mitigating factor [*174*].

Proponents of the psychological and sociological schools of thought charge that the criterion of "willful and premeditated intent" is entirely irrelevant to the question of moral accountability since it is based on the premise of "free will." Our quarrel with the legal definition of responsibility, on the other hand, rests on other grounds. In the first place, the law is too much concerned with the material and formal rights of individuals and too little concerned with intrinsic immorality. The vast majority of acts of cruelty, injustice and treachery are lawful and unpunishable. Secondly, the application of the test of willfulness and intent is not made in a context of psychological analysis of the personality structure and development of the individual. Instead the actual motivation is frequently obscured by concentration on legalistic niceties and the legal rules of evidence; and final judgment may depend more on technical points in the statutory law and on details of precedent in common law—both of which are essentially irrelevant in most cases since they are not taken into account by the offender—than on considerations of equity and justice. Criteria such as "uncontrollable impulse" also, are vague and often applied in a mechanical fashion without careful consideration being given to their relative weight in the causation of a particular act of delinquency.

According to the undiluted sociological point of view, delinquency is an individual behavioral manifestation of social disorganization and pathology. Individuals whose opportunities for normal personality development and constructive endeavor are frustrated by virtue of poverty, unemployment, slum conditions, etc., react with antisocial behavior. Hence, the argument runs, it is society and not the individual who really is the patient. The latter is deviant only as long as he is exposed to a diseased society. As a single factor theory of delinquency, however, this formulation breaks down in failing to explain why children from optimal social environments become wayward, and why the majority of children in a given slum area do not terminate their careers as adult criminals despite fairly regular participation in delinquent activities during childhood and adolescence.

The psychological (also, psychiatric and psychoanalytic) approach is similar to the sociological in de-emphasizing the role of volitional control, but differs from the latter in locating the main etiological factor in the dynamics of early personality development rather than in social pathology. Psychoanalysts contend that criminal behavior is a symptom of mental disturbance. They view the delinquent as an individual equipped with a poorly developed ego and superego but driven by powerful instinctual forces [*3, 85*]. The psychopath, for example, is seen as fixated in the early narcissistic, sexually polymorphous stage of psychosexual development [*3*]. Although social conditions are recognized as contributing factors, greater stress is placed upon various aspects of the early family situation which impinge upon personality development. Nonanalytic psychologists are more concerned with the influence of the parent-child relationship on the latter's socialization process rather than with its effect on sexual maturation. Both, however, would agree in the belief that delinquency is primarily a problem of disordered personality development arising from unfortunate relationships between the child and significant persons in his psychological field rather than a manifestation of disturbance in grosser patterns of social organization.

In the classification of delinquency to be offered below, two basic assumptions will be made: (1) Delinquency like any other behavioral outcome is a resultant of multiple causality. Relevant variables that must be considered in every case are heredity, personality development, other psychological factors (e.g., intelligence, suggestibility), personality disorder, transitional pressures in development, emotional instability, situational factors, family and social environment, etc. Usually, however, one of these factors is prepotent in a given case, allowing it for purposes of convenience to be placed in one of the categories of the classification. (2) While allowing that psychological and social causes of delinquency can be identified, the writer is nevertheless in agreement with the moral and legal approaches to the problem in believing that the identification of the effective cause in an individual case does not necessarily absolve the offender from moral accountability. Objectively valid criteria of culpability are discoverable.

> "There has been too great a tendency in modern psychological thinking about criminality toward divorcing all behavior of its ethical content. In other words, it seems just as one-sided to ascribe all antisocial behavior to underlying psychological disturbances as to see in it only a manifestation of basic immorality. From the standpoint of individual behavior, there is a moral aspect to most purposeful human activity, the psychological reality of which cannot be ignored. And while this aspect is so closely interwoven with the aspect of psychological disturbance that the two can hardly be separated, the relative significance of each in a given case of delinquency is usually clear enough to allow some judgment as to the individual's moral and legal accountability" [*23*].

In the concluding section of this chapter, several hypotheses directed toward this goal will be offered.

Classification of Delinquency

TABLE 5.—*Classification of Delinquency*

I. Delinquency Attributable to Defects in Personality Development
  - A. In Non-Satellizers ("ego hypertrophy" delinquency)
    1. Aggressive, antisocial psychopath
    2. Rejected and overvalued individuals
  - B. In Satellizers ("inadequate psychopath")
    1. Underdominated individuals
    2. Overprotected and overdominated individuals

II. Delinquency Attributable to Transitional Pressures of Adolescence

1. Emotional instability referable to hormonal changes, somatic deviations, status deprivation, etc.
2. Experimentation with moral values; moral confusion, cynicism and disenchantment
3. Peer-group structure and anti-adult orientation

III. Other Psychological Factors Contributing to Delinquency

1. Personality disorder; e.g., psychosis, neurosis
2. Intellectual deficit
3. Hypersuggestibility
4. Hostility and destructiveness as defense and status-getting mechanisms
5. Expiatory need for punishment due to underlying guilt feelings

IV. Social Factors Contributing to Delinquency

1. Status deprivation on basis of class membership, racial or ethnic and religious affiliation
2. Predominant exposure to delinquent moral values in home, peer group and adult culture
3. Segregation of underprivileged youth in socially disorganized areas with opportunity for delinquent gang activities
4. Conditions of prolonged economic exigency; e.g., poverty, unemployment

The third and fourth main categories of this classification are outside the scope of this volume and will not be discussed here except in passing. It is to be noted that they are considered as contributing rather than as effective causes, since it is our contention that in the absence of adequate predisposing factors in personality development, they would be insufficient of themselves to produce permanent delinquency. This interpretation is in accord with the generally accepted fact that the type of delinquency characteristic of disorganized urban areas is a transitory phenomenon for most individuals which is not carried over into adult life. It points to the absence of complete homogeneity in exposure to moral values within a single social class; for despite geographical segregation and continual reinforcement of lower-class value systems, the moral code of the dominant middle-class is eventually adopted by the majority of erstwhile slum dwellers.

Even in the preadolescent and adolescent period, some of the youths in these areas are more heavily influenced by middle-class values than they are by the prevailing norms in their own social class group. While this may be a consequence of exclusion from the peer culture, it may also be a cause of same. We have already referred to the fact that predatory gang behavior tends to become fixed when status deprivation is perceived by the adolescent as the outcome of social discrimination attributable to such permanent characteristics as racial origin instead of as a self-limited affliction shared by all individuals in a given age group.

Sporadic delinquency is also common enough in adolescence even without the contributing influence of adverse social conditions. Prolonged status deprivation leads to an anti-adult orientation in the peer group which sometimes explodes violently in the form of aggressive, antisocial activity. Adolescent emotional instability takes this aggressive form more readily if it is compounded by group interaction, since group resistance is much more effective than individual rebellion and provides moral sanction and anonymity to the participant. The mere pressure for conformity to group norms in adolescence is often sufficient to provoke occasional acts of delinquency in youths who otherwise have high moral standards. However, where there tends to be no large-scale segregation by social class, as in small towns and villages, organized delinquent gangs are not generally found [*171*].

Another factor facilitating the development of delinquent trends in adolescents is the moral confusion and ethical laxity they perceive in the culture at large. Since at this time the sense of moral obligation becomes divorced from parental loyalties, and emulatory models for a rational and reciprocal ethical code are eagerly sought on a societal basis, the moral vacuum tends, unfortunately, to be filled by the readiest and most visible set of standards available.

Delinquency which is rooted in aberrations of conscience development because of deviant parent-child relationships has a far more serious prognosis. In the preceding two sections we have considered the developmental bases for delinquent behavior in satellizers and non-satellizers respectively, and the types of delinquent mechanisms likely to occur in each personality type. However, a relatively rare type of delinquent found among non-satellizers still awaits description—the aggressive antisocial psychopath. This type of individual corresponds to the classic description of "psychopathic personality" who from an early age manifests cruel, impulsive, ruthless, vindictive, and unfeeling tendencies devoid of any remorse or guilt feelings. Such cases are characterized by an early history of parental rejection. However, the needs for counteraggression and vengeance are so great that considerations of expediency are cast aside, and complete and overt rebellion against parental standards takes place. Not only does a sense of personal moral obligation fail to develop, but also any internalization of ethical values whatsoever. The same hostile, rebellious attitude is later carried over in relation to social norms, which the individual identifies with the hateful figures of his parents. Thus, there is no possibility of developing a sense of justice or obligation on rational grounds. Even the interests of self-aggrandizement are subordinated to the need for wanton destructiveness and aggressive retaliation against moral or legal authority.

THE PROBLEM OF MORAL ACCOUNTABILITY[11]

When Oscar Wilde wrote his famous "Ballad of Reading Gaol," decrying man's right to pass moral judgment on the actions of his fellow-man, little did he realize that his position would become so widely accepted only a half century later by social scientists and philosophers concerned with human behavior. The credo of the modern social scientist is predominantly deterministic. It repudiates the notion of free will as reactionary and unscientific, and regards the practice of passing moral judgment as abhorrent, unpsychological, and tinged with the presumption of god-like omniscience. The moral character of an individual is presumed to be shaped by forces beyond his control and, therefore, immune from any judgmental process with ethical implications. Immoral behavior is held to be no different from any other kind of undesirable behavior. It can only be understood psychologically as a type of adjustment mechanism. Caroline Zachry's appraisal of delinquency, for example, is thoroughly representative of current non-legal professional opinion.

> "To isolate certain forms of emotional disturbance and to label them with a term of opprobrium is both scientifically inaccurate and inimical

to the interests of youth. It presupposes an attitude of sitting in moral judgment, of attaching blame for behavior which should be considered as a symptom of disturbance" [*407*].

Fromm's position on moral accountability is particularly interesting in view of the fact that one of the two basic assumptions of his "humanistic ethics" is "the principle that only man himself can determine the criterion for virtue and sin, and not an authority transcending him" [*142*]. Nevertheless he too shies away from the problem of moral responsibility on the grounds that it presupposes "free will." He also vehemently objects to the "absolving" and "condemning" aspects of moral judgment as "tinged by the old concept of a judging god" [*142*], failing to see the inconsistency between this position and the above-quoted proposition on which his ethical system is largely based. Surely if man himself is privileged to determine what is good and evil, he cannot be accused of arrogating prerogatives of transcendental authority by merely taking the next logical step of appraising accountability for wrong-doing. The only type of moral judgment that Fromm would allow begs the question of accountability.

> "Humanistic judgment of ethical values has the same logical character as a rational judgment in general. In making value judgments, one judges facts and does not feel one is godlike, superior and entitled to condemn or forgive. A judgment that a person is destructive, greedy, jealous, envious is not different from a physician's statement about a dysfunction of the heart or lungs. Suppose we have to judge a murderer whom we know to be a pathological case. . . . We can understand how and why he became what he is, but we can also judge him as to what he is. . . . Even if one knows that the odds against the person were overwhelming . . . the judgment about him remains the same. If one fully understands all the circumstances which made him as he is, one may have compassion for him; yet this compassion does not alter the validity of the judgment. Understanding a person does not mean condoning; it only means that one does not accuse him as if one were God or a judge placed above him" [*142*].

We can applaud Fromm's statement that "understanding does not mean condoning," but the kind of judgment he is willing make is devoid of moral content. In his own words, Fromm equates the problem of judging immoral behavior with judging the quality of a painting or a pair of shoes [*142*]. In effect, this approximates Zachry's position that immorality is no different from any other unfortunate adjustment mechanism. To stop at the point of judging behavior as poor in moral quality without attempting to affix accountability is tantamount to saying that moral lapses are to be regarded no more seriously than designing shoes of inferior workmanship or evolving hysterical symptoms that are poor in adjustive quality. It robs the process of "moral judgment" of any semblance of moral content.

Fromm is led to this position by believing implicitly that

"the psychologist is compelled to subscribe to determinism. . . . The child starts his life in an indifferent moral state. . . . His character is shaped by external influences which are most powerful in the early years of his life when he has neither the knowledge nor the power to change the circumstances which determine his character. . . . If we assume that the moral qualities of a person are rooted in his character, is it not true then that since he has no freedom in shaping his character he cannot be judged?"

"Our motives are an outcome of the particular blend of forces operating on our character. Each time we make a decision it is determined by the good or evil forces respectively which are dominant. . . . The will is not an abstract power of man which he possesses apart from his character. On the contrary, the will is nothing but the expression of his character. . . . Even if we would base moral judgment on the premise that a person could have acted differently, the constitutional and environmental factors which make for the development of his character are so numerous and complex that it is impossible, for all practical purposes, to arrive at a conclusive judgment whether or not he could have developed differently" [*142*].

Fromm tempers this determinism slightly by disavowing fatalism.

"Man, while like all other creatures subject to forces which determine him, is the only creature endowed with reason, the only being who is capable of understanding the very forces which he is subjected to, and who by his understanding can take an active part in his own fate and strengthen those elements which strive for the good. . . . We are there-

> fore not helpless victims of circumstance; we are indeed able to change and to influence forces inside and outside ourselves and to control, at least to some extent, the conditions which play upon us" [*142*].

If this is the case, if man can partly control his own destiny, Fromm does not explain why failure to take the proper steps should not be grounds for moral culpability.

Our main quarrel with determinism, however, rests on a more general premise. Contrary to Fromm's assertion, the psychologist is not required to accept the view that the will is not an independent force but merely the executioner of the dominant motive impinging upon the behavioral field—that "free will" is an illusion which confounds awareness of the outcome of the struggle between conflicting forces with the power to determine the outcome. In our study of the development of conscience, we have traced the gradual evolution of a generalized sense of moral obligation. In association with its executive arm of inhibitory self-control, this feeling of obligation constitutes a more or less consistent system of behavior with considerable generality of function that is implicated in every moral decision. The outcome of the latter is not merely a reflection of the relative strengths of a given moral value and its opposing motive, but also of the strength of the generalized sense of obligation to abide by *all* moral values and the vigor of its associated volitional counterpart.

The writer is aware of the fact that a genetic theory of conscience not only provides a basis for ethical conduct and moral accountability, but also establishes a basis in the past for immoral behavior which *was* beyond the individual's control at the time that it impinged on his ethical development.[12] This fact is undeniable and is frequently used as an argument for determinism. In the past history of every individual can be found events which explain his failure to behave morally in certain situations and enable one to predict how he will act in the future. However, the possibility of explaining and predicting an individual's moral lapses on the basis of his developmental history bears no relevance to the problem of moral accountability which requires a judgment with respect to the *present* situation. Regardless of events beyond his control that once transpired, if he can presently recognize a moral obligation and is physically and psychologically capable of exercising inhibitory control, he is accountable for his misdeeds. If in addition a genetic explanation is available for same, it provides a nice demonstration of the fact that behavior, like all events in nature, has causal antecedents (i.e., is deterministic). But what has this to do with moral accountability? Acceptance of behavioral determinism does not oblige one to repudiate the doctrine of responsibility for moral behavior.

If this hypothesis is correct, moral culpability exists whenever the possibility of exercising inhibitory control is present in an ethical problem but nevertheless fails to be exercised. If motives cannot be effectively combatted by volitional restraint because of overpowering emotion, the question of accountability obviously becomes more complicated. The defense of "uncontrollable impulse" generally means that suppression was originally possible but was surrendered to indulgence under special extenuating circumstances. In such cases, culpability is present although undoubtedly in lesser degree than in instances where more deliberate choice was possible. However, lack of awareness of the "true" motives for a misdeed is no defense as long as moral restraint can be exercised.[12] That a murderer fails to appreciate that his hostility is a reaction against parental rejection no more absolves him of responsibility for his crime than the historical fact of parental rejection itself, although our knowledge of the latter fact makes his action more comprehensible.

It is the writer's firm contention that the vast majority of immoral and delinquent acts are committed under conditions where there is clear awareness of a moral issue and reasonable opportunity for exercising inhibitory control in conformity with the perceived direction of moral duty. For example, in instances of criminal behavior committed by a non-satellizer who consciously places himself above the law, or is intellectually dishonest in failing to perceive the incompatibility of his behavior with his professed ethical code, the decision regarding culpability should be unequivocal.

The determination of moral culpability is obviously a highly intricate process requiring considerable psychological analysis. All individuals cannot be judged by the same yardstick. For example, expediency becomes a less legitimate standard of behavior as the degree of freedom from dependency increases. Also, considerations of expediency should become less influential to an individual when interpersonal relationships are based on human values than when relationships are predicated upon his value as a commodity to be bought and sold on the market. Thus, what ostensibly appears to be a double moral standard may when examined genotypically turn out to be a highly consistent ethical code of behavior.

The condemnatory aspects of moral judgment to which Fromm objects so violently are inescapable if such judgment is to have any real moral significance. And condemnation inevitably implies punishment. It need not be assumed, however, that punishment precludes rehabilitative, preventitive or therapeutic efforts if such are indicated, or that it must necessarily be administered in a spirit of vindictiveness. As long as culpability is recognized, punishment is a necessary and relevant aspect of society's reaction to delinquency, providing that it is not employed to the exclusion of such principles as restitution and re-education.

If therapy alone were instituted, culpable immoral behavior would not be distinguishable in any way from other behavior disorders. The notion of liability to punishment following misbehavior is more than a specific product of certain forms of cultural organization. It is an inevitable component of the individual's own concept of moral value and obligation which lies at the root of his conscience formation. As a guilt-reducing mechanism, its therapeutic value should also not be minimized.

The threat of social punishment, therefore, is an important regulatory mechanism in the development of conscience. It thus serves a self-protective function with respect to perpetuating the moral standards of a given social order. After conscience is acquired, of course, it is no longer the main deterrent for misbehavior, merely serving to restrain impulsive acts of "testing the limits." In underdominated satellizers, and non-satellizers, however, it constitutes one of the chief considerations governing the inhibition of antisocial behavior throughout the entire life span of the individual.

With respect to society's right to condemn and punish (without being accused of taking over god-like prerogatives), we must side with the judiciary and against Oscar Wilde and the prevailing opinion of social scientists. The function of holding individuals accountable for their behavior is not only a logical extension of the belief in an objectively valid system of ethics, but is also a legitimate device that society needs to protect its members from predatory individuals. The latter justification is also applicable to the incarceration of both culpable individuals who are dangerous and incorrigible, and non-culpable persons whose freedom would constitute a menace to public safety.

NOTES

[1] According to Fromm, authoritarian ethics "denies" man's capacity to know what is good or bad and answers this question "primarily in terms of the interests of the authority." Humanistic ethics, on the other hand, is "based on the principle that only man himself can determine the criterion for value and sin, and that 'good' is what is good for man" [*142*].

[2] Since our primary concern in this chapter is with the development of conscience, we will only summarize briefly Fromm's discussion of the ethical content of behavior.

[3] Professor Kenneth Benne justly observes that the position taken by the writer in this section could be classified as relativistic by many theorists in the field of ethics on at least three counts: (1) the writer's refusal to claim a privileged status for ethical propositions in contradistinction to other empirically derived scientific data dissociates his position from that of moral absolutists who assert the existence of axiomatic, "revealed," intuitive or dogmatic ethical principles enjoying exemption from the methodological considerations and rules of evidence customarily applied in science; (2) his acceptance of the need for "socially immanent ethics" represents a concession to the flexibility of "'universal ethics" which many moral absolutists are unwilling to grant; and (3) his thesis that norms of ethical conduct must be related to developmental capacities for moral behavior denies the extreme absolutistic assumptions that the moral powers of man are innately and axiomately given, that they undergo no evolution in form, and that they must therefore be judged in relation to a single criterion of value.

If subscribing to these beliefs places him in the camp of the more relativistic of the ethical universalists, the writer is certainly not averse to being grouped with this wing of philosophical thought, especially if this will dissociate him from adherence to the commonly accepted, albeit inaccurate stereotype of what constitutes moral absolutism. The futility of dichotomizing the proponents of moral absolutism and relativism into two polar schools of thought is further illustrated by Professor Benne's observation that both schools are divided on the issue of whether ethical values can ever be given the same type of empirical validation as the laws of a particular scientific discipline. In this connection, the writer's distinction between psychological and philosophical ethical values (see p. 394) might effect some reconciliation between these two points of view.

[4] A more detailed critique of the psychoanalytic concept of superego is presented on pp. 442-444.

[5] In this chapter we have given no systematic attention to the methodology of discovering empirically valid principles which could be applied to the resolution of moral conflict, although we are in agreement with Professor Benne that research in this area is of vital importance if a science of ethics is to be meaningfully applied to everyday behavior in a world marked by moral confusion. However, until the product of such research becomes available, we can do little more than posit on logical grounds alone various criteria for resolving moral conflict.

The source of moral conflict lies not only in social and economic pressures which interfere with the practical implementation of an individual's ethical values, but also in the necessity for choosing between alternative or contradictory value systems. It can be postulated that a person whose chief orientation in the assimilation of values is a satellizing one will find most of his moral conflict in the former area since he usually does not tend to question prevailing norms of conduct. On the other hand, the individual who employs the exploratory orientation is just as apt to experience moral conflict that is generated by the claims and the relative merits of alternative ethical values or value systems.

[6] I am indebted to Barbara K. Haxby for pointing out the significance of this material in the present context.

[7] This critique of Mowrer's views on conscience development is based upon his position as stated in references *286, 287*; and in a symposium on "Cultural Expectations for Children" to be published in the 1952 Yearbook of the Association for Supervision and Curriculum Development.

[8] In older children and adults, repression of hostility is an important adjustive mechanism since it reduces the anxiety produced by guilt feelings and the insecurity referable to anticipation of reprisal.

[9] The reason for this cultural reluctance to perceive wickedness in others is partly a historical reaction to the witch-hunting proclivities of previous generations, and partly an institutionalized defense against insecurity, i.e., there is less reason to be fearful if people are perceived as more benevolent than they really are.

[10] Actual matching of these groups is, of course, impossible since the mere fact of delinquency taints most of the other variables studied.

[11] Recognition of the phenomenological reality of moral accountability and guilt does not, of course, rule out the possibility of utilizing these psychological phenomena for therapeutic or re-educative purposes. We cannot emphasize too strongly, however, that this position does not endorse but stands in oppo-

sition to the current tendency in criminological thought to dichotomize the "disease" versus the "moral accountability" approaches to the causation of delinquency and the "punitive" versus the "rehabilitative" approaches to its treatment. In other words, we would insist that moral accountability enjoys an empirically verifiable phenomenological status apart from and in addition to its potential use in the re-educative process; and that acceptance of the need for re-education in the reorientation of moral behavior does not necessarily imply that the cause of immoral conduct lies solely in faulty education and that judgment of such conduct must therefore be divorced from all considerations of moral accountability.

[12]I am indebted to Professor Foster McMurray for suggesting the need for this paragraph.

PART IV

Ego Development and the Personality Disorders

CHAPTER 17

A Developmental Approach to Psychopathology

In this chapter we shall attempt a systematic application of the dynamics of ego development to the pathogenesis of the behavior disorders. To a very large extent this has already been done in the chapters on developmental crisis and failure, anxiety, and conscience formation. What is needed now is a more formal classification of the behavior disorders so that the relationships of the various diagnostic categories to their developmental matrices and to each other can be more readily perceived.

The proposed system of classification is based on the assumption that developmental factors in ego formation represent the most significant variables in the etiology of behavioral pathology, and account most meaningfully for the differences in onset, symptomatology, and prognosis that hold for the recognized clinical entities. This by no means rules out the importance of genetic, constitutional and situational factors, or of other aspects of personality development. By definition, however, classification in science aims at defining relationships between phenomena in terms of the most prepotent variables responsible for their evolution and with the least possible degree of overlapping between categories.

GENERAL PSYCHOPATHOLOGY

Without attempting to present a definitive exposition of general psychopathology, it would be helpful nevertheless to relate the developmental approach to the more general context of variables in which it is embedded.

Determinants of Behavior Disorder

If we are to abide by the general proposition that any complex behavioral outcome must be considered a resultant of various influences impinging upon an individual's psychological field, what are the relevant variables that should be considered in assessing the possibility that he may or may not develop a behavior disorder or a particular type of behavior disorder? The following is a partial list of factors that should be taken into account: (1) genetic predisposition as determined by a single dominant or two recessive genes [*214*]; (2) inadequacy of constitutional defense factors (based on multifactorial genetic patterns) which do not provide sufficient resistance to disease [*214*]; (3) the objective magnitude of the adjustive stress or deprivation confronting the individual; (4) predispositions arising from aberrant ego development, e.g., lack of ego devaluation or maturation; (5) frustration tolerance, i.e., the amount of frustration an individual can withstand before succumbing to either disruption of performance ability, loss of self-esteem, or lowering of aspiration level; (6) various subjective factors which determine to what extent deprivation will be interpreted as or reacted to as frustration, i.e., general level of prestige aspiration, specific ego-involvement in a given activity, capacity for selective ego-disinvolvement; (7) the self-critical faculty, i.e., the ability or tendency to evaluate oneself more or less severely; (8) introversion-extraversion; (9) previous mode of adjustment to stress, i.e., types of adjustive mechanisms employed, and at what level of integration; (10) accessibility of motivations, attitudes, emotions to consciousness, degree of insight into adjustive techniques; (11) level of energy; (12) complexity of personality organization; (13) level of neurophysiological irritability as influenced by fatigue, emotion, hormonal balance, etc.; (14) level of resistance to stress situations in terms of reacting with somatic dysfunction (adrenocortical sufficiency [*180, 349*]); (15) anatomical and physiological integrity of the nervous system; (16) tolerance for anxiety, guilt, ambiguity, and inconsistency.

The reason why ego development is the central organizing variable in the etiology of behavior disorder (as has been shown in the preceding chapters) is because it crucially affects so many of the other important etiological variables, e.g., level of prestige aspiration, self-critical faculty, introversion-extraversion, frustration tolerance, tolerance for anxiety and guilt, etc.

Experimental Psychopathology

Whether behavior disorder is a peculiar product of man's superior mental processes and the complexity of his cultural organization, or is a more fundamental psychobiological pattern of response to frustration, adjustive stress and conflict than is found among most of the higher vertebrate species is a question that can only be answered by experimental psychopathology. The conclusion to which we are led by the evidence presented below is that behavior disorder in man is continuous in kind with the disturbances manifested by lower animals, differing mainly in complexity, abstractness, degree of verbal symbolism, richness of subjective components, and importance of social determinism and ego relatedness.

We can conceive of behavior disorder in a generic sense as reflective of an altered state of behavioral reactivity with a common core of causes and manifestations that vary in complexity in relation to the various dimensions indicated above. On a purely physiological level this state can be brought about by changes in blood sugar (hunger, diabetic coma, insulin shock), non-protein nitrogen (uremia), hormonal imbalance (thyroid, gonads, adrenals), fatigue, brain damage (hyperirritability in post-concussion syndrome), etc.

On a behavioral level, the same effect can be produced by presenting animals, children and adults with insoluble problems that give rise to prolonged and intense frustration, e.g., the well-known puzzle boxes of Thorndike and Hamilton [*162*], and the experiment by Lewin in which children were separated by a glass partition from attractive new toys [*251*]. We have also referred to the production of "experimental neuroses" in animals by Pavlov, Liddell, Maier and Masserman (see pp. 315-317). Marked behavior changes were induced when an animal's ability to respond and adjust to his environment was impaired by undermining the meaning and reliability of his perceptual cues or when the latter were endowed with incompatible and contradictory meanings. Maier was able to emphasize the element of conflict in the experimental situation by forcing his rats to respond to a negative cue (i.e., a cue eliciting a punished response), the animal's reluctance being overcome by a blast of air [*262, 264*].

Pooling the results of these various experiments, we find the following general pattern emerging as characteristic of the altered state of behavioral reactivity: First, in relation to the problem-solving situation itself, the animal reacts to a less intense and less specific stimulus with greater intensity and less specificity of behavior. There is a loss of differentiated behavior and a tendency toward rigid and "compulsive" perseveration of an unadaptive and even punished response. He "cannot learn new responses even when the situation ceases being insoluble" [*262*]. At other times, complete blocking of response occurs [*268*], or regression to a more primitive type of solution [*251, 262*]. Secondly, various general disturbances in behavior occur in some of the species and individuals studied: restlessness and excitement; tremors, quivering, and convulsive-like seizures; physiological signs of fear; various phobic manifestations; hypersensitivity to stimuli; exaggerated startle responses; cataleptic immobility and aimless hyperactivity; repetition of "compulsive" rituals and stereotyped behavior; extreme retardation of movement; refusal to take food; carelessness in disposition of feces; aggressive attacks on other animals; substitutive bids for affection.

It is evident that this inventory of responses characterizing the altered state of behavioral reactivity is descriptive of the state of panic and disorganization which Goldstein calls the "catastrophic reaction." But whereas Goldstein contends that anxiety is merely the animal's subjective awareness of being immersed in the catastrophic situation, we would insist that the component reactions described above are but a part of the total picture of behavioral disintegration occurring in extreme instances of fear and insecurity induced by catastrophic threats to the organism's life or adjustive capacity.

Maier's conception of the rat's reaction to frustration provides a needed corrective to the prevailing teleological notion which endows all behavior relating to the frustrating situation with adjustive properties (i.e., as reducing the urgency of needs, threats, deprivation and anxiety). In our discussion of anxiety we have already referred to the fact that most of its subjective components (loss of self-esteem, feelings of inadequacy and fear in coping with the environment, etc.) as well as many of its objective manifestations (e.g., its effects on learning) must be regarded as signs of ego damage rather than as compensatory efforts toward adjustment. Maier's position, however, is much more extreme:

> "The studies of abnormal behavior in the rat lead to a new theory of frustration. They demonstrate that behavior elicited during a state of frustration has certain unique properties, and that these properties make frustration-induced behavior different in kind from that produced in a motivated state. This basic separation between motivated and frustrated behavior is in contrast to the view which postulates that all behavior has a motive. When it is assumed that all behavior is motivated it follows that any behavior expressed is a means to some end. . . . Some of the animal experiments show that the type of behavior expressed in frustration is determined by its availability to the individual rather than by its effectiveness. . . . The first step in diagnosis is to determine which condition an individual is in when one attempts to correct behavior. The non-frustrated person is subject to training because he is responsive to training methods, and he can be attracted to substitute goals. The frustrated individual, however, needs relief from frustration" [*262*].

Maier then goes on to differentiate between "motivation-induced" and "frustration-instigated" behavior by characterizing the latter as "not directed toward a goal," aggravated by punishment, rigid and stereotyped, compulsive, destructive and regressive [*262*]. It appears to the present writer, however, that this distinction is unwarranted since these characteristics of "frustration-instigated" behavior are elicited only in instances of extreme frustration amounting to panic. In less catastrophic situations, frustration may lead to behavior which not only is adjustive in terms of need-reduction but is also goal-oriented, flexible, deterred by punishment, resourceful, constructive, etc. The difficulties into which Maier gets by virtue of his oversimplified theory are illustrated by his explanation of enuresis.

> "Believers in the theory that all behavior is motivated have difficulty in explaining such senseless regressive behavior. What problem is solved by this type of behavior? Frequently it is said that the child desires attention. The attention he receives from bed-wetting, however, may be

a spanking and degradation. Is this activity solving a problem for the child or is it aggravating a condition that is already bad? If, however, we assume that frustration produces regression and that this oversimplification of behavior is a direct result of frustration, than our problem is to seek the source of frustration. . . . Love and understanding reduce the state of frustration. . . . Nevertheless, from a motivational point of view, rewarding a bad response with love should strengthen it" [*262*].

To clinicians with experience in treating enuresis, however, it is much more plausible to attribute the enuretic habit to a powerful need on the part of the child to "get even" with a rejecting parent in such a way that he cannot be accused of deliberate aggression; and even if punishment and degradation ensue, the price is not considered excessive for the gratification it brings. The therapeutic efficacy of love can also be explained on a motivational basis, since it reduces the child's need for counter-aggression and vengeance.

In conclusion, while agreeing with Maier that all behavior in response to frustration is neither adjustive nor adaptive, we cannot accept his proposition that "frustration-instigated" behavior is wholly reflective of behavioral disorganization and dichotomous with motivated behavior. This dichotomy is apparent only in catastrophic situations such as confronted by Maier's animals. In less extreme cases of frustration, responses indicative of both disorganization and adjustive effort can be found.

What relevance does the evidence concerning "experimental neuroses" in animals have for behavior disorders in human beings? How does it tie in with our theory of aberrant ego development as the principal variable in the etiology of such disorders? In the first place, it establishes behavior disorder as a fundamental psychobiological response pattern of higher animals to adjustive stress, a pattern which can be designated as a state of altered behavioral reactivity. Continuity prevails not only with respect to the causes of this altered behavioral condition but also with respect to the component responses. These responses are reflective of both behavioral disorganization which is maladaptive and maladjustive, and behavior which is compensatory and directed toward need-reduction. But whereas frustration in animals must be related essentially to the objective magnitude of the threat, in humans subjective factors derived from ego development are more crucial, namely, magnitude and tenacity of aspiration level, frustration tolerance, the availability of intrinsic feelings of security and adequacy, and self-critical faculty; and in terms of response characteristics, human reactions are more verbal, symbolic and ideational rather than occurring on only a motor and emotional plane.

Two of the more recent approaches to psychopathology stressing concepts of ego development might be mentioned in this context. In her latest work, Karen Horney [*190*] emphasizes the conflict between the "real self" and a "neurotic" and illusory idealized image of self as the basic problem in neurosis. This formula, however, like her previous formulas, is a facile oversimplification of the problem and is both poorly systematized and unrelated to empirical evidence in the field of personality development. Silverberg [*359*], on the other hand, specifically recognizes the factor of omnipotence in neurosis as well as the developmental changes occurring in the child's concept of self; but he too constructs a self-contained theoretical system in the psychoanalytic tradition which seeks no connection with empirical data and rests on "simple, sovereign assumptions."

The Ego in Psychopathology

The ego is of such crucial importance in psychopathology because it is the central organizing value in personality structure. Our relationship to the environment is ordered on a hierarchical gradient of ego-involvement. Most motivations bear some relationships to ego needs, e.g., security, adequacy, prestige, status, power. What we wish to derive from life in terms of work, interpersonal relationships, love, position, etc., usually bears some relation to our self-concept, i.e., the magitude of our ego aspirations, how compelling the need for ego enhancement is, how important we think we are or ought to become. The ego is the one value in personality that people are most concerned about. As Gardner Murphy puts it, "whatever else we love, we love our ego best" [*288*]. It elicits greater efforts toward defense and enhancement than any other value.

The causes of frustration and conflict in human beings must also be largely formulated in terms of ego needs. When these are thwarted by delay, denial or conflict, when ego status is debased or threatened, frustration ensues. More important than actual deprivation in determining the degree of frustration experienced is the individual's level of prestige aspiration, his specific ego-involvement in a given task, his frustration tolerance and self-critical faculty. All of these factors are greatly influenced by the course of ego development, which, in addition, helps determine the source from whence status is sought, the degree of volitional and executive dependence desired, the need for hedonistic gratification, the type and degree of security and adequacy feelings possessed, the sense of moral obligation adhered to, as well as tendencies toward introversion-extraversion and egocentrism. In short, ego development forms the core of personality development; hence, it would not be at all surprising if the major predispositions toward acquiring behavior disorder were to be found in aberrant varieties of ego development.

Responses to frustration can likewise be categorized as forms of defense, escape, and damage of self. Defense mechanisms are mainly compensatory attempts to enhance self, to make the ego appear powerful, blameless, and more worthwhile—through substitutive or phantasy achievements, rationalization, disowning weaknesses and perceiving them in others (projection), burying ideas which are unfavorable to self (repression), distorting reality, providing excuses for failure in illness, etc. Escape mechanisms, on the other hand, allow for withdrawal of self beyond the reach of environmental threats, e.g., insulation, negativism, etc. Various forms of ego damage have already been described in Chapter 15. They include loss of self-esteem, anxiety, agitation, depersonalization, fear of death, and depression.

The "Unconscious"

In psychoanalytic theory, "the unconscious" forms the cornerstone of psychopathology. It is the domain of instinctual urges and the locus of repressed libidinal impulses referable to earlier stages of psychosexual development which for some reason had become fixated at a primitive level of evolution. It is also the region to which unacceptable feelings and ideas and regressive desires are banished if they somehow manage to enter the sacred precincts of consciousness. Through the surreptitious influence exerted by unconscious motivation, symptoms are formed which symbolically fulfill the goals of their hidden progenitors. In the absence of the unconscious, behavior disorder is unthinkable in the psychoanalytic sense. Also in Mowrer's "guilt theory" of anxiety we have seen that repression is the all-important factor accounting for the conversion of fear and guilt into anxiety and for whatever behavioral disorganization takes place.

Our objections to this concept of the unconscious are three-fold: (1) We have already objected to the dichotomous notion that all acceptable and self-enhancing motives prevail at the conscious level while their unacceptable, self-debasing, anxiety- and guilt-producing counterparts influence behavior solely from an unconscious base of operations (see page 289). (2) Psychoanalytic theories of the unconscious are topographical rather than functional, implying an all-or-none differentiation between the conscious and the unconscious depending on regional location. It does less violence to modern concepts of psychological functioning to conceive of "varying degrees in the accessibility of a person's behavior to his own analysis" [*61*]. (3) We can agree that unconscious motivation gives rise to symbolic symptom-formation, and that it compounds the seriousness and intensity of guilt and anxiety by impeding integrative and constructive solutions. But we must reiterate that these consequences of repression are not mainly responsible for the evolution of behavior disorders but merely have the status of complications. Furthermore, it should be pointed out that displacement of expression not only proceeds from "unconscious sexual" content to conscious symptom-formation but also in the reverse direction; that is, awareness of current, non-sexual conflicts can be inhibited by identifying them symbolically with repressed sexual material. Because of the widespread prevalence of psychoanalytic theories, many individuals retrospectively interpret innocent childhood experiences (or invent experiences that never occurred) in Freudian terms, which then serve as foci for the symbolic displacement of current conflicts. Since these sexual urges are now considered normal and respectable, it is less traumatic to plead guilty to possessing them than to acknowledge anxiety, weakness, or lack of moral integrity.

In order of importance we may differentiate between four different varieties of inaccessibility: (1) perceptions or motives that are attended to on a sub-threshold level of awareness because of their habitual, autonomous, or unobtrusive nature; (2) experiences occurring in a state of panic or behavioral disorganization with consequent impairment of perceptual and memory functions; (3)

emotional and visceral feelings or attitudes which cannot be formulated in verbal terms, and hence are recalled or reidentified with great difficulty; (4) material which is actively repressed as a form of adjustment. In repression, either (a) motives, attitudes or feelings are repressed, (b) a response to an otherwise adequate stimulus is inhibited, or (c) neither motive nor response is inhibited, but rather the perception of a connection between them. Repression as an adjustive mechanism is resorted to in order to avoid insecurity, guilt or punishment.

Another psychoanalytic concept lacking in clarity and precision but very important for general psychopathology is the concept of regression. Psychoanalytically, the depth of regression with respect to psychosexual development is supposed to account for the degree of behavioral disorganization, e.g., the etiological distinction between neurosis and psychosis. Unfortunately, however, this concept does not differentiate between genuine retrogression (true regression) and mere lack of maturation. Secondly, it conceives of regression only in a psychosexual sense rather than in terms of ego development. Lastly, differences in type and degree of regression are not related to a developmental history of satellization or non-satellization. Most apparent regression in satellizers represents maturational failure, whereas in non-satellizers who rarely fail to undergo maturation, regressive behavior is more indicative of genuine retrogression. Depth of regression is also greater in non-satellizers since the developmental failure to which it relates occurs at an earlier stage of ego development, i.e., the ego devaluation crisis as opposed to the ego maturation crisis.

CLASSIFICATION OF BEHAVIOR DISORDERS

TABLE 6.—*A Classification of Behavior Disorders from the Standpoint of Ego Development*

I. *Personality Disorders Due to Maturational Failure* (in Satellizers)

 A. *Inadequate Psychopath* (Extraversion: hedonistic gratification in reality)

  1. Complete

  2. Partial

 B. *Evolutionary Schizophrenia* (Introversion: hedonistic gratification in fantasy)

II. *Personality Disorders Due to Failure in Ego Devaluation* (in Non-Satellizers)

A. *Maturational or Regressive Disorders*

1. Aggressive antisocial psychopath
2. Delinquency secondary to unstable conscience formation
3. Special problems of adolescent emancipation
4. Alcoholism

B. *Disorders Due to Ego Hypertrophy: The Anxiety States*

1. Manifest anxiety states
2. Latent anxiety states

C. *Defensive Reactions Against Anxiety*

1. Secondary elaborations of anxiety
2. Exhaustion states
3. Hypochondriasis
4. Hysteria
5. Phobia
6. Compulsion
7. Obsession
8. Aggression
9. "Martyrdom"
10. Placation
11. Delusional states
12. Mania

D. *Complications of Anxiety*

1. Withdrawal: Reactive Schizophrenia (especially in introverts)
2. Depressive Reactions (especially in extraverts)
   a. Agitated depression with exaggerated dependency
   b. Retarded depression (cessation of striving)
   c. Manic-depressive cycles

Classification is as necessary in psychiatry as in all scientific disciplines to make possible generalization, concept formation, and investigation of relationships between important variables impinging upon the phenomena encompassed within the discipline. Without classification a separate equation would have to be written for every individual reaction, since identity never prevails phenomenologically. General laws could never be formulated, and anarchy would prevail. Classification does not presume identity, but similarity between events subsumed under a given category. "The use of a given diagnostic entity in this sense does not in the least interfere with the further description of the unique personal evolution of a case within a more general category" [*21*]. Hence, it is indulging in sophistry to urge the abolition of classification in favor of "just understanding the mechanisms underlying each case without worrying about diagnostic labels."

The claim that outmoded classification in psychiatry is retarding the progress of the science also confuses the issue. Generally speaking, classification mirrors the state of clarity prevailing as regards the various concepts and their interrelationships within a given science. Hence an inadequate classification is not the cause of theoretical confusion but a reflection of it. If we still adhere to the Kraepelinian descriptive nomenclature, it means that our so-called "dynamic" systems of psychopathology are lacking in sufficient clarity and self-evident plausibility to command widespread adoption for clinical or research purposes.

PERSONALITY DISORDERS IN SATELLIZERS: MATURATIONAL FAILURE

The defects in ego organization that result from maturational failure as well as its predisposing causes in parental over- and underdomination and in overprotection have already been described in Chapter 13. It will be recalled that ego devaluation as well as attenuation (preliminary maturation) of infantile ego attributes take place normally in satellizers (see Chapter 11). However, the next step in maturation that usually occurs in preadolescence and adolescence—desatellization and the acquisition of adult personality status (volitional independence; striving for long-range, adult ego demands; increased executive independence; societal moral responsibility)—fails to eventuate. Hence, lack of maturation rather than regression is the keynote of this disorder. Because of the presence of intrinsic security and adequacy, neurotic anxiety does not occur and relatively meager reality accomplishment can be tolerated with equanimity. Aspirational tenacity (goal frustration tolerance) is low, while self-esteem and performance frustration tolerance are high. The type of behavior disorder that finally prevails in this type of aberrant ego development is largely influenced by the factors of introversion-extraversion. In either case, characteristic modes of gratifying the hedonistic goal structure are found. And since satisfaction is neither sought nor can be gained through normal adult goals, there is some compensatory retrogression to even more childish levels of goal striving, especially when the individual is removed from the supervision of parents for whose sake attenuation of hedonistic impulses occurred in the first place.

The Inadequate Psychopath

The predominantly extraverted inadequate personality satisfies his hedonistic needs in reality by finding ways of gratifying his pleasure-seeking and childish goals. Since it is obviously impossible for an adult to adapt to an adult world of reality while retaining the goal structure of a child, successful adjustment at a mature level fails to take place.

> "Because of lack of emotional identification with normal goals, the inadequate psychopath is unable to sustain his motivation in striving for them or to derive any satisfaction from their realization. His attitude toward life is passive and dependent. He demonstrates no desire to persevere in the face of environmental difficulties or to accept responsibilities which he finds painful" [*20*].

But despite his underlying sense of intrinsic adequacy, the failure to acquire extrinsic status would still be quite traumatic were it not for a protective inhibition of the self-critical faculty. It would "explode the fiction of serene adequacy so vital to his sense of puerile security" [*20*]. Thus, we find the strange paradox that in the personality disorder in which the most inadequate adaptation to life is made, there are no subjective feelings of inadequacy. Thanks to an impaired self-critical faculty, he is able to deny

> "the very existence of his difficulties and problems as well as his obvious inadequacy. . . . By making unwarranted assumptions about his capacity for meeting new situations, he obviates the necessity for painful planning or preparation. By denying his failures and exaggerating the efficacy of his adjustment, he is thereby required to put forth less effort toward a positive solution of his problems. He becomes preoccupied with the search for an easy, effortless, unearned form of pleasure. All of these factors contribute to the resulting instability and nomadism that is characteristic of the group" [*20*].

From the ranks of the inadequate psychopaths are recruited vagrants, hobos, drug addicts, petty criminals of all varieties, pool-room-hangers-on, carnival operators, confidence men, race-track attaches, etc. Of all these characters, the narcotic drug addict makes the most satisfactory adjustment (from his own point of view). Drug addiction

> "results in positive, immediate, pleasurable sensations which satisfy the quest for effortless, hedonistic satisfaction. It dulls the self-critical faculty to the point where the addict becomes easily contented with his inadequate, hedonistic adjustment to life, and is more easily able to evade and overlook responsibilities; and where in the complete absence of any actual accomplishment, he feels supremely satisfied with himself and his future. By virtue of its analgesic properties and general dulling effect on consciousness, the drug provides a partial escape from the disturbances and distasteful elements of reality. Thus, if he is actually required to work and assume responsibility, the hard, distasteful edge of the task is softened, much in the way a self-indulged child will fulfill his chores as long as he has a lollipop in his mouth.
>
> "The inadequate psychopath who does not discover opiate addiction leads a very unstable, nomadic type of existence characterized by a precarious and marginal vocational adjustment and by frequent, unnecessary changes of employment. . . . He is also predisposed toward alcoholism, addiction to other drugs, and all thrill-seeking forms of vice. He is able to adjust marginally in an optimal environment, that is, one structured in terms of his hedonistic needs, but in no other" [*20*].

A *partial* type of inadequate personality has already been described as occurring in overdominated children who accept parental domination (see pp. 228-232).

Evolutionary Schizophrenia

Clinically, two distinct varieties of schizophrenia are apparent [*21, 120, 385, 386*]:

> "In the first or classical form of schizophrenia, the psychosis is merely the culmination or end result of the natural evolution of the pre-schizophrenic personality: It is the almost invariable and insidious outcome of the continued existence of this type of personality make-up—or, at any rate, if a mental disorder occurs in such a personality, no other

type of psychotic reaction seems conceivable. Most commonly these cases fall into the simple or hebephrenic varieties. On the other hand, in an individual not endowed with the pre-schizophrenic personality, another type of schizophrenic reaction may occur which is, more or less, a paroxysmal, abortive attempt at adjustment upon confrontation with overwhelming environmental demands. Such an individual has previously adopted normal or other abnormal but non-schizophrenic techniques of adjustment and actually and potentially has a better adjustive capacity than the classical type. This second variety of reaction occurs later in life, begins more acutely, is more exogenous in origin and runs a more benign course. There is often a strong affective component present, as in the catatonic variety, or various compensatory paranoid trends. This reaction is not a cumulative or well-nigh inevitable result of a predisposing personality disorder, but a transitory, or sometimes permanent, incident in the adjustment of an essentially non-schizophrenic reaction type to the vicissitudes of life. From this point on, it will be more convenient to refer to the first or classical type of schizophrenia as *evolutionary,* and the second as *reactive*" [*21*].

Schizophrenia represents a marked and functionally complete withdrawal type of adjustment in which the ego is removed beyond the reach of an unsatisfactory objective reality, and imbedded in a subjective, autistic reality of its own making. It occurs in the motivationally inadequate individual who fails to undergo adult ego maturation in goal structure. A strong constitutional predisposition toward introversion facilitates the development of the withdrawal reaction. He is too "tender-skinned," egocentric and inclined toward indirect emotional participation in reality "through the medium of symbols and intellectualization" to venture the alternative of seeking hedonistic gratification in reality against the opposition of parents and cultural agents. Introversion also becomes a compensatory adjustive mechanism since it permits gratification of immature ego demands in fantasy.

"Handicapped by this personality make-up—having no stake in the adult world of reality motivations and little opportunity for gratification of infantile desires (as long as he is required to adjust according to adult standards)—the individual gradually withdraws whatever emotional energy he has invested in adult goals and in reality. . . . [He does this] not because of an overwhelming sense of failure following the frustration of normally motivated drives (for he has no such sense of failure) but because he 'concludes' that reality is an unsuitable medium for the gratification of his immature ego demands, and forsakes it for the obvious superiority of the world of fantasy with whose enchantments he has been progressively flirting. . . . Some precipitating event eventually occurs, often trifling and insignificant enough in itself which convinces him that adult motivations and reality living represent losing propositions; and that he would fare better by dropping all pretense of adult reality adjustment, and frankly expressing his true desires in fantasy" [*21*].

Rogg [*332*] refers to the latter event as the "time of decision."

Clinical evidence substantiates the rationale for differentiating between evolutionary and reactive forms of schizophrenia. The importance of constitutional factors is borne out in a recent somatotypic study by Kline and Tenney [*229*] who found a positive relationship in schizophrenics between mesomorphy and rate of discharge from the hospital. Paranoid schizophrenics tended to be mesomorphic while hebephrenics were primarily ectomorphic [*229*]. Reichard and Tillman [*320*] in reviewing patterns of parent-child relationships in adult schizophrenics found overt maternal rejection in 13 per cent of the cases, covert maternal rejection in 63 per cent of the cases, and overt paternal rejection in 15 per cent of the cases. Covert maternal rejection was expressed most frequently, according to the authors, in overprotective and underdominating child-rearing practices. Unfortunately, however, although these data point to the influence of parent-child relationships on the pathogenesis of schizophrenia, the authors do not distinguish between the reactive and evolutionary types in relation to child-rearing patterns. If our hypothesis were correct, the reactive type would go along with overt rejection, while the evolutionary type would accompany overprotection and underdomination.

The relatively rare occurrence of schizophrenia in children supports the hypothesis that the evolutionary type is the outcome of maturational failure relative to the preadolescent and adolescent periods. Reactive schizophrenia, on the other hand, tends to be a terminal type of maladjustment in the non-satellizer, not generally appearing before the third or fourth decades of life. It would be a fair inference, however, to expect juvenile schizophrenics to conform more to the evolutionary type because of the heavy loading of constitutional and predisposing factors that obviously must operate in such cases. In Clardy's series of thirty cases of juvenile schizophrenia, there was psychosis or extreme maladjustment in the immediate families of twenty of these patients [*67*]. Interestingly enough, his younger group of cases between the ages of three and eleven were characterized by the symptoms of evolutionary schizophrenia (withdrawal, emotional blunting, loss of contact), whereas the older groups (eight to twelve) displayed the delusional, hallucinatory and catatonic features more characteristic of reactive schizophrenia [*67*]. Kanner's study of early infantile autism[1]* brings out the fact that such children

> "take no notice of persons in the environment. They are essentially alone, and when alone, happy; and they resist any effort to encroach upon their aloneness. . . . [Their parents] are detached, lacking in ordinary warmth, mechanical in their relationships. The incidence of divorce among them is extremely low, yet there is an unmistakable unrelatedness between parents. The parent displays a lack of feeling tone toward his children, even though he knows all the details of the child's development" [*216*].

Apparently then, the extreme introversion is a consequence of the convergence of potent constitutional and child-rearing factors.

Evolutionary schizophrenia is characterized more by amaturation than by regression. In addition to the limited form of compensatory regression mentioned above there is also the

> "spurious regression which represents the release of immature drives when the repressive influence of reality censorship is removed. . . . The emotional blunting, apathy and disinterest in surroundings, together with the resulting personality and intellectual deterioration are but the culmination of the process of emotional withdrawal from meager attachments to adult goals and reality. The lack of correlation between emotional expression and mental trend is only to be expected since there is no longer any emotional identification with the ideational content that most normal persons live by" [*21*].

* Notes for this chapter appear on page 518.

These are the essential symptoms characterizing the evolutionary form of the disease, which for the most part conform to the simple and hebephrenic varieties of the old classification. The silliness characteristic of the latter type merely reflects the bizarreness that must inevitably mark the behavior of an individual who lives in his own reality but is judged by persons sharing a social reality. In some cases it seems to possess a sardonic and contemptuous quality, as if the patient pitied the poor mortals who were bound by the conventionality and limitations of an objective existence. Simple schizophrenics, on the other hand, are able to remain in reasonably good contact with their environment and often succeed in making "a partial adjustment to reality as long as they remain within the protected environment of the institution" [*21*]. The hallucinations and delusions which are frequently found in hebephrenics are not comparable to the paranoid type (which are "purposeful distortions of reality"), but are "simple psychological consequences of the greater vividness of the endogenously-derived as compared to the external sources of conscious data. Since the [hebephrenic] variety are not in the least referable to reality, they need not be at all consistent, systematic or logical as the [paranoid] ones are" [*21*].

With respect to course, prognosis, and responsiveness to therapy, the differentiation between evolutionary and reactive types is clear-cut. The former runs a chronic and malignant course, has uniformly a dismal prognosis, and is unresponsive to any form of convulsive therapy. The latter fact is reinforced by the finding that juvenile schizophrenia continues to exhibit a chronic, unremitting course which only rarely is improved by the administration of shock therapy [*249*].

PERSONALITY DISORDERS IN NON-SATELLIZERS: FAILURE IN EGO DEVALUATION

Maturational and Regressive Disorders

The causes and consequences of non-satellization and lack of ego devaluation have been fully described in Chapters 11, 15 and 16. From the standpoint or psychopathological significance, two main types of developmental predispositions toward behavior disorder are attributable to unsuccessful solution of the crisis of ego devaluation: (1) Most important are the characteristics of ego hypertrophy, i.e., the high level of prestige aspiration, ideas of volitional omnipotence and independence, the great need for extrinsic status, the lack of intrinsic security and adequacy, and high goal frustration tolerance. As already pointed out, these personality characteristics are not incompatible with cultural expectations regarding adult personality status, and, in fact, facilitate its acquisition. However, they do predispose toward neurotic anxiety, abnormal defenses against anxiety and deteriorative complications of it. (2) However, another set of predispositions which are also referable to failure in ego devaluation has to do with the infantile ego attributes that are customarily attenuated in the course of satellization, namely, hedonistic needs, the needs for immediate gratification, desire for executive dependence, and moral irresponsibility. In non-satellizers, one sees these ego attributes modified selectively on an expediential basis according to the needs of ego hypertrophy.

While maturation in general is favored by the requirements of ego hypertrophy, two weaknesses are inherent in this situation: (a) The characteristics of mature personality structure which do not contribute to ego aggrandizement are accepted with difficulty. This applies specifically to moral responsibility. (b) The characteristics of mature personality status which do contribute to ego aggrandizement are stable only as long as the individual remains within the framework of his hypertrophied goal structure. In the event of severe behavioral disorganization or psychosis, full-blown regression to these infantile ego attributes will occur since genuine unconditional attenuation has not taken place, and mature behavior no longer serves the interests of expediency.

Referable to the first of these latter two categories are the maturational disorders in conscience development found in non-satellizers, namely, complete moral agenesis (aggressive, antisocial psychopathy), and delinquency secondary to unstable internalization of moral obligation (see page 455). Lack of ego maturation with respect to hedonism and executive dependence occurs sometimes in overvalued children who are harshly rejected later in childhood as a form of aggressive retaliation against parents (see page 244). Regressive manifestations of these same ego attributes are also encountered in psychotic complications of anxiety states, e.g., depression, and reactive schizophrenia.

A type of alcoholism is very common in non-satellizers with hypertrophied ego demands who for constitutional or other reasons find it difficult to maintain the degree of personality maturity necessary for the realization of ego aggrandizement. These individuals lack motivational tenacity and frustration tolerance, are unable to tolerate conscious anxiety, or have excessive needs for visceral and hedonistic satisfactions which interfere with the attainment of long-range goals. Alcoholism serves as a crutch to sustain motivation and self-discipline, as a part-time escape from frustration-laden reality, and (by lowering the self-critical faculty) as an anxiety-reducing mechanism. Because of ego hypertrophy, however, the objectives of maturation are not completely abandoned, and complete surrender to hedonism as occurs in narcotic drug addiction or evolutionary schizophrenia does not take place. Alcoholism, of course, is also very common among satellizers who fail to undergo maturation; but these individuals prefer a more complete form of hedonistic gratification, and quickly abandon the habit once introduced to narcotics. Case histories of drug addicts reveal that approximately one-fifth of the cases have a previous history of alcoholism [*20*].

Personality Disorders Due to Ego Hypertrophy

Anxiety States

Neurotic anxiety has been described as an acquired reaction sensitivity in an individual with impaired self-esteem to over-react with fear to any stimulus which threatens to impair self-esteem further. It is a psychopathological outcome of faulty ego devaluation combined with a history of catastrophic trauma to self-esteem; fundamentally, therefore, it is a disease process, a reflection of ego damage rather than a compensatory mechanism (see Chapter 15).

Nevertheless it must be conceded that anxiety does have some adjustive value *per se:* (1) Before it assumes disorganizing proportions, it mobilizes the individual's adaptive efforts and increases his motivational tenacity. By alerting him in advance, it allows him to prepare responses to threatening stimuli which otherwise might precipitate panic if confronting him unawares. Although this interferes with the capacity for improvisation, it does prevent behavioral disorganization in response to threatening situations which the individual cannot or chooses not to solve by avoidance behavior. (2) It serves as a warning signal to withdraw from certain situations which threaten to bring him defeat and lowered self-esteem. If this entails the loss of gratifications associated with possible success, it also forestalls the painful humiliation that failure would evoke. This protective value of anxiety, however, cannot be utilized in the form of outright avoidance, since fear of failure is not an acceptable justification for withdrawal in our culture. Hence, avoidance must be rationalized by some other device such as illness, gross ineptitude, the virtue of asceticism or self-denial for the sake of others, and in extreme cases by the plea of incapacity due to behavioral disorganization, e.g., panic, agitation. (3) Anxiety is sometimes employed as a bid for help, sympathy, deference, or executive dependence. But since this adjustive use of anxiety is socially hazardous and implies a degree of helplessness that is highly threatening to self-esteem, it is not generally utilized except under conditions of panic.

Although many of the defenses against anxiety help considerably to reduce its tensions and distastefulness, simple conscious anxiety is still a more desirable state of affairs from the standpoint of eventually evolving a contructive adjustment. The defensive reactions tend to become fixed, to acquire a canalized adjustive value, and to limit the variability of behavior which is one of the main hopes of effecting a more wholesome type of adaptation. We must also amend our earlier interpretation of the defenses against and the complications of anxiety to include their role of rationalizing (making more acceptable) the adjustive value of anxiety *per se* as a technique of avoiding situations where loss of self-esteem is feared.

We have held throughout that the main reason for over-reaction with fear to an ostensibly inadequate threat (judged in terms of its objective hazardness to persons not suffering from neurotic anxiety) is an inner feeling of inadequacy reflective of impaired self-esteem. When panic sets in, however, this reason is compounded by the resulting loss of discriminative ability which further prevents the individual from distinguishing between adequate and inadequate threats.

The rejected type of non-satellizer generally suffers from a manifest anxiety neurosis. Many overvalued individuals, however, do not go on to develop frank anxiety states; in a sizeable number of cases where catastrophic impairment of self-esteem does not occur, the anxiety remains latent. Driven by implacable ambition, however, they become obnoxiously aggressive, ruthless, self-centered, rigid, humorless, and determined to achieve success at any price. Later, after experiencing considerable frustration, a note of bitterness and cynicism creeps in. It is at this stage that they are ready to seek compensation through the exploits of their own children, thus perpetuating the same vicious cycle of overvaluation of which they themselves were victims.

Defensive Reactions against Anxiety

The varied and numerous types of adjustive mechanisms through which these defensive reactions are mediated have been described in Chapter 15. Here we shall only attempt to relate these mechanisms to the formal diagnostic entities employed in clinical psychiatry. Their elaboration is facilitated by the altered state of behavioral reactivity induced by anxiety, and their general function is to bolster self-esteem, increase security and rationalize avoidance of threatening situations. Psychosomatic symptoms, for example, may have a dual function: They may explain failure to attain eminence in areas where tremendous effort is obviously expended to achieve success, or they may be utilized to justify to self and others withdrawal from threatening situations (rather than face the risk of possible failure).

The simplest defenses against anxiety utilize the mechanisms of rationalization and displacement in elaborating upon the physiological accompaniments of anxiety states. The *hypochondriac* reduces anxiety by becoming preoccupied with these physiological complaints and believing that they are indicative of organic disease. This conscious attention to normally autonomous physiological functions further impairs their efficiency [*61*]. Belief in organic illness rationalizes both failure and avoidance of striving, and displaces both the source and object of the threat with more palatable and less traumatic surrogates. The same mechanisms are operative in "fatigue" and "exhaustion" states except that the individual concentrates on the fatiguing consequences of anxiety instead of on other somatic complaints. Actual organic symptoms of illness can also be developed *de novo,* apart from the usual manifestations of anxiety (e.g., hysterical anaesthesias, blindness, paralysis, tremors, seizures, tics) through the convergence of intense need to escape from catastrophic threats, extreme suggestibility, and fortuitous physiological accident. For example, a hypersuggestible soldier with intense combat fear can develop hysterical blindness by interpreting the momentary loss of sight induced by the glare of a nearby exploding shell as proof of permanent organic deficit.

In *phobias,* displacement of the source of the threat from impaired self-esteem to specific avoidable objects and situations occurs. The selection of surrogate objects is not arbitrary but depends upon some symbolical connection with the actual threat. In *obsessive* disorders, the source of the threat is not displaced or made more tangible and specific, but consciousness is monopolized by a relatively innocuous and symbolically related idea which relieves anxiety by creating an all-consuming distraction. *Compulsions* add the element of magic and ritualistic defense and provide a rigid formula for meeting new situations, thus banishing anxiety in relation to the unreasonable need for absolute certainty. Dependence on stereotyped ritualism eliminates the need for improvising new adjustments. Compulsive activity, as Maier points out, is also a simple unadjustive consequence of acute behavioral disorganization.

Self-esteem and security can be enhanced by *delusional* distortion of reality in which (a) guilt, responsibility, unacceptable motivations, etc., are disowned and projected onto others, (b) rejecting and unappreciative individuals are unjustifiably deprecated, and (c) the status and accomplishments of self are uncritically inflated or perceived to be the objects of systematic victimization. A related technique is to proclaim the wickedness of all earthly aspirations, to renounce same, and interpret the renunciation as proof of unusual virtue (asceticism), or to believe in one's divinely inspired mission to redeem mankind (religious delusions).

Martyrs assume the role of neglected, self-sacrificing individuals who voluntarily neglect their own interests and aspirations to enhance the welfare or career of others. This not only explains their own lack of eminence but also bestows upon them a saint's mantle of selflessness and devotion. The latter claim is not unfounded in fact, since martyrs either allow themselves to be expoited by others or else manipulate situations in such a way that they are obliged to suffer martyrdom. They frequently start their careers as rejected eldest children in large families who are deprived of childhood joys and are burdened with the responsibility of caring for younger siblings. The role of martyrdom may be assumed initially as a reaction-formation against resulting feelings of hostility and resentment or as a form of expiation for the guilt feelings referable to same. In addition to the later rationalizing and ego-enhancing values of the device, some martyrs also achieve secondary ego gratification by identifying themselves with the accomplishments of those for whom they sacrifice their own lives and fortunes.

Rationalization, projection and delusional distortion of reality all imply some degree of impairment of the self-critical faculty. In *manic* reactions, however, an unusual degree of such impairment constitutes the main adjustive mechanism involved, and is not specifically related to a single belief. Instead there is a general euphoric alteration of mood, boundless optimism, unlimited belief in one's abilities and prospects, and loss of all inhibition and sense of propriety.

Aggression and hostility are among the simplest and commonest outcomes of frustration, and are sometimes used defensively to allay anxiety. But as pointed out earlier, they are themselves highly productive of anxiety because of the anticipation of retaliation, and because they threaten to disrupt the placatory defensive techniques which are more effective in our society [*187*].

Complications of Anxiety

When the burden of anxiety exceeds the individual's level of tolerance because of a breakdown in his defenses or because of new and catastrophic environmental threats to his self-esteem, severe psychotic complications of anxiety may ensue. These reactions represent such marked disorganization of behavior that normal interpersonal relationships or participation in a shared social reality become impossible. The disorganization is in part a reflection of the deterioration of behavior and personality occurring in extreme or panic levels of altered behavioral reactivity, a form of damage which has no adjustive value *per se* and is comparable to Goldstein's "catastrophic reaction" or Maier's "frustration-instigated" behavior in animals. In part, they represent an attempt at adjustment beyond the established framework of ego organization from which the patient derives his usual sense of personal identity, and beyond the social reality which he shares with significant persons in his psychological field. In this sense, and in the sense that they remove him from the field of impossible adjustive situations exceeding his adaptive capacity, they may be considered to have some defensive value.

How are such adjustive crises produced? The anxiety neurotic ordinarily learns how to avoid potentially traumatic situations that he feels might end disastrously in terms of his self-esteem, e.g., rejection by a person with whom he wishes to establish a close emotional relationship. Through various rationalizing techniques he manages to justify avoidance of forming such relationships even though this involves self-frustration and loss of possible gratifications which he deeply desires.

Let us carry the adjustive stress one step further. Suppose that our anxiety patient is confronted with accepting a vocational adjustment below his level of aspiration, a situation which is highly traumatic in terms of his hypertrophic goal structure. Neither fear nor protestations of "being too good for such a job" are valid enough reasons to persuade oneself or others that a practical, modestly-oriented adjustment is unsatisfactory when no other employment is available. When hard-pressed by the inexorable logic of accepting this situation, anxiety may give way to panic which in turn disorganizes behavior, makes any type of adjustment impossible, and induces blocking, paralysis, and exaggerated self-criticism. The patient can claim complete incapacity as a result of "nervous breakdown," justify his dependence on others and enjoy a reprieve from accepting a half-loaf solution that does violence to his needs for prestige, power and exalted ego status.

While immersed in this agitated state of panic, marked by collapse of self-esteem, self-depreciation and dependence on others, a constructive solution is still possible as long as the patient continues to strive on an adult reality plane. If he can perceive the new adjustment as only a short-term setback which does not irreparably frustrate his needs for ego aggrandizement, he may be persuaded to accept it as a temporary expedient. If, on the other hand, he feels that his ambitions are completely blocked and that reconciliation to a life of acknowledged mediocrity of status is inevitable, he may choose instead a psychotic adjustment removed from normal adult strivings and from participation in a social reality.

Reactive Schizophrenia. Reactive schizophrenia is a paroxysmal and extreme form of withdrawal adjustment that occurs in ego-hypertrophic individuals in response to catastrophic adjustive stress. The magnitude of such stress must be evaluated in terms of the individual's particular ego aspirations rather than in relation to conventional criteria of deprivation. For example, to a lawyer who aspires to a professorship in constitutional law, the prospect of becoming reconciled to a $10,000 a year general law practice might represent an unbearable degree of trauma to self-esteem. In contrast to the depressive reactions, reactive schizophrenia is more apt to occur in introverted individuals; but the introversion is seldom as marked as in evolutionary schizophrenia and is by no means an indispensable predisposition, since pronounced extraversion is not a rare finding in the reactive form of the disease. The more crucial differential factors with respect to predisposition are failure of ego maturation in the one (evolutionary type) and lack of satellization and ego devaluation in the other (reactive type). In the reactive type, there is abrupt rather than gradual withdrawal from an objective and shared social reality, and abrupt regressive dematuration from mature adult goals rather than failure to achieve an adult goal structure in the first place. It tends to run a more acute and benign course than the evolutionary type and is much more responsive to shock therapy.

Symptomatically, reactive schizophrenia includes two categories of symptoms not found in the evolutionary form: (1) "Those which are indicative of other non-schizophrenic adjustive techniques (possibly tried before), and directed more within the framework of reality" [*21*]; and (2) manifestations of un-devalued ego aspirations which are expressed on an infantile level and removed from the sphere of adult reality fulfillment. Typical of the first category are "hallucinations and delusions which are referable to the paranoid reaction tendency to negate frustration by distortion of the environment (rationalization and projection)" [*21*]. This condition must be differentiated from the relatively rare disorder, *paranoia,* in which adult goals are not abandoned and loss of contact with reality is neither desired nor attained; but the patient's perception of that portion of his psychological field which is most significant for him is so distorted by a self-consistent delusional system that actual participation in a shared social reality impinging upon this field becomes impossible. Outside of this rather extensive field, however, the attitudes, values and perceptions of patients with paranoia are entirely reasonable and realistic.[2]

> "The most common examples of the second type of supplementary symptoms are active catatonic negativism and the . . . ideas of rebirth, 'eternality,' omnipotence and cosmic identification which recapitulate the corresponding infantile elements of narcissistic solipsism as modified by the greater breadth of adult experience. Catatonic hypersuggestibility, on the other hand, is more indicative of extensive de-maturation and symbolic of complete passivity and dependence. An actively negativistic catatonic schizophrenic . . . tries to destroy the objects and persons in his environment responsible for frustrating his aroused hypertrophic ego; whereas the manic patient is seeking to negate frustration by ceaseless . . . activity the success of which is internally assured by gross impairment of the self-critical faculty" [*21*].

In catatonics, the severance and disinvolvement of self from reality and mature standards of goal structure are most complete and abrupt. There is no acknowledgment of defeat or cessation of striving; the same intense struggle for ego aggrandizement is merely transferred to the patient's subjective reality and carried on at a lower level of goal maturity. This transition may be accomplished within the space of several days or even several hours, and is most apt to occur in proud, vigorous, and volatile individuals capable of intense, uninhibited rage responses.

Depressive Reactions. Instead of regressing to a less mature goal structure and seeking ego aggrandizement in a subjective reality of his own making, another alternative is open to a severely traumatized anxiety neurotic: He may accept the defeat of his ego aspirations, wallow in the misery of his impaired self-esteem, and renounce all further striving. Soon he is overcome by emotional depression and physical and mental retardation. Suffering and hopelessness are acute, and the individual is so completely overwhelmed by his unworthiness that he sees little point in living. The sense of future time in relation to the ego is lost, and there is a strong desire for death. This often leads to refusal to eat, and frequently to suicidal attempts. There is no purposeful withdrawal from reality as such; but preoccupation with his own worthlessness, profound physical and mental retardation, extreme depression of mood and abandonment of striving make participation in social reality completely impossible. When this stage is reached, anxiety can no longer occur since self-esteem could not possibly sink any lower, and since both ego aspirations and the future cease to have any meaning.

Depressive reactions are closely related to acute states of anxiety for several reasons. The anxiety neurotic generally has a well developed self-critical faculty in relation to his own abilities which tends to become even more severe as anxiety increases. Furthermore, he tends to react to frustration with a lowering of self-esteem and a disorganization of performance ability which further increase his feeling of worthlessness. If he is using this state of disorganization as a means of frustrating the acceptance of a "half-loaf adjustment" and of justifying his executive and volitional dependence on others, he has reason to exaggerate his incompetence even further and to erect all kinds of irrelevant barriers and impossibly high standards.

Because of the anxiety sufferer's high goal frustration tolerance, however, defeat is not accepted easily. He continues for some time to maintain his grandiose ego aspirations despite the collapsed state of his self-esteem, looking for some new basis on which to restructure his shattered ambitions. Hence arises the mixture of frantic aimless activity, acute anxiety, emotional depression and intense fear of death (see page 380) that is found in agitated depression. *Involutional melancholia* is a form of agitated depression occurring in menopausal women which is precipitated in part by the threat to biosocial status posed by the prospect of sterility and by the emotional instability secondary to hormonal imbalance. In spite of the characteristic self-condemnatory trend found in this condition, ego hypertrophy betrays itself in the patient's assertion that she is the "*greatest* sinner in the world." The state of agitated depression may either continue chronically or at any point assume the retarded form.

Mania and depression occur singly more frequently than alternately [*61*]. However, the existence of one condition does predispose toward the occurrence of the other. As convalescence from depression begins, the patient realizes how unwarranted and exaggerated his dismal outlook on life was. Thus, in the first intoxication of release from despair, the seeds of mania are sown; for it seems no less miraculous to be delivered from a state in which the reasonable seemed impossible than to pass into a state in which the impossible seems certain. Conversely, when the manic stage collapses, the "let-down" may precipitate depression on the same basis. A tendency toward reaction-formation in relation to the self-critical faculty also predisposes toward violent fluctuations in self-evaluation (see page 458) by interfering with fusion of positive and negative elements.

It is interesting to note that even in the depths of depression there is some attempt to preserve ego grandiosity through displacement of affect. The patient admits worthlessness, but usually for some irrelevantly innocuous reason. Depressions also are sometimes complicated by obsessive perplexity reactions which serve the same defensive functions as ordinary obsessions.

IMPLICATIONS OF EGO DEVELOPMENT FOR PSYCHOTHERAPY[3]

The Overvaluation of Psychotherapy

We are witnessing today a vast but not inexplicable overvaluation of the field of psychotherapy. Exaggerated and unwarranted claims are being made for this relatively new addition to medicine's therapeutic armamentarium. In some quarters it has taken on the status of panacea, promising to all within its reach a fuller and richer life, greater personality integration and self-realization, and freedom from tension, anxiety and disabling psychological symptoms of all varieties. This trend, of course, has its cultural supports. In the first place, there is the tremendous prestige of science in general and of medicine in particular to draw upon. It was relatively easy, therefore, for psychotherapy to establish itself as a branch of medicine and to borrow medicine's mantle of scientific prestige and authority. In the process two weaknesses in the analogy have escaped general detection. It was forgotten that clinical medicine is built upon the firm foundations of anatomy, physiology, biochemistry, pathology, pharmacology, etc., whereas psychotherapy enjoys precious little of an empirical scientific substructure. It is only recently that any attention at all has been given to the problems of evidence in psychotherapy [*54*]. Secondly, the theoretical structure of clinical medicine is cogent, self-consistent and in harmony with the concepts of its parent sciences. In psychotherapy, there are innumerable warring factions with completely antagonistic theories and little concensus with respect to fundamental issues; yet each group claims expertness and reputability, while often formulating its system with consummate disregard for established principles of general psychology.

A second cultural support favoring the overvaluation of psychotherapy has been the sudden public awakening to the importance, prevalence and economic cost of mental illness. The high incidence of psychiatric casualties in World War II increased official willingness to remedy the shortage of psychotherapists; and economic prosperity created for the first time an actual surplus of demand over supply in terms of ability to pay for needed services. The Federal government underwrote training programs in clinical psychology, many new clinical positions opened up, and many general psychologists climbed on the more promising and more remunerative clinical bandwagon. Concurrently private practice in psychiatry greatly expanded.

A third cultural support is traceable to the current tendency to over-psychologize all aspects of modern living. We have already noted this trend in relation to moral problems from which a strong attempt is being made to remove all ethical content and to restate issues simply in behavioral terms. A similar situation has arisen in relation to social, political and economic problems which some psychologists attempt to explain on a psychological plane alone. Within such a conceptual framework, psychotherapy naturally looms as a logical cure for all of the world's ills.

A fourth cultural support stems from a long-seething over-reaction to a core of ideological trends prominent in the first half of the present century which emphasized principles inherently limiting man's capacity for behavioral change. Illustrative of such ideas are Freud's concepts of the id and of a phylogenetically predetermined sequence of psychosexual development; Jung's "racial unconscious"; the concept of "repetition compulsion"; the emphasis upon the prepotent influence of infant experience upon adult personality structure; the notion of a universal Oedipus conflict; Hall's theory of individual psychological growth as a recapitulation of cultural development, etc. The almost inevitable over-reaction to this ideology was the assertion of a rather naive *tabula rasa* doctrine: Human nature is infinitely plastic and malleable; problems of psychological development have no universal common denominator, but reflect in every instance only the operation of unique social conditions; genetic and constitutional factors are of minor importance since man is primarily a creature of his social environment and can be molded into any form his culture wishes him to take.

This new trend was not without its influence on psychotherapy. It led to an unbounded confidence in the patient's capacity to reconstruct his personality on a more wholesome basis regardless of his previous history as long as the stimulus and motivation for same were endogenously derived. This point of view naturally led to a de-emphasis of developmental diagnosis and to a concentration upon the current adjustive situation. Perhaps both the optimism and the preoccupation with present problems stem from the predominant experience of non-directive therapists with clients having minor adjustive difficulties largely of a situational nature.

This unlimited optimism with respect to an adult's ability to remake his personality is not only unsupported by any empirical evidence but seems highly unlikely in the light of theoretical considerations with respect to the reversibility of basic personality patterns (see page 264). A not-to-be ignored consideration also in determining the limits of possible change is the benevolence of an individual's environment and the degree of control he can exercise over it. In the case of children, for example, this latter factor is especially important.

It is obvious, therefore, that the scientific status and role of psychotherapy must be seen in clearer perspective before much progress can be made. Principles of psychotherapy must be related to principles of psychology. Hypotheses regarding the processes of psychotherapy must be empirically validated and related to outcomes. Clinicians must cease demanding exemption from the laws of scientific evidence and must be willing to regard diagnoses as hypotheses to be proven rather than as unchallengeable facts. Clinical hunches and impressions must motivate the search for general psychodynamic principles and for definitive psychological diagnoses rather than be offered *per se* as the equivalent of empirically established data. And finally psychotherapists must avoid arousing extravagant and unwarranted hopes for cure, hopes which when frustrated only augment adjustive stress. Criteria must be established indicating when psychotherapy can be useful, what the objectives are, what limitations exist, and the maximum change that can be expected in terms of developmental history, personality structure, age, diagnostic entity, and the environmental situation of the patient.

The Overvaluation of Unconscious Motivation and Insight

Contributing to the current overvaluation of psychotherapy, but on a conceptual plane rather than as a cultural support, is the psychoanalytic overemphasis upon unconscious motivation as the central etiological mechanism in the production of neurotic symptoms. If behavior disorders could be interpreted as symbolic expressions of or defenses against repressed unconscious motives, then it seemed reasonable to expect complete cure as soon as the patient could be made to appreciate the motivation underlying his symptoms (insight). When this failed to happen in all but a few dramatic cases, analysts explained that intellectual understanding was insufficient and that emotional acceptance and practical application of insight to current life situations ("working through") were also necessary. Emotional acceptance, they argued, was facilitated by catharsis of the affect involved in the repressed complex; and since the source of such complexes supposedly resided in childhood psychosexual development, catharsis could be best effected therapeutically by a "transference" relationship in which the therapist plays the role of parent figure to re-elicit the expression of repressed childhood motives and attitudes. These additional techniques, according to this way of thinking, do not invalidate the crucial role of insight but merely implement it.

Non-directive therapists also stress the role of perceptual reorganization through insight, but decry therapist participation except for purposes of reflection and clarification of the client's feelings. Interpretation and "transference" are tabu, and attention is focused on current conflicts apart from their developmental origins. It is claimed that emotional acceptance of insight is facilitated by the creation of a permissive atmosphere which minimizes resistance to change, by emphasis upon self-discovery of underlying attitudes and motivations, and by emotional relatedness on the part of the therapist to the client. Freeman has recently suggested reinforcement of insight by diagrammatic representation, the use of relevant, instructive films, and opportunity for observation and therapy in reality and role-playing situations [*119*].

The present writer would agree that "working through," catharsis, "transference," optimal permissiveness, self-discovery, and emotional relatedness of therapist to patient are all valuable aids for the implementation of insight. However, acceptance of the therapeutic value of insight does not imply acceptance of the theory that all neurotic symptoms reflect the operation of repression and unconscious motivation. Many neurotic symptoms can occur with complete possession of insight; and lack of conscious accessibility is not necessarily a precondition for lack of insight, since oftentimes, the relation of symptoms to conscious motives is not appreciated. The reason for this, as has already been noted, is that repression is not the primary cause of anxiety, ego immaturity and other forms of ego damage, but a defense against anxiety which facilitates the development of neurotic defenses and interferes with the evolution of more constructive solutions. Hence, it is unrealistic to expect that the acquisition of insight can by itself repair lack of self-esteem or create feelings of security and adequacy. More constructive relief from anxiety might conceivably be achieved by optimal manipulation of the environment, reorganization of goal structure, altering the quality of interpersonal relationships, increasing tolerance for unalterable disabilities, and creating a new set of environmental expectations (see discussion below).

In this connection it should be recalled that displacement of affect not only occurs from "unconscious" material to symbolic conscious equivalents but also in the opposite direction. Unless the therapist is aware of this possibility, he may easily confound cause-and-effect relationships. It should also be realized that the perceptual reorganization achieved as a result of insight does not represent absolute and unconditional change, but change which is stable in relation to a given amount of adjustive stress. Let the degree of stress increase, and retrogression to the former level of insight may readily occur.

The Place of Diagnosis in Therapy

While it is true (as claimed by non-directive therapists) that present personality structure represents a precipitate of all the relevant developmental influences entering into its formation, mere attention to the current adjustive problem without definitive diagnosis in terms of developmental history is not likely to lead to permanent therapeutic benefit. Meaningful insight into the present adjustive situation cannot be gained by patient or therapist by examining only the end product of development. Neither sequence nor process of growth is deducible from eventual outcome although the latter necessarily reflects their operation.

The practical clinical significance of this consideration enters into one of the first decisions that the therapist is obliged to make in every case he undertakes: Are the adjustive difficulties of the patient an outcome of current transitional or situational pressures, or are they reflective of serious abnormalities in ego devaluation or maturation? Until this question can be answered, no intelligent decision with respect to prognosis, length, depth, urgency and type of therapy indicated can be made.

Nevertheless it need not be imagined that all therapy must be postponed until a definitive diagnosis is possible. In acute cases, supportive or drug therapy, environmental manipulation, and relief from immediate pressures and frustration are indicated to forestall imminent psychotic breakdown. Where such breakdown has already occurred, shock therapy may be necessary to make the patient more accessible to interpersonal influences. In less acute cases, concurrently with developmental diagnosis, progress in solving current problems of adjustment must be made if the later acquisition of insight is to have any practical significance; otherwise not only does exploration of the past become an academic pursuit, but also anxiety increases and deterioration of the environmental situation occurs (especially in the spheres of vocational adaptation, social relationships and personal independence), making actual implementation of insight all but impossible.

The common psychoanalytic practice of ignoring situational factors until complete insight is secured is partly a reflection of the Hippocratian concept of the finiteness and single source of drive and affect to which most analysts subscribe. According to this reasoning, as long as affect is bound up in repressed neurotic complexes, the acquisition of more wholesome adjustive mechanisms is impossible since the latter could not be energized by necessary emotional components; only after insight is attained can this "frozen" affect be liberated for other purposes. However, if we adopt the more plausible assumption that "functionally autonomous" motives can arise as the result of new life experiences, new techniques of adjustment can be successfully sustained even though emotional energy is tied up in unsolved conflicts. It is also a common experience that motivation develops retroactively as a result of the interest aroused and the gratification obtained from successful performance of an activity that might have been grudgingly undertaken in the first place.

The Place of Direction in Therapy

The same fetish of permissiveness that we criticized in our chapter on parent-child relationships is gradually capturing the field of psychotherapy. Almost by definition in some quarters, the more permissive a therapist is, the less he structures the therapeutic situation; the fewer his expectations, the less he tends to judge the patient; the wider his limits of tolerance and the less authority he wields, the more superior his professional attitudes and equipment are accounted to be.

The non-directive therapist takes the position that change cannot be imposed upon the individual from without but must originate endogenously. He takes issue with the traditional medical approach in which the physician diagnoses the disorder, explains to the patient the genesis and meaning of his symptoms and prescribes the necessary treatment. Instead the patient does all of these things by himself; and the therapist by clarifying and reflecting the former's own productions merely helps him to make better use of his own inherent resources for acquiring insight and instigating change.

This insistence upon the fact that in the final analysis it is only the individual himself who can actually effect a reorganization of his own personality structure is logical enough providing that it is qualified by certain realistic limitations. In the first place, ego maturation takes place under the impact of mature social expectations and within a realistic framework of interpersonal relations which does not ignore relevant moral problems. Because lasting personality change can occur only when there is genuine internal acceptance of the need for same does not mean that it can or must always be endogenously stimulated. Secondly, patients cannot assume the major responsibility for self-direction when they are disorganized, panic-stricken, or hopelessly caught between the vicious cycle of anxiety and the fixed, perseverative, and maladaptive responses which it tends to engender. The degree of responsibility and self-direction which a patient can assume cannot be fixed dogmatically at the start of therapy and maintained throughout, but must be flexibly modified to meet the requirements of both his original condition and subsequent improvement therein. In many clinical situations, supportive therapy, environmental manipulation, reliance on drugs and physical therapy, and interpretation by the therapist are indicated.

The Need for Realistic Expectations. Throughout this volume we have stressed the fact that ego maturation does not occur spontaneously but largely in response to new social expectations. This principle is supported by evidence from the social psychology of attitude formation and attitude change [*233*]. Goals, ego attributes, and attitudes toward self also change in response to cultural demands and supports, since individuals are dependent upon their social milieu for status, approval, love, acceptance, security and a sense of belongingness [*19*].

To the patient, the therapist represents the expectations of the social reality to which he has not yet succeeded in adjusting adequately. Much of the stimulus for change in motivation, attitude, and adjustive behavior during the period of treatment will come from the expectations of the therapist in his role of social reality surrogate. However, if the latter takes the position that it is the patient's prerogative to structure the framework of expectancy and set the limits[4] in the relationship, the patient not only feels under no pressure to abandon his unrealistic, autistic or immature framework of reference, but also feels justifiably encouraged to seek adjustment within such a framework with the tacit approval, support and sanction of the therapist. The latter, for example, must continue to insist on the patient's acceptance of the need for vocational adjustment on a realistic level, rather than remain non-commital when confronted with grandiose and impractical ambitions that blithely ignore insuperable obstacles of ability and job opportunity.

Part of this framework of realistic and mature expectations in which the therapeutic setting is embedded consists of a code of moral values. Most significant human behavior has an ethical aspect which cannot be ignored without sacrificing much of its essence insofar as interpersonal relationships are concerned. If the therapist articulates no moral expectations and fails to express ethical judgments, the patient is justified in assuming that the former either approves of his immoral behavior, or else considers that any type of ethical solution he (the patient) is satisfied with is also satisfactory to the therapist. In the latter case, therapy takes place in an amoral setting, and the patient is supported in his belief that he is above the moral law which applies to ordinary mortals. Silence on the part of the therapist condones immorality and whitewashes guilt feelings.

Both therapist and patient must face the problem of guilt and moral accountability squarely. If guilt feelings are unfounded, they should be eliminated; if they are warranted they should be acknowledged and dealt with constructively. Proper timing, good rapport, and tact on the part of the therapist are necessary as well as a constructive approach rather than an attitude of final condemnation. However, if in spite of skillful handling the patient discontinues therapy because of the therapist's expression of moral judgment, it is doubtful whether he could have benefited from it in the first place. The pragmatic approach to ethical problems employed by many non-directive therapists, i.e., moral behavior is desirable simply because it makes for more wholesome, stable and predictable interpersonal relationships, is actually devoid of any moral content and lends support to current philosophies of expediency.

It is equally unrealistic to deny the inherent authority residing in the role of therapist and to set up the dictum that therapeutic benefit is limited in instances where the therapist is in a position of authority in relation to the patient. In the first place, the very fact that one individual appeals for help on the basis of another's expert knowledge inevitably injects an authoritarian aspect into the relationship. Secondly, if the therapist plays his necessary role of representing cultural expectations and defining limits for the therapeutic relationship, he automatically becomes invested with authority. Whether he wishes to create a "transference" situation or not, the patient inevitably reacts toward him as an authority figure, since the relationship recapitulates so many features of the parent-child relationship [*240, 336*]. Lastly, the therapist's effectiveness depends upon his being perceived by the patient as an individual of strength, someone to be respected rather than pushed around like an ineffective, underdominating parent [*46, 403*]. Without authority he can set no realistic limits; and in the absence of such limits, therapy can only compound existing ego damage.

It does seem reasonable to expect that there will be less resistance to genuine emotional acceptance of insight if such insight is the product of self-discovery rather than of interpretation by the therapist. However, self-discovery is by no means an indispensable condition for acceptance of insight. Satellizers, for example, are more willing to accept the therapist's interpretations than non-satellizers. Interpretation is also necessary in acute phases of anxiety when panic destroys all ability to think clearly, and in cases where the acquisition of insight is persistently blocked by stubborn "blind-spots."

In a large number of cases also, in which the patient is either hostile, withdrawn, suspicious, or diffident, it is necessary for the therapist to take the initiative in the relationship rather than passively allow the former to explore the situation by himself [*364*]. As the more mature and independent person in the relationship, he has to be willing to make the advances if any need to be made. Anyone who has had experience in treating hostile children and adolescents also recognizes that "warmth, love, understanding and acceptance" (maximal permissiveness) is no magic formula that will automatically diminish the latter's aggressive proclivities [364]. Such is only the case in instances of counteraggression induced by environmental deprivation, and not where hostility is a deeply ingrained orientation toward life or a fixed form of defense against anxiety [364].

By structuring the therapeutic situation in this fashion, the therapist does not necessarily make the patient unduly dependent upon him. Real danger of dependence only arises if direction and support are maintained too long or longer than warranted by the patient's adjustive capacity, especially if during this time no progress has been made toward economic independence. The therapist's presence and support then become necessary conditions upon which the patient's security depends. The therapist also becomes reluctant to terminate the situation since he prefers to earn his living in a familiar setting. The risk of dependency is also greater in the case of satellizers, since non-satellizers do not tend to form deep emotional attachments to their therapists, merely accepting their direction on the basis of its objective validity. Since there is no subservience of self in the latter's acceptance of assistance, volitional independence is not essentially surrendered.

Indications for Directive Therapy. Indications for special forms of directive therapy exist (1) in acute (pre-psychotic) cases of maladjustment; (2) in cases rendered inaccessible to interpersonal intervention because of psychotic inaccessibility; (3) in the treatment of children and adolescents; and (4) in cases of chronic anxiety and other forms of chronic maladjustment.

The first therapeutic consideration in agitated and panic states of anxiety, when patients are confused, helpless, desperate and on the verge of either depressive psychosis or reactive schizophrenia, is symptomatic relief of anxiety and frustration. In terms of psychotherapy, this may involve the extension of immediate emotional support, and the use of reassurance, suggestion, prestige authority, and cautiously advanced interpretation. The patient's environment must be simplified by the elimination of unnecessary pressures and harassments of all kinds; and the therapist must be prepared to intervene actively in the former's personal affairs, and if necessary help make swift decisions for him. Sedation, tolserol [*89, 173*], desensitization to epinephrine [*60*], and even electric shock therapy [*259*] may be necessary to keep acute anxiety under control and prevent the patient from seeking relief in psychotic mechanisms. Explanation of how the surrender of adult strivings in a reality setting may lead to psychosis sometimes has a protective effect. The use of non-directive techniques in such situations can only end in disaster.

In psychotic states where the patient is either preoccupied with his own subjective reality or too overwhelmed by his defeat to remain in contact with objective reality, it is first necessary to make him more accessible by means of shock therapy before psychotherapy has much chance of success. However, Rosen has shown that this difficulty in communication can be greatly reduced in schizophrenia if the therapist is willing to think and feel in terms of the patient's reality in the early stages of treatment [*1, 46, 335, 336*]. This obviously requires a degree of individual attention which would be impossible without increasing the number of psychiatrists in mental hospitals by several thousand per cent. For practical reasons, therefore, shock methods of treatment are presently indispensable.

The use of physical methods of therapy represents in no sense an abandonment of a psychological theory of behavior disorder. If we are ready to concede that an altered state of behavioral reactivity can be induced by fatigue, hormonal imbalance, brain injury, syphilitic encephalitis, uremia, etc., it is no less logical to grant that favorable modification of behavior can be brought about by manipulation of the anatomical or physiological substrate of behavior and consciousness. The more plausible theories of the action of shock therapy (i.e., selective disorganization of the more recently acquired neurotic behavior patterns [*174, 269*], removal of undesirable cortical control [*53*], and impairment of the self-critical faculty [*21*] are quite compatible with psychological approaches to behavior disorder.

Psychiatric treatment of children and adolescents requires considerable reliance on environmental manipulation for two reasons: Independent acquisition of insight is difficult for children because of limitations in their verbal ability; and (2) both children and adolescents are largely under the immediate control of powerful adults who in most cases are largely responsible for the adjustive difficulties involved, and without whose cooperation, improvement in the interpersonal environment and implementation of insight would be impossible.

Since the personality of the parents constitutes the most important variable affecting the child's ego development, it can be safely predicted that psychotherapy with the latter can bring little lasting improvement until favorable modification of parental practices and attitudes is obtained [*371*]. As a matter of fact, this is what is actually found in child guidance centers [*338*]. Where the parent-child relationship is essentially wholesome, simple mediation or interpretation of parent and child to each other is often helpful [*282*]. Acceptance of these therapeutic principles does not in the least rule out an attempt to secure the child's active participation in the process of change [*11*]. Through recognition, objectification and acceptance of his feelings (by means of role-playing and play techniques in a shared reality), the child patient is often enabled to acquire and implement insight and achieve greater security, integration and maturity of personality structure.

Directed guidance is also necessary in chronic maladjustments such as anxiety disorders if progress is to be made in solving current problems of adjustment, and if fixed and rigid defensive mechanisms which prevent efficient learning and working (see page 375) are to be overcome. The anxiety neurotic who has acquired maladaptive ways of learning, perceiving, and setting goals is not free to independently select and utilize beneficial insights (that might arise in the course of therapy) because of potent reaction sensitivities which predispose his behavior along rigidly channelized lines of a defensive nature [*10*]. Guidance in restructuring his environment and response repertory is needed, e.g., selective ego disinvolvment from untenable situations, lowering of aspirational level, formation of satellizing-like relationships, emphasis upon economic security with creative avocational opportunities, avoidance of excessive advance preparation in new learning situations, increasing tolerance for conscious anxiety, minimizing the tendency to achieve security and forestall defeat through abnormal circumscription of the environment, etc.

However, the chief practical implication which a psychology of ego development holds for the treatment of behavior disorders is that prophylaxis is far more effective than therapy. If during the crisis of ego devaluation, a child is accepted and valued for himself, he will satellize and acquire an intrinsic sense of security and adequacy that will prove highly resistant to environmental vicissitudes and will protect him from neurotic anxiety. If during the crisis of ego maturation he is spared from overprotection, underdomination, and overdomination, and given opportunity to undergo desatellization, it is unlikely that he will fail to acquire the mature ego attributes of adult personality structure. And failing the protection of these prophylactic measures, it should be realized that the earlier therapy is instituted, the greater the possibility that damage and distortion are correctible. However, in the light of the paucity of empirical evidence regarding both rationale for and outcome of psychotherapy, it behooves psychiatrists and clinical psychologists to adopt greater caution and humility in appraising the scientific status, the applicability and the probable success of their therapeutic techniques.

NOTES

[1] Despert [*81*] takes essentially the same position with respect to the etiology of autistic behavior in children.

[2] Unpublished data of the writer based on attitude inventories, tests of logical inference and tests of ability to perceive absurdities and unjustifiable conclusions from a given set of conditions.

[3] No attempt will be made to present a definitive discussion of psychotherapy, a task which deserves a volume in itself. Here we shall only be concerned with some of the implications of a psychology of ego development for psychotherapy.

[4] Extreme non-directivists do set limits, but these generally relate to certain minimal formal standards governing the therapeutic relationship (i.e., arriving on time for appointments, avoidance of excessive discussion of irrelevant topics, refraining from physical assault upon the therapist, etc.) and not to the basic framework of the contemplated adjustment.

Bibliography

1. Aarons, Z. A.: Some aspects of theory and treatment of schizophrenia. Psychoan. Rev., *38:* 113-126, 1951.
2. Abraham, K.: Selected Papers. London: Hogarth, 1927.
3. Arahamsen, D.: Psychiatric aspects of criminal behavior. Abstract. Digest Neurol. and Psychiat., *19:* 100, May, 1951.
4. Adler, A.: The Neurotic Constitution. New York: Moffat, Yard, 1917.
14. ——: The Individual and his Religion. New York: Macmillan, 1950. Harcourt, Brace, 1925.
6. Adorno, T. W., et al.: The Authoritarian Personality. Studies in Prejudice Series. New York: Harper, 1950.
7. Aichorn, A.: Wayward Youth. New York: Viking Press, 1925.
8. Albee, G. W.: The prognostic importance of delusions in schizophrenia. J. Abnorm. and Soc. Psychol., *46:* 208-212, April, 1951.
9. Alexander, F.: Development of the Ego-Psychology. In "Psychoanalysis Today: Its Scope and Function" (S. Lorand, Ed.). New York: International Universities Press, 1944.
10. ——, and French, T. M.: Psychoanalytic Therapy. New York: Ronald, 1946.
11. Allen, F. M.: Psychotherapy With Children. New York: Norton, 1942.
12. Allport, G. W.: The ego in contemporary psychology. Psychol. Rev. *50:* 451-478, 1943.
13. ——: Personality, a symposium. III. Geneticism versus ego-structure in theories of personality. Brit. J. Educ. Psychol., *16:* 52-68, 1946.
14. ——: The Individual and his Religion. New York: Macmillan, 1950.
15. Alper, J. G.: Task-orientation vs. ego-orientation in learning and retention. Am. J. Psychol., *59:* 236-248, 1946.
16. Ammons, C. H.: Personality variables in mirror drawing. Mot Skills Res. Exch. *2:* 15, 1950.
17. Anderson, J. E.: The Psychology of Development and Personal Adjustment. New York: Holt, 1949.
18. Angyal, A.: Foundations for a Science of Personality. New York: The Commonwealth Fund, 1941.
19. Auerbach, J. G.: What makes people change. Am. J. Psychother., *5:* 172-186, 1951.
20. Ausubel, D. P.: The psychopathology and treatment of drug addiction in relation to the mental hygiene movement. Psychiat. Quart. Supplement, *22:* Part II, 219-250, 1948.
21. ——: A psychopathological classification of schizophrenia. Psychiat. Quart., *23:* 127-144, 1949.

22. ——: Ego-development and the learning process. Child Developm., *20:* 173-190, 1949
23. ——: Problems of adolescent adjustment. Bulletin of Nat'l. Ass'n. of Secondary School Principals, *34:* 1-84, 1950.
24. ——: Negativism as a phase of ego development. Am. J. Orthopsychiat., *20:* 796-805, 1950.
25. ——: Prestige Motivation of Gifted Children. Genet. Psychol. Monographs, *43:* 53-117, 1951.
26. Bakwin, R. M. M., and Bakwin, H.: Psychologic care of the pre-school child, III. J. of Pediatrics, *16:* 357-374, 1940.
27. Baldwin, A. L.: Socialization and one parent-child relationship. Child Developm., *19:* 128-136, 1948.
28. ——, Kalhorn, J. and Breese, H.: The Appraisal of Parent Behavior. Psychological Monographs No. 299. Washington, D. C.: American Psychological Assn., 1949.
29. Baldwin, J. M.: Social and Ethical Interpretation in Mental Development. New York: Macmillan, 1897.
30. ——: Mental Development in the Child and in the Race. New York: Macmillan, 1906.
31. Balint, M.: Ego strength and education of the ego. Psychoan. Quart., *11:* 87-95, 1952.
32. Barker, R. G., and Wright, H. F.: Psychological ecology and the problem of psychosocial development. Child Developm., *20:* 131-143, 1949.
33. ——: Child Psychology. In "Annual Review of Psychology", Vol. II. Stanford, California: Annual Reviews, 1951.
34. Barrie, J. M.: The Admirable Crichton. London: Hodder and Stoughton, 1914.
35. Bartlett, E. R., and Harris, D. B.: Personality factors in delinquency. Sch. and Soc., *43:* 653-656, 1936.
36. Bartlett, F.: Present trends in psychoanalysis. Science and Society, *9:* 214-231, 1945.
37. Baruch, D.: A study of reported tension in interparental relationships as co-existent with behavior adjustment in young children. J. Exper. Educ., *6:* 187-204, 1937.
38. Bateson, G.: Cultural Determinants of Personality. In "Personality and the Behavior Disorders" (J. Mc.V. Hunt, ed.) New York: Ronald, 1944.
39. Bayley, N.: A study of the crying of infants during mental and physical tests. J. Genet. Psychol., *40:* 306-329, 1932.
40. Benedek, T.: Adaptation to reality in early infancy. Psychoan. Quart., *7:* 200-215, 1938.
41. Benedict, R.: Patterns of Culture. Boston: Houghton, 1934.
42. Bernfeld, S.: Psychology of the Infant. New York: Brentano's, 1929.
43. Bertocci, P. A.: The psychological self, the ego and personality. Psychol. Rev., *52:* 91-99, 1945.

44. Bettelheim, B.: Individual and mass behavior in extreme situations. J. Abnorm. and Soc. Psychol., *38:* 417-452, 1943.
45. Betts, G. H.: Religious attitudes and activities of university students: A report. Relig. Educ., *23:* 917-919, 1927.
46. Betz, B.: Strategic conditions in the psychotherapy of persons with schizophrenia. Am. J. Psychiat. *107:* 203-215, 1950.
47. Biber, B., Murphy, L. B., Woodcock, L. P., and Black, I. S.: Child Life in School. New York: Dutton, 1942.
48. Blos, P.: The Adolescent Personality: A Study of Individual Behavior. New York: D. Appleton-Century, 1941.
49. Blum, G. S.: A Study of the Psychoanalytic Theory of Psychosexual Development. Genet. Psychol. Monographs, *39:* 3-99, 1949.
50. Bradley, C.: Schizophrenia in childhood. Nervous Child, *1:* 199-231, 1942.
51. Bridges, K. M. B.: The School and Emotional Development of the Preschool Child. London: Kegan Paul, 1931.
52. ——: Emotional development in early infancy. Child Developm., *3:* 324-334, 1932.
53. Brisset, Ch., and Gachkel, V.: Médicine psychosomatique en U. R. S. R. 1. La cure de sommeil. Presse méd., *59:* 465-466, 1951.
54. Brody, B., Newman, R., and Redlich, F. C.: Sound recording and the problem of evidence in psychiatry. Science, *113:* 379-380, 1951.
55. Bruner, J. S., and Goodman, C. C.: Value and need as organizing factors in perception. J. Abnorm. and Soc. Psychol., *27:* 203-208, 1948.
56. Burgess, E. W., and Locke, H. J.: The Family: From Institution to Companionship. New York: American Book Company, 1945.
57. Burgum, M.: Constructive values associated with rejection. Am. J. Orthopsychiat., *10:* 312-326, 1940.
58. Bychowski, G.: On relations between the ego and the superego. Psychoan. Rev., *30:* 313-324, 1943.
59. Calkins, M. W.: The self in scientific psychology. Am. J. Psychol., *26:* 495-524, 1915.
60. Cameron, D. E.: Adrenalin administration in persistent anxiety states. Am. J. Med. Sci., *210:* 281, 1945.
61. Cameron, N.: The Psychology of Behavior Disorders: A Biosocial Interpretation. Boston: Houghton Mifflin, 1947.
62. Campbell, A. L.: The personality adjustment of only children. Psychol. Bull., *31:* 193-203, 1934.
63. Cantor, N.: The Dynamics of Learning. Buffalo: Foster and Steward, 1946.
64. Caprio, F. S.: A study of some psychological reactions during prepubescence to the idea of death. Psychiat. Quart., *24:* 495-504, 1950.
65. Champney, H.: The variables of parent behavior. J. Abnorm. and Soc. Psychol., *36:* 525-542, 1941.

66. Chein, I.: The awareness of self and the structure of the ego. Psychol. Rev., *51:* 304-314, 1944.
67. Clardy, E. R.: A study of the development and course of schizophrenia in children. Psychiat. Quart., *25:* 81-90, 1951.
68. Clark, K. B., and Clark, M. P.: Racial Identification and Preference in Negro Children. In "Readings in Social Psychology" (T. Newcomb and E. Hartley, eds.). New York: Holt, 1947.
69. Cogan, L., Conklin A., and Hollingworth, H. L.: An experimental study of self-analysis. Sch. and Soc., *2:* 171-179, 1915.
70. Cohen, M. B., and Cohen, R. A.: Personality as a factor in administrative decisions. Psychiatry, *14:* 46-53, 1951.
71. Cooley, C. H.: Human Nature and the Social Order. New York: Scribner, 1922.
72. Cottrell, L. S., and Dymond, R. F.: The empathic responses. Psychiatry, *12:* 355-359, 1949.
73. Davis, A.: Socialization and Adolescent Personality. In "Adolescence", 43rd Yearbook, Nat'l. Soc. Stud. Educ. Chicago: University of Chicago Press, 198-216, 1944.
74. ——, and Havighurst, R. J.: Social class and color differences in child-rearing. Amer. Sociol. Rev., *11:* 698-710, 1946.
75. De Forest, I.: Anxiety: As experienced in the creation and in the discarding of neuroses. Psychoan. Rev., *37:* 172-177, 1950.
76. ——: The self-dedication of the psychoneurotic sufferer to hostile protest and revenge. Psychiat. Quart., *24:* 706-715, 1950.
77. De Groot, J. L.: On the development of the ego and superego. Internat. J. Psychoan., *28:* 7-11, 1947.
78. Dembo, T.: Der Arger als dynamisches Problem. Psychol. Forsch., *15:* 1-144, 1931.
79. Dennis, W.: Infant development under conditions of restricted practice and of minimum social stimulation. J. Genet. Psychol., *53:* 149-158, 1938.
80. ——: Infant reaction to restraint. Tr. New York Acad. Sci., *2:* 202-218, 1940.
81. Despert, J. L.: Prophylactic aspect of schizophrenia in childhood. Nervous Child, *1:* 199-231, 1942.
82. ——, and Pierce, H. O.: The Relation of Emotional Adjustment to Intellectual Function. Genet. Psychol. Monographs, *34:* 3-56, 1946.
83. ——: Some considerations relating to the genesis of autistic behavior in children. Am. J. Orthopsychiat., *21:* 335-350, 1951.
84. Deutsch, H.: The Psychology of Women, Vol. II. Motherhood. New York: Grune & Stratton, 1945.
85. Deveraux G.: Neurotic crime vs. criminal behavior. Psychiat. Quart., *25:* 73-80, 1951.
86. Dicks, H. V.: In search of our proper ethic. Brit. J. M. Psychol., *23:* 1-14, 1950.

87. Diethelm, O., and Jones, M. R.: Influence of anxiety on attention, learning, retention, and thinking. Arch. Neurol. and Psychiat., *58:* 325-336, 1947.
88. Dimock, H. S.: Rediscovering the Adolescent. New York: Association Press, 1937.
89. Dixon, H. H., Dickel, H. A., and Haugen, G. B.: Clinical observations on tolserol in handling anxiety tension states. Am. J. M. Sc. *220:* 23-29, 1950.
90. Dollard, J., et al.: Frustration and Aggression. New Haven: Yale Uniersity Press, 1939.
91. Dostoyevsky, F. M.: Crime and Punishment. New York: Random House, 1944.
92. Du Bois, C.: Attitudes Toward Food and Hunger in Alor. In "Language, Culture and Personality" (L. Spier, ed.) Menasha, Wisc.: Sapir Memorial Publication Fund, 1941.
93. Düss, L.: Fonction psychologique du nom propre dana la reconstruction de la personalité D'une schizophrene. J. Psychol. Norm. Path., *39:* 350-366, 1946.
94. Edwards, N.: The Adolescent in Technological Society. In "Adolescence", 43rd Yearbook, Nat'l. Soc. Stud. Educ. Chicago: University of Chicago Press, 185-197, 1944.
95. Ellis, A.: An Introduction to the Principles of Scientific Psychoanalysis. Genet. Psychol. Monographs, *41:* 147-212, 1950.
96. English, O. S., and Pearson, G. H. J.: Common Neuroses of Children and Adults: Avoiding the Neurotic Pattern. New York: Norton, 1945.
97. ——, and ——: Emotional Problems of Living. New York: Norton, 1945.
98. Erikson, E. H.: Problems of Infancy and Early Childhood. In "Cyclopedia of Medicine Surgery and Specialties". Philadelphia: Davis, 715-730, 1943.
99. ——: Ego Development and Historical Change. In "The Psychoanalytic Study of the Child", Vol. II. New York: International Universities Press, 1947.
100. ——: Childhood and Tradition in Two American Indian Tribes. In "Personality in Nature, Society and Culture" (C. Kluckhohn and H. A. Murray, eds.). New York: Knopf, 1948.
101. ——: Childhood and Society. New York: Norton, 1950.
102. Escalona, S. K.: An application of the Level of Aspiration Experiment to the Study of Personality. New York: Teachers College, Columbia University, 1948.
103. ——: A commentary upon some recent changes in child-rearing practices. Child Developm., *20:* 157-162, 1949.
104. Federn, P.: Some variations in ego-feeling. Internat. J. Psychoan., *7:* 434-444, 1926.

105. ——: Narcissism in the structure of the ego. Internat. J. Psychoan., *9:* 401-419, 1928.
106. ——: Principles of psychotherapy in latent schizophrenia. Am. J. Psychother., *1:* 129-144, 1947.
107. Fehlman, C.: Parents and Teachers View the Child. New York: Teachers College, Columbia University, 1949.
108. Fenichel, O.: Ego-disturbances and their treatment. Internat. J. Psychoan., *19:* 416-438, 1938.
109. ——: The Psychoanalytic Theory of Neurosis. New York: Norton, 1945.
110. Ferenczi, S.: Steps in the Development of the Sense of Reality. In "Sex in Psychoanalysis". Boston: Badger, 1916.
111. Field, M.: Maternal attitudes found in 25 cases of children with primary behavior disorders. Am. J. Orthopsychiat., *10:* 293-311, 1940.
112. Fitz-Simons, M. J.: Some Parent-Child Relationships as Shown in Clinical Case Studies. Contributions to Education No. 643. New York: Teachers College, Columbia University, 1935.
113. Flügel, J. D.: The Psychoanaltic Study of the Family. Internat. Psychoanalytic Library, No. 3. London: Hogarth, 1921.
114. Folsom, J. K.: The Family. New York: Wiley, 1934.
115. Frank, J. D.: Individual differences in certain aspects of the level of aspiration. Am. J. Psychol., *47:* 119-129, 1935.
116. Frank, L. K.: The fundamental needs of the child. Ment. Hyg., *22:* 353-379, 1938.
117. ——: Freedom for the personality. Psychiatry, *3:* 341-349, 1940.
118. ——: The Adolescent and the Family. In "Adolescence", 43rd Yearbook, Nat'l. Soc. Stud. Educ. Chicago: University of Chicago Press, 240-254, 1944.
119. Freeman, M. J.: Reinforcement therapy: a re-evaluation of the concept of "insight" in psychotherapy. Am. J. Psychother., *5:* 32-37, 1951.
120. French, T. M., and Kasanin, J.: A psychodynamic study of the recovery of two schizophrenic cases. Psychoan. Quart., *10:* 1, 1941.
121. Frenkel-Brunswik, E.: Mechanisms of self-deception. J. Soc. Psychol., *10:* 409-420, 1939.
122. ——, and Sanford, R. N.: Some personality factors in antisemitism. J. Psychol., *20:* 271-291, 1945.
123. ——, Levinson, D. J., and Sanford, N.: The Antidemocratic Personality. In "Readings in Social Psychology" (T. Newcomb and E. Hartley, eds.). New York: Holt, 1947.
124. Freud, A.: The Ego and the Mechanisms of Defence. London: Hogarth Press, 1937.
125. ——: The significance of the evolution of psycho-analytic child-psychology. Congrès Internat. De Psychiatrie, Paris: 1950, Rapports, *5:* 29-48.
126. Freud, S.: A General Introduction to Psychoanalysis. New York: Boni and Liveright, 1921.

127. ——: Beyond the Pleasure Principle. London: International Psychoanalytic Press, 1922.
128. ——: Character and Anal Erotism in "Collected Papers", Vol. II. London: Hogarth, 1924.
129. ——: The Infantile Genital Organization of the Libido. In "Collected Papers", Vol. II. London: Hogarth, 1924.
130. ——: Formulations Regarding the Two Principles in Mental Functioning. In "Collected Papers", Vol. IV. London: Hogarth, 1925.
131. ——: Instincts and Their Vicissitudes. In "Collected Papers", Vol. IV. London: Hogarth Press, 1925.
132. ——: Three Contributions to the Theory of Sex. New York: Nervous and Mental Disease Publishing Company, 1930.
133. ——: New Introductory Lectures on Psychoanalysis. New York: Norton, 1933.
134. ——: The Ego and the Id. London: Hogarth Press, 1935.
135. ——: The Problem of Anxiety. New York: Norton, 1936.
136. Freyhan, F. A.: Clinical evaluations of psychopathic personalities. Delaware State M. J. *22:* 196-200, 1950.
137. Friedlander, K.: Anti-Social Character. In "The Psychoanalytic Study of the Child", Vol. 1, New York: International Universities Press, 189-203, 1945.
138. Fries, M. E.: Psychosomatic relationships between mother and child. Psychosom. Med. *6:* 157-162, 1944.
139. ——: The Child's Ego-Development and the Training of Adults in his Development. In "The Psychoanalytic Study of the Child", Vol. II. New York: International Universities Press, 85-112, 1946.
140. ——, and Lewi, B.: Interrelated factors in development: A study of pregnancy, labor, delivery, lying-in period and childhood. Am. J. Orthopsychiat., *8:* 726-752, 1938.
141. Fromm, E.: Escape from Freedom. New York: Farrar, 1941.
142. ——: Man for Himself: An Inquiry into the Psychology of Ethics. New York: Rinehart, 1947.
143. Fromm-Reichmann, F.: Transference problems in schizophrenics. Psychoan. Quart., *8:* 412, 1939.
144. ——: Principles of Intensive Psychotherapy. Chicago: University of Chicago Press, 1950.
145. Galdston, I.: On the etiology of depersonalization. J. Nerv. and Ment. Dis., *105:* 25-39, 1947.
146. Gardner, G. A.: The mental health of normal adolescents. Ment. Hyg., *31:* 529-540, 1947.
147. Gesell, A. L.: The Individual in Infancy. In "The Foundations of Experimental Psychology" (C. Murchison, ed.). Worcester, Mass: Clark University Press, 1929.
148. Gesell, A.: The Ontogenesis of Individual Behavior. In "Manual of Child Psychology" (L. Carmichael, ed.). New York: Wiley, 1946.

149. ——, and Ilg, F. L. Infant and Child in the Culture of Today. New York: Harper, 1943.
150. ——, and ——: The Child from Five to Ten. New York: Harper, 1946.
151. ——, and Thompson, H.: Twins T and C from Infancy to Adolescence: A Biogenetic Study of Individual Differences by the Method of Co-Twin Control. Genet. Psychol. Monographs, *24:* 256 pp., 1941.
152. Glover,E.: Grades of ego-differentiation. Internat. J. Psychoan., *11:* 1-11, 1930.
153. Glover, J.: The conception of the ego. Internat. J. Psychoan., *7:* 414-419, 1926.
154. Glueck, S., and Glueck, E.: Unraveling Juvenile Delinquency. New York, Commonwealth Fund, 1950.
155. Goldfarb, W.: Psychological privation in infancy and subsequent adjustment. Am. J. Orthopsychiat., *15:* 247-255, 1945.
156. Goldstein, K.: The Organism. New York: American Book Co., 1939.
157. Goodenough, F. L.: Developmental Psychology: An Introduction to the Study of Human Behavior. New York: D. Appleton-Century, 1945.
158. Graham, G. T., Wolf, S., and Wolff, H. G.: Changes in tissue sensitivity associated with varying life situations and emotions: Their relevance to allergy. J. of Allergy, *21:* 478-486, Nov. 1950.
159. Greenacre, P.: The predisposition to anxiety. Psychoan. Quart., *10:* 66-94, 610-638, 1941.
160. ——: Conscience in the psychopath. Am. J. Orthopsychiat., *15:* 247-255, 1945.
161. Grinker, R. R., and Spiegel, S. P.: Men Under Stress. Philadelphia: Blakiston, 1945.
162. Hamilton, G. V.: An Introduction to Objective Psychobiology. St. Louis: C. V. Mosby, 1925.
163. Hankins, D.: The psychology and direct treatment of adolescents. Ment. Hyg., *27:* 238-247, 1943.
164. Harms, E.: Ego-inflation and ego-deflation; a fundamental concept of analytical psychology of childhood. Nerv. Child, *6:* 284-300, 1947.
165. Harris, R. E., and Thompson, C. W.: The relation of emotional adjustment to intellectual function: A note. Psychol. Bull., *44:* 283-287, 1947.
166. Harrower, M. R.: Social Status and the Moral Development of the Child. Brit. J. Educ. Psychol., *1:* 75-95, 1934.
167. Hart, H. H.: Problems of identification. Psychiat Quart., *21:* 274-293, 1947.
168. Hartogs, R.: The clinical investigation and differential measurement of anxiety. Am. J. Psychiat., *106:* 929-934, 1950.
169. Hartshorne, H., May, M. A., et al.: Studies in the Nature of Character. I—Studies in Deceit. II—Studies in Service and Self-Control. III—Studies in the Organization of Character. New York: Macmillan, 1930.
170. Havighurst, R. J. et al.: The development of the ideal self in childhood and adolescence. J. Educ. Res., *40:* 241-257, 1946.

171. Havighurst, R. J., and Taba, H.: Adolescent Character and Personality. New York: Wiley, 1949.
172. Healy, W., and Bronner, A. F.: New Light on Delinquency. New Haven: Yale University Press, 1936.
173. Hecker, A. O., Mercer, M., and Griffin, M. A.: Further clinical investigation of tolserol (myanesin). Dis. Nerv. System, *12:* 99-104, 1951.
174. Henderson, D. K., and Gillespie, R. D.: Textbook of Psychiatry, 6th ed. London: Oxford University Press, 1944.
175. Hendrick, I.: Ego-development and certain character problems. Psychoan. Quart., *3:* 320-346, 1936.
176. ——: Instinct and the ego during infancy. Psychoan. Quart., *11:* 33-58, 1942.
177. Hilgard, E. R.: Theories of Learning. New York: Appleton-Century-Crofts, 1948.
178. ——: Human motives and the concept of self. Amer. Psychologist, *4:* 374-382, 1949.
179. Hill, D., Loe, P., Theobald, J., and Waddell, M.: A central homeostatic mechanism in schizophrenia. J. Ment. Sc., *97:* 111-131, Jan., 1951.
180. Hoagland, H.: Stress and the adrenal cortex with special reference to potassium metabolism. Psychosom. Med., *12:* 142-148, 1950.
181. Hoch, P. H., and Zubin, J. (eds.): Psychosexual Development in Health and Disease, New York: Grune & Stratton, 1949.
182. ——, and —— (eds.): Anxiety. New York: Grune & Stratton, 1950.
183. Hoffer, W.: Mouth, Hand and Ego-Integration. In "The Psychoanalytic Study of The Child" Vol. III/IV. New York: International Universities Press, 1949.
184. Hollingshead, A. B.: Elmtown's Youth. New York: Macmillan, 1949.
185. Hollingworth, H. L.: Psychology and Ethics: A Study of the Sense of Obligation. New York: Ronald, 1949.
186. Holsopple, J. Q.: The social adjustment of delinquents who are unable to inhibit old automatic perceptual responses. J. Soc. Psychol., *3:* 91-96, 1932.
187. Horney, K.: The Neurotic Personality of Our Time. New York: Norton, 1937.
188. ——: New Ways in Psychoanalysis. New York: Norton, 1939.
189. ——: Our Inner Conflicts: A Constructive Theory of Neurosis. New York: Norton, 1945.
190. ——: Neurosis and Human Growth: The Struggle Toward Self-Realization. New York: Norton, 1950.
191. Horowitz, E. L.: Spatial localization of the self. J. Soc. Psychol., *6:* 379-387, 1935.
192. Hyroop, M.: The factor of omnipotence in the development of paranoid reactions. Am. J. Psychother., *5:* 38-44, 1951.
193. Isaacs, S.: Social Development of Young Children. New York: Harcourt, Brace & Co., 1933.

194. Israeli, N.: The social psychology of time. J. Abnorm. and Soc. Psychol., *27:* 209-213, 1932.
195. Jack, L.: An Experimental Study of Ascendent Behavior in Preschool Children. Univ. Iowa Stud. Child Welfare, Vol. 9, No. 3, 1934.
196. Jackson, T. A.: Errors of self-judgment. J. App. Psychol., *13:* 372-377, 1929.
197. James, W.: The Principles of Psychology. New York: Holt, 1890.
198. Jacobson, E.: The effect of disappointment on ego and superego formation in normal and depressive development. Psychoan. Rev., *33:* 129-147, 1946.
199. Jenkins, R. L.: Nature of the schizophrenic process. Arch. Neurol. and Psychiat., *64:* 243-262, 1950.
200. ——, and Glickman, S.: Patterns of personality organization among delinquents. Nerv. Child, *6:* 327-339, 1947.
201. Jersild, A. T.: Child Psychology. New York: Prentice Hall, 1947.
202. ——: Child psychology in the United States. Teach. Coll. Rec., *50:* 114-127, 1948.
203. ——, and Holmes, F. B.: Children's Fears. New York: Teachers College, Columbia University, 1933.
204. ——, et al.: Child Development and the Curriculum. New York: Teachers College, Columbia University, 1946.
205. Jones, E.: Anal-Erotic Character Traits. In "Papers on Psychoanalysis", London: Balliere, 1923.
206. ——: The origin and structure of the super-ego. Internat. J. Psychoan., *7:* 303-311, 1926.
207. Jones, H. E.: Development in Adolescence: Approaches to the Study of the Individual. New York: D. Appleton-Century, 1943.
208. Jones, M. C.: A study of the emotions of pre-school children. Sch. and Soc., *21:* 755-758, 1925.
209. ——, and Burks, B. S.: Personality Development in Childhood. Washington, D. C.: National Research Council, 1936.
210. Jones, V.: Character Development in Children. In "Manual of Child Psychology" (L. Carmichael, Ed.). New York: Wiley, 1946.
211. Josselyn, I. M.: Psychosocial Development of Children. New York: Family Service Association of America, 1948.
212. Jost, H., and Sontag, L. W.: The genetic factor in autonomic nervous-system function. Psychosom. Med., *6:* 308-310, 1944.
213. Kallman, F. J.: The genetic theory of schizophrenia. Am. J. Psychiat., *103:* 309-322, 1946.
214. ——: Modern concepts of genetics in relation to mental health and abnormal personality development. Psychiat. Quart., *21:* 535-553, 1947.
215. Kanner, L.: In Defense of Mothers. Springfield, Ill.: Charles C. Thomas, 1950.
216. ——: A discussion of early infantile autism. Abstract. Digest Neurol. and Psychiat., *19:* 158, April, 1951.

217. Kant, F.: Investigations into the dynamics of paranoid reactions. Dis. Nerv. System, *11:* 268-272, 1950.
218. Kardiner, A.: The Individual and His Society. New York: Columbia University Press, 1939.
219. ——: The Psychological Frontiers of Society. New York: Columbia University Press, 1945.
220. ——: The Change from Dry to Wet Rice Culture in Tanala-Betsileo. In "Readings in Social Psychology" (T. Newcomb and E. Hartley, eds.). New York, Holt, 1947.
221. Karpman, B.: Moral Agenesis. Psychiat. Quart., *21:* 361-399, 1947.
222. Kasanin, J. S., Knight, E., and Sage, P.: The parent-child relationship in schizophrenia. J. Nerv. and Ment. Dis., *79:* 249-263, 1934.
223. ——, et al.: Etxrinsic factors in the treatment of anxiety states in children. Am. J. Orothopsychiat., *12:* 439-456, 1942.
224. Katz, D., and Allport, F. H.: Students' Attitudes. Syracuse, N. Y.: Craftsman Press, 1931.
225. Kinsey, A. C., et al.: Sexual Behavior in the Human Male. Philadelphia: Saunders, 1948.
226. Kirkendall, L. A.: Sex Adjustments of Young Men. New York: Harper, 1940.
227. Kisker, G. W., and Knox, G. W.: The psychopathology of the ego system. J. Nerv. and Ment Dis., *96:* 66-71, 1943.
228 Klein, M.: The Psychoanalysis of Children. London: Hogarth, 1932.
229. Kline, N. S., and Tenney, A. M.: Constitutional factors in the prognosis of schizophrenia. Am. J. Psychiat., *107:* 434-441, 1950.
230. Klineberg, O.: Race Differences. New York: Harper, 1935.
231. Koffka, K.: Principles of Gestalt Psychology. New York: Harcourt, Brace & Co., 1935.
232. Korner, A. F.: Some Aspects of Hostility in Young Children. New York: Grune & Stratton, 1949.
233. Krech, D., and Crutchfield, R. S.: Theory and Problems of Social Psychology. New York: McGraw-Hill, 1948.
234. Kretschmer, E.: Korperbau und Charakter, 7th ed. Berlin: Springer, 1929.
235. Lafore, G. G.: Practices of Parents in Dealing with Preschool Children. Child Develop. Monog. No. 31. New York: Bureau of Publications, Teachers College, Columbia University, 1945.
236. Laird, J.: Problems of the Self. New York: Macmillan, 1917.
237. Landis, C., and Hunt, W.: The Startle Pattern. New York: Rinehart, 1939.
238. Langdon, G., and Stout, I. W.: These Well Adjusted Children. New York: John Day, 1950.
239. Lecky, P.: Self-consistency: A Theory of Personality. New York: Island Press, 1945.

240. Lehrman, S. R.: Transference in psychotherapy. Psychiat. Quart., *24:* 532-542, 1950.
241. Leighton, D., and Kluckholm, C.: Children of the People. Cambridge: Harvard University Press, 1947.
242. Levy, D. M.: On the problems of delinquency. Am. J. Orthopsychiat., *2:* 197-211, 1932.
243. ——: Relation of maternal overprotection to school grades and intelligence test. Am. J. Orthopsychiat., *3:* 23-34, 1933.
244. ——: Primary affect hunger. Am. J. Psychiat., *94:* 643-652, 1937.
245. ——: Studies in Sibling Rivalry. Res. Monog., Am. Orthopsychiat. Assn., No. 2, 1-96, 1937.
246. ——: Psychosomatic studies of some aspects of maternal behavior. Psychosom. Med., *4:* 223-227, 1942.
247. ——: Maternal Overprotection. New York: Columbia University Press, 1943.
248. Levy, J., and Munroe, R.: The Happy Family. New York: Knopf, 1941.
249. Levy, S., and Southcombe, R. H.: Value of convulsive therapy in juvenile schizophrenia. Arch. Neurol. and Psychiat., *65:* 54-59, 1951.
250. Lewin, K., Dembo, T., Festinger, L., and Sears, P. S.: Level of Aspiration. In "Personality and the Behavior Disorders" (J. McV. Hunt, ed.). New York: Ronald, 1944.
251. ——: Behavior and Development as a Function of the Total Situation. In "Manual of Child Psychology" (L. Carmichael, ed.). New York: Wiley, 1946.
252. Liddell, H. S., James, W. T., and Anderson, O. D.: The comparative physiology of the the conditioned motor reflex based on experiments with the pig, dog, sheep, goat and rabbit. Comp. Psychol. Monograph., 11, No. 51, 1934.
253. ——: Conditioned Reflex Method and Experimental Neurosis. In "Personality and the Behavior Disorders" (J. McV. Hunt, ed.). New York: Ronald, 1944.
254. ——: The Role of Vigilance in the Development of Animal Neuroses. In "Anxiety" (P. Hoch and J. Zubin, eds.). New York: Grune and Stratton, 1950.
255. Linton, R.: The Cultural Background of Personality. New York: D. Appleton-Century, 1945.
256. Loewald, H. W.: Ego and reality. Internat. J. Psychoan., *32:* 10-18, 1951.
257. Lorand, S: Character Formation and Psychoanalysis. In "Psychoanalysis Today" (S. Lorand, ed.). New York: Covici, 1933.
258. Louttit, C. M.: The mirror tracing test as a diagnostic aid for emotional instability. Psych. Rec., *5:* 279-286, 1943.
259. Lowenbach, H., and Suitt, R. B.: Alterations of Anxiety Subsequent to Physical Treatment of Psychiatric Disorders. In "Anxiety" (P. H. Hoch and J. Zubin, eds.). New York: Grune & Stratton, 1950. 218-242.

260. Lowry, L.: The family as builder of personality. Am. J. Orthopsychiat., *6:* 117-124, 1936.
261. Mahler, M. S.: Ego Psychology Applied to Behavior Problems. In "Modern Trends in Child Psychiatry" (N. D. C. Lewis and B. L. Pacella, eds.). New York: International Universities Press, 1945.
262. Maier, N. R. F.: Experimentally induced abnormal behavior. The Scientific Monthly, *67:* 210-216, 1948.
263. ——, and Feldman, R. S.: Studies of abnormal behavior in the rat. XXII. Strength of fixation and duration of frustration. J. Comp. and Physiol. Psychol., *41:* 348-363, 1948.
264. ——, and Longhurst, J. U.: Studies of abnormal behavior in the rat. XXI. Conflict and "audiogenic" seizures. J. Comp. and Physiol. Psychol., *40:* 397-412, 1947.
265. Malinowski, B.: Sex and Repression in Savage Society. New York: Harcourt, Brace & Co., 1927.
266. Maslow, A. H.: Deprivation, threat and frustration. Psychol. Rev., *48:* 364-366, 1941.
267. ——, and Mittelmann, B.: Principles of Abnormal Psychology. New York: Harper, 1941.
268. Masserman, J.: Principles of Dynamic Psychiatry. Philadelphia: W. B. Saunders, 1946.
269. ——, Arieff, A. A., Pechtel, C., and Klehr, H.: The effects of direct interrupted electroshock on experimental neuroses. J. Nerv. & Ment. Dis., *112:* 384-392, 1950.
270. May, R.: The Meaning of Anxiety. New York: Ronald, 1950.
271. McGraw, M. B.: Maturation of Behavior. In "Manual of Child Psychology" (L. Carmichael, ed.). New York: Wiley, 1946.
272. McKinnon, K.: Consistency and Change in Personality and Behavior Manifestations During a Five Year Period. Child Development Monographs. New York: Teachers College, Columbia University, 1942.
273. Mead, G. H.: Mind, Self, Society from the Standpoint of a Social Behaviorist. Chicago: University of Chicago Press, 1934.
274. Mead, M.: From the South Seas. New York: Wm. Morrow, 1939.
275. ——: Educative Effects of Social Environment as Disclosed by Studies of Primitive Societies. In "Readings in Social Psychology" (T. Newcomb and E. Hartley, eds.). New York: Holt, 1947.
276. Meyer, A.: Constructive formulation of schizophrenia. Am. J. Psychiat., 1922.
277. ——: Evolution of dementia praecox concept. Proc. Assoc. Research Nerv. and Ment. Dis. (1925), *5:* 3-15, 1928.
278. Meyers, C. E.: Emancipation of adolescents from parental control. Nervous Child, *5:* 251-262, 1946.
279. Miller, N. E.: Experimental Studies in Conflict. In "Personality and the Behavior Disorders" (J. McV. Hunt, ed.). New York: Ronald, 1944.

280. ——: Studies of fear as an acquirable drive: I. Fear as motivation and fear-reduction as reinforcement in the learning of new responses. Exper. Psychol., *38:* 89-101, 1948.

281. Milner, E.: Effects of Sex Role and Social Status on the Early Adolescent Personality. Genet. Psychol, Monographs, *40:* 231-325, 1949.

282. Mittelmann, Bela: Briefer psychotherapy in psychosomatic disorders of children and adolescents. Nerv. Child, *8:* 291-300, 1949.

283. Moreno, J. L.: Who Shall Survive. Washington, D. C.: Nervous and Mental Disease Publishing Co., 1934.

284. Mowrer, O. H.: Anxiety reduction and learning. J. Exper. Psychol., *27:* 497-516, 1940.

285. ——: The law of effect and ego psychology. Psychol. Rev., *53:* 321-334, 1946.

286. ——: Learning Theory and Personality Dynamics. New York: Ronald, 1950.

287. ——, and Kluckhohn, C. Dynamic Theory of Personality. In "Personality and the Behavior Disorders" (J. McV. Hunt, ed.). New York, Ronald, 1944.

288. Murphy, G.: Personality: A Biosocial Approach to Origins and Structure. New York: Harper, 1947.

289. ——, Murphy, L. B., and Newcomb, T.: Experimental Social Psychology. New York: Harper, 1937.

290. Murphy, L. B.: Social Behavior and Child Personality. New York: Columbia University Press, 1937.

291. ——: Childhood Experience in Relation to Personality Development. In "Personality and the Behavior Disorders" (J. McV. Hunt, ed.). New York: Ronald, 1944.

292. ——: Social Factors in Child Development. In "Readings in Social Psychology" (T. Newcomb and E. Hartley, eds.). New York: Holt, 1947.

293. Murray, H. A.: Explorations in Personality. New York: Oxford University Press, 1938.

294. ——, and Kluckhohn, C.: Outline of a Conception of Personality. In "Personality in Nature, Society and Culture" (C. Kluckhohn and H. A. Murray, eds.). New York: Knopf, 1949.

295. Nagy, M.: The child's theories concerning death. J. Genet. Psychol., *73:* 3-27, 1948.

296. Newell, H. W.: The psychodynamics of maternal rejection. Am. J. Orthopsychiat., *6:* 387-399, 1934.

297. ——: A further study of maternal rejection. Am. J. Orthopsychiat., *6:* 576-581, 1936.

298. Newstetter, W. I., Feldstein, M. J., and Newcomb, T. M.: Group Adjustment: A Study in Experimental Sociology. Cleveland: Cleveland School of Applied Sciences, Western Reserve Univ., 1938.

299. Nichols, C. A.: Moral Education Among North American Indians. Contributions to Education, No. 427. New York: Teachers College, Columbia University, 1930.

300. Nunberg, H.: The synthetic function of the ego. Internat. J. Psychoan., *12:* 123-140, 1931.

301. ——: Ego strength and ego weakness. American Imago, *3:* 25-40, August, 1942.

302. Obendorf, C. P.: Child-Parent Relationship. In "Psychoanalysis Today" (S. Lorand, ed.). New York: Covici Friede, 1933.

303. Orlansky, H.: Infant care and personality. Psychol. Bull. *46:* 1-48, 1949.

304. Parten, M. B.: Leadership among preschool children. J. Abnorm. and Soc. Psychol., *28:* 430-440, 1933.

305. Pavlov, I. P.: Conditioned Reflexes. London: Oxford University Press, 1927.

306. Perry, J. D.: The reliability of high-school averages computed from students' estimates of their high school grades. Sch. and Soc., *52:* 63-64, 1940.

307. Peters, H. N.: The mirror tracing test as a measure of social adaptation. J. Abnorm. and Soc. Psychol., *41:* 437-448, 1946.

308. Piaget, J.: Moral Judgment of the child. New York: Harcourt, Brace & Co., 1932.

309. Plant, J. S.: Personality and the Cultural Pattern. New York: Commonwealth Fund, 1937.

310. Pressey, S. L., and Robinson, F. P.: Psychology and the New Education. New York: Harper, 1944.

311. Rabban, M.: Sex Role Identification in Young Children in Two Diverse Social Groups. Genet. Psychol. Monographs, *42:* 81-158, 1950.

312. Radke, M.: The Relation of Parental Authority to Children's Behavior and Attitudes. Minneapolis: University of Minnesota Press, 1946.

313. Rado, S.: Psychodynamics of depression from the etiologic point of view. Psychosom. Med., *13:* 51-55, 1951.

314. Rank, O.: The Trauma of Birth. New York: Harcourt, Brace & Co., 1929.

315. ——: Truth and Reality. New York: Knopf, 1936.

316. ——: Will Therapy: An Analysis of the Therapeutic Process in Terms of Relationship. New York: A. A. Knopf, 1936.

317. Redl, F.: Group emotion and leadership. Psychiatry, *5:* 573-596, 1942.

318. Rees, L.: Body build, personality and neurosis in women. J. Ment. Science, *96:* 426-434, 1950.

319. Reich, W.: Character-Analysis: Principles and Techniques for Psychoanalysts in Practice and Training. New York: Orgone Institute Press, 1945.

320. Reichard, S., and Tillman C.: Patterns of parent-child relationships in schizophrenia. Psychiatry, *13:* 247-257, 1950.

321. Reik, T.: Psychology of Sex Relations. New York: Farrar and Rinehart, 1945.
322. ——: Listening With the Third Ear. New York: Farrar, Straus, 1948.
323. Remmers, H. H., and Weltman, N.: Attitude interrelationships of youths, their parents, and their teachers. J. Soc. Psychol., *26:* 61-68, 1947.
324. ——, Whisler, L., and Duwald, V. F.: Neurotic indicators at the adolescent level. J. Soc. Psychol., *9:* 17-24, 1938.
325. Ribble, M. A.: Disorganizing factors of infantile personality. Am. J. Psychiat., *98:* 459-467, 1941.
326. ——: The Rights of Infants. New York: Columbia University Press, 1943.
327. ——: Infantile Experience in Relation to Personality Development. In "Personality and the Behavior Disorders" (J. McV. Hunt, ed.). New York: Ronald, 1944.
328. Rice, P. B.: The ego and the law of effect. Psychol. Rev., *53:* 307-320, 1946.
329. Richards, B. W.: Childhood schizophrenia and mental deficiency. J. Ment. Science, *97:* 290-312, 1951.
330. Rogers, C. R.: Counseling and Psychotherapy. Boston: Houghton Mifflin, 1942.
331. ——: Some observations on the organization of personality. Amer. Psychol., *2:* 358-368, 1947.
332. Rogg, S. G.: Time of decision. Psychiat. Quart. *24:* 437-447, 1950.
333. Roheim, G.: The Study of Character Development and the Ontogenetic Theory of Culture. In "Essays Presented to C. G. Seligman" (E. E. Evans-Pritchard et al., eds.). London: Paul, Trench, Trubner, 1934.
334. ——: The psychoanalytic interpretation of culture. Internat. J. Psychoan., *22:* 147-169, 1941.
335. Rosen, J. N.: The treatment of schizophrenic psychoses by direct analytic therapy. Psychiat. Quart. *21:* 3-38, 1947.
336. ——: The survival function of schizophrenia. Bull. Menninger Clinic, *14:* 81-91, 1950.
337. Rosenzweig, S.: An Outline of Frustration Theory. In "Personality and the Behavior Disorders" (J. McV. Hunt, ed.). New York, Ronald, 1944.
338. Rotenberg, G.: Need for case work with parents in treatment of adolescents. Abstract of thesis. Smith College Stud. Soc. Work, *17:* 127-128, 1946.
339. Sapir, E.: Cultural anthropology and psychiatry. J. Abnorm. and Soc. Psychol., *27:* 229-242, 1932.
340. ——: The emergence of the concept of personality in a study of cultures. J. Soc. Psychol., *5:* 408-415, 1934.
341. Schilder, P.: Introduction to a Psychoanalytic Psychiatry. Nerv. and Ment. Dis. Monograph Series, No. 50. New York: Nervous and Mental Disease Publishing Co., 1928.

342. ——: The Image and Appearance of the Human Body. Psyche Monograph No. 6. London: Kegan, Paul, Trench, Trubner, 1935.
343. Schmideberg, M.: Methods of approach to the infant mind, a study of his ego activities. Nerv. Child, *6:* 278-283, 1947.
344. Shock, N. W.: Physiological Changes in Adolescence. In "Adolescence", 43rd Yearbook, Natl. Soc. Stud. Educ. Chicago: University of Chicago Press, 56-79, 1944.
345. Sears, P. S.: Levels of aspiration in academically successful and unsuccessful children. J. Abnorm. and Soc. Psychol., *35:* 498-536, 1940.
346. Sears, R. R.: Survey of Objective Studies of Psychoanalytic Concepts. New York: Social Science Research Council, 1943.
347. Seitz, P. F.: A dynamic factor correlated with the prognosis in paranoid schizophrenia. Arch. Neurol. and Psychiat., *65:* 604-606, 1951.
348. Selye, H.: Stress and the general adaptation syndrome. Brit. M. J., *1:* 1383-1392, 1950.
349. ——, and Fortier, C.: Adaptive reaction to stress. Psychosom. Med. *12:* 149-157, 1950.
350. Shaffer, L. F.: The Psychology of Adjustment. Boston: Houghton Mifflin, 1936.
351. Sheerer, E. T.: An analysis of the relationship between acceptance of the respect for self and acceptance of and respect for others in ten counseling cases. J. Consult. Psychol., *13:* 169-175, 1949.
352. Sheldon, W. H.: Constitutional Factors in Personality. In "Personality and the Behavior Disorders" (J. McV. Hunt, ed.). New York: Ronald, 1944.
353. Sherman, M.: The differentiation of emotional responses in infants. J. Comp. Psychol., *7:* 265-284, 1927.
354. Sherif, M., and Cantril, H.: The Psychology of Ego-Involvements. New York: Wiley, 1946.
355. Shirley, M. M.: The First Two Years, Vol. II: Personality Manifestations. Minneapolis: University of Minnesota Press, 1933.
356. ——: Impact of mother's personality on the young child. Smith College Stud. Soc. Work, *12:* 15-64, 1941.
357. Shoben, E. J.: The Assessment of Parental Attitudes in Relation to Child Adjustment. Genet. Psychol. Monographs, 39, 1949.
358. Shulman, A. J.: The etiology of schizophrenia. Psychiat. Quart., *24:* 515-531, 1950.
359. Silverberg, W. V.: The factor of omnipotence in neuroses. Psychiatry, *12:* 387-398, 1949.
360. Silberpfenning, R.: Mother types encountered in child guidance clinics. Am. J. Orthopsychiat., *11:* 475-484, 1941.
361. Simon, B., Holzberg, J., and Unger, J. F.: A study of judgment in the psychopathic personality. Psychiat. Quart. *25:* 132-150, 1951.

362. Simpson, M. S.: Parent Preferences of Young Children. Contributions to Education, No. 652. New York: Teachers College, Columbia University, 1935.

363. Snygg, D., and Combes, A. W.: Individual Behavior: A New Frame of Reference for Psychology. New York: Harper, 1945.

364. Sobel, R.: Treatment of character-conditioned hostility in adolescents. Nerv. Child, *8:* 301-310, 1949.

365. Sontag, L. W.: Some psychosomatic aspects of childhood. Nerv. Child, *5:* 296-304, 1946.

366. ——: The genetics of differences in psychosomatic patterns in childhood. Am. J. Orthopsychiat., *20:* 479-489, 1950.

367. Sperling, M.: Children's interpretation and reaction to the unconscious of their mothers. Internat. J. Psychoanal., *31:* 36-41, 1950.

368. Spitz, R. A.: Anaclitic depression. In "Psychoanalytic Study of the Child", Vol. II, New York: International Universities Press, 313-342, 1946.

369. ——: The role of ecological factors in emotional development in infancy. Child Developm., *20:* 145-154, 1949.

370. ——: Anxiety in infancy: a study of its manifestations in the first year of life. Internat. J. Psychoanal., *31:* 138-143, 1950.

371. ——: Psychiatric therapy in infancy. Am. J. Orthopsychiat. *20:* 623-633, 1950.

372. Stagnell, G.: Relationship of anxiety to solicitude. Abstracted in Psychoan. Rev., *13:* 345, 1925.

373. Stanback, O.: Arrested ego-development and its treatment in conduct disorders and neuroses of childhood. Nerv. Child, *6:* 306-317, 1947.

374. Standish, C. T., Mann, J., and Menzer, D.: Some aspects of the psychopathology of schizophrenia. Implications in treatment. Psychiatry, *13:* 439-445, 1950.

375. Stein, L. H.: A study of overinhibited and unsocialized aggressive children. Part II. A Quantitative Analysis of Background Factors. Smith College Stud. Soc. Work, *15:* 124-125, 1944.

376. Stendler, C. B.: A study of some socio-moral judgments of junior high school students. Child Developm., *20:* 15-29, 1949.

377. ——: Children of Brasstown. Urbana, Ill.: Univ. of Illinois Press, 1949.

378. ——, and Young N.: The impact of beginning first grade upon socialization as reported by mothers. Child Developm., *21:* 241-260, 1950.

379. Stock, D.: An investigation into the interrelations between the self concept and feelings directed toward other persons and groups. J. Consult. Psychol., *13:* 176-180, 1949.

380. Stolz, H. R., and Stolz, L. M.: Adolescent Problems Related to Somatic Variations. In "Adolescence", 43rd Yearbook of the Natl. Soc. Stud. Educ. Chicago: University of Chicago Press, 80-92, 1944.

381. Stone, C. P., and Barker, R. G.: The attitudes and interests of premenarcheal and postmenarcheal girls. J. Genet. Psychol., *54:* 27-71, 1939.
382. Stone, J. T.: The theory and practice of psychoanalysis. Science and Society, *11:* 54-79, 1947.
383. Storch, A.: The Primitive Archaic Forms of Inner Experience and Thought in Schizophrenia. Nerv. and Ment. Dis. Monograph Series, No. 36. Washington, D. C., 1924.
384. Strang, R.: Religious activities of adolescent girls. Relig. Educ., *24:* 313-21, 1929.
385. Strecker, E. A., and Ebaugh, F. G.: Practical Clinical Psychiatry. Philadelphia: Blakiston, 1940.
386. Sullivan, H. S.: Tentative criteria of malignancy in schizophrenia. Am. J. Psychiat., *84:* 759-787, 1928.
387. ——: Conceptions of modern psychiatry. Psychiatry, *3:* 1-117, 1940.
388. Symonds, P. M.: The Psychology of Parent-Child Relationships. New York: D. Appleton-Century, 1939.
389. ——: The Dynamics of Parent-Child Relationships. New York: Teachers College, Columbia University, 1949.
390. ——: The Ego and the Self. New York: Appleton Century Crofts, 1951.
391. Taylor, W. S.: A Critique of Sublimation in Males: A Study of Forty Superior Single Men. Genet. Psychol. Monographs, 13, No. 1, 1933.
392. Thompson, C.: Psychoanalysis: Evolution and Development. New York: Hermitage, 1950.
393. Tietze, T.: A study of mothers of schizophrenic parents. Psychiatry, *12:* 55-65, 1949.
394. Tryon, C.: The Adolescent Peer Culture. In "Adolescence", 43rd Yearbook, Natl. Soc. Stud. Educ. Chicago: University of Chicago Press, 217-239, 1944.
395. Tudor-Hart, B. E.: Are there cases in which lies are necessary? J. Genet. Psychol., *33:* 586-641, 1926.
396. Vaughan, W. F.: Social Psychology. New York: Odyssey, 1948.
397. Weidensall, J.: The Mentality of the Criminal Woman. Baltimore: Warwick and York, 1916.
398. Weingarten, E. M.: A study of selective perception in clinical judgment. J. Personality, *17:* 369-406, 1949.
399. Wilde, O.: The Ballad of Reading Gaol. Portland, Me.: T. B. Mosher, 1905.
400. Wittman, M. P., and Huffman, A. V.: A comparative study of developmental, adjustment, and personality characteristics of psychotic, delinquent, and normally-adjusted teen-age youths. J. Genet. Psychol., *66:* 167-182, 1945.
401. Wolberg, J.: The character structure of the rejected child. Nerv. Child, *3:* 74-88, 1944.

402. Wolberg, L. R.: The problem of self-esteem in psychotherapy. N. Y. State J. Med., *43:* 1415-1419, 1943.
403. Worden, F. G.: Psychotherapeutic aspects of authority. Psychiatry, *14:* 8-17, 1951.
404. Wortis, J.: Freudianism and the psychoanalytic tradition. Am. J. Psychiat., *101:* 814-820, 1945.
405. Young, K.: Parent-child relationship—projection of ambition. Family, *8:* 67-73, 1927.
406. Zachry, C. B., and Lighty, M.: Emotion and Conduct in Adolescence. New York: D. Appleton-Century, 1940.
407. ——: Preparing Youth to Be Adults. In "Adolescence" 43rd Yearbook, Natl. Soc. Stud. Educ. Chicago: University of Chicago Press, 332-346, 1944.
408. Zilboorg, G.: Depressive reactions related to parenthood. Am. J. Psychiat., *10:* 927-962, 1931.
409. ——: Sidelights on parent-child antagonisms. Am. J. Orthopsychiat., *2:* 35-43, 1932.

Index